McGraw-Hill Electrical and Electronic Engineering Series

FREDERICK EMMONS TERMAN, *Consulting Editor*

Harmonics, Sidebands, and Transients In Communication Engineering

McGraw-Hill Electrical and Electronic Engineering Series

FREDERICK EMMONS TERMAN, *Consulting Editor*

BAILEY AND GAULT · Alternating-current Machinery
BERANEK · Acoustics
BRUNS AND SAUNDERS · Analysis of Feedback Control Systems
CAGE · Theory and Application of Industrial Electronics
CUCCIA · Harmonics, Sidebands, and Transients on Communication Engineering
EASTMAN · Fundamentals of Vacuum Tubes
EVANS · Control-system Dynamics
FITZGERALD AND HIGGINBOTHAM · Basic Electrical Engineering
FITZGERALD AND KINGSLEY · Electric Machinery
GEPPERT · Basic Electron Tubes
GLASFORD · Fundamentals of Television Engineering
HAPPELL AND HESSELBERTH · Engineering Electronics
HARMAN · Fundamentals of Electronic Motion
HESSLER AND CAREY · Fundamentals of Electrical Engineering
HILL · Electronics in Engineering
JOHNSON · Transmission Lines and Networks
KRAUS · Antennas
KRAUS · Electromagnetics
LEPAGE · Analysis of Alternating-current Circuits
LEPAGE AND SEELY · General Network Analysis
MILLMAN AND SEELY · Electronics
MILLMAN AND TAUB · Pulse and Digital Circuits
ROGERS · Introduction to Electric Fields
RÜDENBERG · Transient Performance of Electric Power Systems
RYDER · Engineering Electronics
SEELY · Electronic Engineering
SEELY · Electron-tube Circuits
SEELY · Radio Electronics
SISKIND · Direct-current Machinery
SKILLING · Electric Transmission Lines
SKILLING · Transient Electric Currents
SPANGENBURG · Fundamentals of Electronic Devices
SPANGENBURG · Vacuum Tubes
STEVENSON · Elements of Power System Analysis
TERMAN · Electronic and Radio Engineering
TERMAN AND PETTIT · Electronic Measurements
THALER · Elements of Servomechanism Theory
THALER AND BROWN · Servomechanism Analysis
THOMPSON · Alternating-current and Transient Circuit Analysis
TRUXAL · Automatic Feedback Control System Synthesis

Harmonics, Sidebands, and Transients in Communication Engineering

As Studied by the Fourier and Laplace Analyses

C. Louis Cuccia, M.S.

Research Engineer, Radio Corporation of America
RCA Laboratories Division, David Sarnoff Research Center, Princeton, N. J.

New York Toronto London
McGRAW-HILL BOOK COMPANY, INC.
1952

HARMONICS, SIDEBANDS, AND TRANSIENTS
IN COMMUNICATION ENGINEERING

Library of Congress Catalog Card Number: 51-12596

III

In Memory of My Father

PREFACE

In the preface of his well-known book on operational mathematics, Vannevar Bush writes, ". . . I write as an engineer and . . . I do not pretend to be a mathematician. . . . I write in hope that this text will be useful." Such, too, was the philosophy observed at the conception and during the writing of this book.

Applied mathematics and mathematical analysis are no longer the tools of a relatively small number of mathematically inclined engineers. Communication-engineering analysis employing methods of modern operational mathematics has come into its own, a young giant demanding full consideration of its own problems as derived from the systems comprising radio, television, and radar, rather than from generalities drawn from the fields of physics, engineering, and mechanics. In keeping with such demands, this book, dealing with modern communication-engineering analysis, has been written to provide not a collection of solutions but rather an organized and integrated textbook, dealing simultaneously with the Laplace, Fourier, and Taylor analyses. This volume then proceeds with a systematic presentation of the applications of these analyses in all important phases of electrical communications. The associated background of engineering concepts and ideas is included for the express purpose of aiding in the understanding of the processes of these analyses. Also, whenever necessary in this text, the applications and the analyses are developed and extended to bridge any gap which might exist between the tutorial discussions and the literature of the field. This approach is an invaluable aid for providing a fuller understanding of the general principles of communication engineering.

In order to be useful and applicable, communication-engineering analysis must be kept as simple as possible, but not so simple that the teeth of the analysis have been dulled; it must also be to the point, and not so rigorous as to be unwieldy. This demands a working knowledge of such fine points as, for example, when a complex Fourier series rather than a trigonometric Fourier series should be employed or when the use of the Fourier integral is more rewarding than the use of the Laplace transform and also the limitations involved. Any attempt to force a solution of a communication-engineering problem with one method where another method of approach is more suitable may prove dangerously confusing. In addition, the method of approach should be clearly identified lest the analysis prove limited in application and usage.

This book is an outgrowth of lecturing on modulation theory to engineers of the staff of the RCA Laboratories, the teaching of several courses on advanced electrical engineering for the Engineering Science Management War Training Department of Rutgers University, several years of active participation in the field of ultra-high-frequency transmission as a research engineer for the Radio Corporation of America, and as a contributor to the publications of the field. It has been greatly influenced by many persons: in particular, Professor W. G. Dow, of the University of Michigan, who played a large part in creating the author's interest in communication engineering and electronics; Professor R. V. Churchill, whose distinguished courses dealing with the Laplace and Fourier analyses at the University of Michigan kindled the author's enthusiasm for modern operational mathematics; and Doctor Dwight O. North, of the RCA Laboratories, whose keen insight into applied mathematical analysis opened up to the author a vast reservoir of concepts and ideas which revealed the Laplace and Fourier formulations to be powerful tools for determining the behavior of communication systems.

In addition, the author is indebted to Doctors L. S. Nergaard, J. S. Donal, Jr., L. P. Smith, L. Malter, G. L. Fredendall, W. D. Hershberger and to V. D. Landon and E. W. Herold for valuable suggestions and ideas. Appreciation is due to F. H. Norman for much practical information regarding television-receiver circuits; to Doctor I. Wolff for his encouragement; to Deans L. F. Eisenhart and H. S. Taylor of the Graduate School of Princeton University for generously providing the author with the facilities of the Graduate College, where most of the manuscript was written; and again to Professor Churchill for many penetrating and sobering comments pertaining to a very early draft of the manuscript.

The reader's indulgence is requested with regard to any errors which he might encounter. In a work of this length and scope, particularly since it is the work of a single author, it is inevitable that some inaccuracies or errors might be overlooked during the final preparation of the manuscript. The author would deeply appreciate having them brought to his attention.

C. Louis Cuccia

Princeton, N. J.
February, 1952

CONTENTS

CONTENTS

CHAPTER 1

ELEMENTARY FUNCTIONS OF A COMPLEX VARIABLE

> But it must be remembered that the men who have in the past initiated great advances in mathematics have usually been men who were employed in working out physical problems.
>
> HEAVISIDE

> The imaginary number is a fine and wonderful recourse of the divine spirit, almost an amphibian between being and not being.
>
> B. W. LEIBNITZ

1. Introduction. As Joseph Fourier was preparing his monumental treatise "The Analytic Theory of Heat" in Grenoble in the early part of the nineteenth century, it is doubtful that he could have visualized in his wildest dreams the changes that almost a century and a half to follow would bring about in the transmission of information and the part that his mathematical formulations and those of his contemporaries—Laplace and Poisson[1]—would play in the understanding of the mechanism of this transmission. Fourier and Laplace were followed by other brilliant mathematicians, such as James Clerk Maxwell, Oliver Heaviside, and Lord Rayleigh, who made important contributions to the ever-increasing fund of knowledge which was someday to form the basis of the theory of electrical communication. As the world entered the age of radio, the contributions of more modern mathematicians and physicists such as J. R. Carson and B. van der Pol were added to those of their predecessors. At the same time, other gifted and farsighted men in universities and in research laboratories such as those of the Radio Corporation of America were developing and making improvements in the art of communication and communication systems.

Since 1940, the general field of communication has come to include television, radar, facsimile, and many applications of radar and television in the field of ship and airplane traffic control. However, regardless of the specific type of communication system, the majority of the fundamental system components involved are the same and may be analyzed

[1] H. Bateman has pointed out (*Bull. Am. Math. Soc.*, vol. 48, p. 510, 1942) that the method of the Laplace transform was initiated in 1815 by Poisson.

in terms of three fundamental types of waves, *viz.*, harmonics, sidebands, and transients.

This book treats extensively the basic analysis and fundamental concepts associated with these three waves in communication engineering, using Fourier analysis, Laplace analysis, and to a lesser degree, Taylor-series analysis. However, useful applications of any analysis can only be achieved after the analysis itself has been based on a firm mathematical foundation. The foundation of the analyses to be discussed and applied in the present volume is based on the theory of the elementary functions of the complex variable (which will be discussed in this chapter). This is a fortunate circumstance for the communications engineer since many of these elementary functions, such as rotating vectors and complex numbers, form the basis of many of the engineering concepts which are associated with communication-engineering analysis.

BASIC CONCEPTS OF COMPLEX NUMBERS AND ROTATING VECTORS

2. Introduction to Complex Numbers. Alternating-current and voltage phenomena are functions of time and may therefore be written as follows:

$$i = i(t) \tag{1}$$

$$e = e(t) \tag{2}$$

In general, $e(t)$ and $i(t)$ may be described by a combination of both real and imaginary quantities or by real quantities alone. In this chapter we shall associate these basic functions with complex functions and shall extend the discussion of the theory of the functions of a complex variable to include some important properties of complex-plane representation, which will be useful in the Taylor, Fourier, and Laplace analyses.

Consider the complex number

$$z = x + jy \tag{3}$$

where $j = \sqrt{-1}$ is the complex operator which has the property of shifting the length y by an angle of 90° with respect to the length x. x and jy are referred to as the real part and the imaginary part of z, respectively; *i.e.*,

$$\text{Re}\, z = x \tag{4}$$

$$\text{Im}\, z = jy \tag{5}$$

The complex number $x + jy$ may be represented geometrically by either the point x, jy in the complex plane or by the vector of magnitude I which extends from the origin to this point and forms the angle φ with respect to the real axis.

As is seen in Fig. 1, this point may be expressed in terms of its polar coordinates, I, φ, since, according to the Euler formula,

$$z = x + jy \tag{6}$$

$$= I(\cos \varphi + j \sin \varphi) \tag{7}$$

$$= Ie^{j\varphi} \tag{8}$$

where the real part of z in Eq. (7) is its projection on the real axis and the imaginary portion is its projection on the imaginary axis. Note that

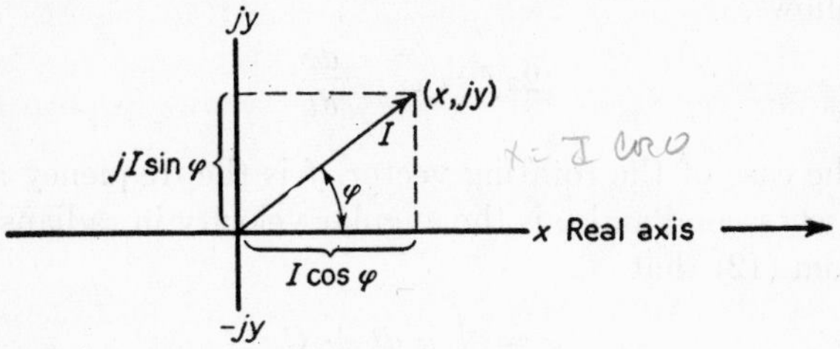

FIG. 1. Rotating vector.

the length I may be described in terms of the absolute magnitude of z as follows:

$$I = |z| = \sqrt{x^2 + y^2} \tag{9}$$

The conjugate of the complex number z, which is denoted by z^*, is

$$z^* = x - jy \tag{10}$$

z and z^* are illustrated in Fig. 2, where it is seen that their real portions are equal and their imaginary portions are opposite in sign. It is evident

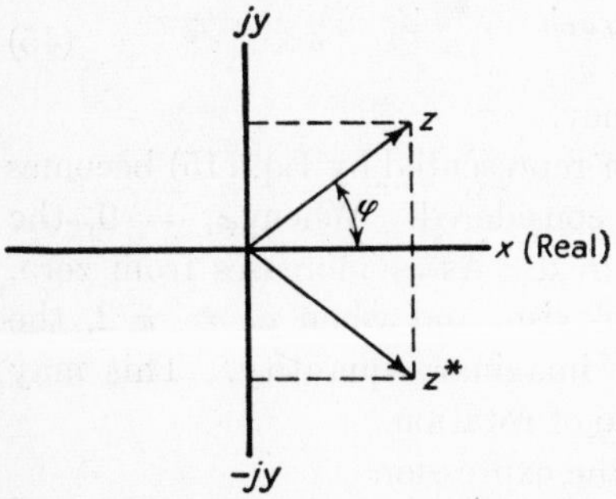

FIG. 2. Conjugate rotating vectors.

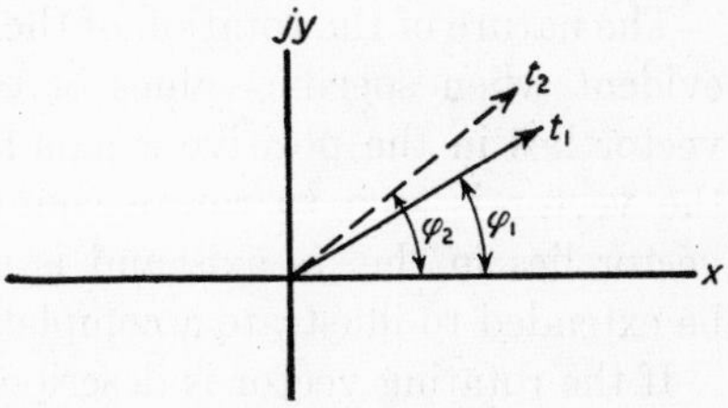

FIG. 3.

from Fig. 2 that a vector summation of the complex-number vector z and its conjugate vector z^* will lie in the real axis and will have a magnitude equal to $2x$.

3. The Rotating Vector. A basic wave concept which includes both real and imaginary quantities is that of the rotating vector in the complex plane.

Let the vector pictured in Fig. 1 rotate about the origin by letting φ either increase or decrease. Since its projections on the real and imaginary axis are $I \cos \varphi$ and $jI \sin \varphi$ and since, owing to the Pythagorean theorem,

$$I = \sqrt{(I \cos \varphi)^2 + (I \sin \varphi)^2} \tag{11}$$

it is evident that the length of the vector is independent of its phase angle φ.

It was first pointed out by Helmholtz that phase and frequency are related as follows,

$$2\pi f = \omega = \frac{d\varphi}{dt} \tag{12}$$

where, for the case of the rotating vector, f is the frequency as measured in rotations per second and ω is the angular velocity in radians per second. It follows from (12) that

$$\varphi = \int \omega \, dt + C \tag{13}$$

It is seen from (13) that each change in phase over a certain period of time is associated with a certain frequency. For example, let us assume the phase angles φ_1 at t_1 and φ_2 at t_2 which are pictured in Fig. 3. From the definition of a derivative, it follows that at t_2

$$2\pi f = \omega = \lim_{(t_2 - t_1) \to 0} \frac{\varphi_2 - \varphi_2}{t_2 - t_1} \tag{14}$$

From this expression arises the concept of instantaneous frequency and phase, and we may relate general expressions for a single rotating vector as follows:

$$Ie^{i\varphi_t} = Ie^{i\int \omega_t dt} \tag{15}$$

where $\omega_t/2\pi$ is the instantaneous frequency.

The nature of the rotation of the vector represented by Eq. (15) becomes evident when specific values of φ_t are considered. When $\varphi_t = 0$, the vector lies in the positive x axis and is real. As φ_t increases from zero, the vector is seen to rotate counterclockwise, and when $\varphi_t = \pi/2$, the vector lies in the jy axis and is a pure imaginary quantity. This may be extended to illustrate a complete cycle of rotation.

If the rotating vector is described by the expression

$$i = Ie^{-i\varphi_t} \tag{16}$$

the rotation will be clockwise. This becomes evident by writing (16) in the form

$$i = I(\cos \varphi_t - j \sin \varphi_t) \tag{17}$$

4. Complex-plane Parts. The physical concept of the complex-plane representation is most easily understood by investigating the significance of the components of the rotating vector, which have been seen to be

$$\text{Re}\, Ie^{j\varphi} = I \cos \varphi \tag{18}$$

$$\text{Im}\, Ie^{j\varphi} = jI \sin \varphi \tag{19}$$

The real part is of interest to us. If the rotating vector represents a current, then the real part represents that current which can be read with meters. It is that current which flows in the physical network and which can be subjected to measurement. The imaginary part is not physically realizable and may be considered to be that part of the current which completes its mathematical representation.

This concept of real and imaginary components must in no way be confused with the concepts associated with the resistive and reactive currents that flow in circuits in which the power factor is other than unity. For such circuits, the quadrature component arises from the voltage and current being out of phase—each being a real quantity.

5. Constant-angular-velocity Representation of a Rotating Vector. If ω is constant

$$\varphi = \int_0^t \omega \, dt = \omega t \tag{20}$$

and the rotating vector may now be written as follows:

$$i = Ie^{j\omega t} \tag{21}$$

$$= I(\cos \omega t + j \sin \omega t) \tag{22}$$

where ωt is the phase angle which increases linearly with time. When the rotating vector makes a complete revolution with respect to its initial position at $t = 0$, ωt will be equal to 2π. For two revolutions, $\omega t = 4\pi$, etc.

The real part of the exponential representation of the rotating vector, $Ie^{j\omega t}$, for constant angular velocity is

$$\text{Re}\, Ie^{j\omega t} = I \cos \omega t \tag{23}$$

6. Addition of Two Complex Numbers. In general, two complex numbers may be added together by adding their real and their imaginary parts; *i.e.*, if

$$z_1 = x_1 + jy_1 \tag{24}$$

$$z_2 = x_2 + jy_2 \tag{25}$$

then

$$z_1 \pm z_2 = (x_1 \pm x_2) + j(y_1 \pm y_2) \tag{26}$$

Sum of Two Rotating Vectors. Consider the two rotating vectors representing the currents,

$$i_1 = I_1 e^{j\omega_1 t} \tag{27}$$

$$i_2 = I_2 e^{j\omega_2 t} \tag{28}$$

The sum $i_1 + i_2$ of these vectors is found to be

$$i_1 + i_2 = (I_1 \cos \omega_1 t + I_2 \cos \omega_2 t) + j(I_1 \sin \omega_1 t + I_2 \sin \omega_2 t) \tag{29}$$

It is often more convenient to add $I_2 e^{j\omega_2 t}$ directly to the tip of $I_1 e^{j\omega_1 t}$. This may seem to be a matter of inconsequential nature, but actually this type of summation is more useful—particularly when ω_2 is considerably larger or smaller than ω_1. Take, for example, the case when $\omega_2 \gg \omega_1$. Then, as far as the motion of $I_2 e^{j\omega_2 t}$ is concerned, $I_1 e^{j\omega_1 t}$ is practically standing still, and we may represent $I_2 e^{j\omega_2 t}$ as a spinning vector at the tip of $I_1 e^{j\omega_1 t}$. This is illustrated in Fig. 4.

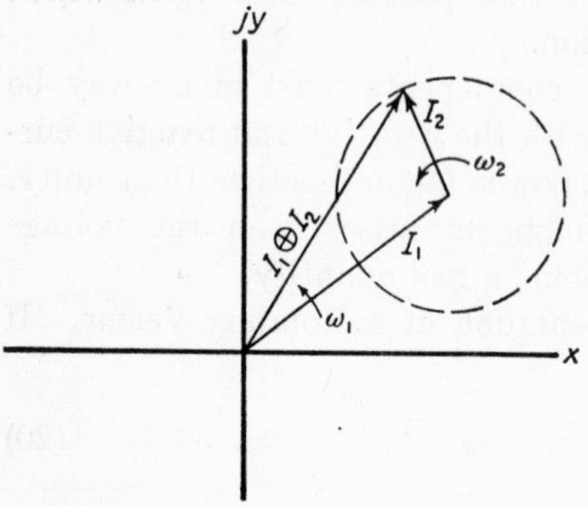

FIG. 4.

For this particular illustration, the phase of the resultant vector leads or lags the vector $I_1 e^{j\omega_1 t}$. If the x, jy plane rotates counterclockwise with ω_1 and if $\omega_2 < \omega_1$, note that $I_1 e^{j\omega_1 t}$ will appear to be *stationary* and $I_2 e^{j\omega_2 t}$ will appear to spin *clockwise.*

Rotating-vector Representation of I cos ωt *and I* sin ωt. Consider the case when the current described by Eq. (1) is a real function of time and is expressed as $I \cos \omega t$. This real current may be represented by rotating vectors by writing $\cos \omega t$ in its exponential form; *i.e.,*

$$i = I \frac{e^{j\omega t} + e^{-j\omega t}}{2} \tag{30}$$

$$= \frac{I}{2} e^{j\omega t} + \frac{I}{2} e^{-j\omega t} \tag{31}$$

i is now represented by two rotating vectors. The magnitude of each rotating vector is $I/2$, and each rotates in the opposite direction with respect to the other with constant angular velocity, ω. Figure 5 shows the positions of the vectors at the phase angles, $\omega t = 0, 45°, 90°, 135°, 180°$.

It is evident from this illustration that although imaginary quantities are involved, the resultant of the two component rotating vectors lies at all times on the real axis, thus corroborating the fact that $i = I \cos \omega t$ is a real quantity.

The real current $i = I \sin \omega t$ can be shown to be a real plane representa-

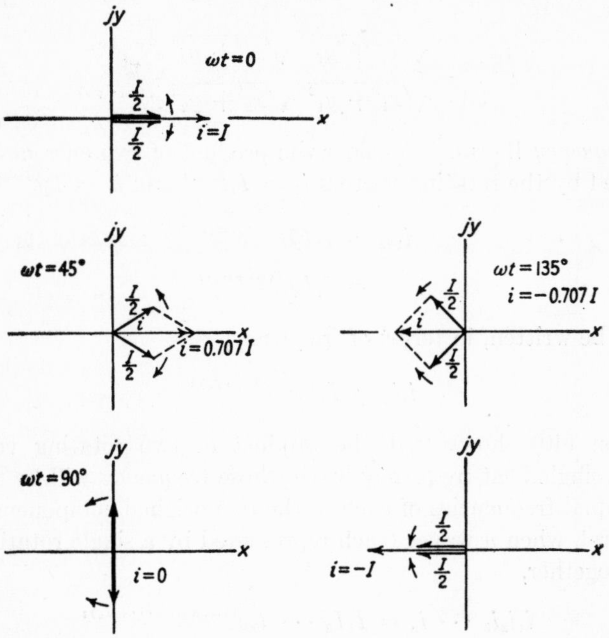

Fig. 5. Rotating-vector representation of $I \cos \omega t$ for case where $\omega t = 0, 45°, 90°, 135°, 180°$.

tion in the same manner which was employed in the preceding discussion. Writing $\sin \omega t$ in its exponential form, the expression for i becomes

$$i = I\,\frac{e^{j\omega t} - e^{-j\omega t}}{2j} \tag{32}$$

$$= -j\,\frac{I}{2}\,e^{j\omega t} + j\,\frac{I}{2}\,e^{-j\omega t} \tag{33}$$

As in Eq. (31), we see that i is made up of two rotating vectors of magnitude $I/2$. However, the presence of the minus sign indicates that the counterclockwise vector is shifted by 180°, and the presence of the j's will produce an additional 90° shift on the part of both vectors. The resultant $i = I \sin \omega t$ will therefore lie at all times on the real axis.

7. Multiplication of Two Complex Numbers. The multiplication of the two complex numbers z_1 and z_2 which are described by Eqs. (24) and (25) is written in terms of both cartesian and polar coordinates as follows:

Cartesian:

$$z_1z_2 = (x_1 + jy_1)(x_2 + jy_2) \tag{34}$$

$$= (x_1x_2 - y_1y_2) + j(x_1y_2 + x_2y_1) \tag{35}$$

Polar:

$$z_1z_2 = \sqrt{x_1^2 + y_1^2}\ \sqrt{x_2^2 + y_2^2}\ e^{j\varphi_1}e^{j\varphi_2} \tag{36}$$

$$= \sqrt{x_1^2 + y_1^2}\ \sqrt{x_2^2 + y_2^2}\ e^{j(\varphi_1+\varphi_2)} \tag{37}$$

Beat-frequency Waves. Consider the product of two currents which are represented by the rotating vectors $i_1 = I_1e^{j\omega_1t}$ and $i_2 = I_2e^{j\omega_2t}$. Then

$$i_1i_2 = I_1I_2e^{j\omega_1t}e^{j\omega_2t} \tag{38}$$

$$= I_1I_2e^{j(\omega_1+\omega_2)t} \tag{39}$$

This may be written, in terms of frequency,

$$i_1i_2 = I_1I_2e^{j2\pi(f_1+f_2)t} \tag{40}$$

Equation (40) shows that the product of two rotating vectors will produce a single beat-frequency wave whose frequency will be the sum of the individual frequencies of each of the two original component waves.

In general, when n waves (each represented by a single rotating vector) are beat together,

$$i_1i_2i_3 \cdots i_n = I_1I_2 \cdots I_ne^{j(\omega_1+\omega_2+\cdots+\omega_n)t} \tag{41}$$

showing that the resulting beat frequency is the sum of the individual frequencies of all of the waves which are beat together.

In physically realizable systems, only real waves will be beat together. We have seen that a real simple harmonic wave may be represented as the sum of two rotating vectors which have the same angular velocity and which rotate in opposite directions. Beating two such real waves together will yield twice as many rotating vectors as the beat of the two waves in Eq. (40).

Consider the product of the two real waves $i_3 = I_3 \cos \omega_3t$ and $i_4 = I_4 \cos \omega_4t$. This product is written

$$i_3i_4 = I_3I_4 \cos \omega_3t \cos \omega_4t \tag{42}$$

$$= \frac{I_3I_4}{4}(e^{j\omega_3t} + e^{-j\omega_3t})(e^{j\omega_4t} + e^{-j\omega_4t}) \tag{43}$$

$$= \frac{I_3I_4}{4}(e^{j(\omega_3+\omega_4)t} + e^{-j(\omega_3+\omega_4)t} + e^{j(\omega_3-\omega_4)t} + e^{-j(\omega_3-\omega_4)t}) \tag{44}$$

$$= \frac{I_3I_4}{2}[\cos(\omega_3 + \omega_4)t + \cos(\omega_3 - \omega_4)t] \tag{45}$$

Equation (45) shows that two beat-frequency waves are produced. These beat-frequency waves are both real, and their frequencies are seen from Eq. (45) to consist of a sum and a difference of the two original wave frequencies.

In general, when n real waves are beat together, 2^{n-1} beat-frequency waves, which are represented by rotating vectors totaling twice this number, will be produced. These beat-frequency waves will have frequencies determined by all possible combinations of the beating frequencies.

The analysis of beat-frequency waves is made simpler when the frequencies of the beating waves are integral multiples of some specified frequency. For instance, consider the product of the two waves $i_1 = I_1e^{j\omega_1 t}$ and $i_5 = I_5e^{j2\omega_1 t}$; that is,

$$i_1 i_5 = I_1 I_5 e^{j\omega_1 t} e^{j2\omega_1 t} \tag{46}$$

$$= I_1 I_5 e^{j3\omega_1 t} \tag{47}$$

In general, the beat of two waves which are represented by the two rotating vectors $i_1 = I_1e^{j\omega_1 t}$ and $i_n = I_ne^{jn\omega_1 t}$ will form the product

$$i_1 i_n = I_1 I_n e^{j(n+1)\omega_1 t} \tag{48}$$

where it is seen that the resulting beat frequency is an integral multiple of ω_1.

8. Other Properties of Complex Numbers. The properties of the division of two complex numbers and the raising of a complex number to the nth power or the taking of its nth root may be summarized as follows:

Consider the complex number $z_1 = I_1e^{j\varphi_1}$:

Division:

If z_1 is divided by $z_2 = I_2e^{j\varphi_2}$, then

$$\frac{z_1}{z_2} = \frac{I_1}{I_2} e^{j(\varphi_1 - \varphi_2)} \tag{49}$$

The nth power:

If z_1 is raised to the nth power, then we get

$$z_1^n = I_1^n e^{jn\varphi_1} \tag{50}$$

$$= I_1^n(\cos n\varphi_1 + j \sin n\varphi_1) \tag{51}$$

The nth root:

The nth root of z_1 is described as follows:

$$z^{1/n} = [I_1(\cos\varphi_1 + j\sin\varphi_1)]^{1/n} \tag{52}$$

$$= I_1^{1/n}(\cos\theta + j\sin\theta) \tag{53}$$

where

$$\theta = \frac{\varphi + 2\pi k}{n} \qquad k = 0, 1, 2, \ldots, n-1 \tag{54}$$

ELEMENTARY FUNCTIONS OF THE COMPLEX VARIABLE[1]—THE TAYLOR AND LAURENT SERIES

9. Introduction. The full significance of the Fourier and Laplace transforms cannot be fully understood without an understanding of the fundamental behavior of functions in the complex plane. The following treatment will discuss this fundamental behavior and will include the development of the Taylor and Laurent series, the former being an important basic formulation in communication-engineering analysis (see Chap. 8) and the latter being a fundamental concept in the calculus of residues, which will be discussed later in the chapter.

10. Elementary Properties of Functions of a Complex Variable. Consider the function of a complex variable z where, as we have seen,

$$z = x + jy \tag{3}$$

In general, we may write

$$f(z) = u(x,y) + jv(x,y) \tag{55}$$

where $u(x,y)$ and $v(x,y)$ are real functions of the variables x and y.

As an illustration, it follows that if

$$f(z) = z^2 \tag{56}$$

then, squaring (3) and separating the real and imaginary parts, we get

$$u(x,y) = x^2 - y^2 \tag{57}$$

$$v(x,y) = 2xy \tag{58}$$

In dealing with the complex plane, we shall be concerned with continuity. In general it may be stated that the function $f(z)$ is continuous at the point z_0, provided that

$$f(z) \rightarrow f(z_0) \tag{59}$$

when

$$z \rightarrow z_0 \tag{60}$$

If the function $f(z)$ is continuous at every point in some region R of the x, jy plane, then $f(z)$ is said to be continuous in the region R. We

[1] N. W. McLachlan, "Complex Variable and Operational Calculus," The Macmillan Company, New York, 1942.

R. V. Churchill, "Modern Operational Mathematics in Engineering," Chap. V, McGraw-Hill Book Company, Inc., New York, 1944.

may establish functional relationships for functions of the complex variables in continuous regions by considering the derivatives of such functions. If an increment Δz is added to z, then

$$z + \Delta z = x + \Delta x + j(y + \Delta y) \tag{61}$$

where it is evident that

$$\Delta z = \Delta x + j\Delta y \tag{62}$$

It follows then that

$$f'(z) = \lim_{\Delta z \to 0} \frac{f(z + \Delta z) - f(z)}{\Delta z} \tag{63}$$

If the limit exists, let us consider the behavior of such a derivative if $f(z + \Delta z)$ is allowed to approach $f(z)$ by any of an infinite number of paths. If, for example, we choose a path such that $\Delta y = 0$ and $\Delta z = \Delta x$, then

$$\frac{df(z)}{dz} = \frac{\partial f(z)}{\partial x} \tag{64}$$

$$= \frac{\partial u}{\partial x} + j\frac{\partial v}{\partial x} \tag{65}$$

If we choose a path such that $\Delta x = 0$ and $\Delta z = j\Delta y$, then

$$\frac{df(z)}{dz} = -j\frac{\partial f(z)}{\partial y} \tag{66}$$

$$= \frac{\partial v}{\partial y} - j\frac{\partial u}{\partial y} \tag{67}$$

Combining (65) and (67), we get the relationships

$$\frac{\partial u}{\partial x} = \frac{\partial v}{\partial y} \qquad \frac{\partial v}{\partial x} = -\frac{\partial u}{\partial y} \tag{68}$$

These are the Cauchy-Riemann differential equations. If these equations hold for a $f(z)$ in a region R, then a unique derivative of $f(z)$ exists and the function is said to be analytic in this region.

As an example, consider the function

$$f(z) = z^2 = x^2 - y^2 + 2jxy \tag{69}$$

which is described by (57) and (58). Then

$$\frac{\partial u}{\partial x} = 2x = \frac{\partial v}{\partial y} \tag{70}$$

$$\frac{\partial v}{\partial x} = 2y = -\frac{\partial u}{\partial y} \tag{71}$$

thus showing that z^2 is analytic at every point where z is finite.

11. Line Integrals and Green's Lemma. Consider a function $f(z)$ which is analytic over a region R which is bounded by a single closed curve, and let C be any curve which lies in R and which connects two points A and B. Let the curve be divided into k sections, $\Delta z_1, \Delta z_2, \ldots, \Delta z_k$, whose projections on the x and jy axes are $\Delta x_1, \Delta x_2, \ldots, \Delta x_k$ and $j\Delta y_1, j\Delta y_2, \ldots, j\Delta y_k$, respectively. Now form the sum

$$\sum_{n=1}^{k} f(z_n)\,\Delta z_n \tag{72}$$

As k approaches infinity such that each subsequent length approaches zero, then, if the limit exists, it follows that

$$\lim_{k\to\infty} \sum_{n=1}^{k} f(z_n)\,\Delta z_n = \int_C f(z)\,dz \tag{73}$$

$\int_C f(z)\,dz$ is the line or contour integral of $f(z)$ along C. C is the field of integration, and its end points will define the limits of the integral such that

$$\int_A^B f(z)\,dz = F(B) - F(A) \tag{74}$$

where $F(B)$ and $F(A)$ represent the evaluation of the integral at B and A, respectively.

Line integrals and surface integrals of the regions enclosed by the contours in the complex plane are related as follows:

Consider the functions $u(x,y)$ and $v(x,y)$ which describe a closed contour

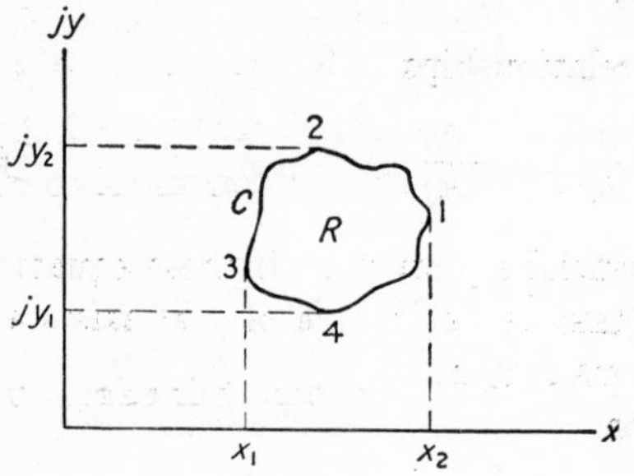

Fig. 6.

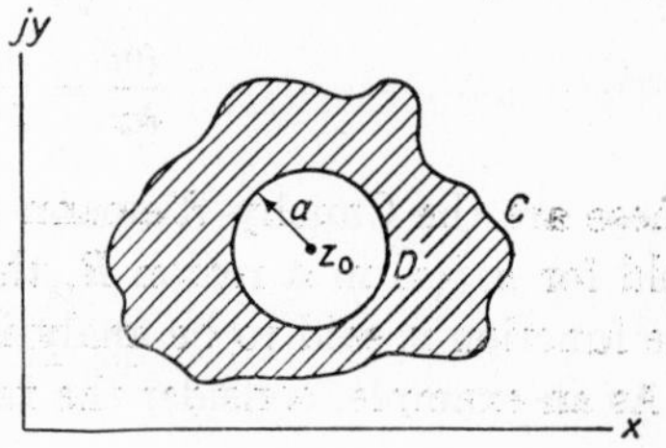

Fig. 7.

C in the x, jy plane. If this contour encloses a region R such as that pictured in Fig. 6, then

$$\int_C f(z)\,dz = \int_C (u\,dx - v\,dy) + j\int_C (v\,dx + u\,dy)$$

$$= \iint_R \left(-\frac{\partial v}{\partial x} - \frac{\partial u}{\partial y}\right) dx\,dy + j \iint_R \left(\frac{\partial u}{\partial x} - \frac{\partial v}{\partial y}\right) dx\,dy \tag{75}$$

This is a form of Green's theorem.[1] It relates the integrand of a contour integral of an analytic region in the complex plane to certain first derivatives which constitute the integrand of a surface integral pertaining to that region. Its statement is basic to concepts in the theory of analytic functions, as will be shown in the discussion of the Cauchy-Riemann equations in the next section.

12. The Cauchy-Goursat Theorem. Consider the function $f(z)$ which is analytic in the region R which is bounded by the closed contour C in the complex plane. Since $f(z)$ must satisfy the Cauchy-Riemann equations, substitution of these equations [see (68)] into (75) yields the Cauchy-Goursat theorem

$$\int_C f(z)\,dz = 0 \tag{76}$$

thus showing that the line integral along the closed contour which bounds a region in which $f(z)$ is analytic is equal to zero. It is also true that if the line integral of a single-valued continuous function around every closed curve in a region R is equal to zero, that function is analytic in R.

13. The Contour Integral of $f(z) = 1/z$. A contour integral of $1/z$ when taken about a closed curve which encloses the point $z = 0$ will not equal zero owing to the singularity at that point. Consider a contour C which is a circle of radius $r = a$ which encloses $z = 0$. Then, since we may replace z by $ae^{i\theta}$ for this contour,

$$\int_C \frac{dz}{z} = \int_0^{2\pi} \frac{1}{ae^{i\theta}}\, jae^{i\theta}\,d\theta \tag{77}$$

$$= j\int_0^{2\pi} d\theta = 2\pi j \tag{78}$$

By the same method, we may show that, for a singular point at $z = z_0$,

$$\int_C \frac{dz}{z - z_0} = 2\pi j \tag{79}$$

14. The Cauchy Integral Formula. Let $f(z)$ be analytic throughout some region R which is enclosed by a curve C. If z_0 is some point in the interior of R as is pictured in Fig. 7, then $f(z)/(z - z_0)$ is analytic at every point in R except at the singular point at $z = z_0$. If z_0 is excluded from the region R by the circle D whose radius is a and which is centered at $z = z_0$, then $f(z)/(z - z_0)$ is analytic in the shaded region in Fig. 7 and it is easily shown, using the Cauchy-Goursat theorem, that

$$\int_C \frac{f(z)}{z - z_0}\,dz = \int_D \frac{f(z)}{z - z_0}\,dz \tag{80}$$

[1] For an extensive discussion of Green's theorem, see Chap. V of I. S. Sokolnikoff, "Advanced Calculus," McGraw-Hill Book Company., Inc., New York, 1939.

This may be written, using Eq. (79), as follows:

$$\int_D \frac{f(z)}{z - z_0}\, dz = \int_D \frac{f(z) - f(z_0)}{z - z_0}\, dz + 2\pi j f(z_0) \tag{81}$$

Note that if we let

$$z - z_0 = ae^{j\theta} \tag{82}$$

then

$$\int_D \frac{f(z) - f(z_0)}{z - z_0}\, dz = j \int_D [f(z) - f(z_0)]\, d\theta \tag{83}$$

and it is easily proved that

$$\lim_{a \to 0} \int_D \frac{f(z) - f(z_0)}{z - z_0}\, dz = 0 \tag{84}$$

Then

$$\int_D \frac{f(z)}{z - z_0}\, dz = 2\pi j f(z_0) \tag{85}$$

whereupon

$$f(z_0) = \frac{1}{2\pi j} \int_D \frac{f(z)}{z - z_0}\, dz \tag{86}$$

where $f(z)$ traverses C in a counterclockwise direction.

This integral relationship is known as Cauchy's integral formula, and it permits us to calculate the value of an analytic function $f(z)$ at any region bounded by a simple closed curve C from the boundary values of $f(z)$ on C.

We may demonstrate the validity of (86) by determining the value of the integral relationship for the case $f(z) = z^2$ at $z = a$. The result should, of course, be $f(a) = a^2$.

In order to evaluate the integral

$$f(a) = \frac{1}{2\pi j} \int_C \frac{z^2}{z - a}\, dz \tag{87}$$

let us make the substitution $z - a = x$ such that

$$\begin{aligned} dz &= dx \\ z &= a + x \end{aligned} \tag{88}$$

Then

$$f(a) = \frac{1}{2\pi j} \int_C \frac{(x + a)^2}{x}\, dx \tag{89}$$

$$= \frac{1}{2\pi j} \int_C \left(x + 2a + \frac{a^2}{x} \right) dx = a^2 \tag{90}$$

which was to be expected.

15. Differentiation of the Integral Relationship (86). The derivative of $f(z)$ is

$$f'(z) = \lim_{\Delta z \to 0} \frac{f(z + \Delta z) - f(z)}{\Delta z} \tag{91}$$

Consider now the derivative of the integral, (86). It follows from (91) that, when evaluated at $z = z_0$,

$$f'(z_0) = \lim_{\Delta z \to 0} \frac{1}{2\pi j} \frac{1}{\Delta z} \left[\int_C \frac{f(z)\, dz}{z - z_0 - \Delta z} - \int_C \frac{f(z)\, dz}{z - z_0} \right] \tag{92}$$

Combining the integrands, we get

$$f'(z_0) = \lim_{\Delta z \to 0} \frac{1}{2\pi j} \int_C \frac{f(z)\, dz}{(z - z_0 - \Delta z)(z - z_0)} \tag{93}$$

$$= \frac{1}{2\pi j} \int_C \frac{f(z)\, dz}{(z - z_0)^2} \tag{94}$$

In like manner, we may show that

$$f^n(z_0) = \frac{n!}{2\pi j} \int_C \frac{f(z)\, dz}{(z - z_0)^{n+1}} \tag{95}$$

If $f(z)$ is analytic, all higher derivatives exist and are analytic.

16. Derivation of Taylor's Series. Consider a function $f(z)$ which is analytic in a region R. Let z_0 be some point in R, and let C be a circle of radius r, which is in R and which is centered at z_0. Then, using the Cauchy integral formula, we may write, letting t be the variable of integration,

$$f(z) = \frac{1}{2\pi j} \int_C \frac{f(t)\, dt}{t - z} \tag{96}$$

$$= \frac{1}{2\pi j} \int_C \frac{f(t)\, dt}{(t - z_0) - (z - z_0)} \tag{97}$$

It is easily shown that

$$\frac{1}{(t - z_0) - (z - z_0)} = \frac{1}{t - z_0} + \frac{z - z_0}{(t - z_0)^2} + \frac{(z - z_0)^2}{(t - z_0)^3} + \cdots + \frac{(z - z_0)^{n+1}}{(t - z_0)^{n+1}(t - z)} \tag{98}$$

Substituting (98) into (97), we get

$$f(z) = \frac{1}{2\pi j} \int_C \frac{f(t)}{t - z_0}\, dt + \frac{z - z_0}{2\pi j} \int_C \frac{f(t)}{(t - z_0)^2}\, dt + \cdots + \frac{(z - z_0)^{n+1}}{2\pi j} \int_C \frac{f(t)\, dt}{(t - z_0)^{n+1}(t - z)} \tag{99}$$

which, using the integral formula listed in (95), yields the *Taylor series* (see Sec. 6, Chap. 8),

$$f(z) = f(z_0) + (z - z_0)f'(z_0) + \cdots + \frac{f^n(z_0)}{n!}(z - z_0)^n + R_{n+1} \tag{100}$$

where R_{n+1} is the Taylor-series remainder, *i.e.*,

$$R_{n+1} = \frac{(z - z_0)^{n+1}}{2\pi j} \int_C \frac{f(t)\,dt}{(t - z_0)^{n+1}(t - z)} \tag{101}$$

Let $|f(t)| \leq M$ on C. Then, since for t on C

$$r = |t - z_0| \tag{102}$$

$$|t - z| \geq r - |z - z_0| \tag{103}$$

it follows from (101) that[1]

$$|R_{n+1}| = \frac{Mr}{r - |z - z_0|}\left(\frac{|z - z_0|}{r}\right)^{n+1} \tag{104}$$

Since $|z - z_0| < r$, $|R_{n+1}|$ may be made very small by making n large.

When $z_0 = 0$ in (100), the resultant series is known as a *Maclaurin series* (both series are often referred to as power series). Taylor and Maclaurin series are widely encountered in communication analysis; for example, the Maclaurin-series expansion of the rotating vector $e^{j\varphi t}$ may be described as follows:

$$e^{j\varphi t} = 1 + j\varphi t - \frac{(\varphi t)^2}{2!} + \cdots \tag{105}$$

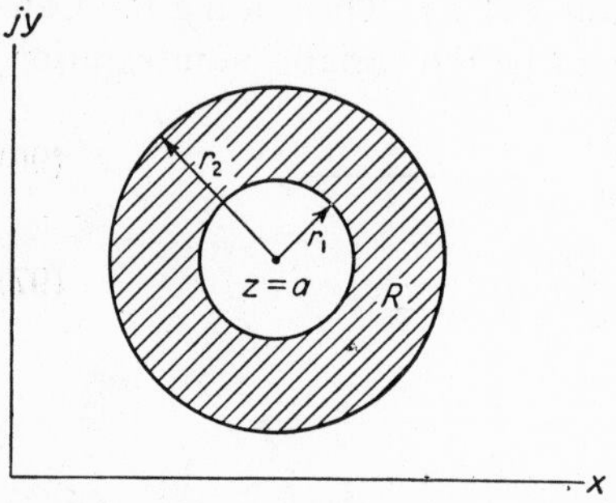

FIG. 8.

17. Laurent's Theorem. We have seen in the preceding section that a power series of the form

$$f(z) = c_1X + c_2X^2 + \cdots + c_nX^n + \cdots \tag{106}$$

may be used to represent $f(z)$ in some region where z is analytic. Consider now an annular ring-shaped region R with smaller radius r_1 and larger radius r_2, which is centered at $z = a$. This region is pictured in Fig. 8. The Taylor series

$$f_1(z) = c_0 + c_1(z - a) + c_2(z - a)^2 + \cdots + c_n(z - a)^n + \cdots \tag{107}$$

[1] See, for example, Secs. 101 and 102 in Reddick and Miller, "Advanced Mathematics for Engineers," 2d ed., John Wiley & Sons, Inc., New York, 1947.

will converge for all values within the larger circle. Consider, too, terms of the type

$$X = \frac{1}{z - a} \tag{108}$$

which yield the series

$$f_2(z) = c_{-1}(z - a)^{-1} + c_{-2}(z - a)^{-2} + c_{-3}(z - a)^{-3} + \cdots + c_{-n}(z - a)^{-n} + \cdots \tag{109}$$

This series contains descending powers; it converges for all values of $f(z)$ outside of the smaller circle. Since both (107) and (109) converge within R, we arrive at Laurent's theorem, which states that the series

$$f(z) = f_1(z) + f_2(z) \tag{110}$$

$$= c_0 + c_1(z - a) + c_2(z - a)^2 + \cdots + c_{-1}(z - a)^{-1} + c_{-2}(z - a)^{-2} + \cdots \tag{111}$$

$$= \sum_{n=-\infty}^{\infty} c_n(z - a)^n \tag{112}$$

is analytic inside the region R.

If a contour C is a circle of radius r, where $r_1 < r < r_2$, then[1]

$$c_n = \frac{1}{2\pi j} \int_C \frac{f(z)\, dz}{(z - a)^{n+1}} \qquad n = 0, \pm 1, \pm 2, \ldots \tag{113}$$

If $n \geq 0$, (113) yields the coefficients of the Taylor series.

In general, we may state that if a function $f(z)$ is analytic in a region R, a power-series representation of this function will be a Taylor series. If the function is not analytic in this region, a Laurent series will be obtained.

INTRODUCTION TO THE CALCULUS OF RESIDUES

18. Introduction. The calculus of residues is absolutely essential to solutions involving the inverse Laplace transform and certain Fourier integrals. Once its essentials are understood, it yields solutions in many problems involving the Laplace transform in a very simple and straightforward fashion.

[1] Actually different contours could be chosen for the calculation of c_{+n} and c_{-n}. However, if the same contour is chosen as indicated, the Laurent series will converge, at most, only on that contour since one part of the series will diverge inside the contour and the other will diverge outside of it. To obtain the greatest annular region of convergence, one contour should be taken at r_1, the smallest radius, and the other at r_2, the largest possible radius before encountering a singularity.

19. Singularities. Points at which a function ceases to be analytic in the complex plane are called singularities of the function. We have already encountered singularities in the functions $f(z) = 1/z$ and $f(z) = 1/(z - a)$, which have singularities at the points $z = 0$ and $z = a$, respectively. There are three important types of singularities. These are listed and discussed as follows:

1. Nonessential singularities or poles. This type of pole is termed nonessential since it can be removed if the function with the singularity is multiplied by the proper factor, for example, multiplying $1/(z - a)$ by $z - a$.

2. A function has essential singularities when it has poles of infinite order. The function $f(z) = e^{1/z}$ has such a singularity in virtue of the fact that its series representation

$$f(z) = 1 + \frac{1}{z} + \frac{1}{2!z^2} + \cdots \tag{114}$$

has an essential singularity at infinity since no multiplying factor may be evolved having a finite value of n which will remove the singularity.

3. A branch point, which occurs when a function has more than one value in the neighborhood of a point, is considered to be a singularity. The nth root of a complex number is a function which yields branch points since, as was seen in Sec. 8, more than one root may exist.

20. Evaluation of a Pole of a Simple Order. Consider the function

$$f(z) = \frac{c_{-1}}{z - a} + c_0 + c_1(z - a) + c_2(z - a)^2 + \cdots \tag{115}$$

which has a pole of order 1 (having a power of unity in the denominator). We may eliminate this nonessential pole by multiplying through by $z - a$ as follows,

$$(z - a)f(z) = c_{-1} + c_0(z - a) + c_1(z - a)^2 + \cdots \tag{116}$$

and it follows that

$$\lim_{z \to a} (z - a)f(z) = c_{-1} \tag{117}$$

c_{-1} is called the residue of the function of the complex variable at the pole.

It can be shown that since the pole is a simple one, (115) is a complete Laurent expansion of $f(z)$ at this pole.

21. Residues. A residue is the result of evaluating a function of complex variable at one of its poles. It is of extreme importance to the communications engineer since most problems in communication engineering which involve complex-plane integration and which have solutions different from zero have poles of various orders or types.

Let us first consider a geometrical interpretation of the residue at a pole.

The region R in Fig. 9a contains two poles, one at $z = a$ and one at $z = b$. Let us deform the contour such that, as is shown in Fig. 9b, the contour passes by each pole and is at all times continuous. The line integrals of the paths 1,4 and 2,3 which lie between the poles and between the pole

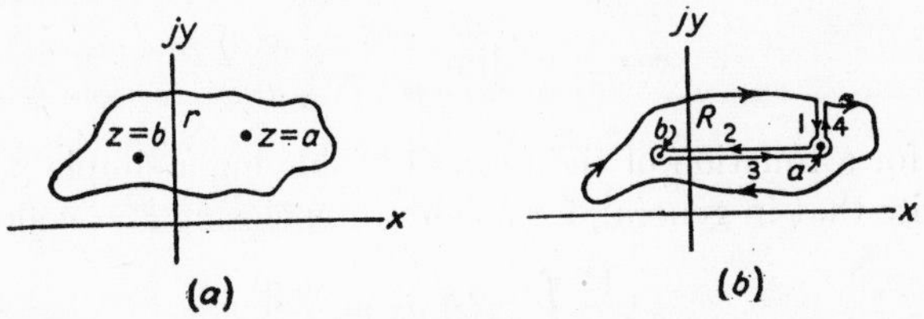

FIG. 9.

$z = a$ and the outer contour, of course, cancel, thus permitting these interpole contours to be entirely arbitrary or to be disregarded, with each of the poles enclosed by a complete circular contour. However, the line integral around each pole yields a residue, and in general we may write that

$$\frac{1}{2\pi j}\int_C f(z)\,dz = \sum^N \text{res} \tag{118}$$

where $\sum^N$ res represents the sum of the residues.

As was pointed out in the preceding section, the residue at each pole, say at $z = a$, of $f(z)$ is the coefficient of the term $1/(z - a)$ in its Laurent expansion such that

$$\text{res}_{z=a} = \frac{1}{2\pi j}\int_{C_a} f(z)\,dz \tag{119}$$

provided that the contour C_a encloses no poles except the one at $z = a$. Equation (118) then states that once each residue has been evaluated, their sum yields the value of the contour integral which encloses these poles.

22. Residues of Functions Having Simple Poles. In most problems, the Laurent expansion of $f(z)$ at each pole is not readily obtainable so that the relatively simple process of determining c_{-1} is not possible.

Consider an $f(z)$ of the form

$$f(z) = \frac{w(z)}{g(z)} \tag{120}$$

where $g(z)$ is factorable and yields a pole at $z = a$, $w(z)$ and $g(z)$ not having common factors. If we write

$$f(z) = \frac{w(z)}{(z - a)h(z)} \tag{121}$$

where $(z - a)h(z) = g(z)$, then for the simple pole at $z = a$ it follows that

$$\frac{w(z)}{(z-a)h(z)} = \frac{c_{-1}}{z-a} + c_0 + c_1(z-a) + c_2(z-a)^2 + \cdots \tag{122}$$

Multiplying both sides by $z - a$, we get for the residue

$$\text{res}_{z=a} = \lim_{z \to a} \frac{w(z)}{h(z)} = \frac{w(a)}{h(a)} \tag{123}$$

Therefore, for a function of the form (120) having a simple pole at $z = a$, we may write that in general, for a contour enclosing $z = a$ alone,

$$\frac{1}{2\pi j} \int_{C_a} f(z)\, dz = \frac{w(a)}{h(a)} \tag{124}$$

This operation represents an amazingly simple procedure for evaluating the contour integral. This simplicity will be found to enhance the use of the Laplace transform, which will be discussed in the chapters to follow.

If $f(z)$ contains more than one simple pole, then we may extend (124) to include considerations of the following:

If $f(z)$ has simple poles at $z = a$, $z = b$, $z = c$, etc., then, for the integral

$$\frac{1}{2\pi j} \int_C f(z)\, dz = \frac{1}{2\pi j} \int_C \frac{w(z)}{[(z-a)(z-b)\cdots]}\, dz \tag{125}$$

the residues at each pole may be listed as follows:

$$\frac{1}{2\pi j} \int_C f(z)\, dz = \sum \text{res} \tag{126}$$

$$= \frac{w(a)}{[(a-b)(a-c)\cdots]} + \frac{w(b)}{[(b-a)(b-c)\cdots]} + \cdots \tag{127}$$

If $g(z)$ is not readily factorable, we may evaluate the contour enclosing a simple pole at $z = a$ as follows: Using L'Hôpital's rule,

$$\text{res}_{z=a} = \lim_{z \to a} \frac{w(z) + (z-a)w'(z)}{g'(z)} \tag{128}$$

$$= \frac{w(a)}{g'(a)} \tag{129}$$

where $g'(a)$ is the derivative of $g(z)$ which is evaluated at $z = a$ (see Sec. 13, Chap. 6, for one of the many applications of Eq. (129) in this volume).

Use of (127). Consider the function

$$f(z) = \frac{e^z}{z^2 + a^2} \tag{130}$$

This may be written

$$f(z) = \frac{e^z}{(z + ja)(z - ja)} \tag{131}$$

thus showing that $f(z)$ has simple poles on the imaginary axis at $z = ja$ and $z = -ja$. These poles and a typical closed contour which encloses both poles are pictured in Fig. 10.

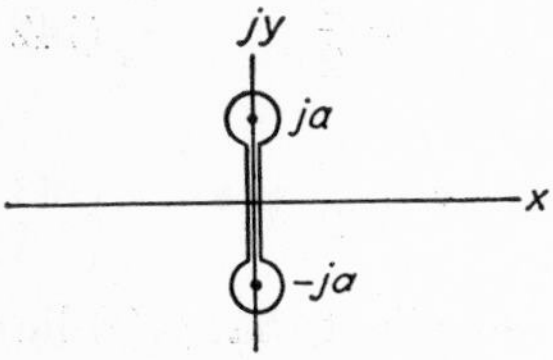

FIG. 10.

It follows from (127) that

$$\frac{1}{2\pi j}\int_C \frac{e^z}{z^2 + a^2}\,dz = \frac{e^{ja}}{2ja} + \frac{e^{-ja}}{-2ja} \tag{132}$$

$$= \frac{1}{a}\frac{e^{ja} - e^{-ja}}{2j} \tag{133}$$

$$= \frac{\sin a}{a} \tag{134}$$

23. Evaluation of the Residue at a Multiple Pole. Consider the function

$$f(z) = \frac{w(z)}{(z-a)^n h(z)} \tag{135}$$

which has a pole of order n at $z = a$. The Laurent expansion of $f(z)$ at $z = a$ is

$$f(z) = \frac{c_{-n}}{(z-a)^n} + \frac{c_{-n+1}}{(z-a)^{-n+1}} + \frac{c_{-n+2}}{(z-a)^{-n+2}}$$

$$+ \cdots + \frac{c_{-1}}{(z-a)^{-1}} + c_0 + c_1(z-a) + \cdots \tag{136}$$

Multiplying through by $(z - a)^n$ and then differentiating $n - 1$ times until the coefficient c_{-1} of $1/(z - a)$ is achieved, we find the residue at $z = a$ to be

$$\text{res}_{z=a} = \frac{1}{(n-1)!}\frac{d^{n-1}}{dz^{n-1}}[(z-a)^n f(z)]_{z=a} \tag{137}$$

Use of (137). Consider the function

$$f(z) = \frac{e^{bz}}{(z-a)^4} \tag{138}$$

which has a multiple pole of order 4 at $z = a$. It follows from (137) that the residue at $z = a$ is

$$\text{res}_{z=a} = \frac{1}{3!}\frac{d^3}{dz^3}[e^{bz}]_{z=a} \tag{139}$$

$$= \frac{b^3}{3!}e^{bz}\Big|_{z=a} \tag{140}$$

$$= \frac{b^3}{3!}e^{ba} \tag{141}$$

24. Branch-point Singularities. Consider the function $f(z) = z^{\frac{1}{2}}$. According to (53), this function has two roots, which are

$$f_1(z) = r^{\frac{1}{2}}\left(\cos\frac{\varphi}{2} + j\sin\frac{\varphi}{2}\right) \qquad \theta = \frac{\varphi}{2} \tag{142}$$

$$f_2(z) = r^{\frac{1}{2}}\left[\cos\left(\frac{\varphi}{2} + \pi\right) + j\sin\left(\frac{\varphi}{2} + \pi\right)\right] \qquad \theta = \frac{\varphi}{2} + \pi \tag{143}$$

If we restrict θ to the region $-\pi < \theta < \pi$, then it is evident that $f_1(z)$ lies in the first and second quadrants and $f_2(z)$ lies in the third and fourth quadrants, $f_1(z)$ and $f_2(z)$ are branches of $z^{\frac{1}{2}}$, and because these branches merge at $z = 0$, $f(z)$ has a branch point at $z = 0$ as a singularity.

Because of the branch point at $z = 0$, any complete contour which is drawn in the complex plane must avoid this point. This is done by placing what is known as a *barrier*[1] in the complex plane such that it passes through the origin and describes any suitable angle θ_0 with the real axis, as shown in Fig. 11. This barrier cannot be crossed, and since a contour such as that drawn in Fig. 11, which includes two lines which are independent and close to the barrier, does not enclose the singularity, the line integral around this contour is equal to zero, according to the Cauchy-Goursat theorem. The function, which has some value at some point on the contour, will regain this value after a complete circuit of the contour is made.

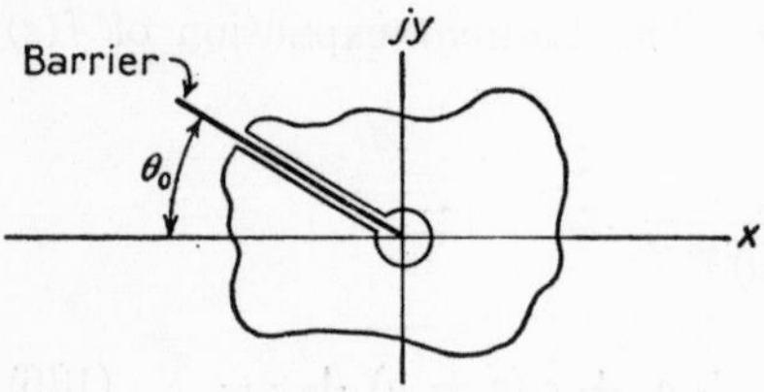

FIG. 11.

If simple or multiple poles are present in addition to a branch point, they may be evaluated as previously described since the contour may be altered to include these singularities, each of which may be treated independently.

PROBLEMS

1. Deduce the product of the complex numbers $3 + j4$ and $2 + j13$ in both cartesian and polar form.

2. Show that

$$\frac{x_1 + jy_1}{x_2 + jy_2} = \frac{x_1x_2 + y_1y_2}{x_2^2 + y_2^2} + j\frac{x_2y_1 - x_1y_2}{x_2^2 + y_2^2}$$

3. Show that

a. $|z_1z_2| = |z_1||z_2|$

b. $|z_1 + z_2| \leq |z_1| + |z_2|$

[1] For an illustration of the use of a barrier, see Chap. 4, Sec. 19.

c. $\left| \sum_{k=1}^{n} z_k \right| \leq \sum_{k=1}^{n} |z_k|$

4. Make a three-dimensional sketch of the vectors comprising the sum $\sin \omega_1 t + \cos \omega_1 t$.

5. Consider the rotating vector which starts its rotation at $\varphi = 0$ and $t = 0$ with an angular velocity of 2,050 radians per sec and continues to $t = \infty$.

a. What is its instantaneous frequency at $t =$ 13 min; 12 sec?

b. What is the total angular displacement achieved by the rotating vector in this interval?

6. What are the beat frequencies produced when the following waves are beat together:

a. $5e^{j7\times 10^8 t}$, $4e^{j10^8 t}$, $5e^{j2.5\times 10^8 t}$

b. $2e^{j10^8 t}$, $4e^{j2\times 10^8 t}$

7. Find the three cube roots of $z = 1 - j$.

8. Show that $f(z) = 1/z$ satisfies the Cauchy-Riemann equations at all points except $z = 0$.

9. Show that $f(z) = x^2 + y^2$ does not satisfy the Cauchy-Riemann equation at any point.

10. Prove the following line integral relationships:

a. $\int_{z_1}^{z_2} e^{kz}\, dz = \frac{1}{k}(e^{kz_2} - e^{kz_1})$

b. $\int_{z_1}^{z_2} \frac{dz}{z^{m+1}} = -\frac{1}{m}(z^{-mz_2} - z^{-mz_1})$

11. If R is a region bounded by a simple curve C,

a. Show that the area of R is

$$\tfrac{1}{2} \int_C (x\, dy - y\, dx).$$

b. Using (*a*), find the area of a circle.

12. Compute the value of

$$\int_{0,0}^{3,2} [(x^2 + y^2)\, dx + (x^2 - y^2)\, dy]$$

along the path $3y^2 = 4x$.

13. Find the Taylor expansion of (*a*) $\cosh z$; (*b*) $\tanh z$.

14. Show that the Laurent expansion of $(4z^2 - 4z + 1)/z^3(1 - z)$ is

$$\frac{1}{z^3} - \frac{3}{z^2} + \frac{1}{z} + 1 + z + z^2 + z^3$$

15. Find the residues of the function $e^z/(z^2 + a^2)(z^2 + b^2)$.

CHAPTER 2

PERIODIC-WAVE ANALYSIS—THE FOURIER SERIES

No one admires Fourier more than I do. It is the only entertaining mathematical work I ever saw. Its lucidity has always been admired. But it is more than lucid. It was luminous. Its light showed a crowd of followers the way to a heap of new problems.

HEAVISIDE

1. Introduction. In this chapter we shall be concerned with the formulation of a mathematical description of the decomposition of a nonsinusoidal periodic wave into a wave set made up of an infinite number of simple harmonic waves. The resulting infinite series describing these component waves is known as a Fourier series.[1]

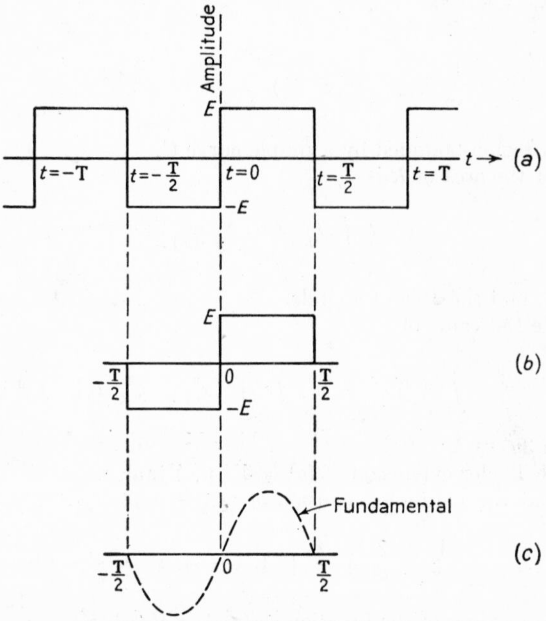

FIG. 1. Periodic square wave and fundamental.

[1] J. Fourier, "The Analytic Theory of Heat," G. E. Stechert & Company, New York, 1945.

As a preliminary illustration of wave superposition, consider the periodic square wave of amplitude E and period T which is illustrated in Fig. 1*a*. A single period has been separated from the main periodic wave and is pictured in Fig. 1*b*. Its form may be compared with that of the sine wave with the same period which is pictured in Fig. 1*c*. This sine wave is known as the *fundamental* of this period since only one complete cycle of the wave is completed in this period.[1] If two complete cycles of any simple harmonic wave were completed in this fundamental period, this wave would be called the *second harmonic.* If three complete cycles of this wave were completed, the wave would be termed the *third harmonic,* etc.

If two electric wave generators are connected in series, the output waveform of the system formed by the two consists of the superposition of the individual waveforms of each generator. One is then led to wonder if, by suitable choice of wave amplitudes and periods of the output of two sinusoidal generators, the square wave in Fig. 1*a* might be approximated. This is accomplished as illustrated in Fig. 2. The wave of frequency f and amplitude E_1 in Fig. 2*a* is superimposed on the wave of frequency $3f$ and amplitude E_2 shown in Fig. 2*b*. The result, which is shown in Fig. 2*c*, is a wave whose shape closely approximates the shape of the square wave in Fig. 1*b*. If more harmonic generators with correct amplitudes and periods were added in series, a better approximation would be obtained, whereas with a suitable infinite set of series generators the output would be an exact representation of the wave shown in Fig. 1*b*.

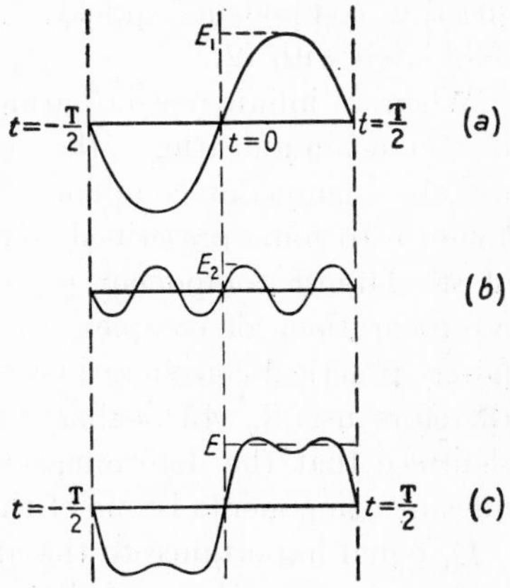

FIG. 2.

If any nonsinusoidal wave may be validly described by a combination of rotating vectors or sinusoidal wave generators [note, for example, that $\sin \omega t = (e^{j\omega t}/2j) - (e^{-j\omega t}/2j)$] of different angular velocity or frequency, then these rotating vectors constitute the *spectrum* of the wave. A chart of the spectral components as a function of frequency or angular velocity is particularly useful to the communications engineer since it permits him to assimilate, at a glance, the spectral information pertaining to the wave being analyzed.

[1] Actually, although this specification is essential, it is not sufficient. For any simple harmonic wave of correct period to be the fundamental or some harmonic of a complex wave, its amplitude and phase must be commensurate with those prescribed by the Fourier analysis of the wave.

Consider, as an illustration, the fundamental, third, and fifth harmonic waves making up the wave pictured in Fig. 2*c*. If this wave may be described by the equation

$$f(t) = E \sin \omega t + \frac{E}{3} \sin 3\omega t + \frac{E}{5} \sin 5\omega t \tag{1}$$

$$= \frac{E}{2j} e^{j\omega t} - \frac{E}{2j} e^{-j\omega t} + \frac{E}{6j} e^{j3\omega t} - \frac{E}{6j} e^{-j3\omega t} + \frac{E}{10j} e^{j5\omega t} - \frac{E}{10j} e^{-j5\omega t} \tag{2}$$

then the rotating vectors listed in (2) may be pictured as shown in Fig. 3 in terms of their absolute amplitudes. It is evident that the chart of

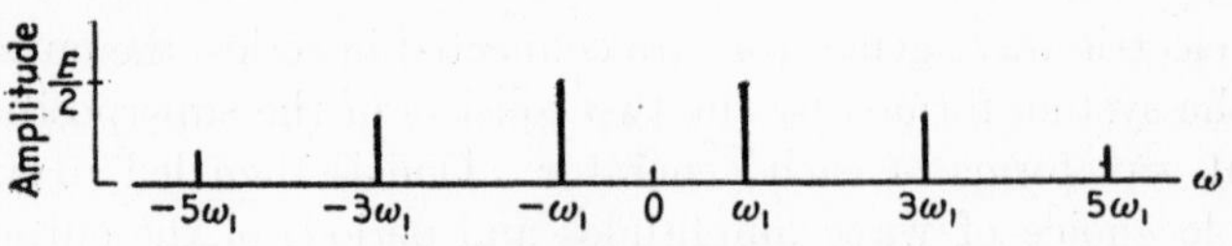

FIG. 3. Amplitude spectrum.

spectral components quickly yields the spectral information which is associated with (2).

When an infinite set of harmonic components is encountered in a problem in communications, the concept of *significant* components becomes useful. Significant components are those components whose amplitudes conform to some prescribed condition—some percentage of the amplitude of the largest component present, for example. In most Fourier-series representations of complex waves, it is not difficult to determine—from purely practical considerations—those harmonics which are significant and therefore useful. In dealing with modulated-wave spectra, however, we shall see that the determination of the position and distribution of significant components is one of the major problems involved.

Of equal importance to the amplitude spectrum of a wave is its energy spectrum. Since in general the energy in a wave will be proportional to the square of the amplitude of that wave, it is evident that the energy corresponding to spectral components of small amplitude will become unimportant in practical considerations, thus making the number of significant *energy* spectral components, corresponding to some nonsinusoidal wave, less in number than the corresponding significant *amplitude* components representing that wave.

There are two ways of writing the Fourier series. The first is the trigonometric form. In certain applications, the use of the trigonometric Fourier series will permit the electrical engineer or physicist to visualize the problem to great advantage since much of his background has been concerned with the real-wave output of sine-wave generators. The other form is known as the complex Fourier series. The use of the word *complex* arises from the fact that the complex Fourier series is a complex-plane representation and will be seen to consist of an infinite set of rotating vectors. This is a limited use of the word, since it will, in general, be used to identify waves which are not simple harmonic (nonsinusoidal), *viz.*, *complex waves.* Owing to the fact that the rotating-vector concept is different from the real-sine-wave-generator concept, a separate section is devoted to each of the two forms of the Fourier series.

In the chapters to follow, the complex Fourier series will enjoy the greatest usage in modulated-wave analysis; the trigonometric Fourier series will be used principally in the analysis of periodic complex waves. In some cases, both types of Fourier series may be used simultaneously, as will be demonstrated in the analysis of complex periodic phase-modulated and frequency-modulated waves in Chap. 18.

THE TRIGONOMETRIC FOURIER SERIES

2. Orthogonal Functions and the Trigonometric Fourier Series. We shall show that a complex periodic wave whose period is $T = 2\pi/\omega$ may be represented by the trigonometric Fourier series

$$f(t) = \frac{a_0}{2} + \sum_{n=1}^{\infty} (a_n \cos n\omega t + b_n \sin n\omega t) \tag{3}$$

$$= \frac{a_0}{2} + a_1 \cos \omega t + a_2 \cos 2\omega t + \cdots$$

$$+ b_1 \sin \omega t + b_2 \sin 2\omega t + \cdots \tag{4}$$

This is an infinite series made up of the sum of both sine and cosine terms whose frequencies are multiples of the fundamental frequency $\omega/2\pi$.

As will be shown in the next section, the Fourier-series representation of a complex periodic wave is due to the orthogonal properties of the trigonometric functions involved. At this point, the question might be asked: Why have we limited ourselves to a series of sine and cosine functions since there are numerous sets of functions which are orthogonal and which could be used to provide a mathematical substitution for the amplitude variation as a function of time in this interval? It would be possible to show, for example, that a set of Legendre functions could be combined to form the square wave in Fig. 1. However, when sine or cosine sets are used, one is able to augment the mathematical concept with a firm physical concept. Every electrical engineer or physicist is familiar with a sine-wave generator. The variation of the amplitude of its output and the relationship between the average, root-mean-square (rms), and peak values of sinusoidal waves are concepts that he has acquired through long experience. The concept of impedance of electrical networks is also a familiar one. In addition, numerous problems in physics, such as the vibrating string problem, in which sinusoidal waves occur, are constantly encountered. These and associated concepts play a large part in clarifying the usage of the Fourier series.

3. Derivation of the Trigonometric Fourier Series. Owing to the fact that the functions

$$1,\ \cos \omega t,\ \sin \omega t,\ \cos 2\omega t,\ \sin 2\omega t,\ \ldots \tag{5}$$

constitute an orthogonal set, the following identities must hold:

$$\begin{aligned} \int_0^{2\pi} \cos n\omega t \cos m\omega t \, d\omega t &= 0 \qquad m \neq n \\ &= \pi \qquad m = n \neq 0 \end{aligned} \tag{6}$$

$$\begin{aligned} \int_0^{2\pi} \sin n\omega t \sin m\omega t \, d\omega t &= 0 \qquad m \neq n \\ &= \pi \qquad m = n \end{aligned} \tag{7}$$

Also

$$\int_{-\pi}^{\pi} \sin n\omega t \cos m\omega t \, d\omega t = \int_{-\pi}^{\pi} \sin n\omega t \, d\omega t = \int_{-\pi}^{\pi} \cos m\omega t \, d\omega t = 0 \tag{8}$$

We wish then to determine the coefficients a_0, a_n, and b_n of the Fourier series (3).

To determine a_0, multiply (3) through by $d\omega t$ and integrate from $-\pi$ to π. It follows, using (8), that

$$\int_{-\pi}^{\pi} f(\omega t) \, d\omega t = \frac{a_0}{2} \omega t \Big|_{-\pi}^{\pi} = a_0 \pi \tag{9}$$

or

$$\frac{a_0}{2} = \frac{1}{2\pi} \int_{-\pi}^{\pi} f(\omega t) \, d\omega t \tag{10}$$

To determine a_n, multiply (3) through by $\cos m\omega t \, d\omega t$ and integrate from $-\pi$ to π. Using (8), we get

$$\int_{-\pi}^{\pi} f(\omega t) \cos m\omega t \, d\omega t = \sum_{n=1}^{\infty} a_n \int_{-\pi}^{\pi} \cos n\omega t \cos m\omega t \, d\omega t \tag{11}$$

Letting $m = n$, it follows from (6) that

$$\int_{-\pi}^{\pi} f(\omega t) \cos n\omega t \, d\omega t = a_n \int_{-\pi}^{\pi} \cos^2 n\omega t \, d\omega t = a_n \pi \tag{12}$$

or

$$a_n = \frac{1}{\pi} \int_{-\pi}^{\pi} f(\omega t) \cos n\omega t \, d\omega t \tag{13}$$

Multiplying (3) through by sin $m\omega t\,d\omega t$, it follows in like manner that

$$b_n = \frac{1}{\pi}\int_{-\pi}^{\pi} f(\omega t) \sin n\omega t\,d\omega t \tag{14}$$

4. The Trigonometric Fourier Series. The complete trigonometric Fourier series is expressed as follows,

$$f(\omega t) = \frac{a_0}{2} + \sum_{n=1}^{\infty} (a_n \cos n\omega t + b_n \sin n\omega t) \tag{15}$$

where

$$\frac{a_0}{2} = \frac{1}{2\pi}\int_{-\pi}^{\pi} f(\omega t)\,d\omega t \tag{10}$$

$$a_n = \frac{1}{\pi}\int_{-\pi}^{\pi} f(\omega t) \cos n\omega t\,d\omega t \tag{13}$$

$$b_n = \frac{1}{\pi}\int_{-\pi}^{\pi} f(\omega t) \sin n\omega t\,d\omega t \tag{14}$$

If this Fourier series is to represent $f(\omega t)$ outside of the interval, $-\pi < \omega t < \pi$, $f(\omega t)$ must be periodic; that is,

$$f(\omega t) = f(\omega t + 2\pi) \tag{16}$$

5. Mathematical Aspects of the Fourier Series. The complete mathematical picture of the Fourier series, taking into consideration the details of existence, convergence, etc., is beyond the scope of this book. However, we may summarize certain important aspects of the convergence, differentiation, and integration of the Fourier series as follows.[1]

Convergence of Fourier Series. Let $f(\omega t)$ satisfy the following conditions:

1. $f(\omega t) = f(\omega t + 2\pi)$.
2. $f(\omega t)$ is sectionally continuous[2] in the interval $-\pi < \omega t < \pi$. Then the Fourier series

$$f(\omega t) = \frac{a_0}{2} + \sum_{n=1}^{\infty} (a_n \cos n\omega t + b_n \sin n\omega t) \tag{17}$$

converges to the value[3]

$$\tfrac{1}{2}[f(\omega t + 0) + f(\omega t - 0)] \tag{18}$$

[1] See R. V. Churchill, "Fourier Series and Boundary Value Problems," McGraw-Hill Book Company, Inc., New York, 1941.

[2] A function is sectionally (or piecewise) continuous in a finite interval if that interval can be divided into a finite number of subintervals in each of which the function is continuous and has finite limits as the function approaches either end point from the interior of one of the subintervals.

[3] The symbol $f(\omega t_1 + 0)$ denotes the limit of $f(\omega t)$ as ωt approaches ωt_1 from the right, and the symbol $f(\omega t_1 - 0)$ denotes the limit of $f(\omega t)$ as ωt approaches ωt_1 from the left.

at every point where $f(\omega t)$ has right- and left-hand derivatives in the domain $-\infty < \omega t < \infty$.

Differentiation of the Fourier Series. Differentiation of Eq. (3), which has been seen to be convergent, yields

$$\frac{d}{d\omega t} f(\omega t) = \sum_{n=t}^{\infty} (-na_n \sin n\omega t + nb_n \cos n\omega t) \tag{19}$$

Each nth term is now multiplied by n. Since the presence of the n in the coefficient will decrease the rate of convergence of the series (if it does not actually cause it to diverge), it can be shown that the Fourier series can be differentiated termwise at every point where $f'(\omega t)$ has a derivative.

Integration of Fourier Series. Consider the integration of Eq. (3), which yields

$$\int f(\omega t)\, d\omega t = \int \frac{a_0}{2}\, d\omega t + \int \sum_{n=1}^{\infty} (a_n \cos n\omega t + b_n \sin n\omega t)\, d\omega t \tag{20}$$

$$= \int \frac{a_0}{2}\, d\omega t + \sum_{n=1}^{\infty} \left(\frac{a_n}{n} \sin n\omega t - \frac{b_n}{n} \cos n\omega t \right) \tag{21}$$

Since (3) was already convergent, the presence of the n in each of the two summations in Eq. (21) causes the series to converge even more rapidly than before integration. In fact, it is not even necessary that Eq. (3) converge to its function to permit integration or that the integrated series integrate to the integral of the function $f(\omega t)$, since the integrated series is not a Fourier series if $a_0 \neq 0$ since it now contains the term $\int (a_0/2)\, d\omega t$. Therefore, we see that termwise integration of the Fourier series is possible under far more general conditions than those for differentiation.

6. The Periodic Square Wave. The first section of this chapter discussed the matter of approximating the output of a square-wave generator by the superposition of the outputs to two sine-wave generators. It is convenient at this point to develop this square-wave output in the form

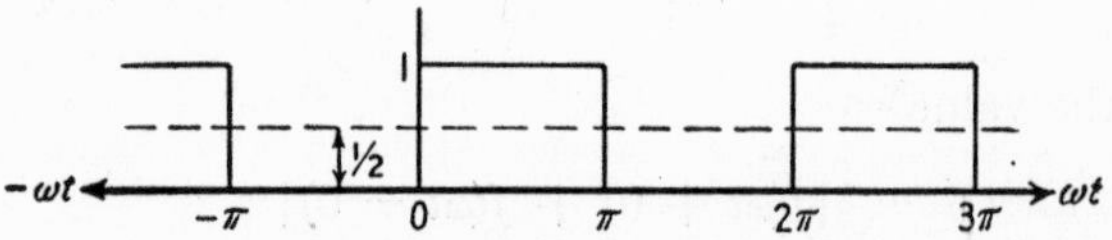

FIG. 4. Periodic square wave.

of a Fourier series. The periodic function pictured in Fig. 4 may be expressed mathematically for the interval $-\pi < \omega t < \pi$ as follows:

$$\begin{aligned} f(\omega t) &= 0 \qquad -\pi < \omega t < 0 \\ &= 1 \qquad 0 < \omega t < \pi \end{aligned} \tag{22}$$

Then, using (10), we get

$$\frac{a_0}{2} = \frac{1}{2\pi}\int_0^\pi d\omega t = \frac{1}{2} \tag{23}$$

This is the average value of $f(\omega t)$ and is shown as a dotted line in Fig. 5. From Eq. (13) we see that

$$a_n = \frac{1}{\pi}\int_0^\pi \cos n\omega t \, d\omega t = 0 \tag{24}$$

which shows that the amplitudes of the cosine terms are equal to zero. The significance of the zero value yielded by this integral for all nonzero values of n will be discussed in Sec. 8 in terms of the odd properties of the wave.[1] From Eq. (14), it follows that

$$b_n = \frac{1}{\pi}\int_0^\pi \sin n\omega t \, d\omega t \tag{25}$$

$$= \frac{1}{\pi n}(1 - \cos n\pi) \tag{26}$$

The Fourier-series representation of (22) is then found to be

$$f(\omega t) = \frac{1}{2} + \sum_{n=1}^{\infty} \frac{1-(-1)^n}{\pi n} \sin n\omega t \tag{27}$$

$$= \frac{1}{2} + \frac{2}{\pi}\sin \omega t + \frac{2}{3\pi}\sin 3\omega t + \frac{2}{5\pi}\sin 5\omega t + \cdots \tag{28}$$

The summation of a set of terms from (28) is shown in Fig. 5. The first term is, of course, the average value of $\frac{1}{2}$. The summation of the first

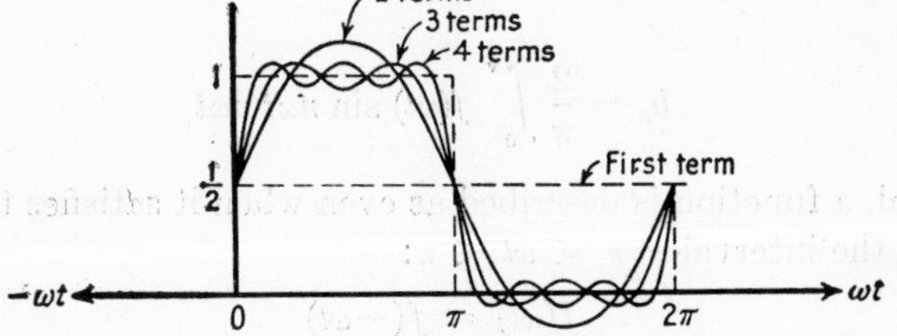

FIG. 5. Summation of terms from (28) showing the formation of the square wave by the superposition of harmonics.

two terms represents the superposition of the average value and the fundamental. The summation of the first three terms shows the result of adding the third harmonic, etc. The close approximation yielded by only four terms to the original square wave is clearly illustrated.

[1] For an illustration of a trigonometric Fourier series having both sine and cosine terms, see, for example, Chap. 8, Sec. 2.

7. Odd and Even Functions. We have seen that when the periodic square wave in Fig. 4 was expanded into a Fourier series, only a sine series resulted. By recognizing the conditions under which either a sine or a cosine series will occur alone, considerable mathematical manipulation can be avoided. These conditions are based on whether the time or phase function is an odd or an even function, even functions producing cosine series and odd functions producing the sine series. In general, a complex wave which is neither even nor odd can be described as the sum of an odd function and an even function, thus causing both a sine series and a cosine series to appear in the general Fourier-series wave representation.

8. The Fourier Cosine and Sine Series. A periodic complex wave which is an odd function will be shown to be representable by a Fourier sine series. Consider first some general aspects of the properties of odd functions. A function is described as odd when it satisfies the following criterion in the interval $-\pi < \omega t < \pi$:

$$-f(\omega t) = f(-\omega t) \tag{29}$$

The graph of an odd function is symmetric with respect to the origin, and the knowledge that a sine wave is an odd function may serve to keep this function type in mind. For an odd function, it follows that

$$-\int_{-\pi}^{0} f(\omega t)\, d\omega t = \int_{0}^{\pi} f(\omega t)\, d\omega t \tag{30}$$

When $f(\omega t)$ is an odd function, the amplitudes of the cosine terms are equal to zero and the Fourier series becomes a Fourier sine series which is written

$$f(\omega t) = \sum_{n=1}^{\infty} b_n \sin n\omega t \tag{31}$$

where

$$b_n = \frac{2}{\pi} \int_{0}^{\pi} f(\omega t) \sin n\omega t\, d\omega t \tag{32}$$

In general, a function is described as even when it satisfies the following criterion in the interval $-\pi < \omega t < \pi$:

$$f(\omega t) = f(-\omega t) \tag{33}$$

A cosine wave, for example, is an even function. The graph is symmetric with respect to the axis of the ordinates, and we may write

$$\int_{-\pi}^{\pi} f(\omega t)\, d\omega t = 2 \int_{0}^{\pi} f(\omega t)\, d\omega t \tag{34}$$

An even periodic complex wave may be represented by a Fourier cosine series.

$$f(\omega t) = \sum_{n=1}^{\infty} a_n \cos n\omega t \tag{35}$$

where

$$a_n = \frac{2}{\pi} \int_0^\pi f(\omega t) \cos n\omega t \, d\omega t \tag{36}$$

since it can be shown that

$$b_n = 0 \tag{37}$$

9. Fourier-series Expansion of an Interference-analysis Function. In some communication problems, the Fourier-series expansion of a function is obtained using somewhat roundabout methods. As an example, let us consider the analysis of a function which occurs frequently in FM interference analysis (see Chap. 17). This function, Ξ, is contained in the expression

$$\tan \Xi = \frac{x \sin y}{1 + x \cos y} \tag{38}$$

Note that Eq. (38) describes a right triangle. If we denote the hypotenuse as σ, then we may write

$$\sigma \sin \Xi = x \sin y \tag{39}$$

$$\sigma \cos \Xi = 1 + x \cos y \tag{40}$$

which may be combined and written in the following way:

$$1 + x \cos y + jx \sin y = \sigma(\cos \Xi + j \sin \Xi) \tag{41}$$

or

$$1 + xe^{iy} = \sigma e^{i\Xi} \tag{42}$$

Taking the logarithms of both sides, we get

$$\log (1 + xe^{iy}) = \log \sigma + j\Xi \tag{43}$$

Upon expanding $\log (1 + xe^{iy})$ in an infinite series,[1] (24) becomes

$$\sum_{n=1}^{\infty} \frac{x^n}{n} (-1)^{n+1}(\cos ny + j \sin ny) = \log \sigma + j\Xi \tag{44}$$

Equating the imaginary terms of (44), we get the following Fourier-series expansion which represents Ξ:

$$\Xi = \sum_{n=1}^{\infty} (-1)^{n+1} \frac{x^n}{n} \sin ny \tag{45}$$

10. Transformation from a Phase Function to a Time Function. The Fourier series

$$f(\omega t) = \frac{a_0}{2} + \sum_{n=1}^{\infty} (a_n \cos n\omega t + b_n \sin n\omega t) \tag{3}$$

[1] See No. 768 in B. O. Pierce, "A Short Table of Integrals," Ginn & Company, Boston, 1929. In No. 768, replace x by xe^{iy}.

may be converted from a phase function to a time function so that it will represent the expansion of $f(t)$ in the interval

$$-\frac{T}{2} < t < \frac{T}{2} \tag{46}$$

Frequency and angular velocity are related to the time T necessary to complete a cycle of the periodic wave, by the expressions

$$T = \frac{1}{f} \tag{47}$$

$$\omega = 2\pi f = \frac{2\pi}{T} \tag{48}$$

The phase angle, $n\omega t$, may be transformed into a time function which is more suitable for use with (46) by use of (48),

$$n\omega t = \frac{2\pi n t}{T} \tag{49}$$

We may check the time limits $t = \pm T/2$ corresponding to the phase limits $\pm\pi$ as follows: Substitution of $t = \pm T/2$ into (49) yields for $n = 1$,

$$\pm\omega \frac{T}{2} = \pm\pi \tag{50}$$

Note too that

$$d\omega t = \frac{2\pi}{T}\, dt \tag{51}$$

It then follows that

$$f(t) = \frac{a_0}{2} + \sum_{n=1}^{\infty} \left(a_n \cos \frac{2\pi n t}{T} + b_n \sin \frac{2\pi n t}{T} \right) \tag{52}$$

$$\frac{a_0}{2} = \frac{1}{T} \int_{-T/2}^{T/2} f(t)\, dt \tag{53}$$

$$a_n = \frac{2}{T} \int_{-T/2}^{T/2} f(t) \cos \frac{2\pi n t}{T}\, dt \qquad n = 1, 2, 3, \ldots \tag{54}$$

$$b_n = \frac{2}{T} \int_{-T/2}^{T/2} f(t) \sin \frac{2\pi n t}{T}\, dt \qquad n = 1, 2, 3, \ldots \tag{55}$$

11. The Gibbs Phenomenon.[1] A phenomenon which exists in connection with the behavior of a Fourier series at points of discontinuity is that which is known as the Gibbs phenomenon. According to Sec. 5, the

[1] Space does not permit an extended discussion of the Gibbs phenomenon here. For an excellent, penetrating study, see E. A. Guillemin, "The Mathematics of Circuit Analysis," Chap. 7, John Wiley & Sons, Inc., New York, 1949.

Fourier series representing $f(t)$ at the point of discontinuity t, where $f(t)$ has right- and left-hand derivatives, will converge to the value

$$\tfrac{1}{2}[f(t+0)+f(t-0)] \tag{56}$$

If, however, we sum the terms of the Fourier series in the vicinity of a discontinuity (such as the jump of a square wave) and then proceed with the summation such that n goes to infinity, the vertical line which connects the points $f(t+0)$ and $f(t-0)$ will overshoot both ends. Bôcher has shown that the amount of overshoot, which we may represent by the symbol ϵ, is equal to

$$\epsilon = \frac{1}{\pi}[f(t+0)-f(t-0)]\int_{\pi}^{\infty}\frac{\sin t}{t}\,dt \tag{57}$$

Evaluation of the integral yields the expression

$$\epsilon = -\frac{0.2808}{\pi}[f(t+0)-f(t-0)] \tag{58}$$

showing that the overshoot is about 9 per cent of the jump.

Further significance of the presence of the integral in Eq. (57) will be found in Chap. 20 (see Sec. 15), where it will be seen that integrals of this type occur in step-function formulation involving the Fourier integral.

THE COMPLEX FOURIER SERIES

12. The Complex Fourier Series.[1] The complex Fourier series is written as a symmetric function of phase in the form

$$f(\omega t) = \sum_{n=-\infty}^{\infty} C_n e^{jn\omega t} \tag{59}$$

where

$$C_n = \frac{1}{2\pi}\int_{-\pi}^{\pi} f(\omega t)e^{-jn\omega t}\,d\omega t \tag{60}$$

for the interval $-\pi < \omega t < \pi$. C_n will be seen to be an amplitude coefficient which corresponds to a combination of a_n and b_n in the trigonometric series. It is important to note that in the infinite series in Eq. (59) the values of n are in the range from $-\infty$ to ∞ rather than 0 to ∞.

13. Derivation of the Complex Fourier Series. It is convenient to derive the complex Fourier series by working backward to show that by suitable mathematical manipulation it can be transformed into the trigonometric form.

[1] E. A. Guillemin, "Communication Networks," vol. 1, Chap. X, John Wiley & Sons, Inc., New York, 1931.

In this derivation, we shall be interested in three cases which will account for all the values of n in the range.

They are

Case 1. $n > 0$

Case 2. $n = 0$

Case 3. $n < 0$

Case 1. $n > 0$:

When n is greater than zero,

$$e^{-j(+n)\omega t} = \cos n\omega t - j \sin n\omega t \tag{61}$$

Then, substituting (61) into (60), we get

$$C_{+n} = \frac{1}{2\pi}\left[\int_{-\pi}^{\pi} f(\omega t) \cos n\omega t \, d\omega t - j \int_{-\pi}^{\pi} f(\omega t) \sin n\omega t \, d\omega t\right] \tag{62}$$

The first and second integrals are recognized as πa_n and πb_n, respectively, in the trigonometric Fourier series. Equation (62) may then be written as

$$C_{+n} = \frac{a_n}{2} - j\frac{b_n}{2} \tag{63}$$

Case 2. $n = 0$:

Substituting $n = 0$ into Eq. (60), we get

$$C_0 = \frac{1}{2\pi}\int_{-\pi}^{\pi} f(\omega t) \, d\omega t \tag{64}$$

This is the term $a_0/2$ in the trigonometric series. Thus,

$$C_0 = \frac{a_0}{2} \tag{65}$$

Case 3. $n < 0$:

When n is less than zero, we see that

$$e^{-j(-n)\omega t} = \cos n\omega t + j \sin n\omega t \tag{66}$$

Substituting (66) into Eq. (60), we get

$$C_{-n} = \frac{1}{2\pi}\left[\int_{-\pi}^{\pi} f(\omega t) \cos n\omega t \, d\omega t + j \int_{-\pi}^{\pi} f(\omega t) \sin n\omega t \, d\omega t\right] \tag{67}$$

which is evidently

$$C_{-n} = \frac{a_n}{2} + j\frac{b_n}{2} \tag{68}$$

Equation (59) may be written in the form

$$f(\omega t) = C_0 + \sum_{n=1}^{\infty} C_n e^{jn\omega t} + \sum_{n=-1}^{-\infty} C_n e^{jn\omega t} \tag{69}$$

Equation (59) may be developed, using (63), (65), and (68), as follows:

$$f(\omega t) = \frac{a_0}{2} + \sum_{n=1}^{\infty} \frac{a_n - jb_n}{2} e^{jn\omega t} + \sum_{n=1}^{\infty} \frac{a_n + jb_n}{2} e^{-jn\omega t} \tag{70}$$

$$= \frac{a_0}{2} + \sum_{n=1}^{\infty} \frac{a_n}{2} (e^{jn\omega t} + e^{-jn\omega t}) + \sum_{n=1}^{\infty} \frac{b_n}{2j} (e^{jn\omega t} - e^{-jn\omega t}) \tag{71}$$

$$= \frac{a_0}{2} + \sum_{n=1}^{\infty} (a_n \cos n\omega t + b_n \sin n\omega t) \tag{72}$$

This is the Fourier trigonometric series, and the equivalence of the two types of Fourier series is demonstrated.

14. The Nature of the Complex Fourier Series. Let us investigate the general form of the Fourier series.

$$f(\omega t) = \sum_{n=-\infty}^{\infty} C_n e^{jn\omega t} \tag{73}$$

Written out, this becomes

$$\begin{aligned} f(\omega t) = {} & C_0 && \text{average value} \\ & + C_1 e^{j\omega t} + C_{-1} e^{-j\omega t} && \text{1st harmonic pair (fundamental)} \\ & + C_2 e^{j2\omega t} + C_{-2} e^{-j2\omega t} && \text{2d harmonic pair} \\ & \cdots\cdots\cdots\cdots\cdots\cdots \\ & + C_n e^{jn\omega t} + C_{-n} e^{-jn\omega t} && n\text{th harmonic pair} \\ & \cdots\cdots\cdots\cdots\cdots\cdots \end{aligned} \tag{74}$$

It is seen from Eq. (74) that the series consists of an infinite number of rotating vectors the angular velocities of which are multiples of the angular velocity of the fundamental harmonic pair. The rotating vector for a positive value of n rotates in counterclockwise direction, while the rotating vector for a negative value of n rotates in the clockwise direction.

15. Nature of C_n. Before continuing with the rotating-vector concept of the complex Fourier series, let us investigate further the nature and properties of C_n. C_n is the amplitude coefficient of the nth rotating vector and is related to the coefficients of the trigonometric Fourier series, a_n and b_n, by the relationships

$$C_{+n} = \frac{a_n}{2} - j\frac{b_n}{2} \tag{75}$$

$$C_{-n} = \frac{a_n}{2} + j\frac{b_n}{2} \tag{76}$$

Thus

$$|C_n| = \sqrt{\left(\frac{a_n}{2}\right)^2 + \left(\frac{b_n}{2}\right)^2} \tag{77}$$

It is evident that the rotating vector for C_{+n} has the same amplitude as the rotating vector for C_{-n}. If it is assumed, for example, that the vector summation of $C_n e^{jn\omega t}$ and $C_{-n}e^{-jn\omega t}$ is a real quantity, then we may diagram the nth harmonic pair as shown in Fig. 6, where it is seen that their vector summation lies on the real axis. It is evident that the component members of the harmonic pair are conjugates.

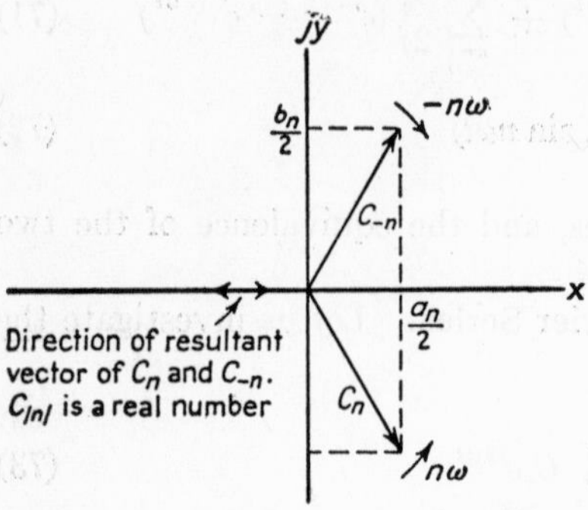

FIG. 6.

C_n is a real, imaginary, or complex number which may be written in the form

$$C_n = C_{n_1} + jC_{n_2} \tag{78}$$

If the periodic function is even, only the real part, C_{n_1}, will result. If the periodic function is odd, the imaginary number, jC_{n_2}, will result. If the periodic function is neither even nor odd, it may be written as the sum of an even and an odd function as described by Eq. (78).

16. Complex Fourier-series Representation of a Square Wave. Consider the complex Fourier-series analysis of the square wave which is pictured in Fig. 4. Its trigonometric Fourier-series expansion is given by Eq. (27). It follows, using (60), that

$$C_n = \frac{1}{2\pi}\int_0^\pi e^{-jn\omega t}\,d\omega t \tag{79}$$

$$= \frac{j}{2\pi n}(e^{-jn\pi} - 1) \tag{80}$$

$$= \frac{j}{2\pi n}[(-1)^n - 1] \tag{81}$$

Because of the n in the denominator of (81) we cannot solve that equation for the case when $n = 0$. Returning to (79), we find that at $n = 0$,

$$C_0 = \frac{1}{2\pi}\int_0^\pi d\omega t = \frac{1}{2} \tag{82}$$

Substituting (81) and (82) into Eq. (59), we get

$$f(t) = \frac{1}{2} + j\frac{1}{2\pi}\sum_{n=-\infty}^{\infty}\frac{(-1)^n - 1}{n}e^{jn\omega t} \qquad n \neq 0 \tag{83}$$

which, when written out, becomes

$$f(\omega t) = \frac{1}{2} - j\frac{1}{\pi}(e^{j\omega t} - e^{-j\omega t})$$
$$- j\frac{1}{3\pi}(e^{j3\omega t} - e^{-j3\omega t})$$
$$- j\frac{1}{5\pi}(e^{j5\omega t} - e^{-j5\omega t}) + \cdots \quad (84)$$

This series may be easily converted into a series of sine functions to yield Eq. (27).

17. Periodic Frequency- and Phase-modulation Functions. A basic rotating-vector function in phase and frequency modulation is

$$f(t) = e^{jx\sin\omega_1 t} \qquad -\frac{\pi}{\omega_1} < t < \frac{\pi}{\omega_1} \quad (85)$$

Substituting (85) into Eq. (60), it follows that

$$C_n = \frac{\omega_1}{2\pi}\int_{-\pi/\omega_1}^{\pi/\omega_1} e^{jx\sin\omega_1 t}e^{-jn\omega_1 t}\,dt \quad (86)$$

Replacing $\omega_1 t$ by φ, (86) can be written in the form

$$C_n = \frac{1}{2\pi}\int_{-\pi}^{\pi} e^{-j(n\varphi - x\sin\varphi)}\,d\varphi \quad (87)$$

This is an integral which has been discussed in the Appendix. According to Eq. (38) in the Appendix, Eq. (87) yields a Bessel function of the first kind; *i.e.*,

$$C_n = J_n(x) \quad (88)$$

whereby we get (see, for example, Sec. 3, Chap. 15)

$$f(t) = \sum_{n=-\infty}^{\infty} J_n(x)e^{jn\omega_1 t} \quad (89)$$

Using other Bessel-function-yielding integrals which are discussed in the Appendix, we may list the following identities which will find considerable application in frequency- and phase-modulation analysis:

$f(t)$		*Fourier-series Expansion*	
$e^{jx\sin\omega_1 t}$	$-\frac{\pi}{\omega_1} < t < \frac{\pi}{\omega_1}$	$\sum_{-\infty}^{\infty} J_n(x)e^{jn\omega_1 t}$	(90)
$e^{-jx\sin\omega_1 t}$	$-\frac{\pi}{\omega_1} < t < \frac{\pi}{\omega_1}$	$\sum_{-\infty}^{\infty} (-1)^n J_n(x)e^{jn\omega_1 t}$	(91)
$e^{jx\cos\omega_1 t}$	$-\frac{\pi}{\omega_1} < t < \frac{\pi}{\omega_1}$	$\sum_{-\infty}^{\infty} j^n J_n(x)e^{jn\omega_1 t}$	(92)
$e^{-jx\cos\omega_1 t}$	$-\frac{\pi}{\omega_1} < t < \frac{\pi}{\omega_1}$	$\sum_{-\infty}^{\infty} e^{j(3\pi n/2)} J_n(x)e^{jn\omega_1 t}$	(93)

THE DOUBLE FOURIER SERIES

18. The Multiple Fourier Series. The multiple Fourier series is of particular use to the electrical-communications engineer since it permits the spectral analysis of waves and functions in more than one variable. Although multiple Fourier series involving more than three variables are of academic interest only, the double and sometimes the triple Fourier series enjoy widespread use in the communications field since they are useful in problems involving television-image scanning (Sec. 3, Chap. 5), multitone-modulated-wave analysis (Chap. 18), and certain types of non-linear-network response (Sec. 3, Chap. 7). The remainder of this chapter will be primarily concerned with establishing and demonstrating the fundamental concepts involved in double Fourier series analysis so that they may be used in the numerous applications which will be included in the chapters to follow.

19. The Double Fourier Series.[1] A complex wave in the phase interval $-\pi < \omega_1 t < \pi$ may be expressed by the following complex Fourier series,

$$f(\omega_1 t) = \sum_{n=-\infty}^{\infty} C_n e^{jn\omega_1 t} \tag{94}$$

where

$$C_n = \frac{1}{2\pi} \int_{-\pi}^{\pi} f(\omega_1 t) e^{-jn\omega_1 t}\, d\omega_1 t \tag{95}$$

This complex Fourier series will converge to $f(\omega_1 t)$ at all continuous segments and to the arithmetic mean at the jump points.

Consider the case when two sets of rotating vectors which represent $f(\omega_1 t)$ and $f(\omega_2 t)$ are so related in phase and amplitude that $f(\omega_1 t)$ in the phase interval $-\pi < \omega_1 t < \pi$ is a function of $f(\omega_2 t)$ in the phase interval $-\pi < \omega_2 t < \pi$. Let $f(\omega_1 t)$ be expressed by the Fourier series which is described by Eq. (94), and let the variation of $f(\omega_2 t)$ for the particular phase $\omega_1 t_1$ be expressed by the Fourier series

$$f(\omega_2 t, \omega_1 t_1) = \sum_{m=-\infty}^{\infty} C_m e^{jm\omega_2 t} \tag{96}$$

where

$$C_m = \frac{1}{2\pi} \int_{-\pi}^{\pi} f(\omega_2 t, \omega_1 t_1) e^{-jm\omega_2 t}\, d\omega_2 t \tag{97}$$

For all of the other values of $\omega_1 t$ in the phase interval $-\pi < \omega_1 t < \pi$, there will exist a Fourier series which describes the variation with respect to $\omega_2 t$ in the phase interval $-\pi < \omega_2 t < \pi$. The expression for C_m in Eq. (97)

[1] P. Mertz and F. Gray, Theory of Scanning, *Bell System Tech. J.*, vol. 13, pp. 464–515, July, 1934.

may be written

$$C_m = \sum_{n=-\infty}^{n=\infty} C_{mn} e^{jn\omega_2 t} \tag{98}$$

Substituting Eq. (98) into Eq. (94), we get the double complex Fourier series

$$f(\omega_1 t, \omega_2 t) = \sum_{n=-\infty}^{\infty} \sum_{m=-\infty}^{\infty} C_{mn} e^{j(n\omega_1 + m\omega_2)t} \tag{99}$$

where

$$C_{mn} = \frac{1}{4\pi^2} \int_{-\pi}^{\pi} \int_{-\pi}^{\pi} f(\omega_1 t, \omega_2 t) e^{-j(n\omega_1 + m\omega_2)t} \, d\omega_1 t \, d\omega_2 t \tag{100}$$

The trigonometric form of the double Fourier series is written

$$f(\omega_1 t, \omega_2 t) = \sum_{n=0}^{\infty} \sum_{m=0}^{\infty} a_{\pm mn} \cos (n\omega_1 \pm m\omega_2)t + \sum_{n=0}^{\infty} \sum_{m=0}^{\infty} b_{\pm mn} \sin (n\omega_1 \pm m\omega_2)t \tag{101}$$

where

$$a_{\pm mn} = \frac{1}{2\pi^2} \int_{-\pi}^{\pi} \int_{-\pi}^{\pi} f(\omega_1 t, \omega_2 t) \cos (n\omega_1 \pm m\omega_2)t \, d\omega_1 t \, d\omega_2 t \tag{102}$$

$$b_{\pm mn} = \frac{1}{2\pi^2} \int_{-\pi}^{\pi} \int_{-\pi}^{\pi} f(\omega_1 t, \omega_2 t) \sin (n\omega_1 \pm m\omega_2)t \, d\omega_1 t \, d\omega_2 t \tag{103}$$

The average term a_{00} may be obtained by solving (102) for the case when $m = n = 0$ and then dividing by 2.

20. Example of the Double Complex Fourier Series. Consider the double Fourier-series expansion, with the exception of C_{00}, of the unit-

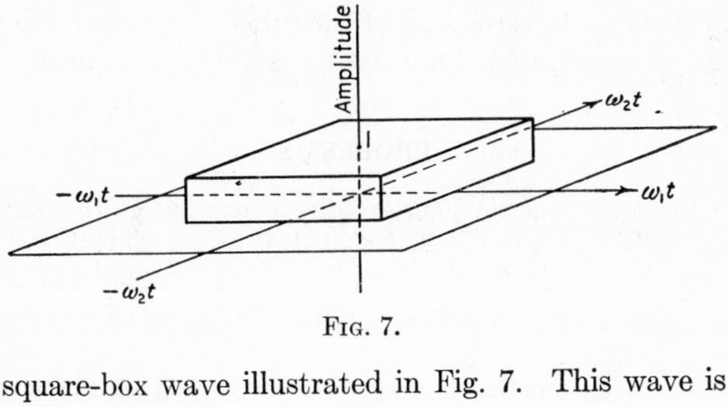

FIG. 7.

amplitude square-box wave illustrated in Fig. 7. This wave is expressed mathematically as follows:

$$\begin{aligned} f(\omega_1 t, \omega_2 t) &= 0 \qquad -\pi < \omega_1 t, \omega_2 t < -\frac{\pi}{2} \\ &= 1 \qquad -\frac{\pi}{2} < \omega_1 t, \omega_2 t < \frac{\pi}{2} \\ &= 0 \qquad \frac{\pi}{2} < \omega_1 t, \omega_2 t < \pi \end{aligned} \tag{104}$$

Substituting (104) into Eq. (100), it follows that

$$C_{mn} = \frac{1}{4\pi^2} \int_{-\pi/2}^{\pi/2} \int_{-\pi/2}^{\pi/2} e^{-j(n\omega_1 + m\omega_2)t} \, d\omega_1 t \, d\omega_2 t \tag{105}$$

Performing the first integration with respect to $\omega_2 t$, we get

$$C_{mn} = \frac{1}{2m\pi^2} \int_{-\pi/2}^{\pi/2} \sin \frac{m\pi}{2} e^{-jn\omega_1 t} \, d\omega_1 t \tag{106}$$

Since sin $(m\pi/2)$ is a function of m alone, a second integration yields

$$C_{mn} = \frac{\sin m(\pi/2) \sin n(\pi/2)}{nm\pi^2} \tag{107}$$

Substituting Eq. (107) into Eq. (99), we find the double Fourier-series expansion of (104) to be

$$f(\omega_1 t, \omega_2 t) = \frac{1}{\pi^2} \sum_{n=-\infty}^{\infty} \sum_{m=-\infty}^{\infty} \frac{\sin m(\pi/2) \sin n(\pi/2)}{nm} e^{j(n\omega_1 + m\omega_2)t} \tag{108}$$

The significance of this double summation may be more clearly visualized by rewriting Eq. (108) in the following way:

$$f(\omega_1 t, \omega_2 t) = \sum_{n=-\infty}^{\infty} \left[\sum_{m=-\infty}^{\infty} \frac{\sin m(\pi/2)}{m\pi} e^{jm\omega_2 t} \right] \frac{\sin n(\pi/2)}{n\pi} e^{jn\omega_1 t} \tag{109}$$

The quantity in the brackets is the single Fourier-series expansion of a unit-amplitude square wave in $\omega_2 t$. It is modified by a single Fourier series in $\omega_1 t$ which converges to unity in the region $-\pi/2 < \omega_1 t < \pi/2$ and which converges to zero at all of the other phase angles in the interval except at $\omega_1 t = \pm\pi/2$, where the arithmetic mean is realized.

PROBLEMS

1. Derive the trigonometric Fourier-series expansion of the wave: $f(t) = 0$, $-T/2 < t < -T/4$; -1, $-T/4 < t < 0$; 1, $0 < t < T/4$; 0, $T/4 < t < T/2$.

Ans. $f(t) = \frac{2}{\pi} \sum_{1}^{\infty} \frac{1 - \cos n(\pi/2)}{n} \sin 2\pi n \frac{t}{T}$

2. Derive the trigonometric Fourier-series expansion of the wave: $f(t) = t$, $-T/2 < t < T/2$.

Ans. $f(t) = 2 \sum_{1}^{\infty} \frac{(-1)^{n+1}}{n} \sin 2\pi n \frac{t}{T}$

3. Derive the trigonometric Fourier-series expansion of the wave: $f(t) = e^t$, $-T/2 < t < T/2$.

Ans. $f(t) = \frac{2 \sinh \pi}{\pi} \left[\frac{1}{2} + \sum_{1}^{\infty} \frac{(-1)^n}{1 + n^2} \left(\cos 2\pi n \frac{t}{T} - n \sin 2\pi n \frac{t}{T} \right) \right]$

4. Derive the trigonometric Fourier-series expansion of the wave: $f(t) = t - 1$, $-T/2 < t < 0$; $t + 1$, $0 < t < T/2$.

$$Ans. \quad f(t) = \frac{2}{\pi} \sum_{1}^{\infty} \frac{1 - (1 + \pi) \cos n\pi}{n} \sin 2\pi n \frac{t}{T}$$

5. Derive the trigonometric Fourier series expansion of the wave: $f(t) = 0$, $-T/2 < t < 0$; t, $0 < t < T/2$.

$$Ans. \quad f(t) = \frac{\pi}{4} + \sum_{1}^{\infty} \left[\frac{(-1)^n - 1}{\pi n^2} \cos 2\pi n \frac{t}{T} - \frac{(-1)^n}{n} \sin 2\pi n \frac{t}{T} \right]$$

6. Show that, when integrated, the complex Fourier-series representation of a unit-amplitude square wave yields the Fourier-series representation of a triangular wave. Diagram the wave, and show its amplitude. What waveform will an additional integration of this wave represent?

7. Derive the complex Fourier-series representation of the wave which is described by the rotating vector

$$f(t) = \exp \left[j\left(\frac{2\pi t}{T_1} + \sigma t^2 \right) \right] \qquad -\frac{T_1}{2} < t < \frac{T_1}{2}$$

Discuss the role played by the Fresnel integrals which contribute to the solution.

8. Derive the complex Fourier-series representation of the wave which is described by the rotating vector

$$f(t) = e^{jx \cos \omega_1 t} \qquad -\frac{\pi}{\omega_1} < t < \frac{\pi}{\omega_1}$$

9. Derive the complex Fourier-series representation of the function

$$e(t) = Ee^{jn\omega_1 t} \qquad -\frac{\pi}{\omega_1} < t < 0$$

$$= Ee^{jm\omega_1 t} \qquad 0 < t < \frac{\pi}{\omega_1}$$

10. Develop the double complex Fourier-series expansion of

$$f(\omega_1 t, \omega_2 t) = e^{j(2\omega_1 t + 3\omega_2 t)} \qquad -\pi < \omega_2 t,\ \omega_1 t < \pi$$

11. Find the triple Fourier-series expansion of

$$f(t) = e^{j(\omega_1 t + a \sin \omega_2 t + b \sin \omega_3 t)}$$

CHAPTER 3

NONPERIODIC WAVES—THE FOURIER TRANSFORM

Fourier's Theorem is not only one of the most beautiful results of modern analysis but it may be said to furnish an indispensable instrument in the treatment of nearly every recondite question in modern physics.

LORD KELVIN AND PETER GUTHRIE TAIT

1. Introduction. A complex Fourier series may be written as follows:

$$f(t) = \sum_{n=-\infty}^{\infty} C_n e^{j(2\pi nt/T_1)} \tag{1}$$

where

$$C_n = \frac{1}{T_1} \int_{-T_1/2}^{T_1/2} f(t) e^{-j(2\pi nt/T_1)}\, dt \tag{2}$$

Equation (1) represents the conversion of a periodic *time* function to a *frequency* function. To express the time function for any time correctly, the relationship

$$f(t) = f(t + T_1) \tag{3}$$

must be satisfied, thus specifying that $f(t)$ is periodic and that it has existed from the beginning of time and will continue until the end of time. It is evident that starting and stopping conditions are implicitly included.

When a function is no longer periodic, in that it does not satisfy Eq. (3) for all time,[1] then the conversion from a time function to a frequency function must be made with the use of a *Fourier transform.*

INTRODUCTION TO THE FOURIER TRANSFORM AND INTEGRAL[2]

2. The Derivation of the Fourier Transform and Integral. According to Eq. (1) and (2), the Fourier-series expansion of a periodic function may be

[1] Mathematically speaking, a wave-train output of a single-tone-harmonic generator which started eons ago and which will cease in the far future will not satisfy Eq. (3) even though a large number of identical repetitions will have taken place. The mathematical and practical aspects of such a wave will be discussed in Chap. 19.

[2] E. A. Guillemin, "Communication Networks," vol. II, Chap. XI, John Wiley & Sons, Inc., New York, 1935.

J. A. Stratton, "Electromagnetic Theory," Chap. V, McGraw-Hill Book Company, Inc., New York, 1941.

written as follows,

$$f(t) = \sum_{n=-\infty}^{\infty} e^{j(2\pi nt/T_1)} \frac{1}{T_1} \int_{-T_1/2}^{T_1/2} f(t)e^{-j(2\pi nt/T_1)}\, dt \tag{4}$$

The derivation of the Fourier transform is an important one since it involves the development of the Fourier series which represents a periodic wave into the Fourier integral which represents a nonperiodic wave.

A nonperiodic wave is a wave which does not satisfy Eq. (3) and which may be considered to be a wave whose period is *infinite*. In the mathematical manipulations leading to Fourier-series representations of periodic waves, we have determined the amplitude coefficients by an integration which in integral (2), for example, was carried out over the time interval $-T_1/2 < t < T_1/2$. A similar amplitude function [which will be found to be $g(\omega)$] for nonperiodic waves will have as its integration limits $-\infty < t < \infty$.

As the integration limits in Eq. (4) are extended to infinity, the summation sign in this equation will be replaced by an integral sign and the Fourier integral, which will contain the Fourier transform, will result.

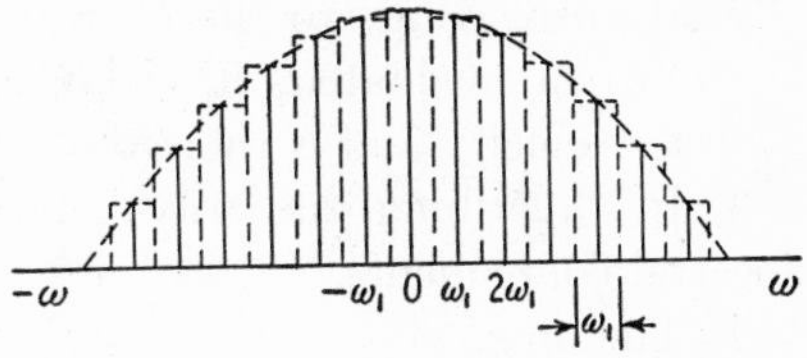

FIG. 1.

Consider the spectral components which are pictured in Fig. 1. It is seen that each spectral component may be identified with an area of width ω_1 and height C_n. Retaining this concept of area for the general case, let the width ω_1 in Eq. (4) be replaced by $\Delta\omega$ when applied to the term $1/T_1$ which precedes the integral sign in this expression. Thus,

$$f(t) = \frac{1}{2\pi} \sum_{n=-\infty}^{\infty} e^{j(2\pi nt/T_1)}\, \Delta\omega \int_{-T_1/2}^{T_1/2} f(t)e^{-j(2\pi nt/T_1)}\, dt \tag{5}$$

Let $\Delta\omega$ decrease in magnitude. As $\Delta\omega$ approaches $d\omega$, the spacing between spectral components becomes differential and the spectrum becomes continuous.

As the following transitions take place,

$$\Delta\omega \rightarrow d\omega \qquad T_1 \rightarrow \infty \tag{6}$$

it is evident that

$$\frac{2\pi}{T_1} \rightarrow 0 \qquad n \rightarrow \infty \qquad \frac{2\pi n}{T_1} \rightarrow \omega \tag{7}$$

Then, by replacing the summation sign by an integral sign, we may write

$$f(t) = \frac{1}{2\pi} \int_{\omega=-\infty}^{\infty} e^{j\omega t}\, d\omega \int_{t=-\infty}^{\infty} f(t)e^{-j\omega t}\, dt \tag{8}$$

This is the Fourier integral which is the nonperiodic counterpart of the Fourier series.

Note that Eq. (8) may be written

$$f(t) = \frac{1}{2\pi} \int_{\omega=-\infty}^{\infty} g(\omega)e^{j\omega t}\, d\omega \tag{9}$$

where

$$g(\omega) = \int_{t=-\infty}^{\infty} f(t)e^{-j\omega t}\, dt \tag{10}$$

$g(\omega)$ is the Fourier transform of $f(t)$.

3. The Nature of the Fourier Transform $g(\omega)$. The nature of the Fourier transform $g(\omega)$ may be summed as follows:

1. $g(\omega)$ is an integral which converts a nonperiodic time function into a frequency function.[1]

2. It corresponds to the C_n which is encountered in the Fourier series since, when evaluated, it yields a relationship between amplitude and angular velocity and is therefore a spectral function.

3. In describing the wave spectrum, it yields the envelope of the spectral components.

4. The integral

$$\int_{-\infty}^{\infty} |f(t)|\, dt \tag{11}$$

shall exist in the interval $-\infty < t < \infty$.

5. The function $f(t)$ shall be piecewise continuous and at points of discontinuity shall have right- and left-hand derivatives. At points of discontinuity, the value of $f(t)$, when recovered from $g(\omega)$ by use of (9), shall converge to the arithmetic mean, i.e., at $t = t_1$,

$$f(t) = \tfrac{1}{2}[f(t_1 + 0) + f(t_1 - 0)] \tag{12}$$

6. If $g(\omega)$ is found to have both real and imaginary parts, then it may be written in the form

$$g(\omega) = G(\omega)e^{j\Theta(\omega)} \tag{13}$$

where $G(\omega)$ describes the amplitude spectrum and $\Theta(\omega)$ describes the phase spectrum.

4. Comparison of the Fourier Series and the Fourier Integral. The expressions for the complex Fourier series and the Fourier integral, when written side by side as follows,

---

[1] See Campbell and Foster, "Fourier Integrals for Practical Applications," D. Van Nostrand Company, Inc., New York, 1942, for an extensive list of transforms.

Fourier Series (*Periodic Functions*)	*Fourier Integral* (*Nonperiodic Functions*)
$f(t) = \sum_{n=-\infty}^{\infty} C_n e^{jn\omega_1 t}$	$f(t) = \frac{1}{2\pi} \int_{\omega=-\infty}^{\infty} g(\omega) e^{j\omega t}\, d\omega$
$C_n = \frac{\omega_1}{2\pi} \int_{-\pi/\omega_1}^{\pi/\omega_1} f(t) e^{-jn\omega_1 t}\, dt$	$g(\omega) = \int_{t=-\infty}^{\infty} f(t) e^{-j\omega t}\, dt$

are seen to be similar in structure. Both employ integrals [C_n and $g(\omega)$] for the determination of spectral amplitudes, and both convert a time function to a frequency function and back.

5. The Spectral Analysis of a Pulse. Pulses of voltage or current are used widely in the radio-communications field, some applications being in radar, as synchronizing signals in television, and in pulse-width-modulation transmission.

The spectral analysis of pulse not only yields information which is extremely valuable to the communications engineer but also serves to give an excellent illustration of the use of the Fourier analysis. The following will illustrate the transition from periodic-pulse analysis (Fourier series) to nonperiodic-pulse analysis[1] (Fourier transform).

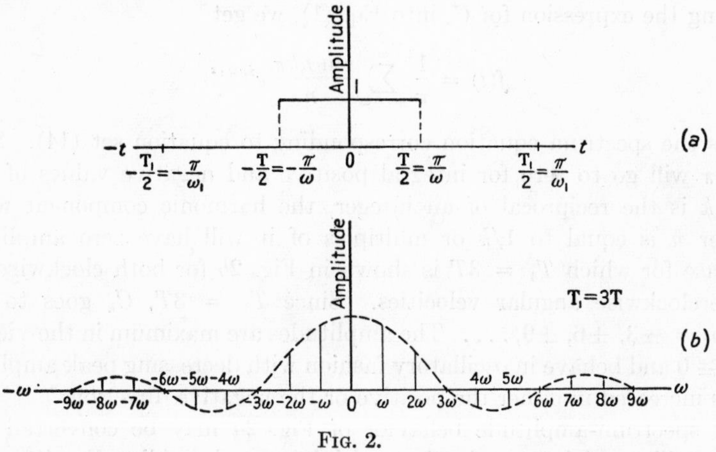

FIG. 2.

Fourier-series Representation of a Periodic Pulse. Consider the complex Fourier-series expansion of a periodic pulse whose time versus amplitude variation for a period T_1 is illustrated in Fig. 2*a* and which is described as

[1] For a discussion of the recovery of the time function of a pulse from the Fourier transform of the pulse, see N. Wiener, "The Fourier Integral," pp. 47–49, Cambridge University Press, London, 1933.

$$
\begin{aligned}
f(t) &= 0 \qquad -\frac{T_1}{2} < t < -\frac{T}{2} \\
&= 1 \qquad -\frac{T}{2} < t < \frac{T}{2} \\
&= 0 \qquad \frac{T}{2} < t < \frac{T_1}{2}
\end{aligned} \tag{14}
$$

Substituting (14) into Eq. (2), we get

$$C_n = \frac{\omega_1}{2\pi} \int_{-\pi/\omega_1}^{-\pi/\omega} 0 \cdot e^{-jn\omega_1 t}\, dt + \frac{\omega_1}{2\pi} \int_{-\pi/\omega}^{\pi/\omega} e^{-jn\omega_1 t}\, dt + \int_{\pi/\omega}^{\pi/\omega_1} 0 \cdot e^{-jn\omega_1 t}\, dt \tag{15}$$

$$= \frac{\omega_1}{-j2\pi n\omega_1} [e^{-j(n\omega_1\pi/\omega)} - e^{j(n\omega_1\pi/\omega)}] \tag{16}$$

$$= \frac{1}{\pi n} \sin nk\pi \tag{17}$$

where

$$k = \frac{T}{T_1} \tag{18}$$

which expresses the ratio of pulse-duration time to the period time. Substituting the expression for C_n into Eq. (1), we get

$$f(t) = \frac{1}{\pi} \sum_{n=-\infty}^{\infty} \frac{\sin nk\pi}{n} e^{jn\omega_1 t} \tag{19}$$

This is the spectrum equation corresponding to equation set (14). Since $\sin nk\pi$ will go to zero for integral positive and negative values of $nk\pi$, when k is the reciprocal of an integer, the harmonic component whose number n is equal to $1/k$ or multiples of it will have zero amplitude. The case for which $T_1 = 3T$ is shown in Fig. 2*b* for both clockwise and counterclockwise angular velocities. Since $T_1 = 3T$, C_n goes to zero when $n = \pm 3, \pm 6, \pm 9, \ldots$. The amplitudes are maximum in the vicinity of $C_n \cong 0$ and behave in oscillatory fashion with decreasing peak amplitude as n is increased in either the positive or the negative direction.

The spectrum-amplitude behavior of Fig. 2*a* may be converted to a more readily useful expression by multiplying and dividing Eq. (17) by k. Thus

$$C_n = k \frac{\sin nk\pi}{nk\pi} \tag{20}$$

and Eq. (19) may be written as follows,

$$f(t) = k \sum_{n=-\infty}^{\infty} \frac{\sin \theta}{\theta} e^{jn\omega_1 t} \tag{21}$$

where $\theta = nk\pi$. Equation (20) no longer yields only the amplitudes of the individual harmonics but is also seen to represent the envelope of the amplitude spectrum. It describes the dotted line connecting the tips of the vectors in Fig. 2*b*. When used in Eq. (21), it yields the amplitudes of only those harmonics which are specified by $n\omega_1$.

The function $(\sin\theta)/\theta$, whose general form is pictured in both Figs. 2*b* and 4, is an important basic function[1] which is very frequently encountered in nonperiodic-wave analysis. It goes to zero when $\theta = \pm\pi, \pm 2\pi, \pm 3\pi, \ldots$ and is well behaved as θ approaches zero since, by use of L'Hôpital's rule, we see that

$$\lim_{\theta\to 0} \frac{\sin\theta}{\theta} = \lim_{\theta\to 0} \cos\theta \tag{22}$$

$$= 1 \tag{23}$$

It is an even function, and its amplitude vanishes at $\theta = \pm\infty$.

The Fourier Transform of a Unit Pulse. The Fourier transform of a unit pulse will be found to yield the previously discussed $(\sin\theta)/\theta$ function which is one of the most important and constantly encountered functions in nonperiodic-wave spectral analysis.

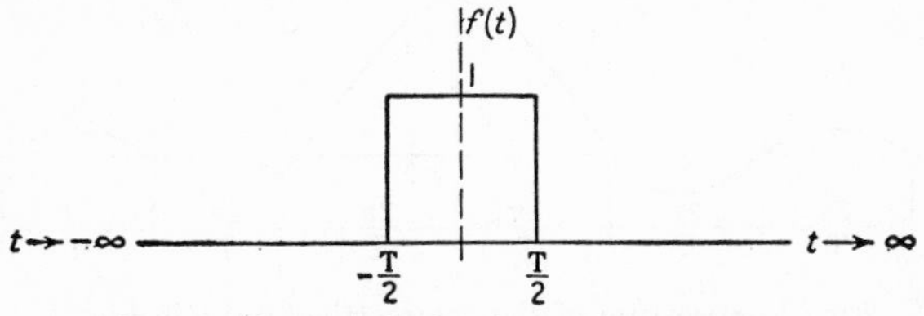

FIG. 3. Symmetrical pulse of duration T.

Consider the symmetrical pulse wave which may be expressed mathematically as

$$\begin{aligned} f(t) &= 0 \qquad -\infty < t < -\frac{T}{2} \\ &= 1 \qquad -\frac{T}{2} < t < \frac{T}{2} \\ &= 0 \qquad \frac{T}{2} < t < \infty \end{aligned} \tag{24}$$

and which is pictured in Fig. 3. The Fourier transform of (24) may be found from Eq. (10) to be

$$g(\omega) = \int_{-\infty}^{-T/2} 0\cdot e^{-j\omega t}\,dt + \int_{-T/2}^{T/2} e^{-j\omega t}\,dt + \int_{T/2}^{\infty} 0\cdot e^{-j\omega t}\,dt \tag{25}$$

[1] See E. A. Guillemin, "The Mathematics of Circuit Analysis," Chap. 7, John Wiley & Sons, Inc., New York, 1949.

The first and last integrals of Eq. (25), which represent the contributions of $f(t)$ for the time intervals $-\infty < t < -T/2$ and $T/2 < t < \infty$, are, of course, equal to zero.

Let us evaluate the second integral. It follows that

$$g(\omega) = \frac{1}{-j\omega}\left(e^{-j\omega(T/2)} - e^{j\omega(T/2)}\right) \tag{26}$$

$$= \frac{T}{\omega(T/2)} \frac{e^{j\omega(T/2)} - e^{-j\omega(T/2)}}{2j} \tag{27}$$

$$= T\frac{\sin \omega(T/2)}{\omega(T/2)} \tag{28}$$

which contains a $(\sin \theta/\theta)$-type function. It is evident that Eq. (28) will go to zero when

$$\frac{\omega T}{2} = \pm\pi, \pm 2\pi, \ldots \tag{29}$$

A graph of Eq. (28) is shown in Fig. 4.

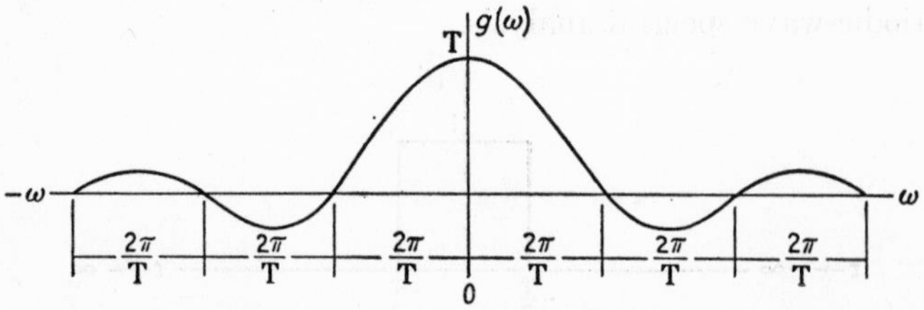

FIG. 4. Spectrum of the symmetrical pulse in Fig. 3.

It is evident from Fig. 4 that the spacing between the zeros is inversely proportional to the duration time of the pulse. Thus for a pulse of extremely *short* duration, the zeros will be far apart, resulting in a *broad* spectrum while for a pulse of *long* duration, a *narrow* spectrum will result. The limiting values occur for either a pulse of infinite duration, in which case the spacing between the zeros becomes infinitesimal, resulting in a single-line spectrum at $\omega = 0$, which of course represents the output of a nonvarying source of constant amplitude, or for a pulse of infinitely short duration, in which case the first zeros are located an infinite distance from the origin, resulting in a band spectrum.

6. The Fourier Transform of an Error Function. Consider the error function of time

$$f(t) = e^{-a^2t^2/2} \tag{30}$$

As may be seen by referring to Fig. 5, $f(t)$ is symmetric about the axis of the ordinates and has an amplitude equal to unity at $t = 0$. It vanishes only as t approaches $t = \pm\infty$. Since the function is symmetric, we may write, by substituting Eq. (30) into Eq. (10),

$$g(\omega) = 2\int_0^\infty e^{-a^2t^2/2}e^{-j\omega t}\,dt \tag{31}$$

$$= 2\int_0^\infty e^{-[(a^2t^2/2)+j\omega t]}\,dt \tag{32}$$

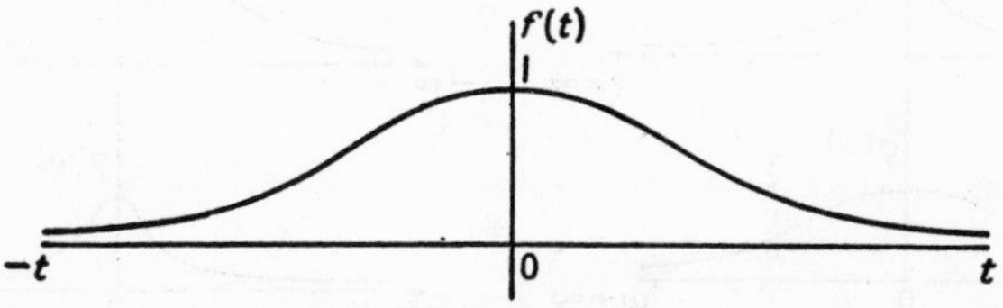

FIG. 5. Error function.

Note that the exponent may be written in the following way by completing the square:

$$\frac{a^2t^2}{2} + j\omega t + \frac{\omega^2}{2a^2} - \frac{\omega^2}{2a^2} = \frac{a^2}{2}\left(t - \frac{j\omega}{a^2}\right)^2 - \frac{\omega^2}{2a^2} \tag{33}$$

Letting

$$b = t - \frac{j\omega}{a^2} \tag{34}$$

and noting that, for the lower limit $t = 0$ of the integral in Eq. (32),

$$b = -\frac{j\omega}{a^2} \tag{35}$$

we may rewrite Eq. (32) as follows:

$$g(\omega) = 2e^{-\omega^2/2a^2}\int_{-j\omega/a^2}^\infty e^{-a^2b^2/2}\,db \tag{36}$$

$$= 2e^{-\omega^2/2a^2}\left(\int_{-j\omega/a^2}^0 e^{-a^2b^2/2}\,db + \int_0^\infty e^{-a^2b^2/2}\,db\right) \tag{37}$$

The first integral is a contour integral on the imaginary axis and may be shown to be equal to zero. The second integral may be shown to yield

$$\int_0^\infty e^{-a^2b^2/2}\,db = \frac{1}{a}\sqrt{\frac{\pi}{2}} \tag{38}$$

Thus, we find that the Fourier transform of the error function is

$$g(\omega) = \sqrt{2\pi}\,\frac{e^{-\omega^2/2a^2}}{a} \tag{39}$$

which is evidently also an error function. Note, however, that there is an a^2 in the denominator of the exponent, whereas in Eq. (30), a^2 is the multiplier of t^2. This is an important result. It shows that if $f(t)$ is narrow as is shown in Fig. 6*a*, the spectrum will be broad; if $f(t)$ is broad as shown in Fig. 6*b*, the spectrum will be narrow.

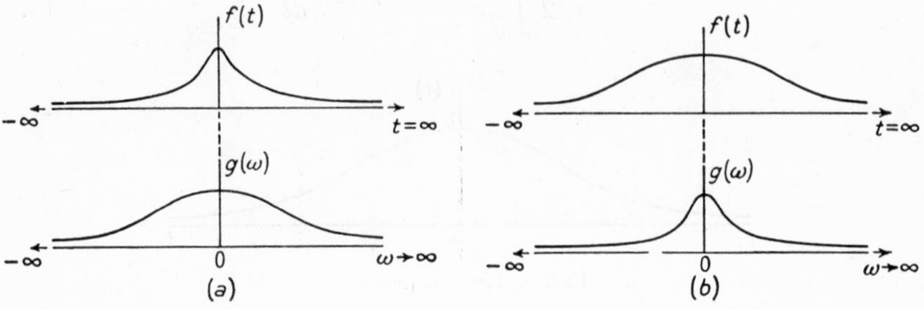

FIG. 6.

7. The Delta Function. Let us stipulate that the area under the curve of (39) at all times be equal to unity; *i.e.*,

$$\int_{-\infty}^{\infty} g(\omega,a)\, d\omega = 1 \tag{40}$$

As a increases in value, the value of the exponent will decrease and the spectrum will become broader with decreasing peak amplitude. However, as a decreases in value, the spectrum will become narrower and narrower and will increase in amplitude. It will eventually form the line $\omega = 0$, whose amplitude will become infinite as a goes to zero. This is known as a delta function of angular velocity if the area which is bounded by this

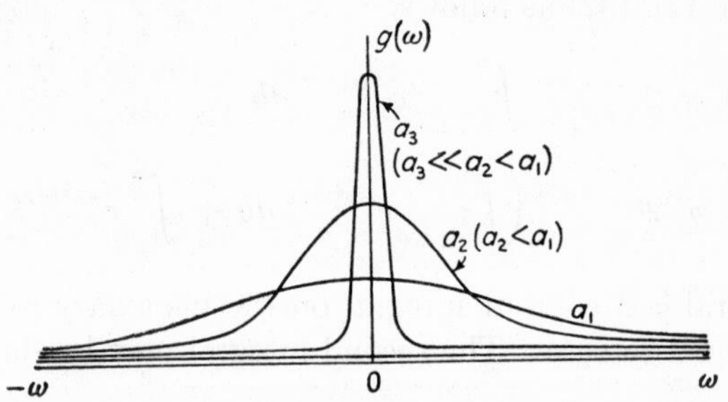

FIG. 7.

spectrum conforms to (40). The behavior of $g(\omega)$, conforming to Eq. (40) for various values of a, is shown in Fig. 7.

If ω in Eq. (39) is replaced by $\omega - \omega_0$ and if a is allowed to approach zero with the area under the curve maintained constant at unity, then

$g(\omega - \omega_0)$ will vanish at all ω except at $\omega = \omega_0$. This is written

$$\delta(\omega - \omega_0) = \lim_{a \to 0} \frac{Ke^{-(\omega-\omega_0)^2/2a^2}}{a} \tag{41}$$

where K is a constant and

$$\int_{-\infty}^{\infty} \delta(\omega - \omega_0)\, d\omega = 1 \tag{42}$$

In general, we may define the delta function $\delta(\omega - \omega_0)$ as a function whose amplitude is equal to zero at every value of ω except at ω_0, where its amplitude is such that Eq. (42) is satisfied.

It follows that we may write a delta function of time, $\delta(t - t_0)$, by replacing ω and ω_0 in Eqs. (41) and (42) by t and t_0, respectively.

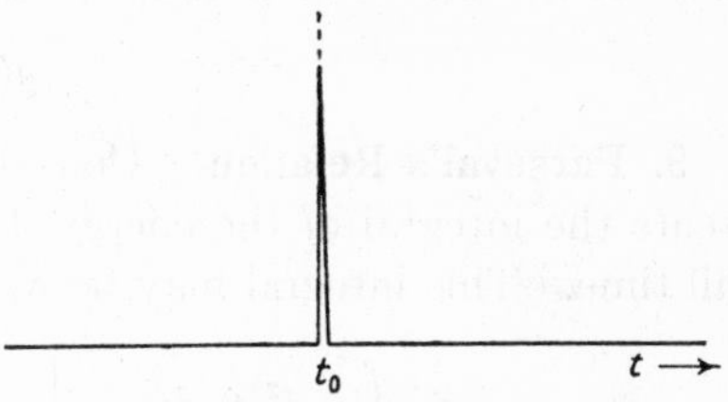

FIG. 8. Delta function at $t = t_0$.

8. Spectrum of the Delta Function $\delta(t - t_0)$. The Fourier transform of the delta function $\delta(t - t_0)$ may be found in the following way: Consider the existence of a delta function at $t = t_0$ as shown in Fig. 8. For all values of t, by definition,

$$\int_{-\infty}^{\infty} \delta(t - t_0)\, dt = 1 \tag{43}$$

and the amplitude of $f(t)$ is equal to zero at all t except at $t = t_0$. The Fourier transform of $\delta(t - t_0)$ is

$$g(\omega) = \int_{-\infty}^{\infty} \delta(t - t_0)e^{-j\omega t}\, dt \tag{44}$$

It is evident that $e^{-j\omega t}$ is a very slowly varying function in the vicinity of $t = t_0$ and therefore may be taken outside of the integral. Thus we may rewrite Eq. (44) as

$$g(\omega) = e^{j\omega t_0} \int_{-\infty}^{\infty} \delta(t - t_0)\, dt \tag{45}$$

which is seen to yield

$$g(\omega) = e^{j\omega t_0} \tag{46}$$

This is in the form,

$$g(\omega) = G(\omega)e^{j\Theta(\omega)} \tag{13}$$

where

$$G(\omega) = 1 \qquad \Theta(\omega) = \omega t_0 \tag{47}$$

Eq. (47) indicates that the spectrum of the delta function is a band spectrum of unit amplitude with spectral components of equal amplitude appearing at each value of ω in the entire range $-\infty < \omega < \infty$. This is illustrated in Fig. 9. Also, since the delta function occurs at $t = t_0$, each

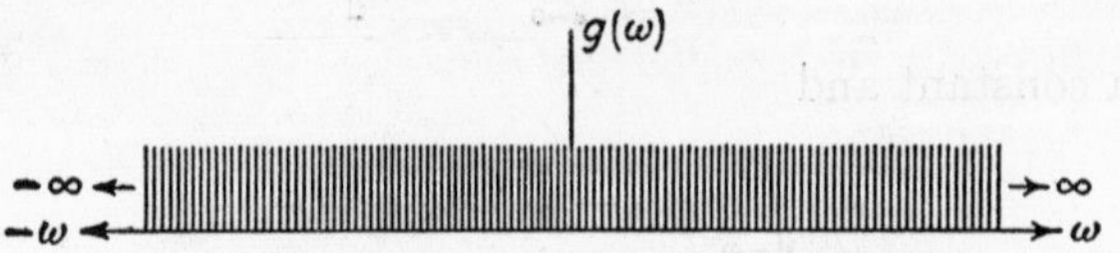

FIG. 9. Spectrum of a delta function.

spectral rotating-vector component is displaced in phase by the phase angle ωt_0. If the delta function occurs at $t = 0$, then it is evident that

$$g(\omega) = 1 \tag{48}$$

9. Parseval's Relation. Consider the integral $\int_{-\infty}^{\infty} f^2(t)\,dt$ which represents the integral of the energy due to a current $i(t)$ or a voltage $e(t)$ for all time. This integral may be written, using (10), as follows:

$$\int_{-\infty}^{\infty} f^2(t)\,dt = \frac{1}{2\pi}\int_{-\infty}^{\infty} f(t)\,dt \int_{-\infty}^{\infty} g(\omega)e^{j\omega t}\,d\omega \tag{49}$$

where $g(\omega)$ represents the Fourier transforms of one of the two $f(t)$'s which form the square, $f^2(t)$. Eq. (49) may be rearranged and written as follows:

$$\int_{-\infty}^{\infty} f^2(t)\,dt = \frac{1}{2\pi}\int_{-\infty}^{\infty} g(\omega)\left[\int_{-\infty}^{\infty} f(t)e^{j\omega t}\,dt\right]d\omega \tag{50}$$

But

$$\int_{-\infty}^{\infty} f(t)e^{j\omega t}\,dt = g^*(\omega) \tag{51}$$

where $g^*(\omega)$ is the conjugate of $g(\omega)$. It follows then that

$$\int_{-\infty}^{\infty} |f^2(t)|\,dt = \frac{1}{2\pi}\int_{-\infty}^{\infty} |g(\omega)|^2\,d\omega \tag{52}$$

This is the Parseval relation. Its use will be demonstrated in Sec. 11, Chap. 5, where it will be applied in the derivation of shot-effect noise in vacuum tubes.

PROBLEMS

1. Develop the Fourier transform of the pulse described as follows:

$$\begin{aligned} f(t) &= 0 \qquad -\infty < t < 0 \\ &= 1 \qquad 0 < t < T \\ &= 0 \qquad T < t < \infty \end{aligned}$$

Write the $g(\omega)$ in the form of Eq. (13), and compare with Eq. (28). Discuss the results in terms of the phase shift of each incremental component.

2. Discuss the delta function, using a development based on the Fourier pulse transform, $(\sin \omega t)/\omega$ rather than the error function.

3. Discuss the energy in the spectrum of a pulse from the standpoint of Parseval's relation.

4. Find the Fourier transform of the damped sine-wave train.

$$e(t) = 0 \qquad -\infty < t < 0$$

$$= e^{-tb} \sin 377t \qquad 0 < t < \infty$$

for the case when (*a*) $b = 50$ and (*b*) $b = 500$. Compare the spectra for both cases.

CHAPTER 4

THE LAPLACE TRANSFORM

Laplace saw in mathematics principally a tool which he modified ingeniously to fit each special problem as it arose—a great philosopher who sought to know nature by making mathematics serve it.

J. L. LAGRANGE

1. Introduction. The Laplace transform is a highly powerful method of operational mathematics for solving the differential equations which describe the transient behavior of many communication networks.

Some of the first major applications of operational mathematics to the problems of electrical communications were formulated by Oliver Heaviside[1] (1850–1925). However, the Heaviside operational calculus, as it was known, was in many cases so obscure in procedure and principle that for many years it was a highly controversial subject, winning both adherents and antagonists. In 1916, Bromwich[2] published a treatise which justified to some extent the Heaviside operational calculus by use of the theory of functions of a complex variable. After Bromwich, others including J. R. Carson, B. van der Pol, and G. Doetsch[3] made contributions which resulted in the system of operational mathematics now known as the method of the Laplace transform, which has won wide acclaim and acceptance in the field of communication-engineering analysis.

In this chapter we shall also discuss a comparison of the Fourier and Laplace integrals. In view of the fact that many decades were to pass between the introduction of the Heaviside operational calculus and both the development of Laplace transform and the understanding of its interpretation in the Fourier sense, it is a tribute to Heaviside that despite the stormy and bitter controversies which raged over his mathematics, he

[1] O. Heaviside, "Electromagnetic Theory," D. Van Nostrand Company, Inc., New York, 1893, vol. 1, 1899, vol. 2, 1912, vol. 3; "Electrical Papers," The Macmillan Company, New York, 1892, 2 vols.

[2] T. J. Bromwich, Normal Coordinates in Dynamical Systems, *Proc. London Math. Soc.*, vol. 2, pp. 401–448, 1916.

[3] G. Doetsch, "Theorie und Anwendung der Laplace-Transformation," Verlag Julius Springer, Berlin, 1937. For an illuminating history of the development of the Laplace transform see Gardiner and Barnes, "Transients in Linear Systems," Appendix C, John Wiley & Sons, Inc., New York, 1942.

retained a considerable amount of respect for Fourier's work, showing remarkable insight and fairness as is evidenced by his statement in his "Electromagnetic Theory" (vol. 2, p. 32): "I may have to point out sometimes that my method leads to solutions much more simply than Fourier's method. I may therefore appear to be disparaging and endeavoring to supersede his work. But it is nothing of the sort. In a complete treatise on diffusion Fourier's and other methods would come in side by side—not as antagonists but as mutual friends helping one another."

INTRODUCTION TO THE LAPLACE TRANSFORM

2. The Laplace Transform. The Laplace transform of some time function $f(t)$ is written as follows,

$$\mathcal{L}[f(t)] = \int_0^\infty f(t)e^{-st}\,dt = f(s) \tag{1}$$

where

$$s = \alpha + j\omega \tag{2}$$

α is a positive number.

Let us compare the Laplace transform with the Fourier transform

$$g(\omega) = \int_{-\infty}^\infty f(t)e^{-j\omega t}\,dt \tag{3}$$

It is immediately evident that the difference lies in the fact that the Laplace transform handles functions which are nonzero for $t_0 < t < \infty$, where $t_0 \geq 0$, such wave functions occurring in transient analysis.[1] In addition, since

$$e^{-st} = e^{-\alpha t}e^{-j\omega t} \tag{4}$$

the integrand of the Laplace transform is seen to contain the decay factor $e^{-\alpha t}$, which does not appear in the Fourier transform.

It is evident that the Fourier transform $g(\omega)$ may be recovered from the Laplace transform for functions of time for which $f(t) = 0$ for $-\infty < t < 0$ by taking the limit[2] of $\mathcal{L}[f(t)]$ as α approaches zero, *i.e.*,

$$g(\omega) = \lim_{\alpha \to 0} \mathcal{L}[f(t)] \tag{5}$$

$$= \lim_{\alpha \to 0} \int_0^\infty f(t)e^{-(\alpha + j\omega)}\,dt \tag{6}$$

[1] For considerations of the Laplace transform for the case when $f(t)$ is not necessarily equal to zero in the interval $-\infty < t < 0$, see van der Pol and Bremmer, "Operational Calculus Based on the Two-sided Laplace Integral," Cambridge University Press, London, 1950.

[2] Provided, of course, that a limit exists.

3. Step-function Analysis Using the Laplace Transform. The unit step function is an important basic concept in radio-communication transient analysis. It is easily handled by the Laplace transform and serves to illustrate concepts arising from the use of the decay factor and from the

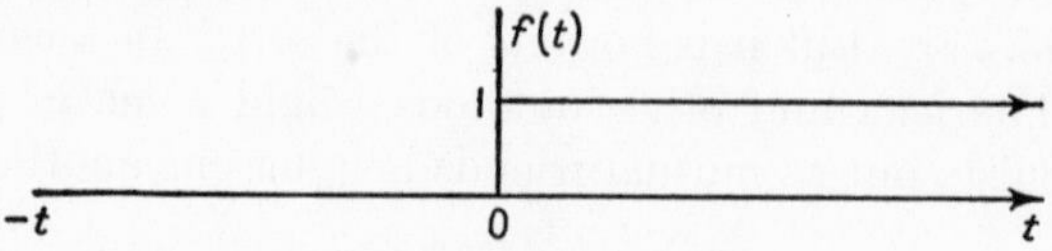

FIG. 1. Step function.

presence of the contour integral. Consider the analysis of the unit step function which is pictured in Fig. 1 and which is described mathematically as

$$\begin{aligned} f(t) &= 0 \qquad -\infty < t < 0 \\ &= 1 \qquad 0 < t < \infty \end{aligned} \tag{7}$$

For this function of time, $\int_{-\infty}^{\infty} |f(t)|\, dt$ does not converge, and (7) cannot be converted directly into a frequency function by use of the Fourier transform. In order to permit the use of the Fourier transform, we may modify equation set (7) and cause the step function to vanish at infinity by introducing the exponential decay factor $e^{-\alpha t}$, where α is a real positive number. If α is sufficiently small, the function pictured in Fig. 1 will be relatively unaffected by the exponential except as time approaches infinity. Equation (7) becomes

$$\begin{aligned} f(t) &= 0 \qquad -\infty < t < 0 \\ &= e^{-\alpha t} \qquad 0 < t < \infty \end{aligned} \tag{8}$$

The Fourier transform of (8) is found to be

$$g(\omega) = \int_{-\infty}^{0} 0 \cdot e^{-j\omega t}\, dt + \int_{0}^{\infty} e^{-\alpha t} e^{-j\omega t}\, dt \tag{9}$$

$$= \frac{1}{\alpha + j\omega} = \frac{1}{s} \tag{10}$$

The Fourier transform of Eq. (7) is therefore

$$g(\omega) = \lim_{\alpha \to 0} \frac{1}{\alpha + j\omega} = \frac{1}{j\omega} \tag{11}$$

which describes the spectrum of the unit step function.

We may derive the expression $1/s$ corresponding to (7) directly, using the Laplace transform as follows:

$$\mathcal{L}[f(t)] = \int_0^\infty e^{-st}\,dt \tag{12}$$

$$= -\frac{e^{-st}}{s}\Big|_0^\infty = \frac{1}{s} \tag{13}$$

4. The Laplace Transform of $f(t) = t^n$. Let us evaluate the Laplace transform of t^n, that is,

$$\mathcal{L}(t^n) = \int_0^\infty t^n e^{-st}\,dt = f(s) \tag{14}$$

Integrating successively by parts, it follows that

$$f(s) = -\frac{t^n e^{-st}}{s}\Big|_0^\infty + \frac{n}{s}\int_0^\infty t^{n-1}e^{-st}\,dt \tag{15}$$

$$= 0 + \frac{n}{s}\left(\frac{n-1}{s}\int_0^\infty t^{n-2}e^{-st}\,dt\right) \tag{16}$$

$$= 0 + \cdots + \frac{n}{s^n}(n-1)(n-2)\cdots 4\cdot 3\cdot 2\cdot 1\int_0^\infty t^0 e^{-st}\,dt \tag{17}$$

$$= \frac{n!}{s^{n+1}} \tag{18}$$

5. Laplace Transform of $e^{j\omega t}$. If $f(t) = e^{j\omega t}$, then

$$\mathcal{L}(e^{j\omega t}) = \int_0^\infty e^{j\omega t}e^{-st}\,dt \tag{19}$$

$$= \frac{1}{j\omega - s}\,e^{-(s-j\omega)t}\Big|_0^\infty \tag{20}$$

$$= \frac{1}{s - j\omega} \qquad s > j\omega \tag{21}$$

6. Laplace Transform of sin ωt and cos ωt. If $f(t) = \sin \omega t$,

$$\mathcal{L}(\sin \omega t) = \int_0^\infty \sin \omega t\, e^{-st}\,dt \tag{22}$$

$$= \frac{1}{2j}\int_0^\infty (e^{-(s-j\omega)t} - e^{-(s+j\omega)t})\,dt \tag{23}$$

$$= \frac{1}{2j}\left(\frac{1}{s-j\omega} - \frac{1}{s+j\omega}\right) \tag{24}$$

$$= \frac{\omega}{s^2+\omega^2} \tag{25}$$

In like manner, we may show that

$$\mathcal{L}(\cos \omega t) = \frac{s}{s^2 + \omega^2} \tag{26}$$

7. Laplace Transform of a Derivative.[1] In electric-network equations, derivatives of the current and voltage (for example, $L\,di/dt$) appear. Consider, for example, the Laplace transform of di/dt, which is derived as follows:

$$\mathcal{L}\left(\frac{di}{dt}\right) = \int_0^\infty \frac{di}{dt} e^{-st}\,dt \tag{27}$$

$$= \int_0^\infty e^{-st}\,di \tag{28}$$

Integrating by parts, we get

$$\mathcal{L}\left(\frac{di}{dt}\right) = ie^{-st}\Big|_0^\infty + s\int_0^\infty ie^{-st}\,dt \tag{29}$$

$$= -i_0 + s\mathcal{L}(i) \tag{30}$$

where i_0 is the value of current at $t = 0$. This is an important result since it includes not only the transform of i but also its initial value. In general, we may write

$$\mathcal{L}[f'(t)] = s\mathcal{L}[f(t)] - f(0) \tag{31}$$

8. Laplace Transform of the Integration, $\int i\,dt$. Consider the Laplace transform of the integral, $\int i\,dt$, which yields the charge on a capacitor. Letting

$$q = \int i\,dt \tag{32}$$

where q is the charge, we get

$$\mathcal{L}(q) = \int_0^\infty qe^{-st}\,dt \tag{33}$$

Integrating by parts, we get

$$\mathcal{L}(q) = -\frac{q}{s}e^{-st}\Big|_0^\infty + \frac{1}{s}\int_0^\infty e^{-st}\,dq \tag{34}$$

Since $dq = i\,dt$, it follows that

$$\mathcal{L}(q) = \frac{q_0}{s} + \frac{\mathcal{L}(i)}{s} \tag{35}$$

[1] See Prob. 3 at the end of this chapter for general formulas relating to the Laplace transform of derivatives of higher order.

The Laplace transform of q is in terms of the initial value of the charge and of the Laplace transform of the current.

9. The Translation of the Laplace Transform. Consider the function $f(t)$, for which the following Laplace transform exists:

$$\mathcal{L}[f(t)] = \int_0^\infty f(t)e^{-st}\,dt \tag{36}$$

Let us multiply each side by the exponential function e^{-st_1} where t_1 is some value of time greater than zero. We get

$$e^{-st_1}\mathcal{L}[f(t)] = \int_0^\infty f(t)e^{-s(t+t_1)}\,dt \tag{37}$$

Substituting σ for $t + t_1$, it follows from the integral on the right-hand side that

$$\int_{t_1}^\infty e^{-s\sigma}f(\sigma - t_1)\,d\sigma = \int_0^{t_1} 0\cdot e^{-s\sigma}\,d\sigma + \int_{t_1}^\infty e^{-s\sigma}f(\sigma - t_1)\,d\sigma \tag{38}$$

which shows that owing to the multiplication by e^{-st_1}

$$\begin{aligned} f(t) &= 0 && -\infty < t < t_1 \\ &= f(t - t_1) && t_1 < t < \infty \end{aligned} \tag{39}$$

10. Example of the Translated Step Function. Consider the step function which is pictured in Fig. 2 and which is expressed mathematically as follows:

$$\begin{aligned} f(t) &= 0 && -\infty < t < t_1 \\ &= 1 && t_1 < t < \infty \end{aligned} \tag{40}$$

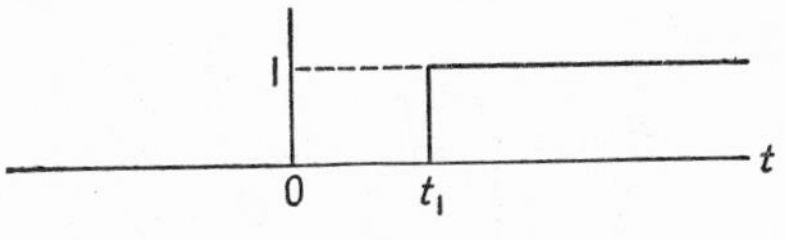

FIG. 2. Translated step function.

Then

$$\mathcal{L}[f(t)] = \int_{t_1}^\infty e^{-st}\,dt \tag{41}$$

$$= -\frac{1}{s}e^{-st}\Big|_{t_1}^{\infty} = \frac{e^{-st_1}}{s} \tag{42}$$

Therefore

$$f(t - t_1) = \frac{e^{-st_1}}{s} \tag{43}$$

Note that by letting α approach zero in (43) we get for the Fourier transform of (40)

$$g(\omega) = \lim_{\alpha \to 0} \frac{e^{-st_1}}{s} = \frac{e^{-j\omega t_1}}{j\omega} \tag{44}$$

It is evident that $e^{-j\omega t_1}$ is a phase-shift term which shifts the phase of the spectral components of (11) by the phase angle ωt_1.

THE INVERSE LAPLACE TRANSFORM

11. The Inverse Laplace Transform. The inverse Laplace transform is expressed as follows: If the Laplace transform of $f(t)$ is $f(s)$, then the inverse Laplace transform provides the recovery of $f(t)$ from $f(s)$, that is,

$$f(t) = \frac{1}{2\pi j} \int_{\alpha - j\infty}^{\alpha + j\infty} f(s) e^{st}\, ds = \mathfrak{L}^{-1}[f(s)] \tag{45}$$

It is not always necessary to resort to contour integration for the recovery of $f(t)$ from $f(s)$ when simple or known functions are involved. For example, it follows from Sec. 5 of this chapter that if

$$f(s) = \frac{1}{s - j\omega} \tag{46}$$

then

$$f(t) = e^{j\omega t} \tag{47}$$

Table 1 represents a compilation of many useful functions of time and their Laplace transforms; far more extensive tables of Laplace transforms are available.[1]

12. The Inverse Laplace Transform and the Fourier Integral. Let us compare the inverse Laplace transform (45) and the Fourier integral which is described as follows:

$$f(t) = \frac{1}{2\pi} \int_{-\infty}^{\infty} g(\omega) e^{j\omega t}\, d\omega \tag{48}$$

The Fourier integral can be written in the form of a contour integral as follows:

$$f(t) = \frac{1}{2\pi j} \int_{-j\infty}^{j\infty} g(\omega) e^{j\omega t}\, dj\omega \tag{49}$$

The Fourier integral is seen to be a contour integral whose path of integration follows the imaginary axis from $-j\infty$ to $+j\infty$. The solution of

[1] Gardiner and Barnes, "Transients in Linear Systems," John Wiley & Sons, Inc., New York, 1942.

R. V. Churchill, "Modern Operational Mathematics in Engineering," McGraw-Hill Book Company, Inc., New York, 1944.

(49) is therefore limited to cases in which singularities do not occur on the imaginary axis.

In the inverse Laplace transform, not only is a factor $e^{\alpha t}$ included in the integrand but the path of integration takes place along a line from $-j\infty$ to $j\infty$ which is displaced to the right of the imaginary axis by α. This path is known as the Bromwich path; its full significance and the role played by the factor $e^{\alpha t}$ will be illustrated in the next section and in Sec. 18.

13. The Inverse Laplace Transform of $1/s$ Using Contour Integration. It follows directly from Sec. 3 that the inverse Laplace transform of $1/s$

TABLE 1
LAPLACE TRANSFORMS

	$f(s)$	$f(t)$		$f(s)$	$f(t)$
(1)	$\frac{1}{s}$	1	(14)	$\frac{1}{s^2(s^2+a^2)}$	$\frac{1}{a^3}(at - \sin at)$
(2)	$\frac{1}{s^2}$	t	(15)	$\frac{1}{(s-a)^2+b^2}$	$\frac{1}{b}e^{at}\sin bt$
(3)	$\frac{1}{s^n}$	$\frac{t^{n-1}}{(n-1)!}$	(16)	$\frac{s-a}{(s-a)^2+b^2}$	$e^{at}\cos bt$
(4)	$\frac{s}{s^2+a^2}$	$\cos at$	(17)	$\frac{1}{s^4-a^4}$	$\frac{1}{2a^3}(\sinh at - \sin at)$
(5)	$\frac{s}{s^2-a^2}$	$\cosh at$	(18)	$\frac{s}{s^4-a^4}$	$\frac{1}{2a^2}(\cosh at - \cos at)$
(6)	$\frac{1}{s-a}$	e^{at}	(19)	$\frac{s^2}{s^4-a^4}$	$\frac{1}{2a}(\sinh at + \sin at)$
(7)	$\frac{1}{(s-a)^2}$	te^{at}	(20)	$\frac{s^3}{s^4-a^4}$	$\frac{1}{2}(\cosh at + \cos at)$
(8)	$\frac{1}{s^2+a^2}$	$\frac{1}{a}\sin at$	(21)	$e^{-a\sqrt{s}}$	$\frac{a}{2\sqrt{\pi t^3}}e^{-a^2/4t}$
(9)	$\frac{1}{(s-a)(s-b)}$	$\frac{1}{a-b}(e^{at}-e^{bt})$	(22)	$\frac{e^{-a\sqrt{s}}}{\sqrt{s}}$	$\frac{1}{\sqrt{\pi t}}e^{-a^2/4t}$
(10)	$\frac{s}{(s^2+a^2)^2}$	$\frac{t}{2a}\sin at$	(23)	$\frac{e^{-a\sqrt{s}}}{s}$	$1 - \operatorname{erf}\frac{a}{2\sqrt{t}}$
(11)	$\frac{a^2}{(s^2+a^2)^2}$	$\frac{1}{2a}(\sin at - at\cos at)$	(24)	$\sqrt{s-a} - \sqrt{s-b}$	$\frac{1}{2\sqrt{\pi t^3}}(e^{bt}-e^{at})$
(12)	$\frac{1}{s^2-a^2}$	$\frac{1}{a}\sinh at$	(25)	$s^{-\frac{3}{2}}$	$2\sqrt{\frac{t}{\pi}}$
(13)	$\frac{1}{s(s^2+a^2)}$	$\frac{1}{a^2}(1-\cos at)$	(26)	$\frac{1}{\sqrt{s}}$	$\frac{1}{\sqrt{\pi t}}$

is the step function pictured in Fig. 1. It is very instructive to demonstrate this, using the contour integral (45).

The inverse Laplace transform of $\mathfrak{L}[f(t)]$, which permits the recovery of the time function from the s function, is written in terms of (7) as follows:

$$f(t) = \frac{1}{2\pi j} \int_{\alpha - j\infty}^{\alpha + j\infty} \frac{e^{st}}{s} \, ds \tag{50}$$

It is evident that only one singularity is present; this is located at $s = 0$. The inverse Laplace transform specifies that the path of integration shall follow the line from $\alpha + j\infty$ to $\alpha - j\infty$. As long as $\alpha > 0$, this path will miss the singularity. In order to close the contour, let us use a semicircle of radius $R \to \infty$, as is shown in Fig. 3a and b.

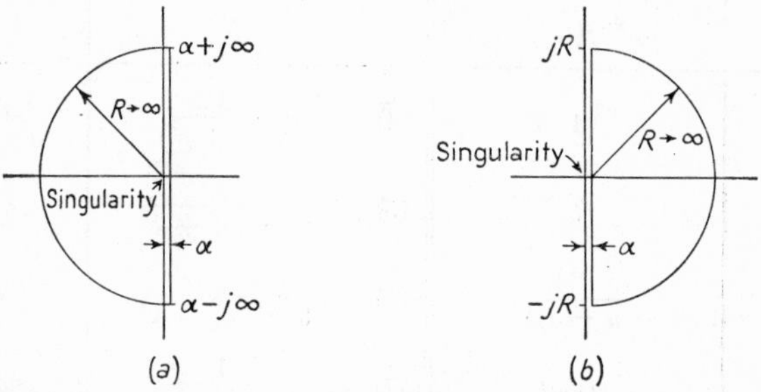

FIG. 3.

When $t < 0$, the semicircle can extend in the positive direction only, as is shown in Fig. 3b, since $e^{\alpha t}$ is present in the integrand and α is positive. This contour does not enclose the singularity, and therefore we see that

$$\frac{1}{2\pi j} \int_{\alpha - j\infty}^{\alpha + j\infty} \frac{e^{st}}{s} \, ds = 0 \qquad t < 0 \tag{51}$$

For $t > 0$, the semicircle must be located as shown in Fig. 3a for the integral to be noninfinite in value. This contour now encloses the one singularity which is present, and since the Laurent expansion of e^{st}/s is

$$\frac{e^{st}}{s} = \frac{1}{s} + t + \frac{st^2}{2!} + \frac{s^2t^3}{3!} + \cdots \tag{52}$$

and since, according to Laurent's theorem, the residue in the vicinity of $s = 0$ is the coefficient of $1/s$, we see that

$$\frac{1}{2\pi j} \int_{\alpha - j\infty}^{\alpha + j\infty} \frac{e^{st}}{s} \, ds = 1 \qquad t > 0 \tag{53}$$

We may determine the value of the contour integral for the special case when $t = 0$ by considering again the contour in Fig. 3b. Denoting the path along the semicircle as R', then, according to the Cauchy-Goursat theorem, we may write for $\alpha \to 0$

$$\int_{-jR}^{jR} \frac{ds}{s} + \int_{R'} \frac{ds}{s} = 0 \tag{54}$$

If

$$s = \text{Re}^{j\theta} \qquad ds = j\,\text{Re}^{j\theta}\,d\theta \tag{55}$$

then it follows that

$$\int_{R'} \frac{ds}{s} = j \int_{-\pi/2}^{\pi/2} d\theta = j\pi \tag{56}$$

whereupon we see that

$$\frac{1}{2\pi j} \int_{\alpha - j\infty}^{\alpha + j\infty} \frac{e^{st}}{s}\,ds = \frac{1}{2} \qquad t = 0 \tag{57}$$

and we find that the full recovery of the time function from the s function yields the following expression:

$$\begin{aligned} f(t) &= 0 \qquad -\infty < t < 0 \\ &= \tfrac{1}{2} \qquad t = 0 \\ &= 1 \qquad t > 0 \end{aligned} \tag{58}$$

Equation (58) describes the unit step function and includes the intermediate value of $f(t) = \frac{1}{2}$ at $t = 0$.

14. Inverse Laplace Transform of $1/s^{n+1}$. Consider the inverse Laplace transform of $1/s^{n+1}$, that is,

$$f(t) = \frac{1}{2\pi j} \int_{\alpha - j\infty}^{\alpha + j\infty} \frac{e^{st}}{s^{n+1}}\,ds \tag{59}$$

This expression can be written in the form

$$f(t) = \frac{1}{2\pi j} \int_{\alpha - j\infty}^{\alpha + j\infty} \left(\frac{1}{s^{n+1}} + \frac{t}{s^n} + \frac{t^2}{2!s^{n-1}} + \cdots + \frac{t^n}{n!s} + \cdots \right) ds \tag{60}$$

The integrand is a Laurent series; the residue is therefore the coefficient of $1/s$, that is,

$$f(t) = \frac{t^n}{n!} \tag{61}$$

This expression is readily deduced from (18).

15. Inverse Laplace Transform of an Irrational Function. In some applications (see, for example, Sec. 8, Chap. 9) of the Laplace transform in communication networks, irrational functions are evolved by the transformation. The following demonstrates a useful method of finding the inverse Laplace transforms of simple irrational functions by use of a series expansion.

Consider the function

$$\mathcal{L}[f(t)] = \frac{1}{\sqrt{s^2 + a^2}} \tag{62}$$

Applying the binomial-expansion theorem to (62), we get

$$\mathcal{L}[f(t)] = \frac{1}{s} - \frac{a^2}{2s^3} + \frac{3a^4}{2^2 2! s^5} - \frac{3 \cdot 5a^6}{2^3 \cdot 3! s^7} + \cdots \tag{63}$$

It follows from Sec. 14 that

$$\mathcal{L}^{-1}\left(\frac{1}{s^n}\right) = \frac{t^{n-1}}{(n-1)!} \tag{64}$$

Then

$$f(t) = 1 - \frac{(at)^2}{2^2} + \frac{(at)^4}{2^2 4^2} - \frac{(at)^6}{2^2 4^2 6^2} + \cdots \tag{65}$$

This infinite series is recognized as that representing a Bessel function of the first kind and zero order [see Appendix, Eq. (7)]. We get finally

$$f(t) = J_0(at) \tag{66}$$

which is valid when $a > 0$.

16. Translation of the Inverse Laplace Transform. We may attribute translational properties to inverse Laplace transformations which are extremely useful in solutions of practical problems. Note that if we replace s by $s - a$ in Eq. (1), it follows that

$$f(s-a) = \int_0^\infty f(t)e^{-(s-a)}\, dt = \int_0^\infty f(t)e^{at}e^{-st}\, dt \tag{67}$$

$$= \mathcal{L}[f(t)e^{at}] \tag{68}$$

Therefore, if a Laplace transform of the form $f(s - a)$ is encountered, it follows that

$$\frac{1}{2\pi j}\int_{\alpha - j\infty}^{\alpha + j\infty} f(s-a)e^{st}\, ds = f(t)e^{at} \tag{69}$$

As an example, consider the function

$$f(s) = \frac{s+a}{(s+a)^2 + \omega^2} \tag{70}$$

Since, according to (26),

$$\mathcal{L}(\cos \omega t) = \frac{s}{s^2 + \omega^2} \tag{71}$$

then

$$\mathfrak{L}^{-1}\left[\frac{(s+a)}{(s+a)^2+\omega^2}\right] = e^{-at} \cos \omega t \tag{72}$$

17. The Faltung Integral. If the two Laplace transforms $f_1(s)$ and $f_2(s)$ exist, where

$$f_1(s) = \mathfrak{L}[f_1(t)] \tag{73}$$

$$f_2(s) = \mathfrak{L}[f_2(t)] \tag{74}$$

then it can be shown[1] that their product is related to $f_1(t)$ and $f_2(t)$ by the Faltung integral (also called the convolution integral),

$$f_1(s) f_2(s) = \int_0^\infty e^{-st} \int_0^t f_1(t-\lambda) f_2(\lambda)\, d\lambda\, dt \tag{75}$$

which may be written in the following way:

$$f_1(t) * f_2(t) = \int_0^t f_1(t-\lambda) f_2(\lambda)\, d\lambda \tag{76}$$

This relationship is particularly useful in evaluating certain inverse Laplace transforms since if $f_1(t)$ and $f_2(t)$ corresponding to each member of the function $f_1(s)f_2(s)$ are known, the inverse Laplace transform of $f_1(s)f_2(s)$ may, in many cases, be readily determined.

As an example of the use of the Faltung integral, consider the function

$$f(s) = f_1(s) f_2(s) \tag{77}$$

$$= \frac{1}{s-a} \frac{1}{s-b} \tag{78}$$

It is readily shown from Sec. 16 that

$$f_1(t) = \mathfrak{L}^{-1}\left(\frac{1}{s-a}\right) = e^{at} \tag{79}$$

$$f_2(t) = \mathfrak{L}^{-1}\left(\frac{1}{s-b}\right) = e^{bt} \tag{80}$$

Then,

$$\mathfrak{L}^{-1}[f(s)] = f_1(t) * f_2(t) = \int_0^t e^{a(t-\lambda)} e^{b\lambda}\, d\lambda \tag{81}$$

$$= \frac{e^{at}}{b-a} e^{(b-a)\lambda} \Big|_0^t \tag{82}$$

$$= \frac{e^{at} - e^{bt}}{a-b} \tag{83}$$

[1] For a detailed proof, see R. V. Churchill, "Modern Operational Mathematics in Engineering," Sec. 14, McGraw-Hill Book Company, Inc., New York, 1944.

18. General Aspects of the Inverse Laplace Transform. In Sec. 13, a contour of the type pictured in Fig. 3*b* was found to be suitable for analysis of the residue due to the singularity at $s = 0$. The following is a generalization of the discussion pertaining to the contour of (45) as specified by the path from $\alpha - j\infty$ to $\alpha + j\infty$.

In most problems encountered in communication-circuit analysis, $\mathcal{L}[f(t)]$ is of the form (do not confuse $g(s)$ with the transform, $g(\omega)$)

$$\mathcal{L}[f(t)] = \frac{a_0 + a_1 s + a_2 s^2 + \cdots + a_n s^n}{b_0 + b_1 s + b_2 s^2 + \cdots + b_m s^m} = \frac{w(s)}{g(s)} \tag{84}$$

where $m > n$ and a_n and b_m are constants. When the denominator of (84) is factored, singularities will be found to be present at $z_1, z_2, \ldots, z_m$.

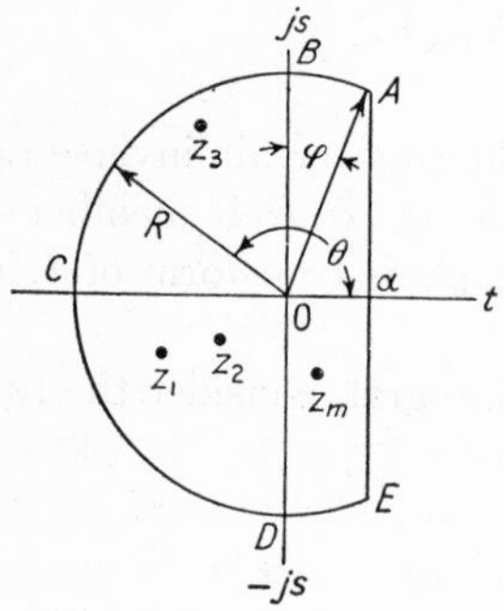

FIG. 4.

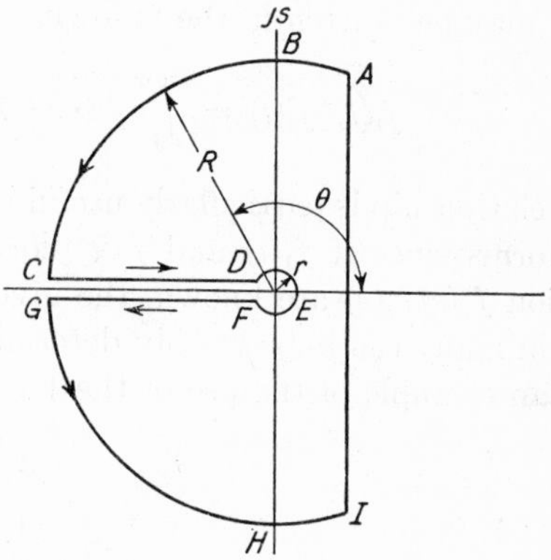

FIG. 5.

These singularities are pictured in Fig. 4, where they are seen to be enclosed by the contour $ABCDEA$, which consists of the line AE, which is parallel to the js axis and at a distance α from the origin, and the circle segment $ABCDE$ of radius R. The value of α is such that the singularities are enclosed by the contour.

Since it is easily shown that the absolute value of a contour integral along a certain path is less than the product of the length of the path and the maximum value of the integrand along the path, it follows that for the contour $ABCDE$, for the case when $R \to \infty$,

$$\lim_{R\to\infty} \left| \int_{ABCDE} \mathcal{L}[f(t)]e^{st}\, ds \right| \leq \lim_{R\to\infty} \left[\frac{a_n e^{tR\cos\theta}}{b_m R^{m-n-1}} (\pi + 2\varphi) \right] = 0 \tag{85}$$[1]

[1] When R is large, we may write $s = R\cos\theta + jR\sin\theta$.

and we find that since the contributions due to the circle segment of radius $R \to \infty$ are equal to zero, then

$$\lim_{R\to\infty}\left\{\frac{1}{2\pi j}\int_{ABCDEA} \mathcal{L}[f(t)]e^{st}\,ds\right\} = \lim_{R\to\infty}\left\{\frac{1}{2\pi j}\int_{EA} \mathcal{L}[f(t)]e^{st}\,ds\right\} \tag{86}$$

The integral on the right-hand side is the inverse Laplace transform as specified by (45). Since the contour encloses all of the singularities, it follows that the inverse Laplace transform is equal to the sum of the residues resulting from the singularities due to (84). Therefore,

$$\frac{1}{2\pi j}\int_{\alpha-j\infty}^{\alpha+j\infty} \mathcal{L}[f(t)]e^{st}\,ds = \sum_{n=1}^{m} \text{res}\,(z_n) \tag{87}$$

Solutions of (87) involving inverse transforms of the type described by (84) will be described in considerable detail with associated electrical circuits in Chap. 6.

19. A Solution of the Inverse Laplace Transform Involving a Branch Point. When $\mathcal{L}[f(t)]$ is not of the form which can be handled by the contour shown in Fig. 4, then the contour integral must be solved for the specific contour prescribed by the problem. Consider, for example, the case when

$$\mathcal{L}[f(t)] = s^{-\frac{1}{2}} \tag{88}$$

This is two-valued and nonanalytic in the neighborhood of the origin where it has a singularity consisting of a branch point.

Let a contour be constructed as shown in Fig. 5, where a large circle of radius R and a small circle of radius r are so connected by AI, CD, and FG that the contour avoids the branch-point singularity at the origin. According to the Cauchy-Goursat theorem, since the entire region enclosed by the contour is analytic,

$$\frac{1}{2\pi j}\int_{A\cdots A} s^{-\frac{1}{2}}e^{st}\,ds = 0 \tag{89}$$

The contour integral for the entire path may be written as follows, with the distances AB and HI presumed negligible and CD and GF as $ae^{i\pi}$ and $ae^{-i\pi}$, respectively ($s = Re^{i\theta}$ on BC and GH; $s = re^{i\theta}$ on DEF):

$$\begin{aligned}\int_{IA} s^{-\frac{1}{2}}e^{st}\,ds &+ \int_{\pi/2}^{\pi} R^{-\frac{1}{2}}e^{-i(\theta/2)}e^{R(\cos\theta+i\sin\theta)t}jRe^{i\theta}\,d\theta \\ &+ \int_{R}^{r} a^{-\frac{1}{2}}e^{-i(\pi/2)}e^{-at}e^{i\pi}\,da + \int_{\pi}^{-\pi} r^{-\frac{1}{2}}e^{-i(\theta/2)}e^{r(\cos\theta+i\sin\theta)t}jre^{i\theta}\,d\theta \\ &+ \int_{r}^{R} a^{-\frac{1}{2}}e^{i(\pi/2)}e^{-at}e^{-i\pi}\,da \\ &+ \int_{-\pi}^{-\pi/2} R^{-\frac{1}{2}}e^{-i(\theta/2)}e^{R(\cos\theta+i\sin\theta)t}jRe^{i\theta}\,d\theta = 0\end{aligned} \tag{90}$$

For the case where

$$R \to \infty \qquad r \to 0 \tag{91}$$

the second, fourth, and sixth integrals vanish, and we arrive at the following relationship, the first integral having transformed into the form given by Eq. (45):

$$\frac{1}{2\pi j}\int_{\alpha-j\infty}^{\alpha+j\infty} s^{-\frac{1}{2}}e^{st}\,ds = \frac{1}{2\pi j}\int_0^\infty a^{-\frac{1}{2}}e^{-at}(e^{j(\pi/2)} - e^{-j(\pi/2)})\,da \tag{92}$$

$$= \frac{1}{\pi}\int_0^\infty a^{-\frac{1}{2}}e^{-at}\,da \tag{93}$$

Letting

$$\vartheta = at \tag{94}$$

we get

$$\frac{1}{2\pi j}\int_{\alpha-j\infty}^{\alpha+j\infty} s^{-\frac{1}{2}}e^{st}\,ds = \frac{1}{\pi\sqrt{t}}\int_0^\infty \vartheta^{-\frac{1}{2}}e^{-\vartheta}\,d\vartheta \tag{95}$$

$$= \frac{1}{\pi\sqrt{t}}\Gamma\left(\frac{1}{2}\right) = \frac{1}{\sqrt{\pi t}} \tag{96}$$

PROBLEMS

1. Derive the following Laplace transforms in Table 1: (*a*) 10; (*b*) 14; (*c*) 20.

2. Show by using contour integration that

$$\mathfrak{L}^{-1}(\log s) = -\frac{1}{t}$$

3. Show that in general

a. $\mathfrak{L}[tF''(t)] = -s^2 f'(s) - 2s f(s) + F(0)$

b. $\mathfrak{L}[F''(t)] = s^2 f(s) - sF(+0) - F'(+0)$

c. $\mathfrak{L}[F^{(n)}(t)] = s^n f(s) - s^{n-1}F(+0) - \cdots - F^{(n-1)}(+0)$

4. Show that

$$\mathfrak{L}\left[\frac{1}{a}e^{(b/a)t}F\left(\frac{t}{a}\right)\right] = f(as - b)$$

5. Prove the following inverse Laplace transforms:

a. $\mathfrak{L}^{-1}\left[\dfrac{(b^2 - a^2)s}{(s^2 + a^2)(s^2 + b^2)}\right] = \cos at - \cos bt$

b. $\mathfrak{L}^{-1}\left[\dfrac{a^2}{s(a^2 + s^2)}\right] = 1 - \cos at$

c. $\mathfrak{L}^{-1}\left[\dfrac{a}{\sqrt{s^2 + a^2}\,(s + \sqrt{s^2 + a^2})}\right] = J_1(at)$

6. Prove parts *a* and *b* of Prob. 5, using the Faltung integral.

CHAPTER 5

COMPLEX WAVES IN RADIO, TELEVISION, AND RADAR

1. Introduction. The complex waves which will be discussed in this chapter are those waves which are fundamental to electrical communications, *i.e.*, *speech*, *music*, *television scanning*, *radar signals*, and *noise*. These waves constitute or decide the nature of the intelligence which is conveyed from one point to another in a communication system. We shall not be concerned here with the actual transducers for converting, for example, sound waves into electrical waves[1] of the same frequencies and general characteristics. Rather, it is the *fundamental waves* and in some cases the *frequency ranges* involved that are of interest to us since these aspects will be important in considerations of modulation, bandwidth, and distortion in general communication systems.

COMPLEX WAVES IN THE AUDIO RANGE

2. Complex Waves in Speech and Music. The musical note, middle C, has a fundamental frequency of 256 cycles. If a singer, an oboe player, or a violinist were to produce this note, for example, the sounds produced by each will be different owing to the fact that in addition to the presence of a fundamental tone whose frequency is 256 cycles, overtones and harmonics are produced which are characteristic of the instrument or voice which produces the note. All sounds associated with speech, music, and the sounds and noises which occur in various types of surroundings are multitone complex waves which differ in the number and amplitudes of the fundamentals, harmonics, and overtones present. Many data on the frequency ranges which are involved for undistorted reproduction of these sounds have been collected, and Fig. 1 shows a compilation of these data.[2] In general, the frequency range of audible sound is from 40 to 15,000

[1] See, for example, the discussion of microphones in H. F. Olson, "Elements of Acoustical Engineering," 2d ed., Chap. VIII, D. Van Nostrand Company, Inc., New York, 1947. For some mathematical aspects of carbon-microphone performance, see E. A. Guillemin, "Communication Networks," Chap. X, Sec. 5, John Wiley & Sons, Inc., New York, 1931.

[2] W. B. Snow, Audible Frequency Ranges of Music, Speech, and Noise, *J. Acoust. Soc. Am.*, vol. 13, No. 1, Part 1, p. 155, 1931.

cycles, with male speech and female speech having spectra in the frequency ranges of 100 to 8,000 and 175 to 10,000 cycles, respectively.

There are many sounds in nature, such as those due to high-velocity winds and to the scraping together of hard materials (for example, chalk

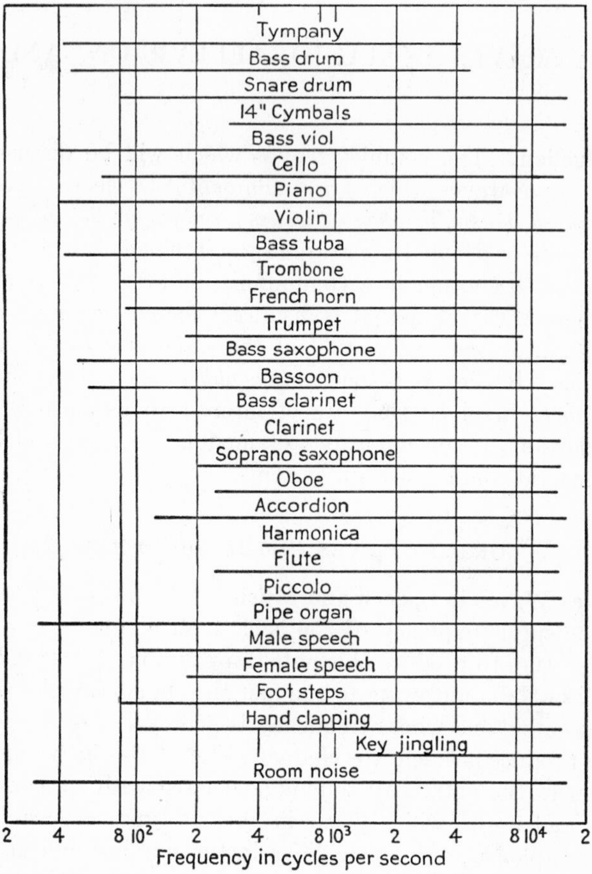

FIG. 1. Frequency ranges of sounds associated with speech, music, and typical everyday noises.

on a blackboard), which have frequencies in their spectra which exceed 15,000 cycles. However, these higher frequencies need not be included in considerations of sound- and speech-communication systems.

COMPLEX WAVES IN TELEVISION

3. Fourier Analysis of Television Scanning. In the transmission of visual information, the method of image scanning[1] has been adopted. A

[1] Because of the point of view and disposition of this book, such practical aspects of image scanning in television as resolution and brightness cannot be included here.

typical process of image scanning is that illustrated in Fig. 2, where it is seen that an exploring element, which has a signal output proportional to either the instantaneous or the short-time average of the brightness at its instantaneous position, moves horizontally across the picture in a series of straight-line paths, the first line path starting at the top of the picture

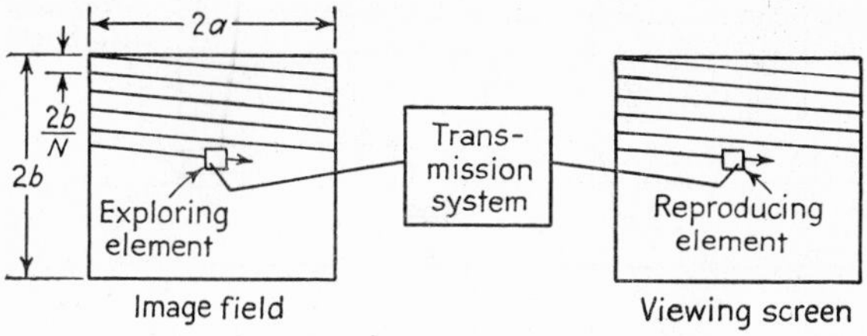

FIG. 2. Typical image-scanning system.

and, for a picture with a total number of N lines, ending with the Nth line, which occurs a distance $2b/N$ below the $(N - 1)$th line. This brightness information is transmitted through a communications system to a reproducing spot, where, using a scanning electron beam which is synchronized with the original image field, the original image is reproduced on the face of a cathode-ray viewing tube (kinescope).

We have seen in Chap. 2 that a two-dimensional field may be represented by a double Fourier series. Consider the case when an image pickup tube such as an iconoscope[1] or an image orthicon[2] is used to convert the scanned two-dimensional image field into an electric wave. This electric wave may be described by the complex Fourier series

$$E(x,y) = \sum_{m=-\infty}^{\infty} \sum_{n=-\infty}^{\infty} C_{mn} \exp \left[j\pi \left(\frac{mx}{a} + \frac{ny}{b} \right) \right] \tag{1}$$

where the height of the picture is $2b$ and its width is $2a$.

Consider first a two-dimensional image field such as that pictured in Fig. 3a for the case when only the component corresponding to $m = 3$, $n = 0$ exists. If this image field is scanned, it is obvious that the output of the image pickup tube will be a simple harmonic wave whose frequency will be a function of the rate of scan and the width, $2a$. For an image field corresponding to the Fourier component, $m = 0$, $n = 3$ as shown in

---

The reader is therefore referred to Zworykin and Morton, "Television," Chap. VI, John Wiley & Sons, Inc., New York, 1940, for a discussion of these considerations.

[1] Zworykin, Morton, and Flory, Theory and Performance of the Iconoscope, *Proc. IRE*, vol. 25, pp. 1071–1092, August, 1937.

[2] Rose and Iams, Television Pickup Tubes Using Low Velocity Electron-beam Scanning, *Proc. IRE*, vol. 27, pp. 547–555, September, 1939.

Rose, Weimer, and Law, The Image Orthicon, A Sensitive Television Pickup Tube, *Proc. IRE*, vol. 34, pp. 424–432, July, 1946.

Fig. 3*b*, it is seen that the signal output of the image pickup tube will have a virtually constant value for a particular scanning line; this value will be a function of the light intensity of the horizontal band involved.

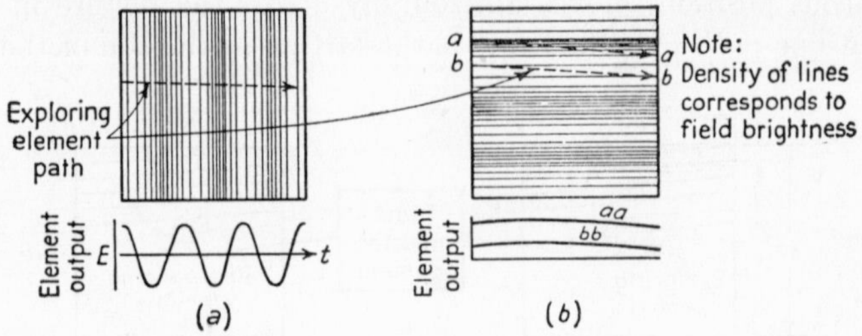

FIG. 3.

Let v_x and v_y be the scanning velocities parallel to the horizontal axis and the vertical axis, respectively, such that

$$x = v_x t \qquad y = v_y t \tag{2}$$

Substituting these values into the exponent of Eq. (1), we find the frequencies of the various Fourier components to be

$$f = \frac{mv_x}{2a} + \frac{nv_y}{2b} \tag{3}$$

If the scanning frame uses N lines, then

$$v_y = \frac{b}{aN} v_x \tag{4}$$

which when substituted into (3) yields the frequency expression

$$f = \frac{v_x}{2a}\left(m + \frac{n}{N}\right) \tag{5}$$

which indicates that various components of the picture signal can exist at the same frequency, thus giving rise to a certain amount of signal confusion since a receiver will be unable to distinguish between these components. Because scanned-image spectral components occur in groups (as we shall see), as long as these groups do not overlap, this signal confusion is reduced to a minimum.

The scanning process does not completely explore the image field. In order to deduce an exact theory which will completely represent a picture, let us include in our considerations, using a solution due to P. Mertz and F. Gray,[1] the function, $F(\gamma,\eta)$, which describes the response or the

[1] Mertz and Gray, Theory of Scanning, *Bell System Tech. J.*, vol. 8, pp. 464–515, July, 1934.

optical transmission of a finite aperture located symmetrically at x, y such that the coordinates γ, η describe a position in the aperture relative to the center of the aperture. This will generalize the analysis such that the output of the image tube will be a signal which will describe a spot of finite area rather than merely a point in this area.

The double Fourier-series representation of the image field in the vicinity of γ, η is

$$E(x+\gamma,\, y+\eta) = \sum_{m=-\infty}^{\infty} \sum_{n=-\infty}^{\infty} C_{mn} \exp\left\{j\pi\left[\frac{m(x+\gamma)}{a} + \frac{n(y+\eta)}{b}\right]\right\} \tag{6}$$

The total light $S(x,y)$ through any portion of the aperture is described by the surface integral

$$S(x,y) = \iint_{\text{ap}} F(\gamma,\eta) E(x+\gamma,\, y+\eta)\, d\gamma\, d\eta \tag{7}$$

which specifies that the total contribution in some incremental area $d\gamma\, d\eta$ is determined by the product of the illumination intensity and the optical transmission of this region.

Substituting (6) into (7), we get

$$S(x,y) = \iint_{\text{ap}} F(\gamma,\eta) \sum_{m=-\infty}^{\infty} \sum_{n=-\infty}^{\infty} C_{mn} \cdot \exp\left\{j\pi\left[\frac{m(x+\gamma)}{a} + \frac{n(y+\eta)}{b}\right]\right\} d\gamma\, d\eta \tag{8}$$

$$= \sum_{m=-\infty}^{\infty} \sum_{n=-\infty}^{\infty} C_{mn} \exp\left\{j\pi\left[\frac{mx}{a} + \frac{ny}{b}\right]\right\} \cdot \iint_{\text{ap}} F(\gamma,\eta) \exp\left[j\pi\left(\frac{m\gamma}{a} + \frac{n\eta}{b}\right)\right] d\gamma\, d\eta \tag{9}$$

which can be written in the form[1]

$$S(x,y) = \sum_{m=-\infty}^{\infty} \sum_{n=-\infty}^{\infty} Y(m,n) C_{mn} \exp\left[j\pi\left(\frac{mx}{a} + \frac{ny}{b}\right)\right] \tag{10}$$

where

$$Y(m,n) = \iint_{\text{ap}} F(\gamma,\eta) \exp\left[j\pi\left(\frac{m\gamma}{a} + \frac{n\eta}{b}\right)\right] d\gamma\, d\eta \tag{11}$$

[1] Compare this equation with the circuit equation in which the driving voltage times the self-admittance, which is independent of the driving voltage, yields the current (see Chap. 6).

$S(x,y)$ represents the sum of Fourier components whose amplitudes are proportional to the components representing the output signal of the image tube. $Y(m,n)$ is the aperture admittance which is comparable with an admittance in an electrical network. It is independent of the scanned picture.

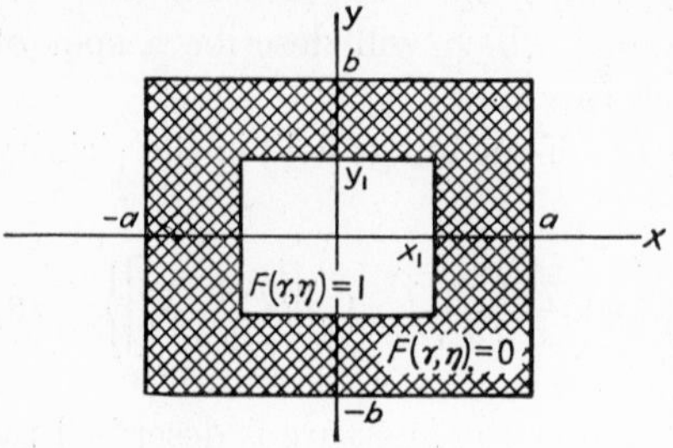

FIG. 4.

As an illustration of the significance of $Y(m,n)$, let us consider the case of a rectangular aperture which is pictured in Fig. 4. Let $F(\gamma,\eta) = 1$ over the entire area of the aperture, and let $F(\gamma,\eta) = 0$ in the area outside of the aperture. It follows from (11) that

$$Y(m,n) = \int_{-y_1}^{y_1}\int_{-x_1}^{x_1} e^{j\pi[(m\gamma/a)+(n\eta/b)]}\,d\gamma\,d\eta \tag{12}$$

$$= 2x_1\frac{\sin(\pi m/a)x_1}{(\pi m/a)x_1}\int_{-y_1}^{y_1} e^{j\pi(n\eta/b)}\,d\eta \tag{13}$$

$$= 4x_1y_1\frac{\sin(\pi m/a)x_1}{(\pi m/a)x_1}\,\frac{\sin(\pi n/b)y_1}{(\pi n/b)y_1} \tag{14}$$

which can be written as follows:

$$Y(m,n) = 4x_1y_1Y_\gamma(m)Y_\eta(n) \tag{15}$$

Equation (14) is diagramed in Fig. 5 and depicts $Y(m,n)$ as a function of $|n|y_1/b$ for various values of $|m|x_1/a$. It is evident that these curves in

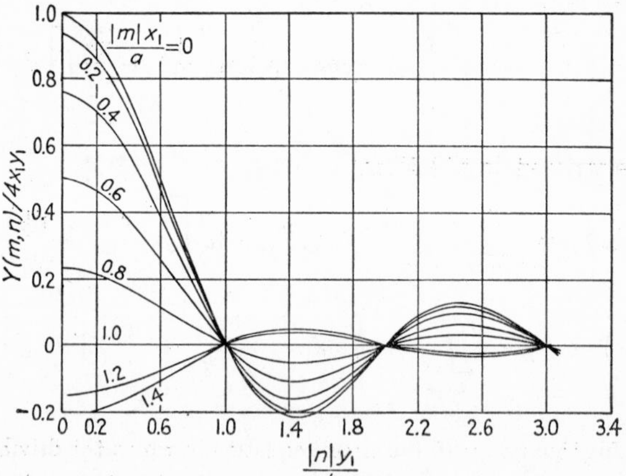

FIG. 5. (*Courtesy of Bell System Technical Journal.*)

this illustration yield values for discrete values of n and m which are related to the number of lines and the scanning velocity by Eq. (5).

Equation (14) shows that for this case, $Y(m,n)$ is determined by the product of two $(\sin \theta)/\theta$ functions whose arguments are functions of the horizontal- and vertical-scanning rates. Since these rates are very different, the product of $Y_\gamma(m)$ and $Y_\eta(n)$, using values from Fig. 4, will yield a set of peaks to an extent which is dependent on the zeros and peaks of each $(\sin \theta)/\theta$ function. These peaks and their associated components will form spectral groups which will be separated by spaces in which the spectral amplitudes are of very low amplitude. These peaks will be located at multiples of the line scanning frequency $v_x/2a$, as shown in Fig. 6. The

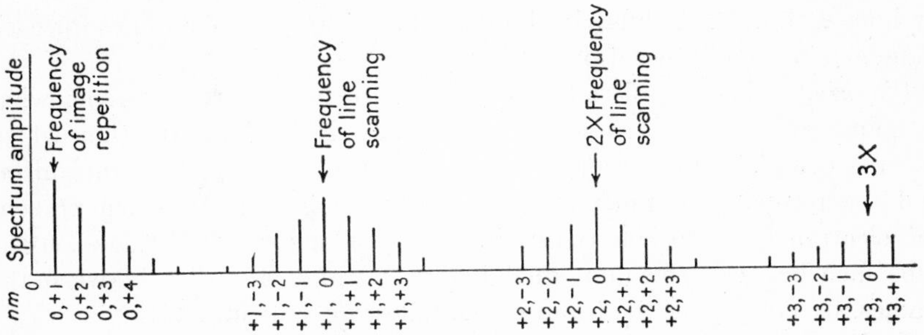

FIG. 6.

components on either side of the peak frequencies will decrease in magnitude as shown. Each component is separated from the adjacent component by the line repetition frequency $v_y/2b$.

This illustration, although elementary and of a special case, yields certain basic patterns which occur in the spectra of typical television images. Figure 7 shows, for example, the spectrum of a human face, accompanied

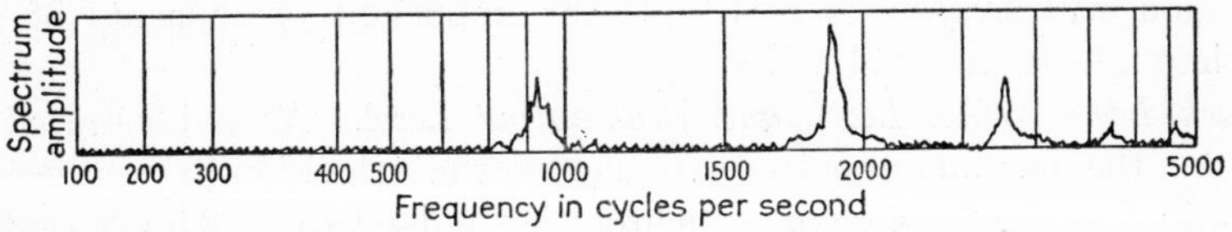

FIG. 7. Spectrum of a human face, accompanied by rapid motions of the hands and head, which is scanned using a 50-line field at a rate of 940 lines per second. (*Courtesy of Bell System Technical Journal.*)

by rapid motions of the hands and head, which is scanned in a field of view with 50 lines at a rate of 940 lines per second. This is, of course, a very slow scanning rate compared with modern television practice, but it serves to demonstrate the occurrence of spectral groups which in this case are located at multiples of 940 cycles. Note that the near-empty spaces between groups are clearly indicated.

4. The Standard American Television Signal.[1] In the transmission of video information, not only must the information as provided by the scanned image be sent, but also synchronizing pulses which will trigger the sweep generators in the receiver so that the scanning voltages in the picture-tube circuits will be accurately synchronized with those at the transmitter.

In commercial television broadcasting in the United States, the picture is scanned thirty times a second, using a frame of 525 lines and a ratio of width to height equal to 4/3. In order to reduce flicker, a system of interlacing is used: lines 1, 3, 5, . . . are first scanned in sequence, followed by lines 2, 4, 6, . . . , thus yielding two image fields of 262.5 lines for each frame. The time interval per field is $\frac{1}{60}$ sec.

Blanking. The complete television signal is in some respects somewhat complicated inasmuch as it must not only include information which ensures complete and accurate synchronization between the transmitter and the receiver but must also produce blanking signals which prevent the electron beam in the kinescope from producing visible traces on the tube face between the individual horizontal lines and also between the frames, by cutting off the beam in the following time intervals:

1. When the scanning spot arrives at the end of one horizontal line and when it starts the next line (horizontal retrace).
2. When the scanning spot arrives at the end of the last line in the field and when it starts the first line of the next field (vertical retrace).

Blanking is produced by superimposing pulses on the television signal which produce properly timed negative pulses of the correct duration and amplitude in the circuit of the control grid of the receiver kinescope so that the beam is cut off for the duration of these pulses. Blanking pulses for both horizontal and vertical blanking will be described in the following discussion with regard to their roles as important components of the complete television signal.

Black Level, White Level, and Peak-output Level. As is illustrated in Fig. 8*a*, the maximum output voltage of the television transmitter is designated as the peak of the synchronizing pulses; 75 ± 2.5 per cent of the maximum is the black level, and from zero to 15 per cent of the maximum the white level. All television signals are referred to the black level as a reference level, the region between black level and peak power being designated as *blacker than black*. By having the synchronizing pulses occur

[1] See "Standards of Good Engineering Practice Concerning Television Broadcast Stations," issued by the Federal Communications Commission, effective Dec. 19, 1945, obtainable from the Superintendent of Documents, Government Printing Office, Washington, D.C. An excellent discussion is provided in F. E. Terman, "Radio Engineering," Chap. 17, McGraw-Hill Book Company, Inc., New York, 1947.

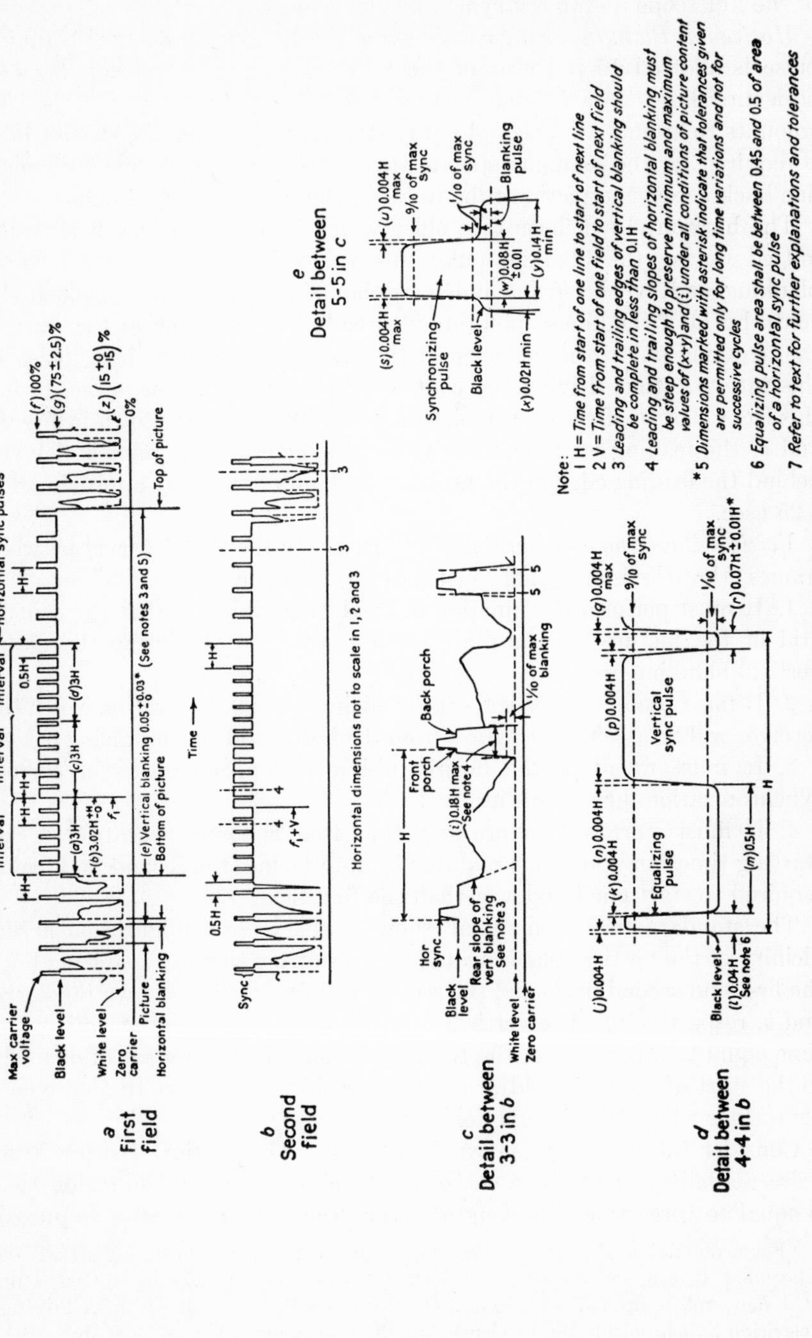

FIG. 8. Standard television synchronizing waveform; $H = 63.5$ μsec, $V = 16{,}667$ μsec.

in the blacker than black region, no visual indication appears on the face of the kinescope due to the synchronizing signals.

Horizontal Blanking and Synchronizing Pulse. The horizontal blanking pulse is allotted 16 per cent of the time available for transmitting one horizontal line. In a 525-line picture using United States standards, this amounts to around 10 μsec and represents the total interval of time which is required for the scanning spot to travel from the end of one horizontal line back across the picture tube to begin the next horizontal line.

The horizontal synchronizing pulse which is 5 μsec in length is transmitted during the blanking-pulse interval so that the combination of blanking and synchronizing pulses is that shown in Fig. 8*e*. Since the control grid of the kinescope beam is already beyond cutoff at the start of the blanking pulse, the inclusion of the horizontal synchronizing pulse in this interval, thus driving the control grid even further negative during this time, has no effect on the picture detail itself. As is shown in Fig. 8*c* and *e*, the leading edge of the horizontal synchronizing pulse is delayed behind the leading edge of the horizontal blanking pulse by approximately 1.25 μsec.

Vertical Blanking and Synchronizing Pulse. In the time interval between frames, the television signal must perform four functions, as follows:

1. It must perform the function of vertical blanking so that the control grid of the picture tube is maintained beyond cutoff during the entire vertical blanking ground.

2. It must produce a vertical synchronizing-pulse configuration which the receiver will be able to distinguish from the horizontal synchronizing pulses.

3. It must maintain the horizontal-line sweep generators in correct synchronization during this interval.

4. It must start the picture at a time that is commensurate with the starting times and positions required by interlacing, the second field being required to start one line lower than the first field.

The standard television signal[1] showing the wave configuration in the vicinity of the vertical blanking and synchronizing signals separating both the first and second fields and the second and first fields is shown in Fig. 8*a* and *b*, respectively. The vertical blanking pulse is allotted an interval of time equal to 5 per cent of the total field time (from the start of one field to the start of the next field). Included in this interval are the pulse configurations which satisfy functions 2 to 4.

Consider the waveform shown in Fig. 8*a*. The vertical synchronizing pulse actually consists of a set of six blocks whose total duration time is equal to three times the length of time required by one line—approxi-

[1] For a discussion of apparatus for generating television synchronizing signals, see Schoenfeld, Brown, and Milwitt, New Techniques in Synchronizing Signal Generators, *RCA Rev.*, vol. 8, pp. 237–250, June, 1947. See also Bedford and Smith, A Precision Television Synchronizing Signal Generator, *RCA Rev.*, vol. 10, pp. 51–68, July, 1940.

mately nineteen times the length of time required by a horizontal synchronizing pulse. The serrations in this pulse have a frequency equal to twice that of the horizontal synchronizing pulse. The vertical synchronizing pulse is preceded by and also followed by a group of six short pulses, which are referred to as equalizing pulses. The equalizing pulses also have a frequency equal to twice the frequency of the horizontal synchronizing pulse and, like the vertical synchronizing pulse, have a duration time per group of 6, equal to the time required for three horizontal lines. Using a frequency equal to twice the frequency of the horizontal synchronizing pulse serves the following functions:

1. Every other pulse or serration triggers the horizontal sweep circuit in the receiver and therefore maintains horizontal synchronization during the vertical blanking period.

2. Having the frequency of the vertical-synchronizing-pulse components equal to twice the frequency of the horizontal synchronizing pulses permits the television system to account for the fact that each field either ends or begins with half a line and thus permits correct registry of the interlaced fields.

3. It assists the receiver system to differentiate between the vertical synchronizing pulse and the horizontal synchronizing pulse.

The entire pulse set, consisting of the two sets of equalizing pulses and the serrated vertical synchronizing pulse, is identical for both fields and immediately follows the end of the field. The remainder of the vertical blanking period consists of a succession of horizontal synchronizing pulses in order to assure correct synchronization when the next field starts.

Because the vertical synchronizing and blanking waveform has a duration time of 5 per cent of the total frame time, the total number of useful lines in the frame is actually in the neighborhood of 500 lines.

5. Frequency Ranges in Commercial Television. The lower frequencies in a television signal should theoretically approach direct current if little change in picture background or detail is being televised. However, a lower frequency limit of around 20 cycles is sufficient to yield satisfactory reproduction of picture detail involving practical gradations of detail and tone.

To determine the extent of the highest frequencies required, assume that it is required that the picture will make a transition from white to black and then back to white sinusoidally in a length of picture element equal to the spacing between adjacent lines. If the frame frequency is $\frac{1}{30}$ sec, then the time per line in a 525-line picture with a useful-line percentage of 0.95 is

$$\text{Time per line} = \frac{1}{30 \times 525 \times 0.95} \tag{16}$$

$$= 6.7 \times 10^{-5} \text{ sec} \tag{17}$$

In a scanned picture whose ratio of length to width is 4/3 and whose horizontal blanking pulse occupies an interval of 16 per cent of the horizontal scan time, the time that is required to scan a line segment equal to the spacing between adjacent lines is approximately

$$t = \frac{3}{4} \frac{6.7 \times 10^{-5} \times 0.84}{525} \tag{18}$$

$$= 0.802 \times 10^{-7} \text{ sec} \tag{19}$$

Since this time represents the duration of a half cycle of the desired variation of picture intensity, we get for the frequency corresponding to this variation

$$f = \frac{1}{2 \times 0.802 \times 10^{-7}} \tag{20}$$

$$= 6.23 \times 10^{6} \text{ cycles} \tag{21}$$

Actually, the use of a band of frequencies from 20 cycles to from 4.5 to 5 Mc will yield a picture of high quality. Reducing the upper limit will result in loss of picture detail, although even at 2 Mc the picture quality may be satisfactory for many applications.

COMPLEX WAVES IN RADAR

6. Radar.[1] Echo sounding with electromagnetic waves was first used in 1924 by Breit and Tuve for proving the existence of a conducting layer of ionized gas in the upper atmosphere. These experiments laid the foundation of what is now known as radar; a radio wave is beamed at a target from which it is reflected, a small amount returning to a receiver. The echo will be received at the receiver a time τ after the signal leaves the transmitter, thus yielding an accurate method of measuring the distance to the target. τ is defined as

$$\tau = \frac{2D}{c} \tag{22}$$

where D is the distance to the target, c is the speed of propagation, or 983.24 ft per μsec in normal sea-level air. If a highly directional antenna is used at the transmitter, the precise position of the target relative to the transmitter may also be determined.

7. Complex Waves in Radar. There are three major types of radar;

[1] See L. N. Ridenour, "Radar System Engineering," Radiation Laboratory Series, McGraw-Hill Book Company, Inc., New York, 1947. For a historical survey of radar, see C. D. Tuska, Historical Notes on the Determination of Distance by Timed Radio Waves, *J. Franklin Inst.*, vol. 237, Nos. 1, 2, pp. 1–20, 83–102, January, February, 1944.

each is identified by the type of radiated wave used. These types and their associated waveforms are listed as follows:

1. Pulse radar. In this type of radar, a periodic pulsed wavetrain using pulses of very short duration is transmitted; the time elapsing until the return of the echoes of this wave from the target is accurately measured and used to deduce the distance to the target. This type of radar and its numerous ramifications are widely used, particularly for military applications, aircraft traffic control, and ship navigation.

2. FM radar.[1] In this type of radar, a continuous-wave periodic triangular FM wave is transmitted. The returning echo is heterodyned with the wave leaving the transmitter at the instant of echo return, thus yielding a beat note which is a function of the time required for the wave to travel to the target and return. This type of radar is widely used in aircraft altimeter applications.

3. Doppler radar. In this type of radar, a continuous simple harmonic wave is radiated. If either the transmitter or the target is moving, there will be an apparent increase or decrease in frequency of the wave depending on the relative speed between the radar and the target; this is due to the Doppler effect. Doppler radar is used in systems involving projectiles and moving targets.

NOISE IN COMMUNICATION SYSTEMS

8. Introduction. Complex waves representing information are accompanied during transmission by waves inherent in communication networks and in nature known as noise. Were it not for noise, any signal could be transmitted at any amplitude and rendered intelligible at the point of reception, all other factors such as bandwidth being suitable. Because noise of one or more kinds does accompany transmission or is present in all communications, criteria and standards of the ratio of signal level to noise level must be established; the following is intended to serve as an introduction to those types of noise which are encountered in communication systems so that their presence may be included in general considerations of communications.

9. Room Noise. Speech, music, and other sounds which are to be transmitted are accompanied by a certain amount of ambient room or location noise since the ideal of a completely quiet place (no noise) is seldom realized. D. F. Hoth[2] and others have shown that the average

[1] See Wolff and Luck, Principles of Frequency Modulated Radar, *RCA Rev.*, vol. 9, pp. 50–75, March, 1948.

[2] D. F. Hoth, Room Noise Spectra at Subscriber's Telephone Locations, *J. Acoust. Soc. Am.*, vol. 12, No. 4, p. 499, April, 1941.

H. Fletcher, Hearing, The Determining Factor for High Fidelity Transmission, *Proc. IRE*, vol. 30, No. 6, p. 266, 1942.

noise spectrum for residences, homes, and factories is that pictured in Fig. 9. The ordinates, which give in decibels[1] the spectrum level, are obtained from the expression

$$\text{Spectrum level} = 10 \log_{10} \frac{I}{I_0(f_2 - f_1)} \quad \text{(db)} \tag{23}$$

where I = sound intensity in the frequency bandwidth, $f_2 - f_1$
I_0 = zero reference level of 10^{-16} watt per sq cm

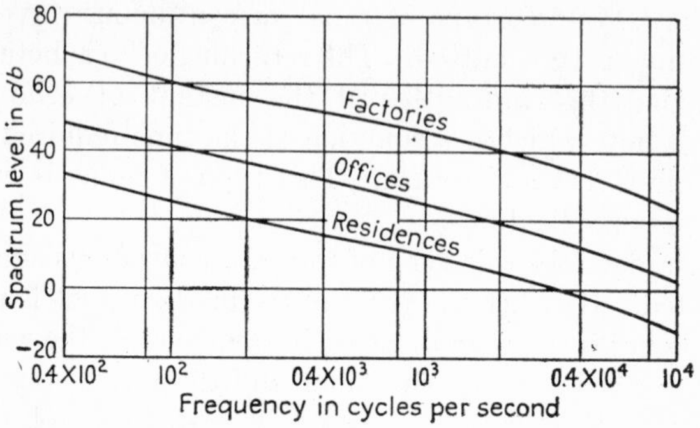

FIG. 9.

The spectrum shown for average room noise is that for a room having a total noise of 43 db.

10. Tube Noise.[2] The major sources of tube noise can be listed as follows:

1. Shot-effect noise, representing random variations in the rate of emission of electrons from the emitter. As will be derived in the next section, shot-effect noise[3] in a temperature-limited region is described by the equation

$$\overline{\Delta i^2}(t) = 2eI(f_2 - f_1) \tag{24}$$

[1] Decibel level in amplifiers is in general defined as follows:

$$\text{Decibels above or below zero level} = 10 \log_{10} \frac{\text{watts at level to be measured}}{\text{zero-level watts}}$$

where zero level is 6 mw.

[2] See Thompson, North, and Harris, Fluctuations in Space-charge-limited Currents at Moderately High Frequencies, *RCA Rev.*: Part I, General Survey, B. J. Thompson, Vol. 4, No. 3, January, 1940; Part II, Diodes and Negative-grid Triodes, D. O. North, vol. 4, No. 4, April, vol. 5, No. 1, July, 1940; Part III, Multi-collectors, D. O. North, vol. 5, No. 2, October, 1940; Part IV, Fluctuations Caused by Collision Ionization, B. J. Thompson and D. O. North, vol. 5, No. 3, January, 1941; Part V, Fluctuations in Vacuum Tube Amplifiers and Input Systems, W. A. Harris, vol. 5, No. 4, April, 1941, vol. 6, No. 1, July, 1941. This series also contains an excellent bibliography.

[3] W. Schottky, Spontaneous Current Fluctuations in Various Conductors, *Ann. Physik*, vol. 57, pp. 541–567, 1918.

where $\overline{\Delta i^2}(t)$ = rms value of noise current in amperes having components whose frequencies are in the range $f_2 - f_1$

e = charge on electron, coulombs

I = d-c current, amp

$f_2 - f_1$ = frequency range in cycles over which the noise current is described

2. Partition noise, due to the random variations in the distribution of current between two or more positive electrodes.

3. Induced grid noise, due to the random variations of an electron stream passing adjacent to a grid.

4. Gas noise, due to random variations in the rate of production of ions by collision.

5. Secondary-emission noise, due to the random variation in the rate of production of secondary electrons.

6. Flicker effect, a low-frequency (l-f) variation in emission that occurs with oxide-coated cathodes.

7. Microphonics, due to mechanically induced vibrations in the tube structure and components.

11. Derivation of the Shot-effect-noise Equation.[1] The derivation of Eq. (24) involves not only concepts which illustrate the true nature of shot-effect noise but also two fundamental concepts which are instrumental in the understanding of electron-tube performance, *i.e.*, the current induced in an electron-tube circuit by an electron of finite velocity traveling from the cathode to the anode and the spectrum of the current due to the passage of the electron. This derivation is presented as follows:

Consider the case when a negatively charged particle travels from the

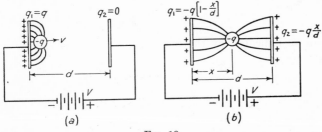

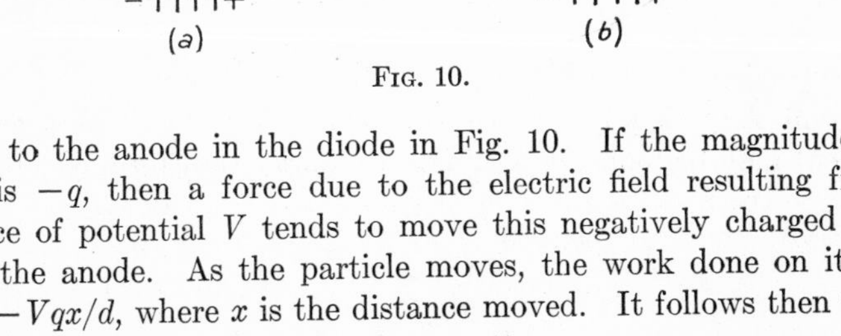

FIG. 10.

cathode to the anode in the diode in Fig. 10. If the magnitude of the charge is $-q$, then a force due to the electric field resulting from the difference of potential V tends to move this negatively charged particle toward the anode. As the particle moves, the work done on it by the field is $-Vqx/d$, where x is the distance moved. It follows then that the

[1] From a set of lectures on noise by D. O. North at the RCA Laboratories in 1944.

charge q_2 on the anode is

$$q_2 = -q\frac{x}{d} \tag{25}$$

and the charge q_1 on the cathode is

$$q_1 = -q\left(1 - \frac{x}{d}\right) \tag{26}$$

The instantaneous current, which will flow in the circuit as the result of the motion of the charge, is equal to the rate of change of the charge on the anode. In general, we may write the current $i(t)$ due to the motion of the charge as

$$i(t) = -\frac{dq_1}{dt} = \frac{dq_2}{dt} \tag{27}$$

$$= q\frac{v}{d} \tag{28}$$

Thus we see that the current which flows because of the particle motion is a function of velocity and plate separation and not of position. Figure 10*a* and *b* shows the change in distribution of charge as the particle moves.

If we assume that Laplace's equation holds for the region between the anode and the cathode, then the electric potential will increase linearly from cathode to anode in the absence of space charge and an electron of charge e in this region will encounter constant electric-field intensity and constant acceleration a. If the electron transit time is τ where the passage from cathode to anode has taken place in the interval $0 < t < \tau$, then the current which flows through the meter during the transit time is

$$i(t) = e\frac{at}{\frac{1}{2}a\tau^2} \tag{29}$$

The current as indicated by the meter for all time may then be written as follows:

$$\begin{aligned} i(t) &= 0 & -\infty < t < 0 \\ &= e\frac{2t}{\tau^2} & 0 < t < \tau \\ &= 0 & \tau < t < \infty \end{aligned} \tag{30}$$

This current shape is a saw tooth as shown in Fig. 11. The spectrum of this current may be found by taking the Fourier transform of (30); *i.e.*,

$$g(\omega) = \int_{-\infty}^{\infty} i(t)e^{-i\omega t}\,dt \tag{31}$$

$$= \frac{2e}{\tau^2}\int_0^{\tau} te^{-i\omega t}\,dt \tag{32}$$

If we define Φ as the transit angle such that $\Phi = \omega\tau$ (note that $\Phi = 2\pi$ if the time of transit is equal to one period of the angular velocity ω) and if we let $x = j\omega t$, then we get

$$g(\omega) = \frac{2e}{(j\Phi)^2}\int_0^{j\Phi} xe^{-x}\,dx \tag{33}$$

$$= \frac{2e}{(j\Phi)^2}\,[1 - (1 + j\Phi)e^{-j\Phi}] \tag{34}$$

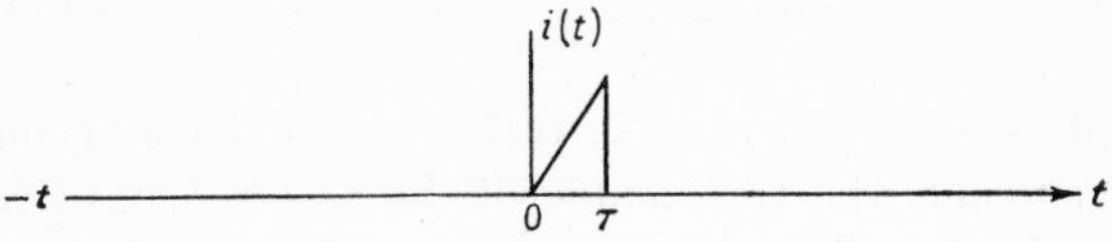

FIG. 11.

The energy spectrum corresponding to (30) is proportional to the square of (34); it follows that

$$|g(\omega)|^2 = \frac{4e^2}{\Phi^4}\,[2(1 - \cos\Phi) + \Phi(\Phi - 2\sin\Phi)] \tag{35}$$

$$= e^2\left(1 - \frac{\Phi^2}{18} + \frac{\Phi^4}{720} - \frac{\Phi^6}{50{,}400} + \cdots\right) \tag{36}$$

$$= e^2 \qquad \Phi \leq 1 \tag{37}$$

thus showing that the passage of a single electron produces a near band spectrum for small values of transit angle.

If N electrons pass in the interval $-T/2 < t < T/2$ in purely random order such that the transit time of any single electron is small compared with T, we may deduce a voltage versus frequency distribution which, when separated from the spectrum of some preferred electric wave in the system, constitutes noise. This problem was first worked out by Schottky in 1912.

Consider the currents due to the random distribution of electrons

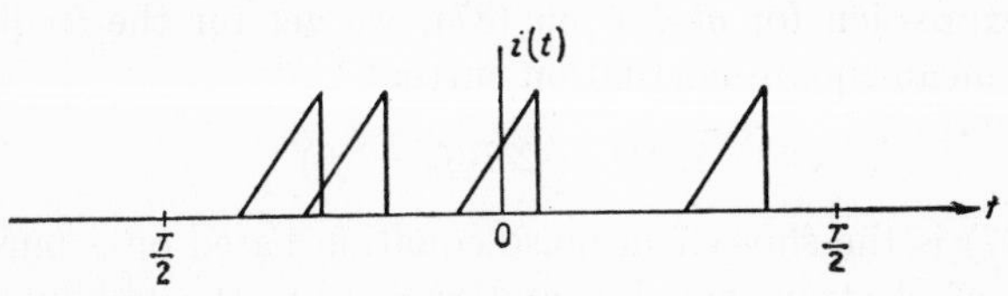

FIG. 12.

flowing in a diode in the time interval $-T/2 < t < T/2$. For purposes of illustration, some of these currents are pictured in Fig. 12. If we let $f(t - t_\kappa)$ be the transient due to an electron emitted at t_κ, then we may write the total current as

$$i(t) = \sum_{k=1}^{N} f(t - t_\kappa) \tag{38}$$

The mean-square value of the current may then be written, as

$$\overline{i^2}(t) = \lim_{T\to\infty} \frac{1}{T} \int_{-T/2}^{T/2} i^2(t)\, dt \tag{39}$$

$$= \lim_{T\to\infty} \frac{1}{T} \sum_{\kappa=1}^{N} \sum_{l=1}^{N} \int_{-T/2}^{T/2} f(t - t_\kappa) f(t - t_l)\, dt \tag{40}$$

The subscripts κ and l are used in order to avoid confusion. If there is no constant current, the transients will be as often positive as negative and the integral sum will be zero when $\kappa \neq l$. Thus it follows from (40) that

$$i^2(t) = \lim_{T\to\infty} \frac{N}{T} \int_{-T/2}^{T/2} f^2(t)\, dt \tag{41}$$

But

$$\lim_{T\to\infty} \frac{N}{T} = n \tag{42}$$

We therefore get

$$\overline{i^2}(t) = n \int_{-\infty}^{\infty} f^2(t)\, dt \tag{43}$$

Using Parseval's relation, (43) may be written

$$\overline{i^2}(t) = 2n \int_0^\infty |g(\omega)|^2\, df \tag{44}$$

Recalling that the current I may be expressed in terms of n electrons as

$$I = en \tag{45}$$

it then follows from (44) that

$$\overline{i^2}(t) = \frac{2I}{e} \int_0^\infty |g(\omega)|^2\, df \tag{46}$$

Using the expression for $g(\omega)$ from (37), we get for the frequency band $f_2 - f_1$ the mean-square fluctuation current

$$\overline{\Delta i^2}(t) = 2eI(f_2 - f_1) \tag{47}$$

Equation (47) is the shot-effect-noise equation based on a purely random distribution of electron emission and represents the minimum that can be expected from any emitting surface in the absence of space charge.[1]

[1] It can be shown that if full space charge exists in a diode with large anode-cathode voltage, the noise component of the current corresponds to the thermal-agitation noise current generated by a resistance having a magnitude equal to the dynamic plate resist-

To illustrate the orders of magnitude involved in (47), a circuit of 50,000 ohms impedance having an effective bandpass of 10,000 cycles through which a temperature-limited current of 1 ma flows will develop a voltage of 89 μv across its terminals, independent of the resonant frequency.

12. Thermal-agitation Noise.[1] An important source of complex waves as represented by noise is fluctuation current due to thermal agitation in resistors. Nyquist has shown that a short-circuited resistor produces a mean-square fluctuation current $\bar{i}^2(t)$ in the frequency band Δf which is described by the equation,

$$\bar{i}^2(t) = 4\kappa T g \, \Delta f \qquad (48)$$

where g is the conductance of the resistor, κ is Boltzman's constant, 1.372×10^{-23} joules per deg, and T is the temperature in degrees Kelvin.

If the resistance is R, then the mean-square thermal-agitation voltage across the resistor is

$$\bar{e}^2(t) = 4\kappa T R \, \Delta f \qquad (49)$$

Note that for a near room temperature of 290°K

$$\bar{e}^2(t) = 1.59 \times 10^{-20} R \, \Delta f \qquad (50)$$

As an illustration of (50), consider the case when R is a 0.5-megohm resistor and the band of frequencies is 10 kc wide. It then follows from (50) that if the room temperature is 290°K, the noise voltage will be almost 13μv rms.

13. Noise-equivalent Resistance. It is convenient to express the shot-effect noise in a triode or a pentode in terms of an equivalent resistance R_{eq} which is termed the noise-equivalent resistance. To this resistance is attributed a value equal to the magnitude of a resistor which would generate a noise voltage at the grid of a noiseless tube to produce the noise current present.

For a triode with an oxide-coated cathode, the noise-equivalent resistance is closely approximated by the expression

$$R_{eq} = \frac{2.5}{g_m} \qquad (51)$$

---

ance of the diode and a temperature equal to 0.64 times the cathode temperature. See Thompson, North, and Harris, Fluctuations in Space-charge-limited Currents at Moderately High Frequencies, Part II, D. O. North, Diodes and Negative-grid Triodes, *RCA Rev.*, vol. 4, April, 1940, vol. 5, July, 1940.

[1] H. Nyquist, Thermal Agitation of Electric Charge in Conductors, *Phys. Rev.*, vol. 32, No. 1, pp. 110–113, July, 1928.

J. B. Johnson, Thermal Agitation of Electricity in Conductors, *Phys. Rev.*, vol. 32, No. 1, pp. 97, 109, July, 1928.

For a pentode, the partition noise must be included with the shot-effect noise; the noise-equivalent resistance for such tubes may be approximated by the equation

$$R_{eq} = \frac{I_b}{I_b + I_{c_2}}\left(\frac{2.5}{g_m} + 20\,\frac{I_{c_2}}{g_m^2}\right) \tag{52}$$

where I_b and I_{c_2} are the d-c plate current and screen current in amperes, respectively.

Table 1, due to W. A. Harris, giving the calculated and measured noise-equivalent resistance of various tubes, shows the noise-equivalent resistance of the multigrid tubes listed to be approximately three times the value for the comparable negative-grid triodes.

14. Impulse Noise.[1] An important type of noise which is encountered in communication systems is impulse noise, which is produced by atmospherics, lightning, ignition systems, and similar sources. In general,

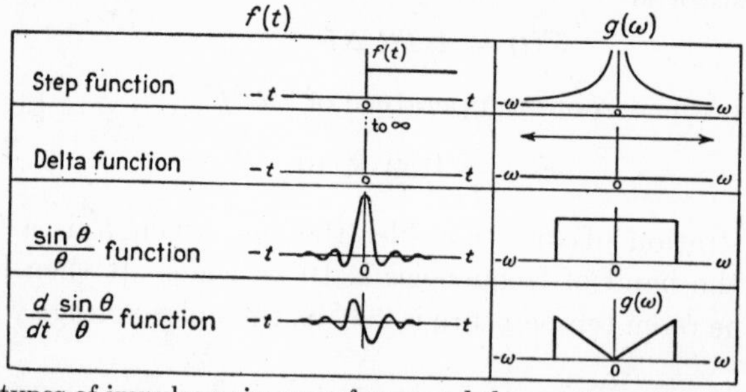

FIG. 13. Four types of impulse-noise waveforms and the spectrum associated with each.

impulse noises have characteristics which permit them to be described by delta functions and step functions, *viz.*:[2]

Step function:

$$\begin{aligned} f(t) &= 0 \qquad -\infty < t < 0 \\ &= 1 \qquad 0 < t < \infty \end{aligned} \tag{53}$$

$$g(\omega) = \frac{1}{j\omega} \tag{54}$$

Delta function:

$$f(t) = \delta(t - t_0) \tag{55}$$

$$g(\omega) = e^{j\omega t_0} \tag{56}$$

The step function and delta function and their respective spectra are diagramed in Fig. 13, where their spectral contributions to noise are seen to exist in large or infinite ranges of ω.

[1] See V. D. Landon, Impulse Noise in F.M. Reception, *Electronics*, February, 1941, pp. 26–30, 73–76.

[2] See Eq. (46), Chap. 3, and Eq. (11), Chap. 4.

TABLE 1*

TUBE NOISE VALUES

Type	Application	Voltages			Currents			Transconductance µmhos	Noise-equivalent resistance		Noise-equivalent input voltage µv
		Plate volts	Screen volts	Bias volts	Plate ma	Screen ma	Cathode ma		Calculated ohms	Measured ohms	
6SK7	Pentode amplifier	250	100	−3	9.2	2.4	11.6	2,000	10,500	9,400–11,500	0.94
6SJ7	Pentode amplifier	250	100	−3	3	0.8	3.8	1,650	5,800	5,800	0.70
6SG7	Pentode amplifier	250	125	−1	11.8	4.4	16.2	4,700	3,300	....	0.53
6AC7/1852	Pentode amplifier	300	150	−2	10	2.5	12.5	9,000	720	600–760	0.25
956	Pentode amplifier	250	100	−3	5.5	1.8	7.3	1,800	9,400	....	0.90
1T4	Pentode amplifier	90	45	0	2.0	0.65	2.65	750	20,000	....	1.3
6J5	Triode amplifier	250	...	−8	9.0	....	.....	2,600	960	1,250	0.28
955	Triode amplifier	180	...	−5	4.5	....	.....	2,000	1,250	....	0.32
6AC7/1852	Triode amplifier	150	150	−2	....	....	12.5	11,200	220	200	0.14

*See Thompson, North, and Harris, Fluctuations in Space-charge-limited Currents at Moderately High Frequencies, Part V, W. A. Harris, Fluctuations in Vacuum Tube Amplifiers and Input Systems, *RCA Rev.*, vol. 5, pp. 505–523, April, 1941. (Courtesy of *RCA Review.*)

An important consideration in the study of impulse noise in communication systems is the circuit response due to this noise. We shall see in Chap. 20 that when a modulated step function is applied to a linear transmission network having a certain pass band, the output is a function which is described in the *form*

$$N_1(t) = A \frac{\sin \theta}{\theta} \cos \omega_0 t \tag{57}$$

where ω_0 is the center of the pass band and A is an amplitude coefficient.

In many transmission networks with limited bandwidths and in circuits employing inductive coupling, differentiation of $N_1(t)$ often takes place, thus yielding the function,

$$N_2(t) = \frac{d}{dt} N_1(t) \tag{58}$$

$N_1(t)$ and $N_2(t)$ and their spectra are also pictured in Fig. 13, where it is seen that $g_1(\omega)$ is a band spectrum while $g_2(\omega)$ is zero at ω_0 and increases linearly as ω increases or decreases.

While other types of noise such as shot-effect and thermal-agitation noise will demand certain signal levels for intelligible transmission and must therefore be considered in all communication-systems design, impulse noise is capable of completely disrupting communications because of the high intensity level at which these impulses frequently occur. One of the main advantages of FM transmission over AM transmission is that interference with the intelligibility of FM transmission due to impulse noise may be reduced to a minimum or eliminated.

PROBLEMS

1. Discuss the frequency ranges corresponding to television images employing the following number of lines: (*a*) 405; (*b*) 441; (*c*) 625; (*d*) 1,000.

2. Show that for a circular aperture of radius c

$$Y(m,n) = \frac{2J_1\left[\pi\sqrt{\left(\frac{mc}{a}\right)^2 + \left(\frac{nc}{b}\right)^2}\right]}{\pi\sqrt{\left(\frac{mc}{a}\right)^2 + \left(\frac{nc}{b}\right)^2}}$$

3. Discuss the general aspects of pulse width and minimum detection distance in pulse radar.

4. Let an electron pass from cathode to plate of a triode with constant velocity, and let the transit time through each of the grid-cathode and the grid-plate regions be τ. Show that a meter in the grid circuit will read the noise current,

$$\overline{\Delta i^2}(t) = 2eI\phi^2 \left[\frac{\sin (\phi/2)}{\phi/2}\right]^4 (f_2 - f_1)$$

where $\phi = \omega\tau$.

5. Plot the noise-equivalent resistance of a 6J5 tube as a function of g_m in the range $0 < g_m < 3 \times 10^{-3}$ mho.

CHAPTER 6

LINEAR-NETWORK ANALYSIS

1. Introduction. For many decades, numerous great scientists, such as Ohm, Kirchhoff, Heaviside, Steinmetz, and van der Pol, have contributed to the furthering of the study of electric-circuit behavior. Despite the apparent simplicity of the analysis of many of the circuits in the light of present-day knowledge, the path was difficult; each new step and principle was won only after much labor and hardship. Linear-network analysis has come far, although even today we have only scratched the surface of many of the solutions demanded by modern communication systems and components. There are many refinements to be made, much clarification yet to be achieved, new theories of communication processes yet to be investigated.

The Fourier and Laplace methods have become great tools for solving linear-network problems but they are not, as is often supposed, special methods or approaches. Rather they are logical extensions of elementary linear-circuit analysis based on the rotating vector, thus permitting the communication engineer to retain and employ his basic concepts involving impedance and response.

This chapter will first discuss the fundamentals of analysis involving rotating vector operators. It will then develop and discuss the concepts associated with the Fourier and Laplace analysis, concluding with applications of the superposition-integral theorem. Whereas the more general mathematical considerations of linear networks will be presented, the circuits which will be analyzed will be limited to important communication networks which are not essentially transfer networks whose theory, applications, and response behavior will be discussed in Chaps. 9, 10, and 20.

FUNDAMENTALS OF LINEAR-CIRCUIT ANALYSIS

2. Certain Aspects of Linear Differential Equations. Consider the solution of any linear differential equation of the type

$$A_1 \frac{d^nF(t)}{dt^n} + A_2 \frac{d^{n-1}F(t)}{dt^{n-1}} + \cdots + A_nF(t) = f(t) \tag{1}$$

where A_1, A_2, . . . are constant coefficients and $f(t)$ is the force which is impressed in the system. The solution of (1) is of the form

$$F(t) = F_c(t) + F_p(t) \tag{2}$$

$F_c(t)$ is known as the *complementary function* and is the solution of the homogeneous differential equation [when $f(t) \equiv 0$]. This solution is the transient solution of the system and provides a description of the starting behavior of $f(t)$.

$F_p(t)$ is known as the *particular-integral* solution and is the solution or the sum of all of the solutions which satisfy the nonhomogeneous differential equation (1). It is a solution which corresponds to the steady-state response to $f(t)$.

The general aspects of the complementary function and the particular integral may be illustrated by considering the series RLC circuit which is pictured in Fig. 1. It can be shown, using Kirchhoff's second law, which is stated in Sec. 4, that the differential equation describing this circuit is

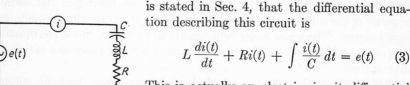

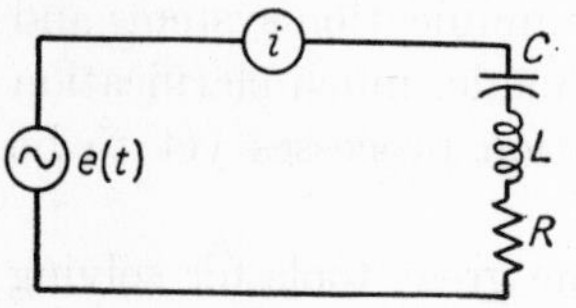

FIG. 1.

$$L\frac{di(t)}{dt} + Ri(t) + \int \frac{i(t)}{C}\,dt = e(t) \tag{3}$$

This is actually an electric-circuit differential equation with constant coefficients *of a very general kind* since its form will appear in even the most complicated multimesh-circuit equations.

Consider first the complementary-function solution of Eq. (3), *viz.*, when $e(t) \equiv 0$. The equation becomes

$$L\frac{di(t)}{dt} + Ri(t) + \int \frac{i(t)}{C}\,dt = 0 \tag{4}$$

Taking the derivative of each member with respect to time, we get

$$L\frac{d^2i(t)}{dt^2} + R\frac{di(t)}{dt} + \frac{i(t)}{C} = 0 \tag{5}$$

or

$$\frac{d^2i(t)}{dt^2} + \frac{R}{L}\frac{di(t)}{dt} + \frac{1}{LC}\,i(t) = 0 \tag{6}$$

Assume an exponential solution of the form $i(t) = e^{mt}$. It follows that

$$m^2 + \frac{R}{L}\,m + \frac{1}{LC} = 0 \tag{7}$$

This is known as the characteristic equation of (4). It has two roots, *viz.*,

$$m_1 = -\frac{R}{2L} + \sqrt{\left(\frac{R}{2L}\right)^2 - \frac{1}{LC}} \tag{8}$$

$$m_2 = -\frac{R}{2L} - \sqrt{\left(\frac{R}{2L}\right)^2 - \frac{1}{LC}} \tag{9}$$

Since there are two roots of the characteristic equation, there will be two solutions of the homogeneous differential equation;

$$F_c(t) = e^{m_1 t} + e^{m_2 t} \tag{10}$$

Since (10) is a solution, then

$$F_c(t) = Ae^{m_1 t} + Be^{m_2 t} \tag{11}$$

is also a solution, A and B being arbitrary constants. A and B must be determined from the initial conditions using classical methods or by use of the Laplace transform on the original differential equations, the inclusion of the boundary conditions into the analysis being provided for by the Laplace formulation. (Note that the roots of (7) could be real and distinct, equal, or complex.)

Consider now the particular-integral solution of (3). It is in the performance of this operation that the rotating-vector type of solution proves itself to be one of the most important and basic functions in communication-circuit analysis.

Let $e(t)$ be a rotating-vector voltage consisting of a single rotating vector with constant angular velocity ω; that is,

$$e(t) = Ee^{j\omega t} \tag{12}$$

Assume that a current

$$i(t) = Ie^{j\omega t} \tag{13}$$

will flow in the circuit owing to $e(t)$. Let us now determine under what conditions this assumption is valid. Substituting (12) and (13) into (3), we get

$$RIe^{j\omega t} + j\omega LIe^{j\omega t} + \frac{Ie^{j\omega t}}{j\omega C} = Ee^{j\omega t} \tag{14}$$

Canceling the exponential $e^{j\omega t}$ from both sides, we get

$$I\left(R + j\omega L + \frac{1}{j\omega C}\right) = E \tag{15}$$

whereupon it follows that

$$\frac{E}{I} = R + j\left(\omega L - \frac{1}{\omega C}\right) = Z(\omega) \tag{16}$$

The assumption that $i(t) = Ie^{j\omega t}$ is valid when (16) holds, $Z(\omega)$ being the self-impedance of the circuit (see Sec. 5) and E and I the rotating-vector amplitudes at the particular angular velocity ω.

Since the total particular-integral solution of (3) is the sum of all the particular-integral solutions of (3), then, if $e(t)$ is of the form

$$e(t) = E_1e^{j\omega t} + E_2e^{j2\omega t} + \cdots + E_ne^{jn\omega t} + \cdots \tag{17}$$

it follows that

$$i(t) = I_1e^{j\omega t} + I_2e^{j2\omega t} + \cdots + I_ne^{jn\omega t} + \cdots \tag{18}$$

provided that

$$\frac{E_n}{I_n} = R + j\left(n\omega L - \frac{1}{n\omega C}\right) \tag{19}$$

This yields an insight into the use of the general complex Fourier series for solving for particular-integral solutions of linear communications networks which is allied with the principle of superposition, this principle stating that when several voltages are simultaneously applied to a linear network with fixed parameters, each produces its own effect independently of all the rest. The effect of each voltage alone may be calculated and the values of current, corresponding to each voltage component, added together to obtain the final result.

3. Rotating-Vector Circuit Analysis. The rotating vector is an important tool in the operational solution for the particular integrals of the linear differential equations with constant coefficients which are encountered in communication circuits.

We have seen from the preceding section that

$$\frac{1}{C}\int_0^t Ie^{j\omega t}\,dt = \frac{Ie^{j\omega t}}{j\omega C} \tag{20}$$

$$L\frac{d(Ie^{j\omega t})}{dt} = j\omega LIe^{j\omega t} \tag{21}$$

A $1/j\omega$ has resulted from the integration, whereas a $j\omega$ has resulted from the differentiation. This shows that a definite relationship can be deduced in rotating-vector formulation which can be used to reduce a linear differential equation with constant coefficients to a simple algebraic equation from which the nature of the particular integral can be deduced.

In his well-known method of operational calculus, Oliver Heaviside has employed operations of the following type,

$$\begin{aligned} \frac{d^2}{dt^2} &\approx p^2 & \int_0^t dt &\approx \frac{1}{p} \\ \frac{d}{dt} &\approx p & \iint dt^2 &\approx \frac{1}{p^2} \end{aligned} \tag{22}$$

such that, for example,

$$\frac{df(t)}{dt} = \approx pf(t) \tag{23}$$

Note that in (23) a multiplication does not actually take place. *$f(t)$ is said to be operated upon by p.*

Heaviside's operational calculus may be used to produce the complete solution for many differential equations. If we wish to limit ourselves to the particular-integral solution, however, the formulation becomes simple and we may evolve the following set of rotating-vector operators based on (20), (21), and (22):

$$\begin{aligned} p^2 &= -\omega^2 \qquad & p &= j\omega \\ \frac{1}{p} &= \frac{1}{j\omega} \qquad & \frac{1}{p^2} &= -\frac{1}{\omega^2} \end{aligned} \tag{24}$$

As an illustration of the use of (24), we see that

$$\frac{d}{dt}(Ie^{j\omega t}) \rightarrow pIe^{j\omega t} = j\omega Ie^{j\omega t} \tag{25}$$

An actual multiplication now takes place between $j\omega$ and $Ie^{j\omega t}$, the validity of the process of multiplication being true for rotating-vector operators in general.

As a further illustration, consider Eq. (3) when $e(t) = Ee^{j\omega t}$ and $i(t) = Ie^{j\omega t}$: We may write, using (22),

$$Lpi(t) + Ri(t) + \frac{1}{C}\frac{i(t)}{p} = Ee^{j\omega t} \tag{26}$$

Using the rotating-vector operators listed in (24), we get, after the cancellation of exponentials,

$$Lj\omega I + RI + \frac{1}{C}\frac{I}{j\omega} = E \tag{27}$$

whereupon

$$\frac{E}{I} = R + j\left(\omega L - \frac{1}{\omega C}\right) \tag{28}$$

which is identical to (16).

4. Steady-state Solution of a Linear Electrical Network. Having discussed the rotating-vector operational solution of the simple series circuit which is illustrated in Fig. 1, let us now consider the rotating-vector operational solution of a general linear electrical network which consists of a coupled group of circuits made up by branches, each of which may contain resistances, inductances, capacitances, and sources of rotating-vector voltage in series.

In general, Kirchhoff's laws for electrical circuits state:

I. At any junction point of three or more branches, the algebraic sum of the currents, considered as positive when flowing toward the point and negative when flowing away from the point, is zero.

II. The algebraic sum of all of the emfs and potential drops around any circuit is zero.

As an illustration of the application of Kirchhoff's laws to an electrical mesh—this illustration will yield basic concepts regarding procedure and notation which will aid in the formulation of a general theory—let us evolve the equations of the network shown in Fig. 2. The emf source in

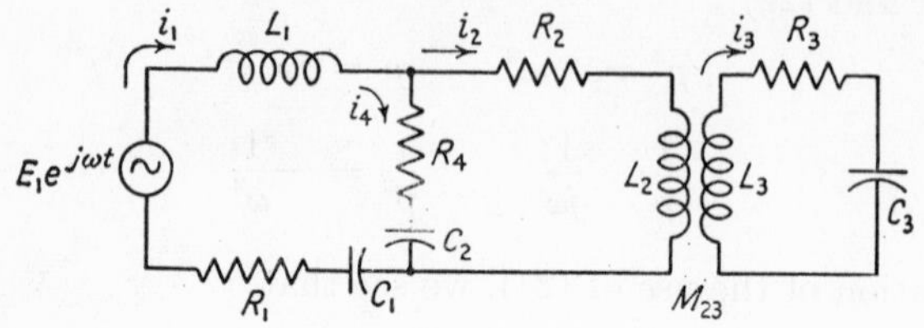

FIG. 2.

the first mesh is a rotating-vector voltage generator whose output is $E_1e^{j\omega t}$. The various circuit parameters will be identified with the circuit branch in which they occur by their subscripts, and the mutual inductance will be written as M_{jk}, where j and k represent the jth and kth circuits which are coupled with this mutual inductance.

According to Kirchhoff's laws, the equations which describe the circuit in Fig. 2 are as follows:

Law I:

$$i_1 = i_2 + i_4 \tag{29}$$

Law II:

$$L_1 \frac{di_1}{dt} + R_4 i_4 + \frac{1}{C_2}\int i_4\,dt + \frac{1}{C_1}\int i_1\,dt + R_1 i_1 = E_1 e^{j\omega t} \tag{30}$$

$$R_2 i_2 + L_2 \frac{di_2}{dt} + M_{23}\frac{di_3}{dt} - \frac{1}{C_2}\int i_4\,dt - R_4 i_4 = 0 \tag{31}$$

$$R_3 i_3 + \frac{1}{C_3}\int i_3\,dt + L_3\frac{di_3}{dt} + M_{23}\frac{di_2}{dt} = 0 \tag{32}$$

Using (29), we can eliminate i_4 from (30) and (31) and get

$$L_1 \frac{di_1}{dt} + (R_1 + R_4)i_1 + \left(\frac{1}{C_1} + \frac{1}{C_2}\right)\int i_1\,dt - R_4 i_2 - \frac{1}{C_2}\int i_2 e^{j\omega t} = E_1 e^{j\omega t} \tag{33}$$

$$-R_4 i_1 - \frac{1}{C_2}\int i_1\,dt + L_2\frac{di_2}{dt} + (R_2 + R_4)i_2 + \frac{1}{C_2}\int i_2\,dt + M_{23}\frac{di_3}{dt} = 0 \tag{34}$$

$$M_{23}\frac{di_2}{dt} + L_3\frac{di_3}{dt} + R_3 i_3 + \frac{1}{C_3}\int i_3\,dt = 0 \tag{35}$$

Since the currents which will flow in the three branches are $I_1e^{j\omega t}$, $I_2e^{j\omega t}$, and $I_3e^{j\omega t}$, Eqs. (33) to (35) may be written, using rotating-vector operators, as follows:

$$\begin{aligned} Z_{11}(\omega)I_1 + Z_{12}(\omega)I_2 + Z_{13}(\omega)I_3 &= E_1 \\ Z_{21}(\omega)I_1 + Z_{22}(\omega)I_2 + Z_{23}(\omega)I_3 &= 0 \\ Z_{31}(\omega)I_1 + Z_{32}(\omega)I_2 + Z_{33}(\omega)I_3 &= 0 \end{aligned} \tag{36}$$

where

$$\begin{aligned} Z_{11}(\omega) &= (R_1 + R_4) + j\omega L_1 + \frac{1}{j\omega}\left(\frac{1}{C_1} + \frac{1}{C_2}\right) \\ Z_{12}(\omega) &= -R_4 - \frac{1}{j\omega C_2} \\ Z_{13}(\omega) &= Z_{31}(\omega) = 0 \\ Z_{21}(\omega) &= -R_4 - \frac{1}{j\omega C_2} \\ Z_{22}(\omega) &= (R_2 + R_4) + j\omega L_2 + \frac{1}{j\omega C_2} \\ Z_{23}(\omega) &= Z_{32}(\omega) = j\omega M_{23} \\ Z_{33}(\omega) &= R_3 + j\omega L_3 + \frac{1}{j\omega C_3} \end{aligned} \tag{37}$$

Let us extend the formulation to include the rotating-vector solution of an m-mesh electrical network[1] which includes a rotating-vector voltage generator, $E_1e^{j\omega t}$, in its first mesh. It follows then that the set of equations representing this m-mesh network may be written

$$\begin{aligned} Z_{11}(\omega)I_1 + Z_{12}(\omega)I_2 + \cdots + Z_{1m}(\omega)I_m &= E_1 \\ Z_{21}(\omega)I_1 + Z_{22}(\omega)I_2 + \cdots + Z_{2m}(\omega)I_m &= 0 \\ \cdots\cdots\cdots\cdots\cdots\cdots\cdots\cdots\cdots\cdots \\ Z_{m1}(\omega)I_1 + Z_{m2}(\omega)I_2 + \cdots + Z_{mm}(\omega)I_m &= 0 \end{aligned} \tag{38}$$

Each equation in this set is a linear algebraic equation. It is therefore easily verified that the solution for the complex magnitude of the kth rotating-vector current $I_ke^{j\omega t}$ is

$$I_k = \frac{D_k(\omega)}{D(\omega)} E_1 \tag{39}$$

[1] For an extensive discussion of the steady-state solution of a general linear network, see E. A. Guillemin, "Communication Networks," vol. 1, Chap. IV, John Wiley & Sons, Inc., New York, 1931.

where $D(\omega)$ is the determinant of the system; *i.e.*,

$$D(\omega) = \begin{vmatrix} Z_{11}(\omega) & Z_{12}(\omega) & \cdots & Z_{1m}(\omega) \\ Z_{21}(\omega) & Z_{22}(\omega) & \cdots & Z_{2m}(\omega) \\ \cdots & \cdots & \cdots & \cdots \\ Z_{m1}(\omega) & Z_{m2}(\omega) & \cdots & Z_{mm}(\omega) \end{vmatrix} \tag{40}$$

and $D_k(\omega)$ is the cofactor, that is, $(-1)^{k-1}$ times the minor of $Z_{1k}(\omega)$.

Since the equations in (38) are linear with constant coefficients, then in virtue of the principle of superposition, if a number of rotating-vector voltage generators are present in the circuit, the effect of each generator can be calculated separately and the final action of the currents in the network will be the sum of responses to the individual generators. The principle of superposition will hold regardless of the number and location of generators and the magnitudes and angular velocities of their outputs.

5. Self-impedance and Transfer Impedance.[1] In many applications of the Fourier formulation to circuit analysis, we shall be concerned with two types of impedance, which are described as follows:

1. Self-impedance $Z_S(\omega)$. Self-impedance, or driving-point impedance, is described by the ratio

$$Z_S(\omega) = \frac{e_1}{i_1} = |Z_S(\omega)|\, e^{i\phi_S} \tag{41}$$

where ϕ_S is a phase angle due to the fact that e_1/i_1 is a complex number. It follows from (39) that

$$Z_S(\omega) = \frac{D(\omega)}{D_1(\omega)} \tag{42}$$

where it is readily shown that

$$D_1(\omega) = [Z_{22}(\omega)Z_{33}(\omega) \cdots Z_{mm}(\omega) - Z_{2m}(\omega)Z_{3m-1}(\omega) \cdots Z_{m2}(\omega)] \tag{43}$$

As is seen from Eq. (41), $Z_S(\omega)$ relates the driving generator voltage to the current which is delivered by the generator to the network.

2. Transfer impedance $Z_T(\omega)$. Transfer impedance relates the driving generator voltage to the current in the *m*th mesh and is described by the ratio

[1] In general, $Y(\omega) = 1/Z(\omega)$, where $Y(\omega)$ is the admittance of the circuit and may be described as $Y(\omega) = G(\omega) + jB(\omega)$, where $G(\omega)$ and $B(\omega)$ are the conductance and susceptance, respectively, of the circuit. A fundamentally different type of admittance—indicial admittance, $A(t)$—will be discussed in Sec. 19.

$$Z_T(\omega) = \frac{e_1}{i_m} = \frac{D(\omega)}{D_m(\omega)} = |Z_T(\omega)|\, e^{j\phi_T} \tag{44}$$

Transfer impedance is of the utmost importance in communications circuits. For example, it may be used to relate the a-c component of the plate current of the first tube in a vacuum-tube amplifier to the driving grid voltage in some succeeding stage. It also enables us to describe the ratio of the driving voltage to the voltage across some series impedance $Z_a(\omega)$ in the mth mesh since such a multimesh-element voltage is determined by the relationship

$$E_a = I_m Z_a(\omega) \tag{45}$$

6. Bandwidth in Communication Networks. There are several varieties of bandwidth which are associated with communication engineering. Spectral bandwidth and, to a lesser degree, noise bandwidth will be discussed in the text to follow. In the design and consideration of communication networks, circuit bandwidth plays an important role, being closely associated with the fidelity of the transmission involved.

The bandwidth of a network[1] is usually defined as the width of the band of frequencies over which the power across or gain through the network does not drop to less than some fraction of the power or gain at resonance. In many systems, this fraction, for considerations of power, is $\frac{1}{2}$, corresponding to a 3-db loss.

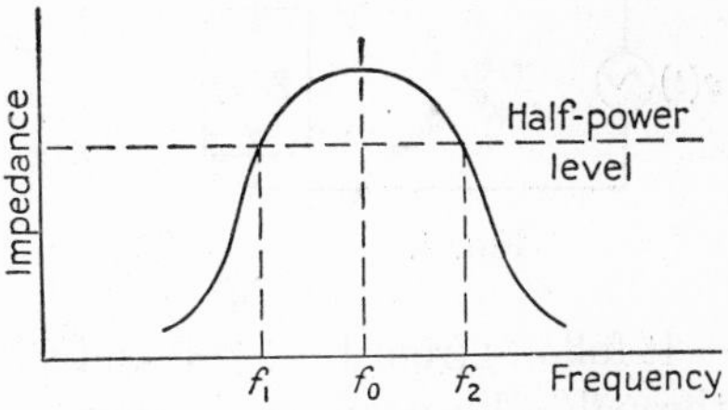

FIG. 3.

In dealing with a resonant circuit of the parallel resonant type, for example, whose impedance versus frequency curve is that pictured in Fig. 3, the bandwidth $f_2 - f_1$, which is the distance between half-power points on this curve, is defined as

$$f_2 - f_1 = \frac{f_0}{Q} \tag{46}$$

where f_0 and Q represent the resonant frequency and the figure of merit of the circuit, respectively. The Q of the circuit is defined as 2π times the ratio of the stored energy $\mathcal{E}$ in the circuit to the power lost per cycle W/f; that is,

$$Q = 2\pi \frac{\mathcal{E}}{W/f} = \frac{\omega \mathcal{E}}{W} \tag{47}$$

[1] See, for example, F. E. Terman, "Radio Engineering," p. 341, McGraw-Hill Book Company, Inc., New York, 1947, for a discussion of bandwidth considerations in tuned amplifiers.

FOURIER ANALYSIS OF A LINEAR NETWORK

PERIODIC WAVES

7. Current through a Linear Network. Consider the circuit which consists of a linear network whose self-impedance is $Z_S(\omega)$. Let it be excited by a complex periodic voltage which may be represented by the Fourier series

$$e(t) = \sum_{-\infty}^{\infty} E_n e^{in\omega t} \tag{48}$$

where, in the interval $-\pi/\omega < t < \pi/\omega$, E_n is described by the integral

$$E_n = \frac{\omega}{2\pi} \int_{-\pi/\omega}^{\pi/\omega} e(t) e^{-in\omega t}\, dt \tag{49}$$

$e(t)$ is expressed as a complex Fourier series rather than by a trigonometric Fourier series in order to simplify the mathematics.

Owing to the principle of superposition, the current delivered by the complex voltage generator to the network in Fig. 4 is

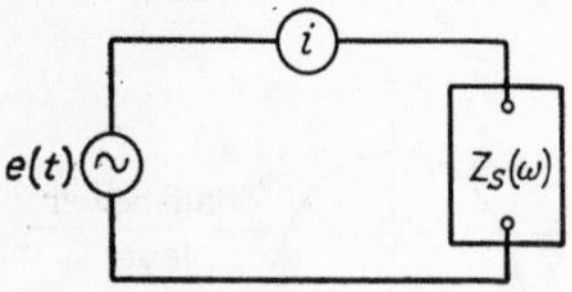

FIG. 4.

$$i(t) = \sum_{-\infty}^{\infty} I_n e^{in\omega t} \tag{50}$$

where

$$I_n = \frac{E_n}{Z_S(n\omega)} \tag{51}$$

It follows from Eqs. (48) and (50) that if a complex current $i(t)$ is passed through a linear network whose self-impedance is $Z_S(\omega)$, then the voltage across the network is

$$e(t) = \sum_{n=-\infty}^{\infty} I_n Z_S(n\omega) e^{in\omega t} \tag{52}$$

8. Demonstration of the Evaluation of Equation (51). Consider the series RLC circuit shown in Fig. 1. Using Eqs. (48) and (50), the response of this network to the complex periodic exciting voltage $e(t)$ is expressed as follows:

$$R \sum_{n=-\infty}^{\infty} I_n e^{in\omega t} + L \frac{d}{dt}\left(\sum_{n=-\infty}^{\infty} I_n e^{in\omega t}\right) + \frac{1}{C} \int \sum_{n=-\infty}^{\infty} I_n e^{in\omega t}\, dt = \sum_{n=-\infty}^{\infty} E_n e^{in\omega t} \tag{53}$$

This reduces to

$$\sum_{n=-\infty}^{\infty} I_n \left[R + j\left(n\omega L - \frac{1}{n\omega C}\right)\right] e^{in\omega t} = \sum_{n=-\infty}^{\infty} E_n e^{in\omega t} \tag{54}$$

Canceling the exponentials, we get, in terms of the nth component,

$$I_n = \frac{E_n}{R + j[n\omega L - (1/n\omega C)]} \tag{55}$$

9. Periodic Square-wave Voltage Impressed on a Series RL Circuit. When a step voltage of amplitude E, such as that pictured in Fig. 5a, is

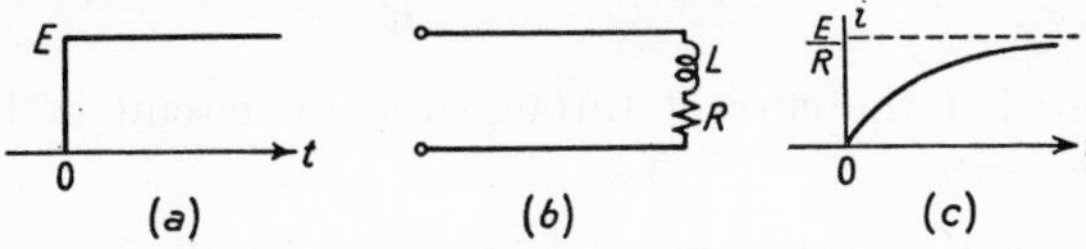

FIG. 5.

impressed on the series RL circuit shown in Fig. 5b, the current which will flow in the circuit is pictured in Fig. 5c and is expressed as (see Sec. 11)

$$i(t) = \frac{E}{R}(1 - e^{-(R/L)t}) \tag{56}$$

R/L is the time constant of the circuit and determines the rate of rise of the amplitude of the current which flows in the circuit.

Let a periodic square-wave voltage of amplitude E and period $2\pi/\omega_1$, such that pictured in Fig. 6a, be impressed on the series RL circuit.

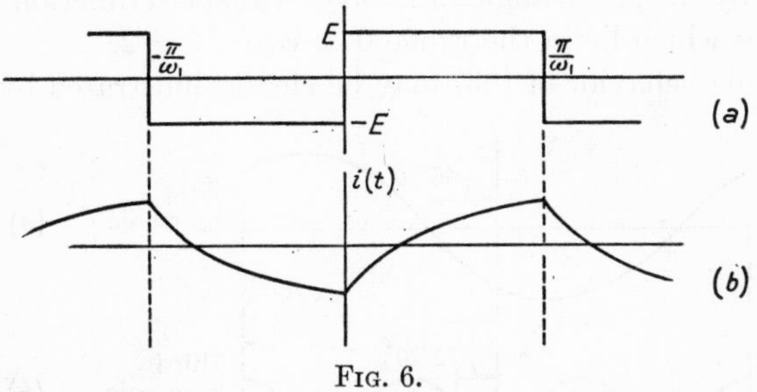

FIG. 6.

If $R/L \ll \pi/\omega_1$, thus permitting the current to approach its asymptotic value E/R when the voltage step is in the positive direction, the current $i(t)$ will flow as shown in Fig. 6b since at the start of each half cycle the circuit will have a step voltage impressed on it.

We may derive the waveform shown in Fig. 6b by using the Fourier analysis. The Fourier analysis to follow will serve to illustrate both the general concepts of the general analysis and the role played by the phase functions of the impedance in wave superposition. The Fourier representation of the square wave in Fig. 6a is

$$e(t) = \frac{4E}{\pi}\left(\sin \omega_1 t + \frac{1}{3}\sin 3\omega_1 t + \frac{1}{5}\sin 5\omega_1 t + \cdots\right) \tag{57}$$

In general, the self-impedance of any series RL circuit is expressed as

$$Z_S(\omega) = R + j\omega L \tag{58}$$

$$= \sqrt{R^2 + \omega^2 L^2}\, e^{j\phi(\omega)} \tag{59}$$

where

$$\phi(\omega) = \tan^{-1}\frac{\omega L}{R} \tag{60}$$

It follows then that the current through the RC circuit in Fig. 5b is expressed by the series

$$i(t) = \frac{4E}{\pi}\left\{\frac{\sin[\omega_1 t - \phi(\omega_1)]}{\sqrt{R^2 + \omega_1{}^2 L^2}} + \frac{\sin[3\omega_1 t - \phi(3\omega_1)]}{3\sqrt{R^2 + (3\omega_1 L)^2}} + \cdots\right\} \tag{61}$$

If we make the substitution,

$$Q_1 = \frac{\omega_1 L}{R} \tag{62}$$

in Eq. (61), we get

$$i(t) = \frac{4E}{\pi R}\left\{\frac{\sin[\omega_1 t - \phi(\omega_1)]}{\sqrt{1 + Q_1{}^2}} + \frac{\sin[3\omega_1 t - \phi(3\omega_1)]}{3\sqrt{1 + 9Q_1{}^2}} + \cdots\right\} \tag{63}$$

The nth current harmonic listed in (63) lags behind the nth voltage harmonic in (57) by the phase angle $\tan^{-1} nQ_1$, which is a function of frequency and has values which lie in the range $0 < \phi(\omega) < \pi/2$.

The harmonic behavior of (63) may be clearly illustrated by considering

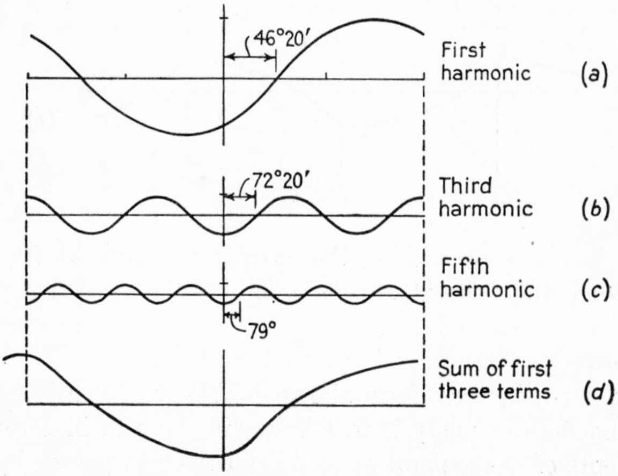

FIG. 7.

the case when $Q_1 = \pi/3$. Let Q_1 yield a time constant such that during a half cycle of the square-wave voltage the current will rise exponentially to 95 per cent of its maximum possible value. Substituting this value of

Q_1 into (63), we get

$$i(t) = (E/R)[0.88 \sin (\omega_1 t - 46°20') + 0.128 \sin (3\omega_1 t - 72°20') + 0.0476 \sin (5\omega_1 t - 79°) + \cdots] \qquad (64)$$

The fundamental and the third and fifth harmonics are pictured in Fig. 7*a*, *b*, and *c* in proper phase, and their summation, which is pictured in Fig. 7*d*, is in the form of the wave depicted in Fig. 6*b*.

Nonperiodic Waves

10. Current through a Linear Network. Consider the case when a nonperiodic complex voltage $e(t)$ is applied to a linear network whose self-impedance is $Z_S(\omega)$. Since the impressed voltage is nonperiodic, it may be represented by a Fourier transform $g(\omega)$, where

$$g(\omega) = \int_{-\infty}^{\infty} e(t)e^{-j\omega t}\, dt \qquad (65)$$

This is a spectral function (see Chap. 3) which converts the voltage from a time function to a frequency function. Once $g(\omega)$ has been determined, we may recover the time function by using the inverse Fourier transform as follows:

$$e(t) = \frac{1}{2\pi} \int_{\omega=-\infty}^{\infty} g(\omega)e^{j\omega t}\, d\omega \qquad (66)$$

If the current behavior is desired, the recovery of the time function may be made in terms of the current by using the self-impedance $Z_S(\omega)$ or the self-admittance $Y_S(\omega)$ of the network. It therefore follows that

$$i(t) = \frac{1}{2\pi} \int_{-\infty}^{\infty} \frac{g(\omega)}{Z_S(\omega)} e^{j\omega t}\, d\omega \qquad (67)$$

Similarly, if a nonperiodic current is representable by a Fourier transform such that

$$g(\omega) = \int_{-\infty}^{\infty} i(t)e^{-j\omega t}\, dt \qquad (68)$$

and if this current passes through the linear network having a self-impedance $Z_S(\omega)$, then the voltage across this network is described by the inverse Fourier transform,

$$e(t) = \frac{1}{2\pi} \int_{-\infty}^{\infty} g(\omega)Z_S(\omega)e^{j\omega t}\, d\omega \qquad (69)$$

In most applications in electrical communications, Eqs. (67) and (69) are of academic interest only because of the difficulty in performing the integrations. Except for certain elementary applications such as that which will follow, it is necessary to resort to impedance expressions for idealized networks, which are discussed in detail in Chap. 20, in order to achieve usable expressions.

11. Step Voltage Impressed on a Series RL Circuit.[1] Consider the Fourier-integral solution[2] of the case when the step-function voltage pictured in Fig. 5a is impressed on the series RL circuit which is pictured in Fig. 5b. This step-function voltage is described mathematically as

$$\begin{aligned} e(t) &= 0 \qquad -\infty < t < 0 \\ &= E \qquad 0 < t < \infty \end{aligned} \tag{70}$$

We have seen in Chap. 4 [see Eq. (11) in that chapter] that the Fourier transform of (70) is

$$g(\omega) = \frac{E}{j\omega} \tag{71}$$

The self-admittance of the series RL circuit is readily shown to be

$$Y_S(\omega) = \frac{R}{R^2 + \omega^2 L^2} - j\frac{\omega L}{R^2 + \omega^2 L^2} \tag{72}$$

The following Fourier integral represents the current due to (70):

$$i(t) = \frac{E}{2\pi}\int_{-\infty}^{\infty}\left(\frac{R}{R^2 + \omega^2 L^2} - j\frac{\omega L}{R^2 + \omega^2 L^2}\right)\frac{e^{j\omega t}}{j\omega}\,d\omega \tag{73}$$

Let us rewrite integral (73) as follows:

$$i(t) = \frac{E'}{R} + \frac{E}{2\pi}\int_{-\infty}^{\infty}\left(\frac{R}{R^2 + \omega^2 L^2} - \frac{1}{R} - j\frac{\omega L}{R^2 + \omega^2 L^2}\right)\frac{e^{j\omega t}}{j\omega}\,d\omega \tag{74}$$

The prime indicates that this term is to be considered only when $t > 0$. Applying Euler's formula to $e^{j\omega t}$ and rearranging the terms, we get the real expression [the imaginary terms are equal to zero since $e(t)$ is real].

$$\begin{aligned} i(t) &= \frac{E'}{R} - \frac{E}{2\pi R}\int_{-\infty}^{\infty}\frac{\sin \omega t}{\omega}\,d\omega \\ &\quad + \frac{E}{2\pi}\int_{-\infty}^{\infty}\left[\left(\frac{R}{R^2 + \omega^2 L^2}\right)\frac{\sin \omega t}{\omega} - \left(\frac{\omega L}{R^2 + \omega^2 L^2}\right)\frac{\cos \omega t}{\omega}\right]d\omega \end{aligned} \tag{75}$$

But

$$\int_{-\infty}^{\infty}\frac{\sin \omega t}{\omega}\,d\omega = \pi \qquad t > 0 \tag{76}$$

[1] See V. Bush, "Operational Circuit Analysis," Chap. X, John Wiley & Sons, Inc., New York, 1937.

[2] This is a special case of the formulation to be discussed in Sec. 23.

Thus we find that for $t > 0$

$$i(t) = \frac{E}{2R} + \frac{E}{2\pi}\int_{-\infty}^{\infty} \frac{R}{R^2 + \omega^2 L^2} \frac{\sin \omega t}{\omega} \, d\omega$$

$$- \frac{E}{2\pi}\int_{-\infty}^{\infty} \frac{\omega L}{R^2 + \omega^2 L^2} \frac{\cos \omega t}{\omega} \, d\omega \qquad (77)$$

If we substitute $-t$ for t in Eq. (75), thus causing it to equal zero [since $i(-t) = 0$], we may also write for $t > 0$

$$0 = \frac{E}{2R} - \frac{E}{2\pi}\int_{-\infty}^{\infty} \frac{R}{R^2 + \omega^2 L^2} \frac{\sin \omega t}{\omega} \, d\omega - \frac{E}{2\pi}\int_{-\infty}^{\infty} \frac{\omega L}{R^2 + \omega^2 L^2} \frac{\cos \omega t}{\omega} \, d\omega \qquad (78)$$

Combining (77) and (78), we find that $i(t)$ may be expressed in either of the two following ways:

Expression I:

$$i(t) = \frac{E}{R} + \frac{2E}{\pi}\int_{0}^{\infty} \frac{\omega L}{R^2 + \omega^2 L^2} \frac{\cos \omega t}{\omega} \, d\omega \qquad (79)$$

Expression II:

$$i(t) = \frac{2E}{\pi}\int_{0}^{\infty} \frac{R}{R^2 + \omega^2 L^2} \frac{\sin \omega t}{\omega} \, d\omega \qquad (80)$$

Either of these expressions may be evaluated[1] to yield

$$i(t) = \frac{E}{R}(1 - e^{-(R/L)t}) \qquad (81)$$

which is, of course, equal to Eq. (56) for $t > 0$.

We were able to obtain this solution only because the conductance and susceptance of the RL circuit are well-behaved functions and because the solutions of the final integrals are known. In general, in problems involving step-function excitation of linear networks, it is more advantageous to use a more powerful approach—the Laplace-transform method—so that contour integration can be used to bring about the solution in a more direct fashion. Note that *only* the conductance or the susceptance *alone* was necessary for either solution (see Sec. 23).

[1] See Bierens de Haan, "Nouvelles tables d'intégrales définies," p. 252, No. 1, p. 223, No. 5, Leide, Engels, 1867; *viz.*,

$$\int_0^{\infty} \frac{\sin ax}{x(b^2 + x^2)} \, dx = \frac{\pi}{2b^2}(1 - e^{-ab})$$

$$\int_0^{\infty} \frac{\cos ax}{b^2 + x^2} = \frac{\pi}{2b} e^{-ab}$$

LINEAR-CIRCUIT ANALYSIS USING THE LAPLACE TRANSFORM[1]

12. Laplace Transform and Linear-circuit Analysis. The Laplace transform is more suitable for use in the transit analysis of many communications networks because it is easier to use and arrive at a result and because it handles step functions and other functions for which $\int_0^t |f(t)|\, dt$ does not converge.

In dealing with the Fourier transform and integral, an impedance function $Z(\omega)$ has been evolved. In using a Laplace transform a corresponding impedance function $Z(s)$ will be obtained. It follows from Secs. 7 and 8 in Chap. 4 that, for example, the impedance functions resulting from the Laplace transforms of the voltage drops across capacitors and inductances are

$$\mathcal{L}\left[L\,\frac{di(t)}{dt}\right] = Z(s) = sL\mathcal{L}[i(t)] + Li_0 \qquad (82)$$

$$\mathcal{L}\left[\frac{\int i(t)\,dt}{C}\right] = Z(s) = \frac{q_0}{Cs} + \frac{\mathcal{L}[i(t)]}{Cs} \qquad (83)$$

where i_0 and q_0 are the initial current and charge, respectively. These expressions demonstrate some aspects of the power of the Laplace transform since unlike the case of the Fourier transform the initial conditions are explicitly included in the problem.

Note in the following tabulation the similarity between corresponding expressions for voltage drops across resistances, inductances, and capacitances when rotating-vector operators and Laplace transforms are used. In this tabulation it is assumed that i_0 and q_0 are equal to zero.

	Rotating-vector operator	Laplace transform
Resistance	$RIe^{j\omega t}$	$R\mathcal{L}[i(t)]$
Inductance	$j\omega LIe^{j\omega t}$	$sL\mathcal{L}[i(t)]$
Capacitance	$\frac{1}{j\omega C}\,Ie^{j\omega t}$	$\frac{1}{sC}\,\mathcal{L}[i(t)]$

The general procedure for analyzing an electrical network using the Laplace transform may be summarized in the following four essential steps:

1. Write down the differential equations of the network.

[1] Gardiner and Barnes, "Transients in Linear Systems," vol. I, John Wiley & Sons, Inc., New York, 1942.

Carslaw and Jaeger, "Operational Methods in Applied Mathematics," Oxford University Press, New York, 1941.

2. Take the Laplace transforms of these equations.
3. If a final expression for $i_k(t)$, for example, is desired, solve the resulting algebraic equations for $\mathcal{L}[i_k(t)]$.
4. Obtain $i_k(t)$ by solving the inverse Laplace transform; *i.e.*,

$$i_k(t) = \frac{1}{2\pi j} \int_{\alpha - j\infty}^{\alpha + j\infty} \mathcal{L}[i_k(t)]e^{st}\, ds \tag{84}$$

Eq. (84) actually involves the adding up of the residues of $\mathcal{L}[i_k(t)]e^{st}$ at all of its poles. These residues, which comprise the solution of (84), are easily obtained by employing the formulas in Chap. 1. In many problems, the inverse Laplace transform may be obtained immediately by consulting the table of transforms in Chap. 4.

13. Laplace-transform Solution of a Series RL Circuit. Consider the Laplace-transform solution for the current flowing in the series RL circuit (see Secs. 9 and 11) pictured in Fig. 5*b* when the step voltage

$$\begin{aligned} e(t) &= 0 \qquad -\infty < t < 0 \\ &= E \qquad 0 < t < \infty \end{aligned} \tag{85}$$

is impressed on its terminals for the case when $i_0 = 0$. The differential equation of the circuit is

$$L\frac{di(t)}{dt} + Ri(t) = e(t) \tag{86}$$

Taking the Laplace transform of each term, we get

$$Ls\mathcal{L}[i(t)] + R\mathcal{L}[i(t)] = \frac{E}{s} \tag{87}$$

or

$$\mathcal{L}[i(t)] = \frac{E}{s[Ls + R]} \tag{88}$$

The current $i(t)$ may be determined by taking the inverse Laplace transform of (88); *i.e.*,

$$i(t) = \frac{E}{2\pi j} \int_{\alpha - j\infty}^{\alpha + j\infty} \frac{e^{st}}{s[s + (R/L)]L}\, ds \tag{89}$$

which has simple poles at $s = 0$ and $s = -R/L$.

The residue at the pole, $s = 0$, is found as follows: Since, according to Eq. (129), Chap. 1,

$$\text{res} = \left.\frac{w(s)}{g'(s)}\right|_{s=0} \tag{90}$$

then,

$$\begin{aligned} w(s) &= \frac{Ee^{st}}{[s + (R/L)]L} \qquad & w(0) &= \frac{E}{R} \\ g(s) &= s & g'(s) &= 1 \end{aligned} \tag{91}$$

It follows that

$$\text{res} = \frac{E}{R} \tag{92}$$

For the pole at $s = -R/L$, let

$$w(s) = E\frac{e^{st}}{s} \qquad g(s) = Ls + R \tag{93}$$

Then

$$\frac{w(-R/L)}{g'(-R/L)} = -\frac{E}{R}e^{-(R/L)t} \tag{94}$$

Summing the residues, we get finally [see (81)]

$$i(t) = \frac{E}{R}(1 - e^{-(R/L)t}) \tag{95}$$

14. Laplace-transform Solution of a Series *RC* Circuit. Consider the Laplace-transform solution for the current flowing in a series *RC* circuit when the step-function voltage

$$\begin{aligned} e(t) &= 0 \qquad -\infty < t < 0 \\ &= E \qquad 0 < t < \infty \end{aligned} \tag{96}$$

is impressed on its terminals, for the case when

$$q_0 = 0 \tag{97}$$

The differential equation of the circuit is

$$\frac{1}{C}\int i(t)\,dt + Ri(t) = e(t) \tag{98}$$

Taking the Laplace transform of each member, we get

$$\frac{\mathfrak{L}[i(t)]}{sC} + R\mathfrak{L}[i(t)] = \frac{E}{s} \tag{99}$$

Then

$$\mathfrak{L}[i(t)] = \frac{E}{(1/C) + sR} \tag{100}$$

Since

$$i(t) = \frac{E}{2\pi j}\int_{\alpha - j\infty}^{\alpha + j\infty} \frac{e^{st}}{[(1/RC) + s]R}\,ds \tag{101}$$

it is evident that we must solve for the residue at the simple pole at

$$s = -\frac{1}{RC} \tag{102}$$

According to Eq. (129), Chap. 1,

$$i(t) = \left. \frac{w(s)}{g'(s)} \right|_{s=-1/RC} \tag{103}$$

Then

$$\begin{aligned} w(s) &= E\frac{e^{st}}{R} \qquad & w\left(-\frac{1}{RC}\right) &= \frac{E}{R}e^{-t/RC} \\ g(s) &= \frac{1}{CR} + s \qquad & g'\left(-\frac{1}{RC}\right) &= 1 \end{aligned} \tag{104}$$

and we get

$$i(t) = \frac{E}{R}e^{-t/RC} \tag{105}$$

15. Pulser Circuit with a Resistive Load. Consider the Laplace-transform solution,[1] of the resistance-loaded hard-tube pulser discharging circuit which is pictured in Fig. 8*a*. Here the hard tube is depicted as an ideal switch in series with a plate resistance r_p and a battery E_b. We shall be interested in determining the waveform of the voltage, across the resistive

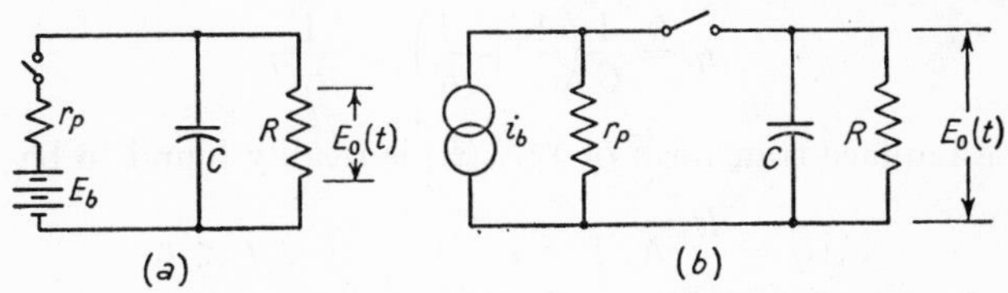

FIG. 8. (*a*) Hard-tube (vacuum-tube) pulser circuit. (*b*) Equivalent circuit of the pulser circuit using a constant-current generator.

load, as a function of time. If it is assumed that the capacitor is charged to the full battery voltage E_b and that the capacitance C is so large that the change in voltage during a pulse is extremely small, then the voltage pulse appearing across R may be deduced in the following two steps:

1. The tube is turned on (switch closed) in the time interval $0 < t < t_1$.
2. The tube is biased off (switch opened) for $t \geq t_1$.

The voltage source E_b and the series resistance r_p, may be replaced by a current source i_b in shunt with the resistance r_p such that

$$i_b = \frac{E_b}{r_p} \tag{106}$$

The resulting equivalent circuit is pictured in Fig. 8*b*. When the switch is closed at $t = 0$, then according to Kirchhoff's first law

[1] See Glasoe and Lebacqz, "Pulse Generators," Sec. 22, Radiation Laboratory Series, McGraw-Hill Book Company, Inc., New York, 1948. This book contains one of the finest treatments of pulse circuits available in addition to many excellent applications of the Laplace transform.

$$\left(\frac{1}{r_p} + \frac{1}{R}\right)E_0(t) + C\,\frac{dE_0(t)}{dt} = i_b \tag{107}$$

Taking the Laplace transform of each member, we get

$$\left(\frac{1}{r_p} + \frac{1}{R}\right)\mathcal{L}[E_0(t)] + C\{s\mathcal{L}[E_0(t)] - E_0(0)\} = \frac{i_b}{s} \tag{108}$$

If the capacitor is assumed to be discharged at $t = 0$ such that $E_0(0) = 0$, then it follows that

$$\mathcal{L}[E_0(t)] = \frac{i_b}{s}\,\frac{1}{sC + [(1/r_p) + (1/R)]} \tag{109}$$

which can be evolved, using partial fractions, into the form

$$\mathcal{L}[E_0(t)] = \frac{E_b}{r_p}\,R_1\left(\frac{1}{s} - \frac{1}{s+\gamma}\right) \tag{110}$$

where

$$R_1 = \frac{Rr_p}{R + r_p} \tag{111}$$

$$\gamma = \frac{1}{C}\left(\frac{1}{r_p} + \frac{1}{R}\right) = \frac{1}{R_1C} \tag{112}$$

The inverse Laplace transform of $\mathcal{L}[E_0(t)]$ is readily found to be

$$E_0(t) = \frac{E_b}{r_p}\,R_1(1 - e^{-\gamma t}) \qquad 0 < t < t_1 \tag{113}$$

This yields the expression for the leading edge of the pulse which will have an amplitude, $(E_b/r_p)R_1$, if $t_1 \gg R_1C$.

If we denote the pulse amplitude at $t = t_1$ as $E(t_1)$, where

$$E(t_1) = \frac{E_b}{r_p}\,R_1 \tag{114}$$

such that the capacitor is charged to this potential, then, when the switch is opened at $t = t_1$,

$$i_b = 0 \qquad r_p = 0 \qquad E_0(t_1) = E(t_1) \tag{115}$$

It follows that, for the time interval after t_1,

$$\mathcal{L}[E_0(t)] = \frac{E(t_1)}{s + (1/CR)} \qquad t > t_1 \tag{116}$$

from which we get, as an expression for the trailing edge of the pulse,

$$E_0(t) = E(t_1)e^{-(t-t_1)/RC} \tag{117}$$

$$= \frac{E_b}{r_p}\,R_1e^{-(t-t_1)/RC} \qquad t > t_1,\ t_1 \gg RC \tag{118}$$

As an illustration of the use of Eqs. (113) and (118), a pulse wave for $R = 1{,}000$ ohms, $C = 50\ \mu\mu f$, and $r_p = 150$ ohms is shown plotted in Fig. 9 and is seen to be satisfactory with regard to rectangularity of shape.

16. An *m*-mesh Electrical Network. In a general m-mesh electrical network, the voltage drops in the kth mesh are summed as follows:

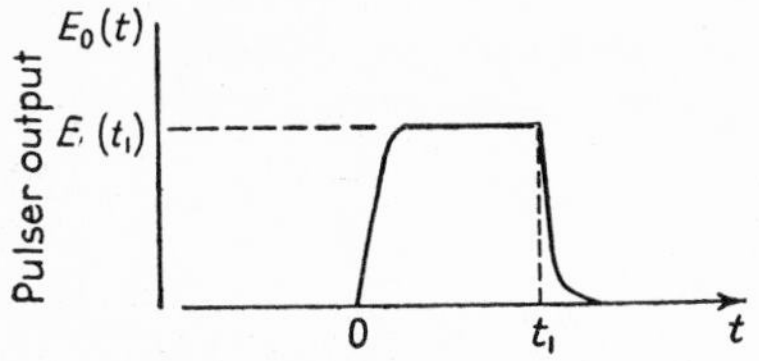

FIG. 9.

$$L_k \frac{di_k}{dt} + R_k i_k + \frac{q_{0k}}{C_k} + \frac{1}{C_k}\int i_k\,dt + \sum M_{kr}\frac{di_r}{dt} = e_k(t) \tag{119}$$

where $\sum M_{kr}\, di_r/dt$ refers to the mutual coupling between the kth and rth mesh, $e_k(t)$ is a series voltage appearing in the kth mesh, L_k, R_k, and C_k are the lumped-circuit parameters, and i_{0_k} and q_{0_k} are the initial currents and charge in the kth mesh, respectively. Taking the Laplace transform of both sides, we get

$$Z_{kr}(s)\mathfrak{L}[i_{kr}(t)] = \mathfrak{L}[e_k(t)] - \frac{q_{0k}}{sC_k} + L_k i_{0k} + \sum_{r\neq k} M_{kr} i_{0_r} \tag{120}$$

where

$$r = k \qquad i_{kr}(t) = i_k(t) \qquad Z_{kk}(s) = R_k + sL_k + \frac{1}{sC_k} \tag{121}$$

$$r \neq k \qquad i_{kr}(t) = i_r(t) \qquad Z_{kr}(s) = sM_{kr} \tag{122}$$

When these are summed over m meshes, we get finally

$$\sum_{k=1}^{m} Z_{kr}(s)\mathfrak{L}[i_{kr}(t)] = \sum_{k=1}^{m}\left(L_k i_{0_k} + \sum_{r\neq k} M_{kr} i_{0_r} - \frac{q_{0_k}}{sC_k}\right) + \sum_{k=1}^{m}\mathfrak{L}[e_k(t)] \tag{123}$$

where $\sum_{k=1}^{m}\mathfrak{L}[e_k(t)]$ is the sum of the Laplace transforms of the applied emfs in the closed circuit.

When $i_0 = q_0 = 0$, Eq. (123) becomes

$$\sum_{k=1}^{m} Z_{kr}(s)\mathfrak{L}[i_{kr}(t)] = \sum_{k=1}^{m}\mathfrak{L}[e_k(t)] \tag{124}$$

which may be written out as

$$\begin{aligned} Z_{11}(s)\mathfrak{L}[i_1(t)] + \cdots + Z_{1m}(s)\mathfrak{L}[i_m(t)] &= \mathfrak{L}[e_1(t)] \\ Z_{21}(s)\mathfrak{L}[i_1(t)] + \cdots + Z_{2m}(s)\mathfrak{L}[i_m(t)] &= \mathfrak{L}[e_2(t)] \\ \cdots\cdots\cdots\cdots\cdots\cdots\cdots\cdots\cdots\cdots\cdots & \\ Z_{m1}(s)\mathfrak{L}[i_1(t)] + \cdots + Z_{mm}(s)\mathfrak{L}[i_m(t)] &= \mathfrak{L}[e_m(t)] \end{aligned} \tag{125}$$

Equation (125) is easily solved for the Laplace transform of the kth current by using determinants as in Eq. (38); *i.e.*,

$$\mathcal{L}[i_k(t)] = \frac{\begin{vmatrix} Z_{11}(s) & Z_{12}(s) & \cdots & \mathcal{L}[e_1(t)] & \cdots & Z_{1m}(s) \\ Z_{21}(s) & Z_{22}(s) & \cdots & \mathcal{L}[e_2(t)] & \cdots & Z_{2m}(s) \\ \cdots & \cdots & \cdots & \cdots & \cdots & \cdots \\ Z_{m1}(s) & Z_{m2}(s) & \cdots & \mathcal{L}[e_m(t)] & \cdots & Z_{mm}(s) \end{vmatrix}}{D(s)} \tag{126}$$

in which the Laplace transforms $\mathcal{L}[e_1(t)]$, $\mathcal{L}[e_2(t)]$, . . . replace the kth row and $D(s)$ is the determinant of the system [Eq. (40), in which $j\omega$ is replaced by s]. In most problems in communication circuits, the determinantal quotient is readily solved for $\mathcal{L}[i_k(t)]$, and the expression for $i_k(t)$ is determined by using the inverse Laplace transform; *i.e.*,

$$i_k(t) = \frac{1}{2\pi_j} \int_{\alpha - j\infty}^{\alpha + j\infty} \mathcal{L}[i_k(t)]e^{st}\, ds \tag{127}$$

$$= \sum \text{res}\ \rho_n \tag{128}$$

where ρ_n is the residue at the nth pole of $\mathcal{L}[i_k(t)]e^{st}$. When a pole s_n is a simple pole, then

$$\rho_n = \lim_{s \to s_n} (s - s_n)e^{st}\mathcal{L}[i_k(t)] \tag{129}$$

$$= e^{s_n t} \lim_{s \to s_n} (s - s_n)\mathcal{L}[i_k(t)] \tag{130}$$

Heaviside Expansion Theorem. If $\mathcal{L}[i_k(t)]$ has the fractional form [see Eq. (84), Chap. 4],

$$\mathcal{L}[i_k(t)] = \frac{a_0 + a_1 s + a_2 s^2 + \cdots + a_n s^n}{b_0 + b_1 s + b_2 s^2 + \cdots + b_m s^m} \tag{131}$$

$$= \frac{a_0 + a_1 s + a_2 s^2 + \cdots + a_n s^n}{(s - s_1)(s - s_2) \cdots (s - s_m)} \tag{132}$$

$$= \frac{w(s)}{g(s)} \tag{133}$$

where $m > n$, and $a_0, a_1, \ldots, a_n, b_1, b_2, \ldots, b_m$ are constants; if a pole exists at $s = s_n$ such that $\omega(s)$ and $g(s)$ are analytic at $s = s_n$ and $g'(s) \neq 0$, then

$$\rho_n = \frac{w(s_n)}{g'(s_n)} e^{s_n t} \tag{134}$$

If all of the poles are simple poles, then

$$i_k(t) = \sum_{n=1}^{m} \frac{w(s_n)}{g'(s_n)} e^{s_n t} \tag{135}$$

This is known as the Heaviside expansion theorem. Its derivation and form serve forcibly to demonstrate the fact that the use of the Laplace transform reduces the solution of many transient problems in complicated communication systems to a succession of relatively simple mathematical manipulations.

17. Solution for a Mesh Circuit Using the Heaviside Expansion Theorem. Consider the Laplace-transform solution[1] for the current i_1 in the circuit in Fig. 10 when $e_1(t)$ is a unit step function; *i.e.*,

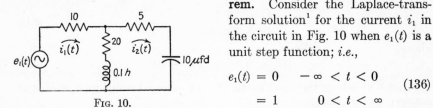

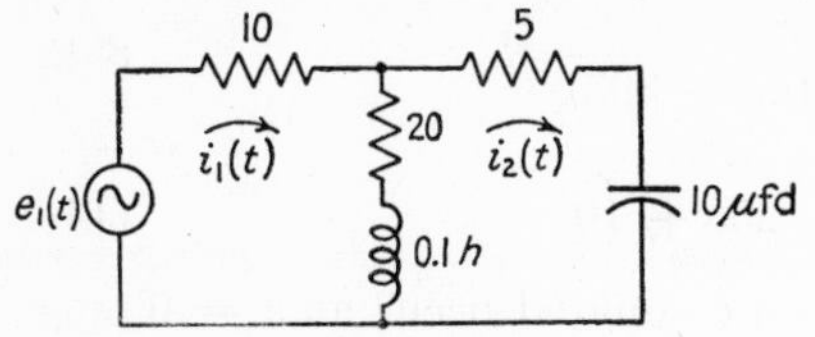

FIG. 10.

$$\begin{aligned} e_1(t) &= 0 \qquad -\infty < t < 0 \\ &= 1 \qquad 0 < t < \infty \end{aligned} \tag{136}$$

According to Kirchhoff's second law, the differential equations of the network are

$$0.1\,\frac{di_1}{dt} + 30i_1 - 0.1\,\frac{di_2}{dt} - 20i_2 = 1 \tag{137}$$

$$25i_2 - 0.1\,\frac{di_1}{dt} - 20i_1 + 0.1\,\frac{di_2}{dt} + 10^5 q_2 = 0 \tag{138}$$

Taking the Laplace transforms of these equations, we get

$$(0.1s + 30)\mathcal{L}(i_1) - (0.1s + 20)\mathcal{L}(i_2) - 0.1i_{10} + 0.1i_{20} = \frac{1}{s} \tag{139}$$

$$- (0.1s + 20)\mathcal{L}(i_1) + \left(0.1s + 25 + \frac{10^5}{s}\right)\mathcal{L}(i_2) + 0.1i_{10} - 0.1i_{20} + \frac{10^5 q_{20}}{s} = 0 \tag{140}$$

where i_{10}, i_{20}, and q_{20} are the initial currents and charge, respectively, at $t = 0$.

If we assume that the network is initially at rest, then

$$q_{20} = 0 \qquad i_{10} - i_{20} = 0 \tag{141}$$

Solving for $\mathcal{L}(i_1)$, we get

$$\mathcal{L}(i_1) = \frac{0.1s^2 + 25s + 10^5}{s(1.5s^2 + 10{,}350s + 3 \times 10^6)} \tag{142}$$

[1] From an illustrative example by Jacob Millman, Laplacian Transform Analysis of Circuits with Linear Lumped Parameters, *Elec. Eng.*, vol. 61, pp. 197–205, April, 1942. This is one of the finest introductory discussions of the applications of Laplace analysis to electric circuits available. Comparisons of the Heaviside calculus, the Carson infinite-integral theorem, and the Laplace transform are also given.

Let us solve for i_1. According to the Heaviside expansion theorem,

$$i_1(t) = \sum_{n=1} \frac{w(s_n)}{g'(s_n)} e^{s_n t} \tag{143}$$

where

$$\frac{w(s)}{g(s)} = \mathfrak{L}(i_1)e^{st} \tag{144}$$

$$= \frac{A(s)}{s(s + 6{,}600)(s + 303)} e^{st} \tag{145}$$

where

$$A(s) = 0.1s^2 + 25s + 10^5 \tag{146}$$

The poles at which the residues must be evaluated occur at $s = 0$, $s = -6{,}600$, and $s = -303$.

To find the residue at $s = 0$, let

$$\omega(s) = \frac{A(s)}{1.5s^2 + 10{,}350s + 3 \times 10^6} e^{st} \tag{147}$$

$$g(s) = s \tag{148}$$

Then

$$\operatorname*{res}_{s=0} = \frac{w(0)}{g'(0)} = 0.033 \tag{149}$$

For the residue at either $s = -6{,}600$ or $s = -303$, let

$$w(s) = \frac{A(s)}{s} e^{st} \tag{150}$$

$$g(s) = 1.5s^2 + 10{,}350s + 3 \times 10^6 \tag{151}$$

Note that

$$g'(s) = 3s + 10{,}350 \tag{152}$$

The residue at $s = -303$ is

$$\operatorname*{res}_{s=-303} = \frac{w(-303)}{g'(-303)} \tag{153}$$

$$= \frac{[0.1(-303)^2 + 25(-303) + 10^5]e^{-303t}}{(-303)[3(-303) + 10{,}350]} = 0.0355e^{-303t} \tag{154}$$

Solving in like manner for the residue at $s = -6{,}600$, we get finally

$$i_1(t) = 0.033 - 0.0355e^{-303t} + 0.0689e^{-6{,}600t} \tag{155}$$

18. Laplace-transform Analysis for Linear-network Response.[1] Consider first a simple series RLC circuit across whose terminals is impressed

[1] For an extensive mathematical study of this subject, see J. H. Mulligan, The Effect of Pole and Zero Locations on the Transient Response of Linear Dynamic Systems, *Proc. IRE*, vol. 37, pp. 516–529, May, 1949.

a voltage $e(t)$. The differential equation describing the circuit is

$$Ri(t) + L\frac{di(t)}{dt} + \frac{1}{C}\int i(t)\,dt = e(t) \tag{156}$$

If the system is initially at rest, the Laplace transform of (156) may be written as follows:

$$\mathcal{L}[i(t)] = \mathcal{L}[e(t)]Y(s) \tag{157}$$

where

$$Y(s) = \frac{1}{R + sL + (1/sC)} \tag{158}$$

$Y(s)$ is the Laplace admittance function, which may be easily obtained by replacing $j\omega$ by s in the expression for $Y(\omega)$ representing the circuit.

The product of two Laplace transforms which are found on the right-hand side of (157) is typical of the general expressions which are obtained in both two-terminal and four-terminal Laplace analysis. For any four-terminal network, we may write

$$\mathcal{L}[i_0(t)] = \mathcal{L}[e_1(t)]Y_T(s) \tag{159}$$

where $i_0(t)$ is the output current and $Y_T(s)$ is the transformed transfer admittance [$j\omega$ replaced by s in $Y_T(\omega)$ for the system initially at rest, for example]. It follows then that

$$i_0(t) = \frac{1}{2\pi j}\int_{\alpha - j\infty}^{\alpha + j\infty} \mathcal{L}[e_1(t)]Y_T(s)e^{st}\,ds \tag{160}$$

If the output voltage $e_0(t)$ is desired, we may write

$$e_0(t) = \frac{1}{2\pi j}\int_{\alpha - j\infty}^{\alpha + j\infty} \mathcal{L}[e_1(t)]h(s)e^{st}\,ds \tag{161}$$

where $h(s)$ is the transformed complex transmission-frequency function [see the discussion of $h(\omega)$ in Chap. 20], *i.e.*,

$$h(s) = \frac{\mathcal{L}[e_0(t)]}{\mathcal{L}[e_1(t)]} \tag{162}$$

For an illustration of use of Eq. (162), see Sec. 28, Chap. 20.

In some solutions arising from transient analysis in certain communication networks, it may be easier to achieve a solution of (160) or (161) by using the Faltung integral theorem: if we write

$$\begin{aligned} \mathcal{L}^{-1}[Y_T(s)] &= y(t) \\ \mathcal{L}^{-1}[h(s)] &= h(t) \end{aligned} \tag{163}$$

and if the inverse Laplace transforms $y(t)$ and $h(t)$ are known, then, according to the Faltung integral theorem

$$i_0(t) = \int_0^t e_1(\lambda)y(t - \lambda)\, d\lambda \tag{164}$$

$$e_0(t) = \int_0^t e_1(\lambda)h(t - \lambda)\, d\lambda \tag{165}$$

LINEAR-NETWORK ANALYSIS USING THE SUPERPOSITION-INTEGRAL THEOREM

19. Indicial Admittance. The two types of a-c admittance which we have encountered earlier in this chapter were seen to relate a current and a voltage in a network at some frequency. It is convenient at this point to introduce a new basic concept for linear electrical networks, *viz.*, indicial admittance.

Indicial admittance $A(t)$ is defined as the response of a linear network to a unit step-function voltage. If the current is in the same loop as the impressed unit step-function voltage, then this current is called the *self indicial admittance* $A_s(t)$. In a general network, the current flowing in mesh b due to an impressed unit step-function voltage is called the *transfer indicial admittance* $A_T(t)$.

20. The Superposition-integral Theorem. If the voltage $e_1(t)$ which is impressed upon the network is a time-varying function rather than a step function, then we may consider $e_1(t)$ to be made up of a number of step functions as shown in Fig. 11.

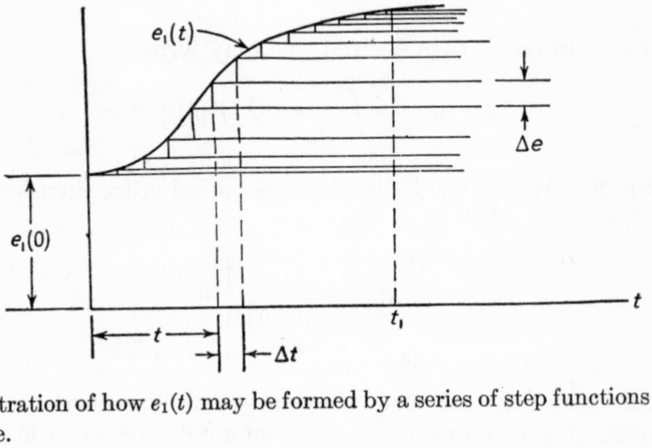

FIG. 11. Illustration of how $e_1(t)$ may be formed by a series of step functions of appropriate amplitude.

The current $i_L(t)$ in the output loop due to the impressed unit step function is equal in magnitude to $A_T(t)$. Consider the time interval $0 < t < t_1$ in Fig. 11, where $t_1 > 0$. At some arbitrary time t where $0 < t < t_1$ the indicial transfer admittance is $A_T(t_1 - t)$. The current contribution in the differential time Δt is

$$i_{\Delta t} = A_T(t_1 - t)\, \Delta e \tag{166}$$

where Δe is the magnitude of the step function occurring at the start of Δt. Note that since by definition

$$\frac{de_1(t)}{dt} = e_1'(t) \tag{167}$$

if

$$\Delta e_1(t) = e_1'(t)\ \Delta t \tag{168}$$

then

$$i_{\Delta t} = A_T(t_1 - t)e_1'(t)\ \Delta t \tag{169}$$

For the time interval $0 < t < t_1$, we must add the contributions from all the step functions in this interval as follows:

$$\sum_0^{t_1} i_{\Delta t} = \sum_0^{t_1} A_T(t_1 - t)e_1'(t)\ \Delta t \tag{170}$$

If the steps are made smaller and smaller, we may write, letting $t_1 \to t$ and $t \to \lambda$, and denoting the initial current as $e_1(0)A_T(t)$, the superposition integral theorem

$$i_L(t) = e_1(0)A_T(t) + \int_0^t A_T(t - \lambda)e_1'(\lambda)\ d\lambda \tag{171}$$

This integral is found to occur very often in analysis and is often called the Duhamel integral.

21. Application of the Superposition-integral Theorem. Consider the solution for the current in the series RL circuit which is pictured in Fig. 5*b* when the voltage

$$\begin{aligned} e(t) &= 0 \qquad & -\infty < t < 0 \\ &= E \sin \omega t \qquad & 0 < t < \infty \end{aligned} \tag{172}$$

is applied to its terminals. In Sec. 13, we found that the current flowing in the circuit due to the step-function voltage of amplitude E is

$$i(t) = \frac{E}{R}(1 - e^{-(R/L)t}) \tag{173}$$

By definition, the indicial admittance of the circuit is then, for $A(0) = 0$,

$$A_s(t) = \frac{1}{R}(1 - e^{-(R/L)t}) \tag{174}$$

From the superposition integral theorem, it follows that

$$i(t) = \frac{E}{R}\int_0^t (1 - e^{-(R/L)(t-\lambda)})\omega \cos \omega\lambda\ d\lambda \tag{175}$$

which is easily solved to yield the final result,

$$i(t) = \frac{E}{R^2 + \omega^2 L^2}(R \sin \omega t - \omega L \cos \omega t + \omega L e^{-(R/L)t}) \tag{176}$$

22. Laplace-transform Analysis Using the Superposition-integral Theorem. As an often convenient and useful approach for determining the response of a linear network, we may combine the use of the Laplace transform and the superposition integral to produce a method of response analysis which can be very useful, particularly when applied to networks in cascade. Such an analysis is in two steps, which are listed as follows:

1. The Laplace transform is used to find the indicial transfer admittance $A_T(t)$ of the linear network. $A_T(t)$ is, by definition, the current which flows in the output loop due to an impressed unit step-function voltage at the input terminals of the network and may be described in terms of $Y_T(s)$ and the Laplace transform of a unit step function (which is $1/s$), as follows:

$$A_T(t) = \frac{1}{2\pi j}\int_{\alpha - j\infty}^{\alpha + j\infty} \frac{1}{s} Y_T(s) e^{st}\, ds \tag{177}$$

$$= \frac{1}{2\pi j}\int_{\alpha - j\infty}^{\alpha + j\infty} \frac{e^{st}}{sZ_T(s)}\, ds \tag{178}$$

2. Once $A_T(t)$ is determined, the response of the linear network may be deduced using the superposition integral; it follows that

$$i_0(t) = e(0)A_T(t) + \int_0^t A(t-\lambda)\frac{d}{d\lambda}e(\lambda)\, d\lambda \tag{179}$$

where $e(0)$ is the impressed voltage at the time $t = 0$ and $e(\lambda)$ is the impressed-voltage wave as a function of λ, the integration being performed for $0 < \lambda < t$.

If the output voltage $e_{0S}(t)$ due to a unit step-function voltage at the input is known, then we may determine the output voltage due to any impressed wave $e(t)$ by using the following integral relationship:

$$e_0(t) = e(0)e_{0S}(t) + \int_0^t e_{0S}(t-\lambda)\frac{d}{d\lambda}e(\lambda)\, d\lambda \tag{180}$$

where the subscript S denotes the unit step function.

23. Indicial Admittance and A-C Admittance.[1] Using the same approach as in Sec. 11, it can be shown that indicial admittance and a-c admittance are related by the pair of equations

$$\text{I.} \qquad A(t) = G(0) + \frac{2}{\pi}\int_0^\infty \frac{B(\omega)}{\omega}\cos \omega t\, d\omega \qquad t > 0$$

$$\text{II.} \qquad A(t) = \frac{2}{\pi}\int_0^\infty \frac{G(\omega)}{\omega}\sin \omega t\, d\omega \qquad t > 0 \tag{181}$$

where $G(\omega)$ and $B(\omega)$ represent the conductance and susceptance, re-

[1] See V. Bush, "Operational Circuit Analysis," Chap. X, John Wiley & Sons, Inc., New York, 1937.

spectively. These integrals are more or less of academic interest since they are very difficult to solve for even the simplest networks. However, they yield a fact which is of considerable interest to a communication engineer, *viz.*: once either the amplitude or the phase characteristics of a network[1] are specified, the other is automatically exactly defined for the network.

Failure to adhere rigidly to this specification in the design and analysis of electrical networks will yield anomalous results such as that described in Sec. 18, Chap. 20.

PROBLEMS

1. Find the self-impedance and transfer impedance of the circuit shown in Fig. 10.

2. Calculate the amplitude of the current due to the significant harmonics of a square wave of unit amplitude which is impressed on the circuit shown in Fig. 1 of this chapter for the case when

a. $R = 40$ ohms, $C = 5\ \mu$f, $L = 10$ henrys, fundamental frequency = 120 cycles

b. $R = 100$ ohms, $C = \mu\mu$f, $L = 5 \times 10^{-6}$ henry, fundamental frequency = 10^6 cycles

3. Repeat Prob. 2 for the pulse wave where the ratio of pulse width τ to period time T is

a. $\dfrac{\tau}{T} = 0.1$

b. $\dfrac{\tau}{T} = 0.01$

4. Plot the pulse shape of $E_0(t)$ in Fig. 8*b* for the case when

a. $R = 5{,}000$ ohms, $C = 50\ \mu\mu$f, $t_1 = 5\ \mu$sec

b. $R = 10{,}000$ ohms, $C = 50\ \mu\mu$f, $t_1 = 5\ \mu$sec

c. $R = 5{,}000$ ohms, $C = 150\ \mu\mu$f, $t_1 = 5\ \mu$sec

5. Derive an expression for the current which flows through the capacitor in Fig. 8*b* during the pulse.

6. Discuss the validity of the assumption that $i_{10} - i_{20} = 0$ in Sec. 17. Prove, using a solution for $i_2(t)$.

7. Evolve general criteria relating rise time and decay time to repetition rate of the pulses. Discuss these criteria with respect to maximizing the repetition rate.

8. Prove, using Laplace-transform analysis, the equivalence of the circuit in Prob. 8*a* and *b* to the circuit in Fig. 8. Show that the battery potential in (*a*) is $E_bR/(r_p + R)$; in (*b*), E_b.

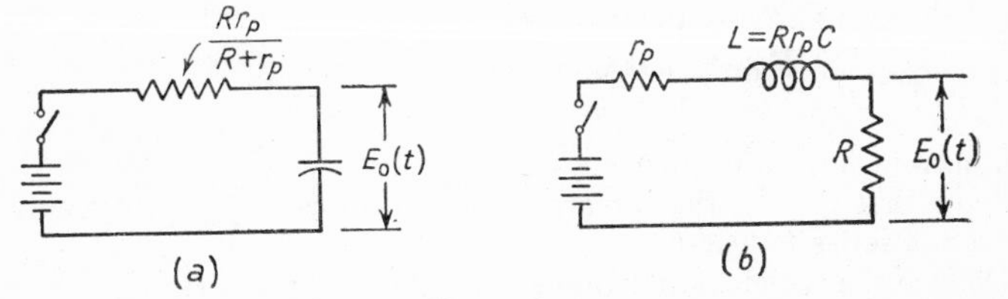

PROB. 8.

[1] This is, of course, true only for minimum-phase-shift networks. See H. W. Bode, "Network Analysis and Feedback Amplifier Design," D. Van Nostrand Company, Inc., New York, 1945.

9. The most important type of load used with a hard-tube pulser in radar and pulse equipment is the multicavity magnetron. The magnetron is a nonlinear device in that it has a current-voltage characteristic somewhat like that pictured

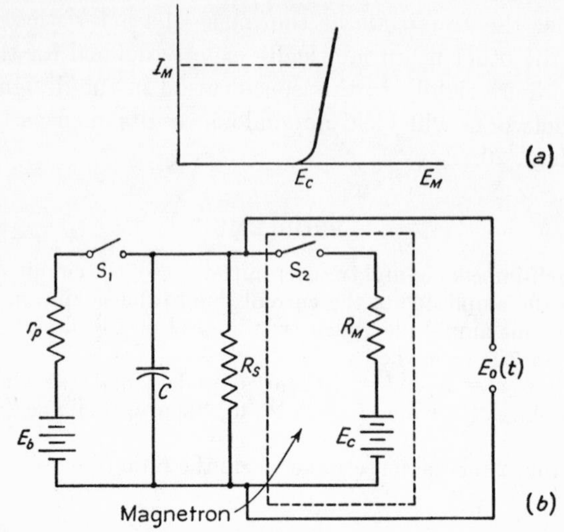

PROB. 9.

in Prob. 9*a* with cutoff ideally occurring at E_c. Since the magnetron is also a hard tube in which current can flow only one way, it acts as a biased diode, which may be represented in the equivalent circuit by a switch in series with a dynamic resistance R_M and a battery potential E_c. The basic equivalent circuit of a hard-tube pulser with a magnetron load is illustrated in Prob. 9*b*.

a. Discuss the boundary conditions associated with the following sequence of four incidents, which are associated with the operation of this circuit for pulse operation:

(1) S_1, closed
(2) Magnetron voltage rises above cutoff (S_2 closed)
(3) S_1, opened
(4) Magnetron voltage drops below cutoff (S_2 open)

b. Derive the equation for the output pulse shape, using the Laplace transform.

c. Plot the pulse shape for the case where

$$r_p = 200 \text{ ohms} \qquad E_b = 5{,}000 \text{ volts}$$
$$R_s = 10{,}000 \text{ ohms} \qquad E_c = 4{,}000 \text{ volts}$$
$$R_M = 5{,}000 \text{ ohms}$$
$$C = 100\ \mu\mu\text{f}$$

Time of current flow in magnetron, 5 μsec

10. Show that the Fourier-integral formulation used in Sec. 5 would fail if the circuit were a series *RC* circuit.

11. Deduce the indicial admittance of a series *RC* network.

CHAPTER 7

HARMONIC DISTORTION—AMPLIFIER OPERATION

1. Introduction. A linear network is one which conforms to Ohm's law. In the circuits used in electrical communications, there are numerous system components such as electron tubes and semiconductor devices which may be either linear or nonlinear depending on the nature of their operating characteristics and regions; these components are the heart of radio, radar, and television, performing such important functions as rectification, amplification, conversion, and detection. The discussion to follow will discuss both the basic principles of operation and fundamental concepts associated with these components and the harmonics and electrical waves which are inherent in their systems.

HARMONIC DISTORTION IN NONLINEAR CIRCUITS

2. Harmonic Distortion and Nonlinear Circuits. When a simple harmonic wave is applied to the input of a nonlinear circuit, harmonics are produced and the output will be nonsinusoidal. When two or more simple harmonic waves are applied to the input, we get sum and difference terms in addition to the harmonics whose frequencies are multiples of the frequencies of the applied waves. The extent and nature of the new waves will depend upon the voltage-current characteristic of the nonlinear network. The appearance of these waves at the output in addition to the original waves constitutes harmonic distortion.

3. The Dynamic Characteristic of an Electron-tube System. Analyses of multielement electron-tube operation and harmonic distortion in electron-tube systems are in general based on considerations of the dynamic characteristic of the system.[1] Consider the triode which is connected as shown in Fig. 1. Its plate-voltage plate-current characteristics as a func-

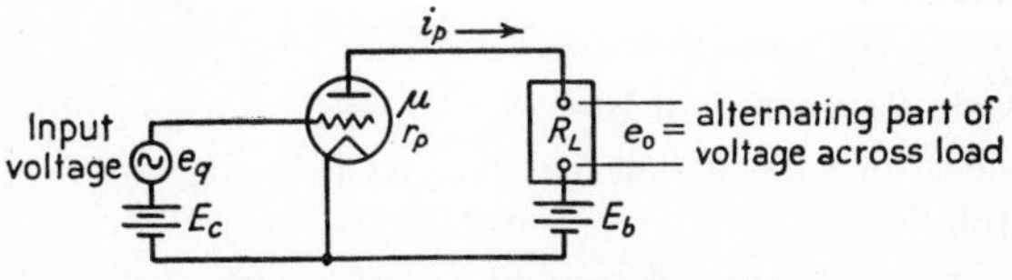

FIG. 1. Basic amplifier circuit.

[1] For an excellent, detailed account of the subject, see W. G. Dow, "Fundamentals of Engineering Electronics," Chap. VII, John Wiley & Sons, Inc., New York, 1937.

tion of grid voltage are diagramed in Fig. 2*b*. Since the plate voltage will be determined by both the battery voltage E_b and the voltage drop across the load resistance due to the plate-current flow, the instantaneous plate voltage e_p will be determined by the expression

$$e_p = E_b - i_p R_L \tag{1}$$

and thus we may include in Fig. 2*b* the graphical representation of (1) which is called the *load line*. Its slope is the reciprocal of the load resistance.

Figure 2*a* shows the grid-voltage versus plate-current variation. It is

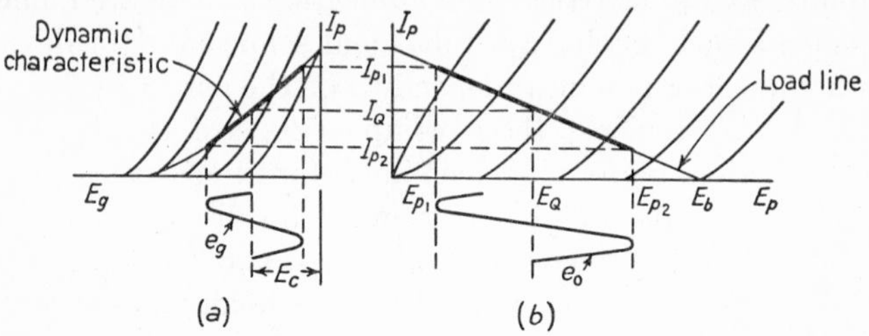

FIG. 2. Dynamic characteristic and load line as derived from the characteristics of an electron-tube amplifier.

derived from the plate characteristics in Fig. 2*b* and is pictured using curves of constant plate voltage. These curves are the mutual characteristic curves, and when we transfer the load line in Fig. 2*b* to the set of mutual characteristic curves, we obtain the curve which is called the dynamic characteristic. The dynamic characteristic is the most important curve to the communications engineer since its properties and shape are a function of both the tube and the external circuit and with it we are able to determine the waveform of the plate current corresponding to the variation of grid potential. If a signal-voltage generator whose output is e_g is placed in series with a bias-voltage battery whose constant voltage is E_c, then as is shown in Fig. 2, the plate current and the plate voltage will vary between the values I_{p_1} and I_{p_2} and E_{p_1} and E_{p_2}, respectively. Note that a value of plate current and plate voltage, namely, I_Q and E_Q, correspond to the point of zero excitation which is determined by E_c. Note also that, in addition, the dynamic-characteristic curve yields the plate-current cutoff point.

4. Some Basic Properties of Electron Tubes. Three fundamental properties of an electron tube which are derived from its characteristic curves are listed as follows:

1. Plate resistance R_p may be evaluated at any point on the plate characteristics by measuring the slope at that point (grid-potential constant): *i.e.*,

$$R_p = \frac{\partial E_p}{\partial I_p} = r_p \tag{2}$$

2. Mutual conductance g_m measures the incremental change in plate current corresponding to an incremental change in grid voltage (plate-voltage constant): *i.e.*,

$$g_m = \frac{\partial I_p}{\partial E_g} \tag{3}$$

3. Amplification factor μ relates the incremental change in plate voltage corresponding to an incremental change in grid voltage (plate-current constant): *i.e.*,

$$\mu = -\frac{\partial E_p}{\partial E_g} \tag{4}$$

5. Second Harmonic Distortion in a Triode Circuit. Before proceeding with a discussion of the mathematical aspects of nonlinear-network formulation, let us illustrate certain useful basic concepts which will aid our over-all understanding of the properties of nonlinear networks by a graphical demonstration of how a second harmonic wave is produced in a triode circuit.

Figure 3 illustrates the dynamic-characteristic curve of a triode. This

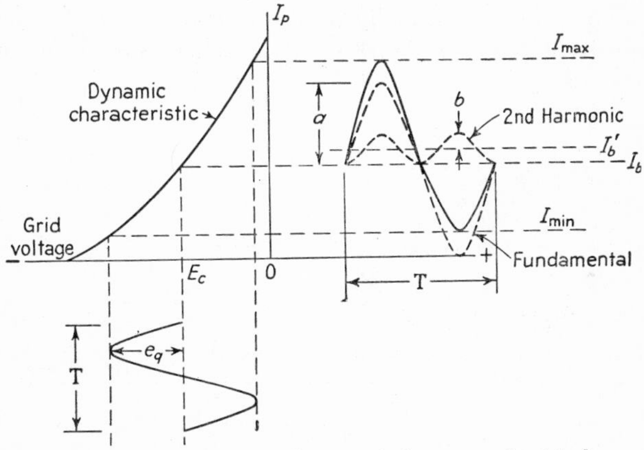

FIG. 3. Nonlinear dynamic-characteristic curve of a triode.

curve is seen to be nonlinear. Since this dynamic-characteristic curve relates the grid voltage and the plate current, we may graphically determine the plate-current variation due, for example, to a real simple harmonic wave $E_g \sin \omega_1 t$ which is impressed on the grid in series with a grid-bias voltage E_c as shown. The plate current is seen to vary between $I_{\max}$ and $I_{\min}$. It is seen in Fig. 3 that the curved dynamic characteristic heightens the top loop and flattens the bottom loop. Let I_b be the value of plate current corresponding to E_c, and let a and b represent the peak amplitudes of the fundamental and second harmonic, respectively. From Fig. 3, it is easily verified that

$$\begin{aligned} I_{\max} &= I_b + a + 2b \\ I_{\min} &= I_b - a + 2b \end{aligned} \tag{5}$$

Solving for a and b in terms of $I_{\max}$, $I_{\min}$, and I_b, we get

$$\begin{aligned} a &= \tfrac{1}{2}(I_{\max} - I_{\min}) \\ b &= \frac{\tfrac{1}{2}(I_{\max} + I_{\min}) - I_b}{2} \end{aligned} \tag{6}$$

b may also be shown to be the difference between the average value of the plate current I_b' and I_b. Thus the percentage of second harmonic distortion in terms of the fundamental is

$$\text{Per cent second} = 100\,\frac{a}{b} = 100\,\frac{\tfrac{1}{2}(I_{\max} + I_{\min}) - I_b}{I_{\max} - I_{\min}} \tag{7}$$

6. The Taylor-series Representation of a Nonlinear Characteristic Curve. We may obtain a useful analytic expression for a nonlinear voltage-current characteristic curve by representing it by a Taylor series. Before writing the Taylor series, let us discuss the physical significance of what is known mathematically as the *Law of the Mean*. Consider the nonlinear grid-voltage plate-current dynamic-characteristic curve of a

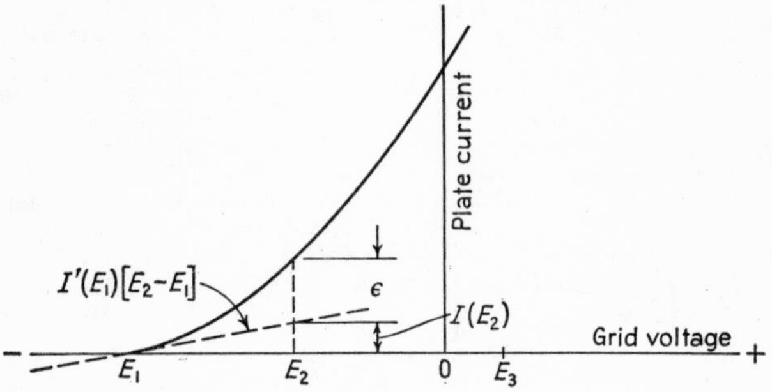

FIG. 4.

triode which is pictured in Fig. 4. In terms of this diagram and the voltages E_1 and E_2, we may write the law of the mean to describe approximately the current at E_2 in terms of the voltage at E_1 as

$$I[E_2] = I[E_1] + I'[E_1](E_2 - E_1) \tag{8}$$

where

$$I'[E_1] = \left[\frac{dI}{dE}\right]_{E=E_1}$$

Thus we see that if we wish to determine the value of the current at E_2, we must add the current at E_1 (which is zero in this case) to the product of the difference between E_1 and E_2 and the slope of the voltage-current curve at E_1, which will thus yield the current at E_2. It is evident that although (8) properly represents a linear function passing through E_1, it does not yield the correct current corresponding to E_2 since it is seen in Fig. 4 that the correct value of current and the current predicted by the law of the mean differ by the quantity ϵ. It is clear, however, that as $E_2 - E_1$ is made smaller, ϵ will decrease in value and the quality of the approximation will improve. If we try to use (8) to represent E_3 in terms of E_1, however, the error will become one of considerable magnitude.

If, in evaluating the true value of I corresponding to E_2, we were to add correction terms to the right-hand side of (8) whose combined values would approach ϵ, we should find ourselves using an extended form of the law of the mean which would actually add or subtract increments such that, after a succession of correction quantities, we should arrive at the true value of I corresponding to any voltage greater than E_1. The final expression would be found to be the Taylor series

$$I = I[E_1] + \left[\frac{dI}{dE}\right]_{E=E_1}(E - E_1) + \frac{1}{2!}\left[\frac{d^2I}{dE^2}\right]_{E=E_1}(E - E_1)^2 + \cdots + \frac{1}{n!}\left[\frac{d^nI}{dE^n}\right]_{E=E_1}(E - E_1)^n + \cdots \tag{9}$$

We may list the first three correction terms in (9) as follows:

First correction term:

$$\left[\frac{dI}{dE}\right]_{E=E_1}(E - E_1) \qquad \text{straight line}$$

Second correction term:

$$\frac{1}{2!}\left[\frac{d^2I}{dE^2}\right]_{E=E_1}(E - E_1)^2 \qquad \text{square-law curve}$$

Third correction term:

$$\frac{1}{3!}\left[\frac{d^3I}{dE^3}\right]_{E=E_1}(E - E_1)^3 \qquad \text{cubic parabola}$$

Thus we see that we are representing the nonlinear voltage-current characteristic curve as the sum of a set of elementary curves, each successive curve producing a tendency to bend. The amplitude characteristics of the nth curve are seen to be governed by the coefficient $1/n!\ [d^nI/dE^n]_{E=E_1}$. Note that dI/dE has the dimensions of a conductance such that $dI/dE = g_m$, for example, if I represents plate current and E represents grid voltage. The use of the Taylor series for representing nonlinear characteristics[1] (see

[1] J. R. Carson, A Theoretical Study of the Three Element Vacuum Tube, *Proc. IRE*, vol. 7, p. 187, April, 1919.

Sec. 12) is limited only to those curves or portions of curves which have continuous derivatives of all orders.

For most applications in communication-circuit analysis, the use of the first two or three terms in the Taylor-series representation of a nonlinear voltage-current characteristic curve is sufficient—more terms being needed only when the characteristic curve is greatly distorted or, in some cases, when the input voltage is particularly large in amplitude.

The actual contributions of the first two terms in the Taylor series to the output of a nonlinear device may be listed as follows:

1. The linear term, of course, yields the undistorted input wave.
2. The quadratic or square-law term yields (*a*) the second harmonic of each input wave plus (*b*) a d-c wave based on the amplitude of each input wave and (*c*) waves whose frequencies are the sum and difference frequencies of each possible group of pairs of input waves. This is demonstrated as follows:

Let the output current of an electron tube be described as

$$I = g'e_g^2 \tag{10}$$

where e_g is the applied signal voltage to the grid, and g' is the derivative, with respect to plate voltage, of the conductance of the tube. If

$$e_g = E_1 \sin \omega_1 t + E_2 \sin \omega_2 t \tag{11}$$

then, substituting (11) into (10), we get

$$I = \frac{g'}{2}(E_1^2 + E_2^2) - \frac{g'}{2}(E_1^2 \cos 2\omega_1 t + E_2^2 \cos 2\omega_2 t) + g'E_1E_2[\cos(\omega_1 - \omega_2) - \cos(\omega_1 + \omega_2)] \tag{12}$$

Taylor-series Representation of Triode Plate Current. Simple Taylor-series representations involving linear, square-law, and cubic curves find considerable usefulness in, for example, solutions of class C amplifier operation (see Sec. 12), receiver operation (see Chap. 22), and free and forced oscillations in linear dynamical systems.[1] However, if the Taylor series is developed to include two independent variables, it may be applied to triode vacuum-tube operation in which $I_p = f(E_p, E_g)$ where I_p, E_p, and E_g are the instantaneous plate current, plate voltage, and grid voltage respectively; J. R. Carson has shown the solution to be

$$i_p = \frac{\mu}{r_p + R_L} e_g - \frac{\mu^2 r_p r_p'}{2(r_p + R_L)^3} e_g^2 + \cdots \tag{13}$$

where R_L is the resistive load, e_g and i_p are the a-c components of the grid voltage and plate current, respectively, and $r' = \partial r_p/\partial E_p$.

[1] See, for example, B. van der Pol, The Nonlinear Theory of Electric Oscillations, *Proc. IRE*, vol. 22, pp. 1051–1086, September, 1934.

7. Fourier-series Representation of a Voltage-Current Curve.[1] In this section, we shall discuss the representation of a nonlinear characteristic curve by a limited Fourier series. This method is not as transparent as the Taylor-series method when used for the determination of harmonic distortion since the first varying term in the Fourier-series representation of the voltage-current characteristic curve is sinusoidal in form. However, as a general approach for determining the complete solutions of nonlinear problems which involve complicated characteristic curves and large impressed voltages, the Fourier-series method may be easier to use despite the apparent mathematical complexity of the solution.

Consider the Fourier-series representation of the triode voltage-current characteristic curve which is pictured in Fig. 5*a*. Note that if a Fourier

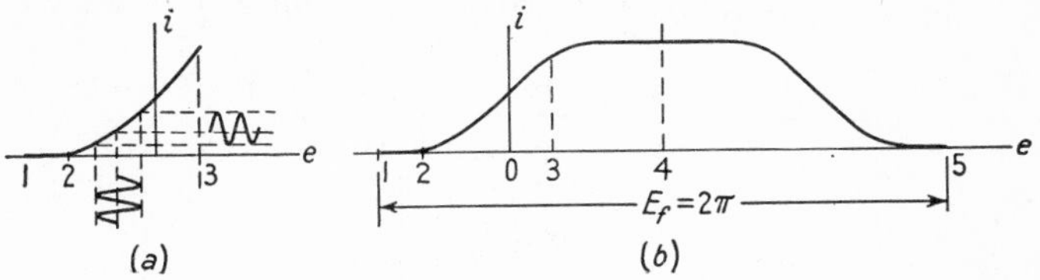

FIG. 5.

representation of the curve in Fig. 5*a* is to be used, a large number of significant Fourier components will be necessary to describe the sharp bend at 2 and the abrupt drop at 3. In order to reduce the number of significant terms which will appear in the Fourier series, it is practical, without any loss of validity since the voltage swing takes place in the same region, to construct a dynamic-characteristic curve such as that illustrated in Fig. 5*b*. This artificial characteristic is even about the point 4, and the position from 1 to 4 has odd symmetry about $e = 0$. The interval 1, 5 is designated as the period 2π of the Fourier-series representation fundamental and is expressed in terms of voltage as E_f.

If i represents the current and e_g the voltage, then owing to the fact that the characteristic curve in Fig. 5*b* is even, it follows that[2]

$$i = \frac{a_0}{2} + \sum_{n=1}^{N} a_n \cos\left(\frac{2\pi n}{E_f} e_g + \Theta_n\right) \tag{14}$$

where N is the number of significant terms which represent the curve. $a_0/2$, a_n, and Θ_n are the Fourier coefficients and phase angles which may be obtained from a graphical analysis of the tube dynamic-characteristic

[1] W. L. Barrow, Contribution to the Theory of Nonlinear Circuits with Large Applied Voltages, *Proc. IRE*, vol. 22, pp. 964–980, August, 1934.

[2] For an illustration of the use of (14) as applied to a 101-D tube, see example due to R. S. Morse in W. L. Barrow, *loc. cit.*

curve once the choice of the tube and its operating voltage and load resistance is made.

Let a grid voltage,

$$e_g = E_c + E_1 \sin \omega_1 t \tag{15}$$

where E_c is the grid bias, be applied to a triode which has a resistance load and whose plate current is expressible by (14). If the distance, 0, 4 in Fig. 5b is chosen as E_a for the tube, then the voltage e_g may be written as follows:

$$e_g = E_0 + E_1 \sin \omega_1 t \tag{16}$$

where $E_0 = E_a + E_c$. It then follows that

$$i = \frac{a_0}{2} + \sum_{n=1}^{N} a_n \cos (u_n + v_n \sin \omega_1 t) \tag{17}$$

where

$$\begin{aligned} u_n &= \frac{2\pi n}{E_f} E_0 + \Theta_n \\ v_n &= \frac{2\pi n}{E_f} E_1 \end{aligned} \tag{18}$$

Equation (17) may be expanded into the form,

$$i = \frac{a_0}{2} + \sum_{n=1}^{N} a_n[\cos u_n \cos (v_n \sin \omega_1 t) - \sin u_n \sin (v_n \sin \omega_1 t)] \tag{19}$$

Using Eqs. (26) and (27) from the Appendix, it follows that the mth harmonic of the plate current is described by the expression

$$|i_m| = \left| 2 \sum_{n=1}^{N} a_n J_m(v_n) \cos \left(u_n + \frac{m\pi}{2}\right)\right| \tag{20}$$

8. Fourier Analysis of Beam-deflection Tube Operation. As an illustration of the application of the Fourier-series method to problems involving voltage-current characteristic curves of unusual shape, let us consider the solution, due to E. W. Herold,[1] for the plate-current representation of the beam-deflection tube[2] which is pictured in Fig. 6a. As the potential between the deflecting electrodes is varied, the beam of finite cross section swings across the beam space from one side of the final aperture to the anode and then to the other side of the final aperture to yield the voltage-current characteristic curve which is pictured in Fig 6b.

[1] E. W. Herold, Superheterodyne Conversion Using Phase Reversal Modulation, *Proc. IRE*, vol. 34, No. 4, pp. 184–197, April, 1946.

[2] For a description of modern beam-deflection tubes of this type, see Herold and Mueller, Beam Deflection Mixer Tubes for U.H.F., *Electronics*, vol. 22, pp. 76–80, May, 1949.

Using the Fourier-series method of representing the nonlinear voltage-current characteristic, let us consider the representation of the multi-

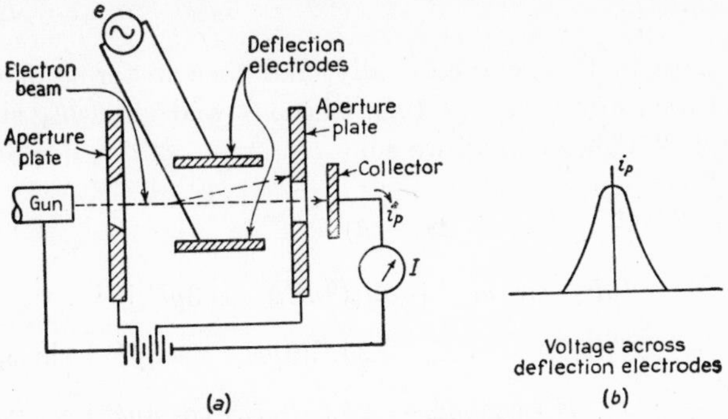

FIG. 6. Beam-deflection tube.

humped characteristic curve which is pictured in Fig. 7, in which the actual excursion of the deflection-electrode potential difference is maintained in the region a, b. Since the characteristic curve is very nearly cosinusoidal in form, we may express the current by the limited Fourier series

$$i_p = I_b - a_1 \cos y(e - E_c) + a_3 \cos 3y(e - E_c) \tag{21}$$

where $y = 2\pi/E_f$, E_f is the base-line voltage, I_b is the average current, E_c is the d-c bias on the deflection electrodes, and a_1 and a_3 are coefficients which depend on the shape of the characteristic curve. In Fig. 7, $E_f = a, c$.

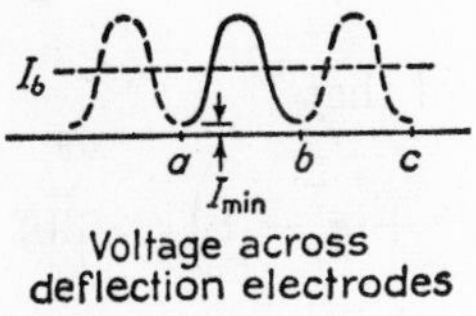

FIG. 7.

Let us use the notation

$$\frac{a_3}{a_1} = \vartheta \qquad \frac{I_{p\min}}{I_{p\max}} = \sigma \tag{22}$$

where it can be shown that $-0.037 < \vartheta < 0.11$ for proper representation. For any practical case, σ is a very small number. From Eq. (21), it follows that we may express $I_{p\max}$ and $I_{p\min}$ as

$$I_{p\max} = I_b + (1 - \vartheta)a_1 \tag{23}$$

$$I_{p\min} = I_b - (1 + \vartheta)a_1 \tag{24}$$

It then follows that

$$i_p = \frac{I_{p\max}}{2} (1 + \vartheta - \sigma)[(1 + 2\sigma - \vartheta) - \cos y(e - E_c) + \vartheta \cos 3y(e - E_c)] \tag{25}$$

Let a voltage $e = E_1 \sin \omega_1 t$ be applied to the deflecting electrodes of the tube. Then

$$i_p = \frac{I_{p_{max}}}{2}(1 + \vartheta - \sigma)[(1 + 2\sigma - \vartheta) - \cos y(E_1 \sin \omega_1 t - E_c) + \vartheta \cos 3y(E_1 \sin \omega_1 t - E_c)] \tag{26}$$

Expanding (26), first trigonometrically, and then in terms of the Bessel-function representations of cos $(yE_1 \sin \omega_1 t)$ and sin $(yE_1 \sin \omega_1 t)$ [see Eqs. (26) and (27), Appendix], we get

$$\begin{aligned} i_p = \frac{I_{p_{max}}}{2}(1 + \vartheta - \sigma)\{[(1 + 2\sigma - \vartheta) \\ - J_0(yE_1) \cos yE_c + \vartheta J_0(3yE_1) \cos 3yE_c] \\ - [2J_1(yE_1) \sin yE_c - 2\vartheta J_1(3yE_1) \cos 3yE_c] \sin \omega_1 t \\ - [2J_2(yE_1) \cos yE_c - 2\vartheta J_2(3yE_1) \cos 3yE_c] \cos 2\omega_1 t \\ - \cdots\} \end{aligned} \tag{27}$$

ϑ may be found by investigating the expression for the transconductance of the tube as follows: Using (25), we see that

$$g_m = \frac{di_p}{de} = y\frac{I_{p_{max}}}{2}(1 + \vartheta - \sigma)[\sin y(e - E_c) - 3\vartheta \sin 3y(e - E_c)] \tag{28}$$

whose maximum value will occur when $y(e - E_c) = \pi/2$. Therefore

$$g_{m_{max}} = y\frac{I_{p_{max}}}{2}(1 + \vartheta - \sigma)(1 + 3\vartheta) \tag{29}$$

from which we find that

$$\vartheta \cong \frac{1}{4}\left(\frac{E_f}{\pi}\frac{g_{m_{max}}}{I_{p_{max}}} + \sigma - 1\right) \tag{30}$$

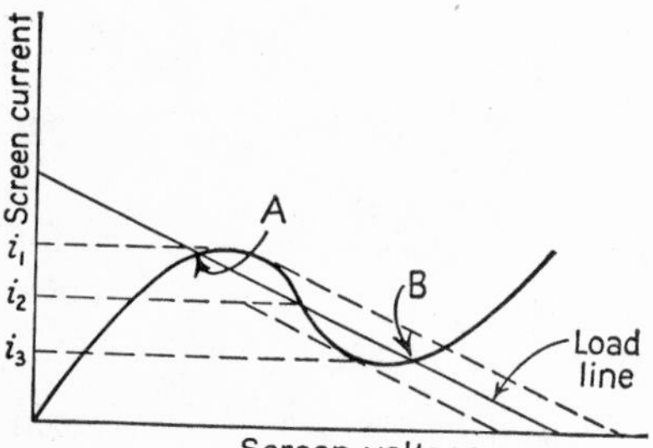

FIG. 8.

9. Bistable Systems. In certain multigrid tubes, nonlinear current-voltage characteristics occur which can be utilized in certain communication circuits for triggering (gating). Such a characteristic is the tetrode screen-current screen-voltage characteristic which is illustrated in Fig. 8 for the case where the suppressor grid is connected to the screen grid in such a way that a change in screen voltage is accompanied by a proportional change in suppressor voltage, the suppressor being maintained negative and the plate positive.

Consider the case where a load resistance is introduced into the screen-grid circuit, thus producing the load line pictured in Fig. 8. It is evident that, for the particular value of control-grid voltage shown, the circuit is at equilibrium at three values of screen current. However, i_2 is in a state of unstable equilibrium. An increase or decrease in current would not cause a change in voltage of the correct sign across the load resistance and is not observed experimentally. This leaves two stable points of equilibrium A and B.

It is evident from Fig. 8 that if the screen voltage is raised or lowered, the screen current can be made to jump from point A to point B and back by a voltage pulse of suitable polarity impressed in the grid circuit, thus making possible a trigger action. Trigger circuits, which are based on any tube system having two stable conditions of equilibrium at fixed values of applied voltages and circuit parameters, form the basis of the switching and pulse-forming circuits[1] which are used in modern television and radar systems.

FUNDAMENTALS OF CLASS A, B, AND C OPERATION

10. Classes of Amplifier Operation. In a vacuum-tube system such as that pictured in Fig. 1, we are, in general, interested in considerations of the ratio of the input voltage e_g to the output voltage e_0. If, as is generally the case, $e_0/e_g > 1$, the vacuum-tube system is an amplifier. Three important classes of amplifiers are called, respectively, class A, B, and C amplifiers. The definitions of these amplifier types as given by the standardization committee, Institute of Radio Engineers,[2] are presented as follows:

Class A Amplifier. An amplifier in which the grid bias and alternating grid voltages are such that plate current in a specific tube flows at all times.

Class AB Amplifier. An amplifier in which the grid bias and alternating grid voltages are such that plate current in a specific tube flows for appreciably more than half but less than the entire electrical cycle.

Class B Amplifier. An amplifier in which the grid bias is approximately equal to the cutoff value so that the plate current is approximately zero when no exciting grid voltage is applied, and so that plate current in a specific tube flows for approximately one-half of each cycle when an alternating grid voltage is applied.

Class C Amplifier. An amplifier in which the grid bias is appreciably greater than the cutoff value so that the plate current in each tube is zero when no alternating grid voltage is applied, and so that plate current in a specific tube flows for appreciably less than one-half of each cycle when an alternating grid voltage is applied. (Note—To denote that grid current does not flow during any part of the

[1] See H. J. Reich, New Vacuum Tube Counting Circuits, *Rev. Sci. Instruments*, vol. 9, pp. 222–223, July, 1938.

Eccles and Jordan, A Trigger Relay Utilizing Three Electrode Thermionic Vacuum Tubes, *Radio Rev.*, vol. 1, pp. 143–146, December, 1919.

[2] See *Proc. IRE*, vol. 38, No. 4, p. 430, April, 1950.

input cycle, the suffix 1 may be added to the letter or letters of the class identification. The suffix 2 may be used to denote that current flows during some part of the cycle.)

In each of these classes of amplifier operation, the dynamic characteristic and the biasing voltages play an important part. Since the over-all dynamic characteristic is nonlinear, the class of amplifier serves to relate the plate current to the exciting grid voltage. The adjustment from one class of operation to another is made by changing the grid bias. Assume

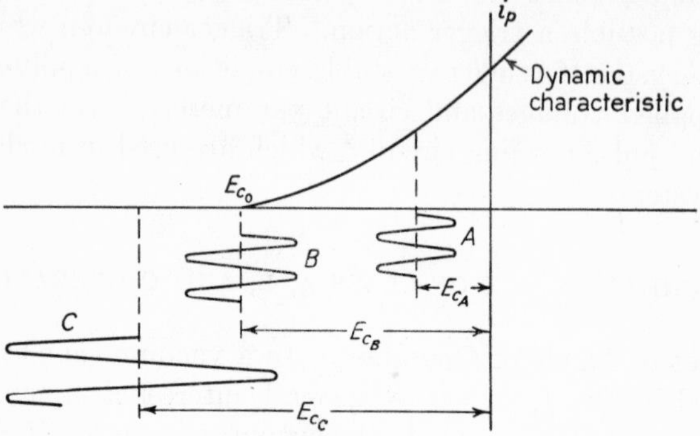

FIG. 9.

a resistive load in the circuit in Fig. 1. Then Fig. 9 shows the relative position of the exciting voltages with respect to the cutoff point of the dynamic-characteristic curve at E_{c_0}. It is evident that for class A operation, $|E_{cA}| < |E_{c_0}|$; for class B operation, $|E_{cB}| \cong |E_{c_0}|$, and for class C operation, $|E_{cC}| > |E_{c_0}|$.

11. Equivalent Circuit of a Triode Circuit Operating Class A. If the triode circuit in Fig. 1 is operating class A, we may evolve an equivalent circuit for the tube based on either a constant-current generator or a constant-voltage generator.

We may deduce from the expression for the plate-current density of the triode the following expression for plate current:

$$i_p \approx D\left(e_g + \frac{e_0}{\mu}\right) \tag{31}$$

In the range of current values within which the tube characteristics are straight lines, D is a constant which may be evaluated by differentiating (31) with respect to the excitation voltage e_g; that is,

$$D = \frac{\partial i_p}{\partial e_g} \tag{32}$$

D is seen to be equal to g_m, the mutual conductance, and may be written using (2) and (4) as follows:

$$D = \frac{\mu}{r_p} \tag{33}$$

Substituting (33) into (31) and recognizing the reversal in phase of the voltage appearing across Z_L with respect to e_g, we get

$$-\mu e_g = i_p r_p + e_0 \tag{34}$$

This is completely general and actually applies to any load. If e_0 is the voltage across the output load Z_L, we may rewrite (33) as follows:

$$-\mu e_g = i_p(r_p + Z_L) \tag{35}$$

A schematic diagram based on (35) is shown in Fig. 10*a*, where the triode is seen to be replaced by a constant-voltage generator of output $-\mu e_g$, which is in series with its internal impedance r_p. It is easily shown[1] that we may also represent the triode by a constant-current generator whose output is $g_m e_g$ and which is shunted by both r_p and Z_L as shown in Fig. 10*b*.

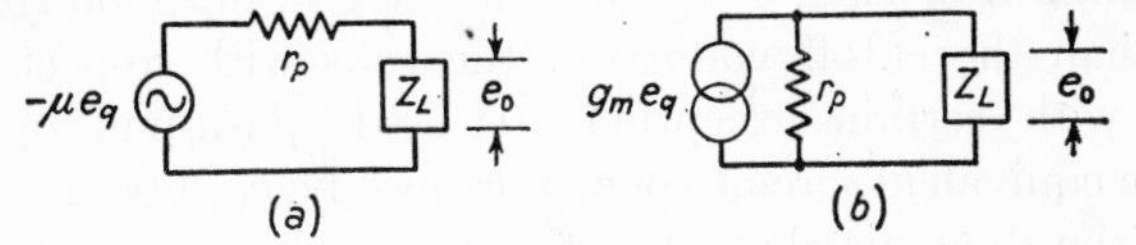

FIG. 10.

Both circuits are identical, the constant-voltage generator circuit being more readily suitable for use with loads consisting of series elements and the constant-current generator circuit being more readily usable for loads consisting of shunt elements. These equivalent circuits may be shown to also apply to multigrid tubes, the constant-current-generator equivalent circuit being particularly applicable to pentodes.

These equivalent circuits are of the utmost importance with regard to Fourier-analysis concepts since e_g is unspecified and, being a time function, may be expressed as a Fourier series or a Fourier transform. Consider for example, a periodic complex signal voltage e_g which is applied to the grid circuit and which may be expressed by the Fourier series

$$e_g = \sum_{n=-\infty}^{\infty} C_n e^{jn\omega_1 t} \tag{36}$$

If the output load may be written in the form

$$Z_L = Z_L(\omega) = Z_L(n\omega_1) \tag{37}$$

[1] See, for example, the discussion of Norton's theorem in W. L. Everitt, "Communication Engineering," 2d ed., Chap. II, McGraw-Hill Book Company, Inc., New York, 1937.

it follows that the substitution of (36) into (35) yields the following Fourier-series representation of the output voltage e_0:

$$e_0 = -\sum_{n=-\infty}^{\infty} \frac{\mu Z_L(n\omega_1)C_n}{r_p + Z_L(n\omega_1)} e^{jn\omega_1 t} \tag{38}$$

If e_g is nonperiodic and representable by the Fourier transform $g(\omega)$, then the output voltage e_0 may be described by the Fourier integral,

$$e_0 = \frac{1}{2\pi} \int_{\omega=-\infty}^{\infty} \frac{-\mu Z_L(\omega)}{r_p + Z_L(\omega)} g(\omega)e^{j\omega t}\, d\omega \tag{39}$$

Since r_p and μ are virtually constant during class A operation, it is evident from (38) and (39) that the determination of the output voltage is governed by the load impedance. The general problem in class A operation is therefore reduced to a problem which deals with the excitation of linear or nonlinear networks by complex or nonperiodic exciting waves.

12. Certain Aspects of Class B and C Operation. When a vacuum tube is operated class B or class C so that the d-c grid-bias voltage is equal to or greater than the cutoff voltage of the tube with respect to absolute magnitude, with certain exceptions (class B push-pull operation, for example) the equivalent-circuit concept cannot be used because of the nonlinearity of the dynamic-characteristic curve taken as a whole and it is necessary to resort to graphical or mathematical methods for solutions.

If the class B or class C amplifier is connected to a resistive load, then we may employ a Fourier method for determining the plate current by using the dynamic characteristic. Two cases will follow; the solutions derived in these cases will be used in determining the performance of class C amplifiers, which will be discussed in Sec. 15 of this chapter.

Case 1. Class C Amplifier with a Linear Dynamic-characteristic Curve. Consider a vacuum-tube system with a resistive load whose linear dynamic-characteristic curve (ideal case) is that illustrated in Fig. 11. If an

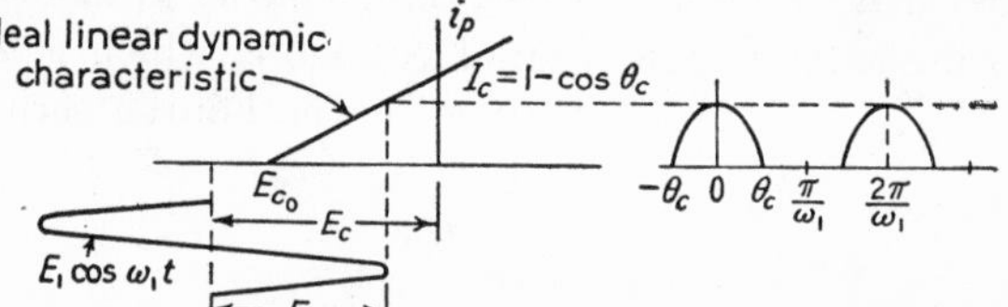

FIG. 11.

excitation a-c voltage $E_1 \cos \omega_1 t$ is applied to the grid in series with a bias voltage E_c, such that $|E_c| > |E_{c_0}|$, where E_{c_0} is the cutoff voltage, then the plate current will be a series of cosine-loop pulses. The duration of each current loop will be for less than half a cycle; we shall denote the operating angle as θ_c, where the entire current flow per cycle occurs in the total phase angle $-\theta_c < \omega_1 t < \theta_c$.

Assuming a loop peak amplitude of $1 - \cos\theta_c$, we may mathematically describe a loop in the period $-\pi < \omega_1 t < \pi$ as

$$\begin{aligned} i_p &= 0 && -\pi < \omega_1 t < \theta_c \\ &= \cos\omega_c t - \cos\theta_c && -\theta_c < \omega_1 t < \theta_c \qquad (40) \\ &= 0 && \theta_c < \omega_1 t < \pi \end{aligned}$$

It follows that (40) may be represented by the Fourier cosine series,

$$i_p = \frac{1}{\pi}(\sin\theta_c - \theta_c\cos\theta_c) + \frac{1}{\pi}\left(\theta_c - \frac{1}{2}\sin 2\theta_c\right)\cos\omega_1 t$$
$$+ \frac{1}{\pi}\sum_{n=2}^{\infty}\left[\frac{\sin(n+1)\theta_c}{n+1} + \frac{\sin(n-1)\theta_c}{n-1} - \frac{2}{n}\cos\theta_c\sin n\theta_c\right]\cos n\omega_1 t \quad (41)$$

Case 2. Class C Amplifier with a Square-law Dynamic-characteristic Curve. Consider a vacuum-tube system with a resistive load and with a square-law dynamic characteristic which is illustrated in Fig. 12. If the

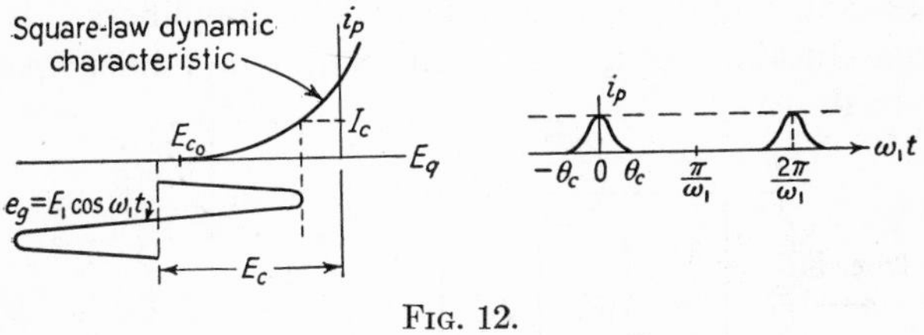

FIG. 12.

operating angle is θ_c ($\theta_c < \pi/2$), then the current pulses of amplitude $1 - \cos\theta_c$, which are illustrated in Fig. 12, may be described mathematically as

$$\begin{aligned} i_p &= 0 && -\pi < \omega_1 t < -\theta_c \\ &= (\cos\omega_1 t - \cos\theta_c)^2 && -\theta_c < \omega_1 t < \theta_c \qquad (42) \\ &= 0 && \theta_c < \omega_1 t < \pi \end{aligned}$$

This current pulse may be represented by the following Fourier cosine series:

$$i_p = \frac{1}{2\pi}\left(\theta_c - \frac{3}{2}\sin 2\theta_c + 2\theta_c \cos^2 \theta_c\right)$$
$$+ \frac{1}{\pi}\left(-2\theta_c \cos \theta_c + \frac{3}{2}\sin \theta_c + \frac{1}{6}\sin 3\theta_c\right)\cos \omega_1 t$$
$$+ \frac{1}{\pi}\left[\frac{1}{4}(1 + 6\cos^2 \theta_c)\sin 2\theta_c\right.$$
$$\left. - 2\left(\sin \theta_c + \frac{1}{3}\sin 3\theta_c\right)\cos \theta_c + \frac{\theta_c}{2}\right]\cos 2\omega_1 t$$
$$+ \cdots \qquad (43)$$

Class C Amplifiers, Oscillators, and Frequency Multipliers

13. Introduction. In class C amplifiers and frequency multipliers, the analysis of performance must include considerations of both the nonlinearity of the vacuum tube and the selectivity of the resonant networks which are included in the circuits. Since in such systems the grid is so biased that a simple harmonic voltage applied to the grid circuit produces a complex-wave plate current, in class C amplifiers we shall be interested in the fundamental, in frequency doublers—the second harmonic—and in frequency triplers—the third harmonic—etc. We shall discuss here an important method[1] of application of the Fourier analysis to the determination of the performance of these systems.

14. Current and Voltage Relations in Class C Amplifiers. If an amplifier is connected as shown in Fig. 13 for class C amplifier operation, the

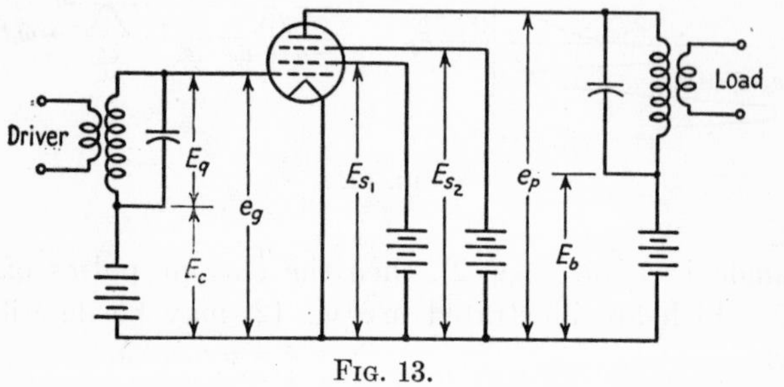

FIG. 13.

instantaneous plate voltage e_p, plate current i_p, grid voltage e_g, and grid current i_g vary as pictured in Fig. 14. By referring to Fig. 14, we see that e_p is the sum of the plate battery voltage E_b and the voltage swing $E_p \cos \omega t$ across the plate tank circuit and that e_g is the sum of the bias battery voltage E_c and the voltage swing $E_g \cos \omega t$ across the grid tank circuit; *i.e.*,

[1] W. G. Wagener, Simplified Methods of Computing Performance of Transmitting Tubes, *Proc. IRE*, vol. 25, No. 1, pp. 47–78, January, 1937.

$$e_p = E_b - E_p \cos \omega t \tag{44}$$

$$e_g = E_c + E_g \cos \omega t \tag{45}$$

The plate-current cutoff will occur at the phase angle $\pm\theta_c$ which occurs when

$$\mu e_g = -e_p \tag{46}$$

θ_c is the operating angle of the tube, and plate current will flow in the interval determined by $2\theta_c$. At $\omega t = \theta_c$, the magnitude of the grid voltage is equal to $-E_c$, and it follows that

$$\left(E_g - \frac{E_p}{\mu}\right) \cos \theta_c = -\left(E_c + \frac{E_b}{\mu}\right) \tag{47}$$

whereby

$$\cos \theta_c = -\frac{E_c + (E_b/\mu)}{E_g - (E_p/\mu)} \tag{48}$$

which defines the cosine of the operating angle in terms of the quantities listed in (44) and (45) and the amplification factor μ of the tube.

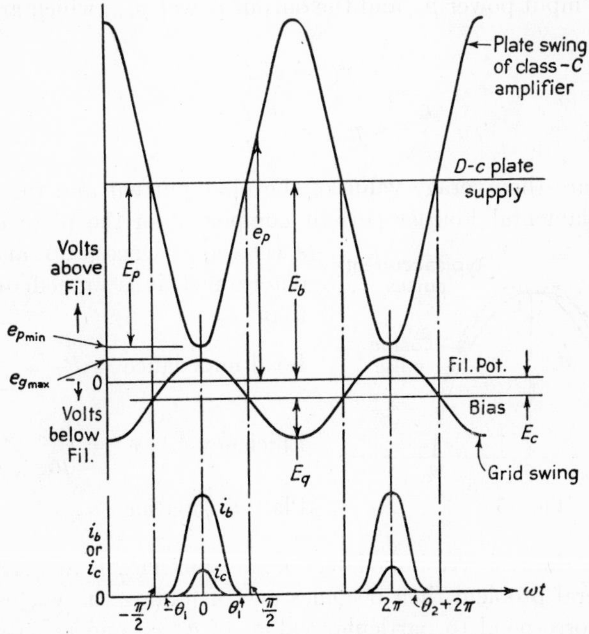

FIG. 14. Instantaneous current and potentials in the plate and grid circuits during class C operation.

In considering the theory of the class C amplifier, we must recognize the fact that it is inherently an equilibrium device in that the amplifier will satisfy the requirements of a certain tank voltage $E_p \cos \theta$, grid variation e_g, and a current angle θ_c only if the impedance of the output load as seen by the tube is of the correct magnitude. Since analytic expressions for the plate current are impractical, solutions based on either graphical or Fourier analysis are found to be useful. Graphical methods, which are described in any volume dealing with radio engineering, are lengthy and cumbersome although exact, but inasmuch as the load is generally specified beforehand (by an antenna or by a particular industrial application), numerous solutions using various values of e_g, e_p, and θ_c must usually be tried before the proper values of all parameters are determined.

15. Fourier Analysis of Class C Amplifier Operation.[1] A Fourier-analysis solution due to W. G. Wagener effectively reduces the amount of labor and time involved for arriving at a class C amplifier solution. This type of solution, although somewhat approximate, is extremely useful in practical applications and also serves as a demonstration of a general approach to problems involving nonlinearity and distortion in vacuum-tube circuits.

Plate-circuit considerations. In order to arrive at a solution, we must determine two power relationships in the plate circuit of the tube. They involve the input power p_{in} and the output power p_{out}, which are described as follows:

$$p_{\text{in}} = E_b I_b \tag{49}$$

$$p_{\text{out}} = \frac{E_p I_{p_1}}{2} \tag{50}$$

I_b and I_{p_1} are the average value of the plate current and the peak value of the fundamental Fourier current component of the plate current, respectively. Once (49) and (50) are determined, it is immediately evident that

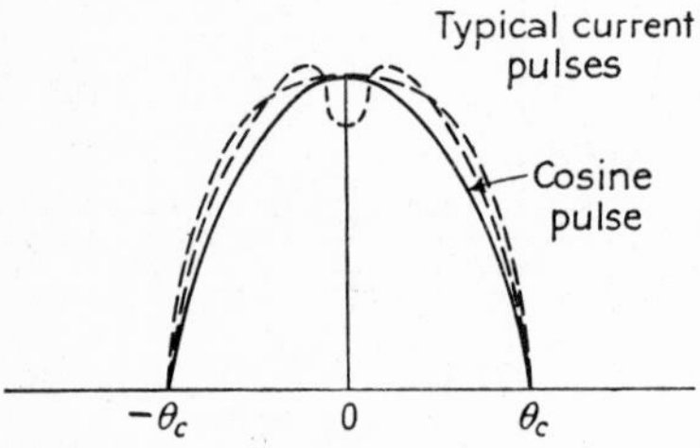

FIG. 15.

$$\text{Load impedance} = R_L = \frac{E_p^2}{2p_{\text{out}}} \tag{51}$$

$$\text{Efficiency} = \frac{p_{\text{out}}}{p_{\text{in}}} \times 100 \tag{52}$$

$$\text{Plate dissipation} = p_{\text{in}} - p_{\text{out}} \tag{53}$$

where R_L is the resistive impedance of the tank circuit at resonance.

The general problem then becomes one of finding the values of I_b and I_{p_1} which correspond to particular values of θ_c, e_p, and e_g. Consider the current pulses which are drawn in Fig. 15 for the case when $\theta_c = 75°$.

[1] The Wagener-Fourier method reduces the difficult and laborious task of deducing class C operation to a relatively simple operation. However, this method is not intended to be a substitute for thought. The reader should augment his understanding of this method with a broad knowledge of all fundamentals involved. See, for example, F. E. Terman, "Radio Engineering," Chap. 7, McGraw-Hill Book Company, Inc., New York, 1947.

Although in practice these representative current loops either will be flat on top or will actually dip in at the crest, the average current loop may be described approximately as a cosine loop. Earlier in this chapter, we developed the Fourier series for such a cosine loop of duration $2\theta_c$ in the interval $-\pi < \omega t < \pi$ [see Eq. (41)]. It was shown in Sec. 12 that, for a cosine loop of amplitude $1 - \cos\theta_c$ and total duration time $2\theta_c/\omega$,

$$I_b = \text{d-c component} = \frac{1}{\pi}(\sin\theta_c - \theta_c\cos\theta_c) \tag{54}$$

$$I_{p_1} = \text{first harmonic component} = \frac{1}{\pi}\left(\theta_c - \frac{1}{2}\sin 2\theta_c\right) \tag{55}$$

Equations (54) and (55) have been evaluated and the ratios of the peak value of the pulse to the average value of the pulse and to the peak value of the fundamental Fourier component are charted in Fig. 16.

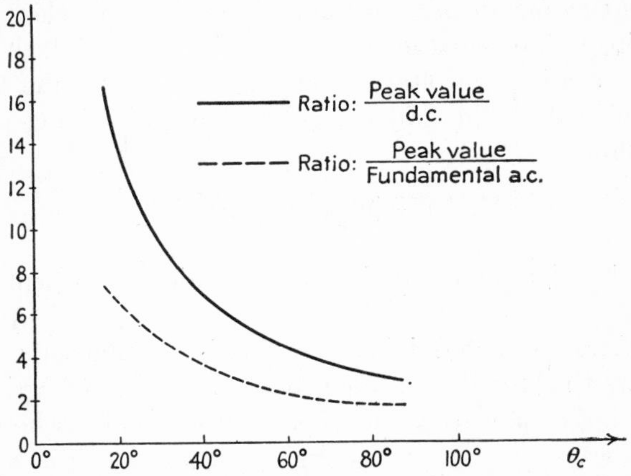

FIG. 16.

To solve for values of power and load, it is necessary to establish the operating angle θ_c, the minimum value of plate potential $e_{p_{\min}}$, and the maximum value of grid potential $e_{g_{\max}}$. Once these values are established, the peak value of plate current is found by consulting a set of characteristic curves for the particular tube to be used. This value of peak current along with a suitable choice of θ_c is used in Fig. 16 to determine I_b and I_{p_1}, which, when substituted into (49) to (53) yield the plate-circuit solution. Successive solutions employing appropriate changes in θ_c and in the other parameters will enable us to arrive quickly at a final solution which satisfies the plate-circuit loading conditions.

Note that at $\omega t = 0$, which yields $e_{p_{\min}}$ and $e_{g_{\max}}$,

$$E_g = e_{g_{\max}} - E_c \tag{56}$$

Substituting (56) into (48), we get

$$E_c = \frac{1}{1 - \cos\theta_c}\left[\left(-e_{g_{\max}} + \frac{E_b - e_{p_{\min}}}{\mu}\right)\cos\theta_c - \frac{E_b}{\mu}\right] \tag{57}$$

which relates E_c to θ_c and to the potentials concerned in the Fourier analysis.

By operating class C, plate current is passed only when the potential on the plate is in the vicinity of its minimum value, thus reducing the plate dissipation and raising the over-all system efficiency. In fact, efficiencies in excess of 80 per cent are possible as compared with the 50 per cent maximum possible efficiency which is obtainable for class A operation in which a linear portion of the dynamic-characteristic curve is used, thus demonstrating the fact that linear-network usage is not necessarily conducive to optimum operating conditions for all applications in communication systems.

Grid-circuit Considerations. In the grid circuit of the class C amplifier, we are principally interested in the grid driving power, which is described in terms of the grid a-c voltage swing $E_g \cos\omega t$, and the fundamental Fourier component of the grid current. The grid driving power is described as follows:

$$\text{Grid driving power} = \frac{E_g I_{p_1}}{2} \tag{58}$$

I_{g_1} is the peak value of the fundamental Fourier component of the grid current.

The procedure for determining the Fourier components of the grid current follows that for the plate current except that the grid current is more closely approximated by a squared cosine pulse whose operating angle is θ_2, where

$$\cos\theta_2 = -\frac{E_c}{E_g} \tag{59}$$

The total operating angle during which the grid draws grid current is $2\theta_2$. We have seen in Sec. 12 [see Eq. (43)] that for a squared cosine current pulse of peak amplitude, $1 - \cos\theta_2$, we get

$$I_g = \frac{1}{2\pi}\left(\theta_2 - \frac{3}{2}\sin 2\theta_2 + 2\theta_2\cos^2\theta_2\right) \tag{60}$$

$$i_{g_1} = \frac{1}{\pi}\left(-2\theta_2\cos\theta_2 + \frac{3}{2}\sin\theta_2 + \frac{1}{6}\sin 3\theta_2\right)\cos\omega t \tag{61}$$

where I_g and i_{g_1} are the average value and the fundamental Fourier component of the grid current, respectively.

Figure 17 is a plot of the ratio of the peak value of the grid current to the average value and to the maximum value of the fundamental Fourier component. After the peak grid current is determined from the tube characteristics, and after θ_2 is deduced from E_c and E_g, we may quickly find the average grid current and the grid driving power.

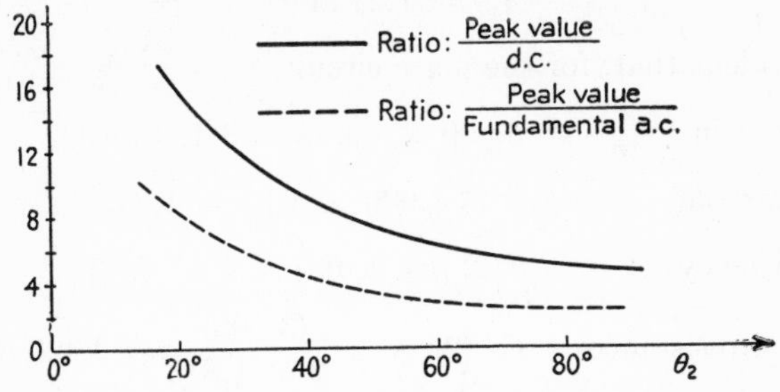

FIG. 17.

16. Illustrative Example of the Wagener-Fourier Method. Consider the performance of the class C amplifier using an RCA 207, whose characteristics are pictured in Fig. 18, when

$$E_b = 5{,}000 \text{ volts} \qquad \theta_c = 65° \qquad \mu = 20$$
$$E_p = 3{,}000 \text{ volts} \qquad e_{g_{max}} = 400 \text{ volts} \tag{62}$$

It follows directly from Fig. 18 that these values of E_b, E_p, and $e_{g_{max}}$

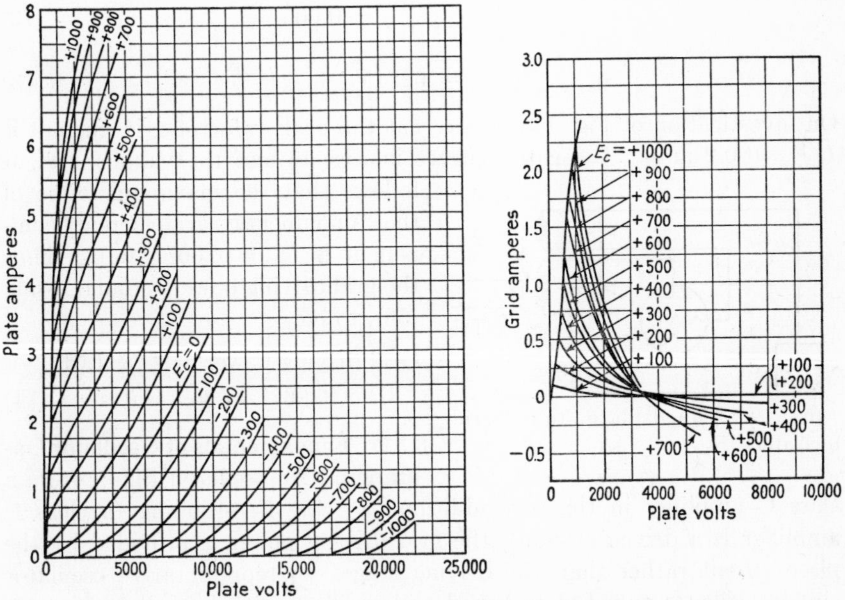

FIG. 18. Plate and grid characteristics of an RCA 207 electron tube.

correspond to a peak plate-current value of $I_{p_{\max}} = 3$ amp. Using this value and the operating angle $\theta_c = 65°$ in Fig. 16, we find that

$$I_b = 0.682 \text{ amp} \tag{63}$$

$$I_{p_1} = 1.21 \text{ amp} \tag{64}$$

It is then evident that, for the plate circuit,

$$\text{Power in} = 5{,}000 \times 0{,}682 = 3{,}410 \text{ watts} \tag{65}$$

$$\text{Power out} = \tfrac{1}{2} \times 3{,}000 \times 1.21 = 1{,}815 \text{ watts} \tag{66}$$

$$\text{Efficiency} = 53.2 \text{ per cent} \tag{67}$$

$$\text{Load resistance} = E_p^2/2p_{\text{out}} = \frac{(3{,}000)^2}{2 \times 1{,}815} = 2{,}490 \text{ ohms} \tag{68}$$

In order to determine the grid driving power, we must first find E_g and θ_2. It follows from (57) and (59) that

$$E_g = e_{g_{\max}} - E_c \tag{69}$$

$$= 400 - \frac{1}{1 - \cos 65°}\left[(-400 + 150) \cos 65° - \frac{5{,}000}{20}\right] \tag{70}$$

$$= 400 + 613 = 1{,}013 \text{ volts} \tag{71}$$

and

$$\cos \theta_2 = \frac{613}{1{,}013} = 0.605 \tag{72}$$

$$\theta_2 = 62°45' \tag{73}$$

On investigation of Fig. 18, we see that the peak value of grid current is $I_{g_{\max}} = 0.2$ amp. Using the curves in Fig. 17 and the value for θ_2, it follows that the maximum value of the fundamental grid-current component is $I_{g_1} = 0.0677$ amp. Thus the grid driving power is found, using (58), to be

$$\text{Grid driving power} = \tfrac{1}{2} \times 1{,}013 \times 0.0677 = 34.3 \text{ watts} \tag{74}$$

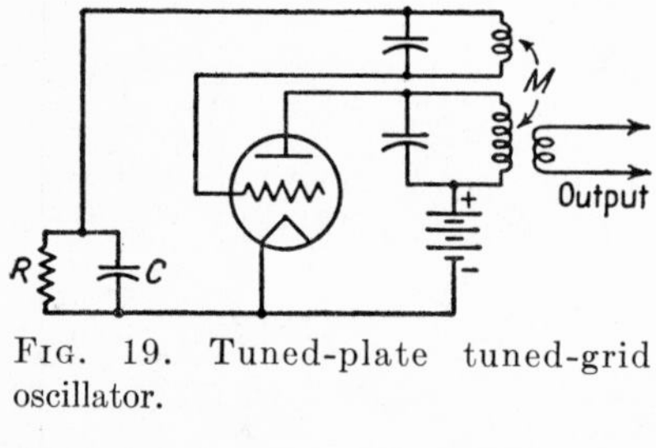

FIG. 19. Tuned-plate tuned-grid oscillator.

17. Fundamentals of Oscillator Operation. An oscillator differs from a class C amplifier in that, in addition to being free-running (a class C amplifier is a driven system), the grid driving power is provided by the plate circuit rather than the driving stage. A representative oscillator circuit, called a tuned-plate tuned-grid oscillator, is pictured in Fig. 19, where it is seen that the resonant circuits in the plate and grid circuits are coupled in such a way that a voltage of proper amplitude is applied to the grid, this voltage being 180° out of phase with respect to the plate voltage. In addition, an RC circuit is included in the grid circuit to provide the d-c bias necessary for the oscillator to function with class C amplifier operation.

18. Blocking-oscillator Operation. The circuit shown in Fig. 20*a* is known as a blocking oscillator and is widely used in television and radar

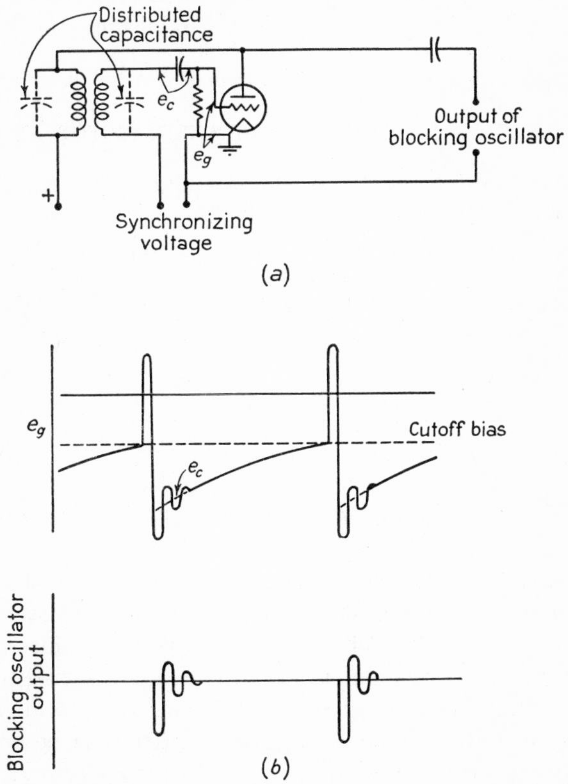

FIG. 20. (*a*) Blocking-oscillator circuit. (*b*) Typical blocking-oscillator waveforms.

circuits to produce short pulses of large amplitude; this circuit has a behavior somewhat like that of a relaxation oscillator. By making the coupling coefficient M large, the time constant C_gR_g large compared with the duration time of one cycle of the resonant circuit, and the L/C ratio of the resonant system sufficiently large, the blocking oscillator will bias itself off shortly after the start of oscillation, thus producing short pulses of voltage which may be produced in a free-running fashion or at a rate and phase determined by a synchronizing pulse. Typical blocking-oscillator waveforms are illustrated in Fig. 20*b*.

19. Frequency Multipliers. A frequency multiplier is an electronic circuit which is widely used in AM and FM transmitters. Its basic circuit is that of a class C amplifier in which the tank circuit in the plate system pictured in Fig. 13 is replaced by a resonant circuit which is tuned to some integral multiple of the resonant frequency of the grid tank circuit. If the frequency of the input wave and grid system is f_0 and if the output tank circuit is tuned to Nf_0, then this tank circuit will be excited by the Nth harmonic of the plate current, thus establishing the system as a frequency multiplier.

FUNDAMENTALS OF OPERATION OF SEMICONDUCTOR AMPLIFIERS

20. The Transistor—A Semiconductor Amplifier. The transistor is an amplifying semiconductor control impedance consisting of a slab of germanium crystal with a base contact and two contacts of small area as shown in Fig. 21*a*. The assembly is mounted in a cartridge with the two small-area point contacts made by phosphor-bronze cat whiskers; these

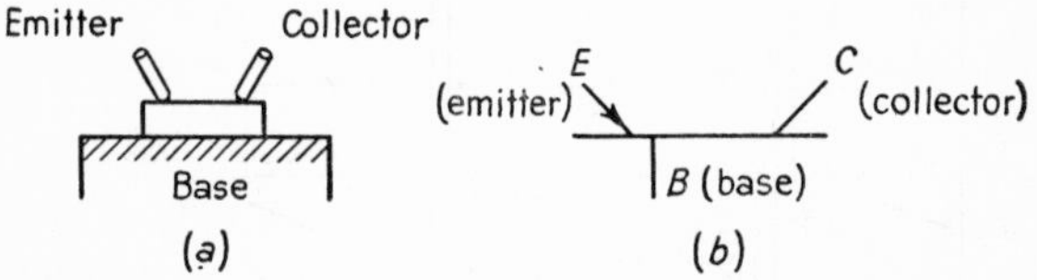

FIG. 21. (*a*) Transistor. (*b*) Equivalent circuit of a transistor.

two terminals are known as the emitter and the collector. The large-area contact is known as the base. The schematic symbol denoting the transistor is pictured in Fig. 21*b*. As in the case of crystal rectifiers, a potential barrier is formed in the germanium near the collector owing to this electrode being biased in the low-conduction direction. By placing appropriate voltages on the emitter, anomalous charge carriers can be emitted from this electrode which can influence the action of the collector.

There is perhaps a tendency at first encounter with transistors to think of this semiconductor device as being somewhat replaceable by a triode vacuum tube and then to attribute near-normal vacuum-tube behavior to it. Actually, except for some particular ranges of operation where the equivalent circuits of the triode and the transistor exhibit similarity, the transistor should be considered in view of its fundamental characteristics[1] alone and will be so discussed here. At least two characteristics are inherent in the transistor which make it either difficult or unwise to attempt

[1] See Ryder and Kircher, Some Circuit Aspects of the Transistor, *Bell System Tech. J.*, vol. 28, No. 3, pp. 367–400, July, 1949.

to establish an analogy between it and a vacuum tube. They are as follows:

1. Whereas a vacuum tube in general has a current gain in the vicinity of unity (the ratio of the current in the plate lead to the current in the cathode lead), the transistor is capable of values of current gain considerably greater than unity.

2. The transistor is not a true unilateral (one-way) impedance, some feedback being inherent due to the nature of the semiconductor, thus creating a need for criteria of stability. In fact, with care the transistor can be made to act as a bilateral impedance, power gains being realized in both directions.

Consider, for example, the *grounded-base* transistor amplifier circuit shown in Fig. 22*a*. (The transistor may also be operated with grounded

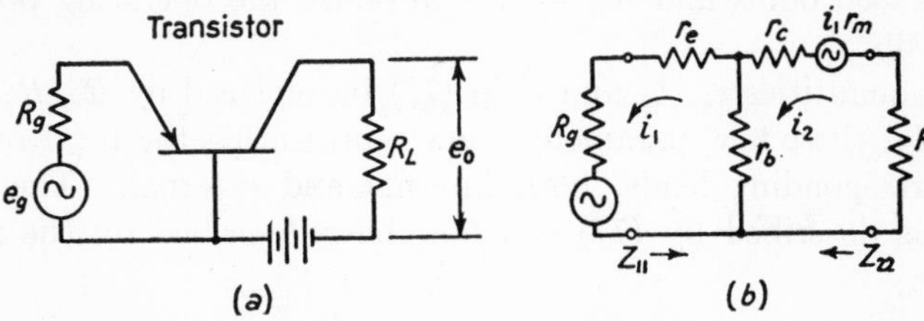

FIG. 22. (*a*) Grounded-base transistor circuit. (*b*) Equivalent circuit of grounded-base transistor circuit.

emitter or grounded collector.) If the transistor is to be operated with an input signal of small amplitude, an equivalent circuit—shown in Fig. 22*b*—due to R. M. Ryder and R. J. Kircher[1] may be used to represent the transistor system, with r_m representing the net mutual resistance of the transistor. For this circuit

$$i_1(R_g + r_e + r_b) + i_2r_b = e_g \tag{75}$$

$$i_1(r_b + r_m) + i_2(r_b + r_c + R_L) = 0 \tag{76}$$

from which it can be shown that, for stability, the following criterion must be satisfied:

$$(R_g + r_e + r_b)(R_L + r_c - r_b) - r_b(r_b + r_m) > 0 \tag{77}$$

In addition, it follows[2] from the four-pole-network analysis of the circuit in Fig. 22*b* that

$$R_{11} = r_e + r_b - \frac{r_b(r_b + r_m)}{R_g + r_e + r_b} \tag{78}$$

$$R_{22} = r_c + r_b - \frac{r_b(r_b + r_m)}{R_g + r_e + r_b} \tag{79}$$

[1] See also Webster, Eberhard, and Barton, Some Novel Circuits for the Three-Terminal Semiconductor Amplifier, *RCA Rev.*, vol. 10, pp. 5–16, March, 1949.

[2] See Ryder and Kircher, *loc. cit.*

where R_{11} and R_{22} are the input impedance and output impedance of the transistor, respectively. Denoting the operating power gain as $\mathcal{G}_p$, it can then be shown that

$$\mathcal{G}_p = 4R_gR_L \frac{-(r_b + r_m)^2}{(R_g + r_e + r_b)(R_L + r_c + r_b) - r_b(r_b + r_m)} \tag{80}$$

Consider the transistor circuit having the following characteristics:

$$I_e = 0.6 \text{ ma} \qquad r_e = 240 \text{ ohms}$$
$$I_c = -2 \text{ ma} \qquad r_b = 290 \text{ ohms}$$
$$V_e = 0.7 \text{ volt} \qquad r_c = 19{,}000 \text{ ohms}$$
$$V_c = -40 \text{ volts} \qquad r_m = 34{,}000 \text{ ohms}$$

If $R_g = 500$ ohms and $R_L = 20{,}000$ ohms, the operating power gain will be 17 db.

Let the quantities r_e, r_c, and r_b in (77) be replaced by R_e, R_c, and R_b, respectively, these new parameters now representing the total resistances in the corresponding leads, both internal and external. The stability criterion as described by (77) can now be redescribed by the following inequality:

$$\frac{r_m}{R_c} < 1 + \frac{R_e}{R_b} + \frac{R_e}{R_c} \tag{81}$$

It is evident that the base resistance R_b is an important factor in the stability criterion, which is not surprising since it is seen in Fig. 22*b* to comprise the network feedback element. It follows from (81) that if $R_b \to 0$, the circuit can be stable. If $R_b > 0$, stability can be achieved if R_e and R_c are sufficiently large or if r_m is sufficiently small.

If a signal of large amplitude is to be applied to the transistor, it is more advantageous to resort to the load-line current-voltage characteristics of the transistor. Ryder and Kircher describe four large-signal operating conditions and attendant distortion in transistor circuits as follows:

1. One may drive the emitter positive into the cutoff region where the collector current fails to respond to changes in emitter potential corresponding to grid cutoff in an electron tube.
2. One may drive the emitter positive into an emitter overload region where nonlinear distortion may be encountered because the emitter impedance changes with its voltage. The corresponding tube phenomenon is positive grid distortion. For both tubes and transistors, this effect is a minor one which may be actually beneficial in practical cases.
3. The collector may be driven down to low potential where it can no longer draw the current required to follow the impressed emitter current variations. This distortion corresponds to plate "bottoming" in electron tubes.
4. The collector may be driven up to high currents where it overloads because of

the nonlinear voltage response in that region arising from heating effects. This effect has practical consequences something like the overloading of electron tubes which may arise from insufficient cathode emission.

Since the transistor may become unstable if the electrode voltages are not maintained constant, the transistor currents are taken as the independent variables in evolving the transistor characteristics; *i.e.*,

$$V_e = f_1(I_e, I_c) \tag{82}$$

$$V_c = f_2(I_e, I_c) \tag{83}$$

There are several methods of representing, either analytically or graphically, the static characteristics of the transistor. The discussion here will be limited to the static characteristics showing the collector voltage and current as a function of emitter current since this case is closely analogous to the static triode characteristics pictured in Fig. 2*b*, where the grid voltage is the independent variable. A representative transistor-char-

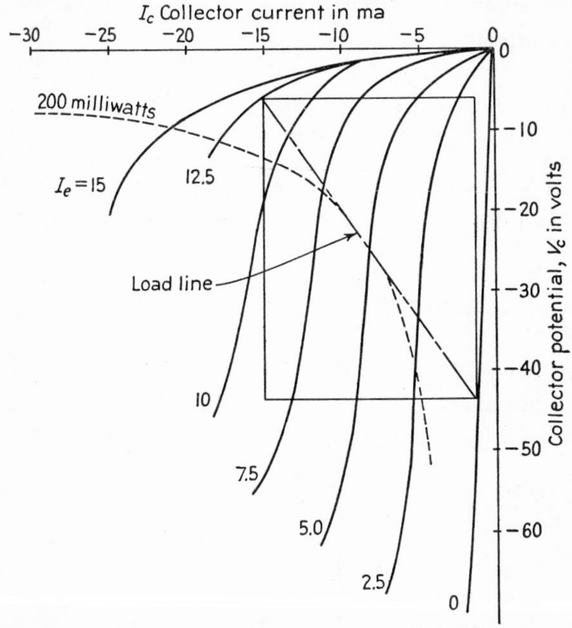

FIG. 23. Static characteristics of a typical transistor, showing the collector voltage and current as a function of emitter current. (*Courtesy of Bell System Tech. J.*).

acteristic chart is pictured in Fig. 23, which includes a load line corresponding to a load resistance of 2,800 ohms and a dotted line represents an operating input power of 200 mw.

21. Bistable Characteristic of a Transistor. Owing to the fact that a transistor can be made to exhibit two states of operating equilibrium for one output load, it has considerable application in fields using trigger circuits since in addition to the mechanical simplicity involved, one transistor may be used to produce triggering in a circuit normally requiring two electron tubes.

The bistable characteristics of a transistor are readily obvious from the measurable characteristics of the device. Consider the representative values of r_e, r_c, and r_m as a function of I_e which produce the curves pictured

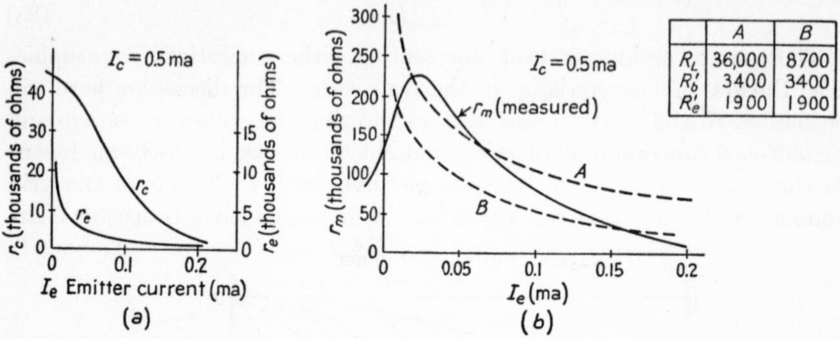

FIG. 24. Transistor stability curves. R_b' and R_e' are the *external resistances in the leads* to the base and emitter, respectively. (*Courtesy of RCA Review.*)

in Fig. 24*a* and *b*. Included in Fig. 24*b* are two lines of stability which are deduced from Eq. (81) based on the following derivable equation, which yields

$$r_m = \frac{(R_e + R_b)(R_c + R_L)}{R_b} + R_e \tag{84}$$

It is seen that, for each of the stability lines pictured in Fig. 24*b*, I_c is constant at 0.5 ma and the calculated stability line crosses the measured curve for r_m twice, indicating two stability limits for each value of R_L.

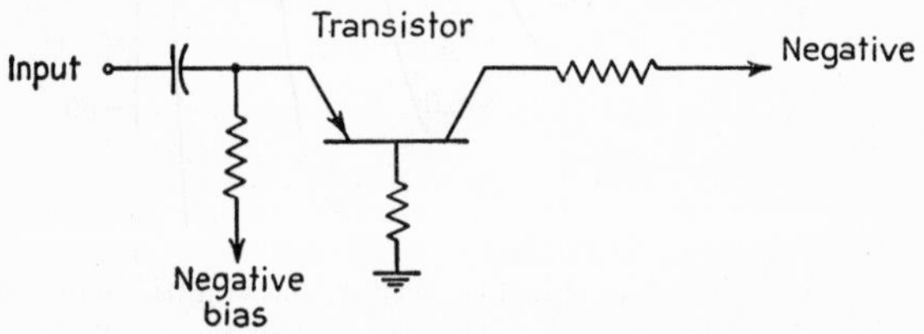

FIG. 25. Transistor trigger circuit.

A simple transistor circuit which utilizes this bistable effect for triggering action is pictured in Fig. 25.[1]

[1] For a discussion of the bistable characteristics of transistors and related applications, see Eberhard, Endres, and Moore, Counter Circuits Using Transistors, *RCA Rev.*, vol. 10, pp. 454–476, December, 1949.

FUNDAMENTALS OF OPERATION OF VELOCITY-MODULATION AMPLIFIERS

22. Introduction. Because of transit time effects, multigrid vacuum tubes are difficult to design for use as amplifiers at the ultra-high frequencies,[1] and velocity-modulation (VM) amplifier tubes, making use of transit-time effects, have become important components in u-h-f transmission systems. As we shall see, VM tubes resemble class C amplifier[2] circuits since an input signal will generate harmonics in the current in the output circuit; this complex current may be used to excite the output resonant circuit at proper frequency. In addition, a portion of the output circuit power may be fed into the input circuit, thus permitting operation as an oscillator.

23. Velocity-modulation (VM) Tubes. If an electron beam passes through a region which contains a varying electric field whose direction is parallel to the direction of the electrons, the electrons will emerge from this region with varying speeds depending on whether they are accelerated, decelerated, or subjected to interaction whose net effect on electron velocity is zero. If a drift space is provided after this region, then the electrons will travel down this space with varying individual velocities and electron bunching and debunching will take place depending on the distance and the system parameters involved.

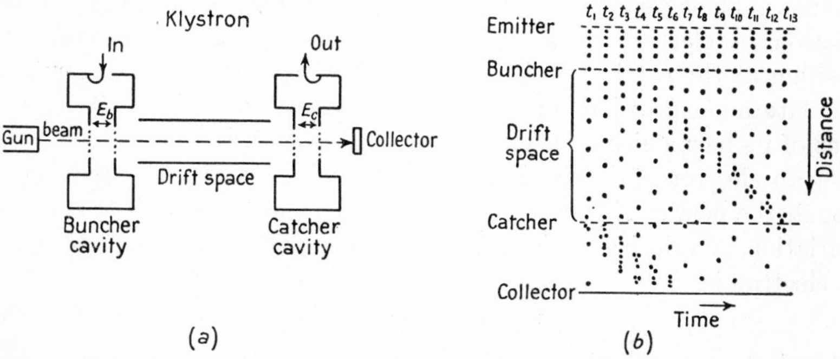

FIG. 26. (*a*) Basic klystron system. (*b*) Electron behavior as a function of time, showing the formation of the electron bunches.

Such a bunching system is found in VM tubes, of which the klystron is typical. A basic tube structure is pictured in Fig. 26*a*, where we see

[1] For an extensive discussion of the performance of conventional tube systems at ultra-high frequencies, see K. Spangenberg, "Vacuum Tubes," Chap. 12, McGraw-Hill Book Company, Inc., New York, 1948.

[2] An attempt to force a full analogy between class C amplifier operation and VM tube operation will fail because of the lack of a parameter in a VM tube which is equivalent to μ in a vacuum tube and because the current through the catcher cavity in a VM tube is relatively independent of the r-f voltage except for a limited range of operating parameters.

an electron gun, a buncher cavity and a catcher cavity separated by a drift space, and a collector. Either the two cavities are tuned to the same frequency, as in an amplifier or an oscillator, or the catcher-cavity frequency is tuned to an integral multiple of the buncher-cavity frequency, thus producing frequency multiplication.

Once electron bunching occurs, these bunches must be passed through the catcher cavity before debunching takes place. The phase of the electric field in the catcher cavity should be such that the electron bunches are decelerated, thus transferring the electron energy to the cavity fields and thence to the output load. As the catcher-cavity electric field assumes a direction which will accelerate any electrons passing through the cavity, the number of electrons entering the cavity from the drift space at this time should, of course, be kept at a minimum. If no bunching takes place and a steady stream of electrons passes through the catcher cavity, the net exchange of energy between the electrons and the electric field will be equal to zero and no power will reach the load.

We are not concerned here with the specific mechanisms of interaction in VM tubes, such considerations being beyond the scope of this book. Rather, we are interested in the production and analysis of harmonics in these tubes, these considerations to be discussed in the next section.

24. Fourier Analysis of Bunching in Velocity-modulated Electron Streams. The actual behavior of the electrons is pictured in Fig. 26*b*, the variation in electron velocity at the buncher producing the electron bunching at the catcher cavity, as shown. The following treatment will formulate an expression for the current passing through the catches in terms of its harmonics by using a Fourier series.

Let an electron enter the buncher cavity with velocity v_0. If it passes through the center of the buncher cavity at time t_1 and if it experiences a variation in velocity $v_1 \sin \omega_1 t$, then at some later time the velocity of this electron is

$$v = v_0 + v_1 \sin \omega_1 t \tag{85}$$

If the electron passes through the center of the catcher cavity at time t_2, where

$$t_2 = t_1 + \frac{x}{v_0 + v_1 \sin \omega_1 t_1} \tag{86}$$

x being the distance from the center of the buncher cavity to the center of the catcher cavity, then we may write the phase at t_2 as follows,

$$\omega t_2 = \omega t_1 + \frac{\omega x}{v_0} - \omega x \frac{v_1}{v_0^2} \sin \omega_1 t_1 \tag{87}$$

which follows from the fact that

$$\frac{x}{v_0 + v_1 \sin \omega_1 t_1} \cong \frac{x}{v_0} - x \frac{v_1}{v_0^2} \sin \omega_1 t_1 \tag{88}$$

provided that $v_1 \ll v_0$. This provides us with an expression for phase which is useful in the Fourier analysis of bunching. In general, we may write the current due to electron bunching at t_2 as the complex Fourier series,

$$i(t_2) = \sum_{m=-\infty}^{\infty} i_m e^{jm\omega t_2} \tag{89}$$

where

$$i_m = \frac{1}{2\pi} \int_{-\pi}^{\pi} i(t_2) e^{jm\omega t_2}\, d(\omega t_2) \tag{90}$$

The current in the velocity-modulated electron stream must satisfy a criterion of continuity; *i.e.*,

$$i(t_1)\, dt_1 = i(t_2)\, dt_2 \tag{91}$$

so that

$$i(t_2) = i(t_1) \frac{dt_1}{dt_2} \tag{92}$$

We may extend this equation to state that

$$i(t_2) = i_0 \sum_{t_1(t_2)} \left| \frac{dt_1}{dt_2} \right| \tag{93}$$

where i_0 is the d-c beam current arriving at the catcher at t_2 and $\sum_{t_1(t_2)} |dt_1/dt_2|$ describes the summation of the absolute values of the derivatives dt_1/dt_2 corresponding to the arrival time t_2.

If $\omega(xv_1/v_0^2) < 1$, then (93) reduces to

$$i(t_2) = i_0 \frac{dt_1}{dt_2} \tag{94}$$

Substituting (94) into (90), we get

$$i_m = \frac{i_0}{2\pi} \int_{-\pi}^{\pi} e^{-jm\omega t_2}\, d\omega t_1 \tag{95}$$

Replacing ωt_2 in the exponential by the value given by (87), we get

$$i_m = \frac{i_0}{2\pi} e^{-jm\omega(x/v_0)} \int_{-\pi}^{\pi} e^{-jm[\omega t_1 - \omega(xv_1/v_0^2)\sin\omega_1 t]}\, d\omega_1 t \tag{96}$$

Using Eq. (90), Chap. 2, we get

$$i_m = i_0 J_m\!\left(\frac{m\omega x v_1}{v_0^2}\right) e^{-jm(\omega x/v_0)} \tag{97}$$

which when substituted into (89) yields

$$i(t_2) = i_0 \sum_{m=-\infty}^{\infty} J_m\!\left(\frac{m\omega x v_1}{v_0^2}\right) e^{+jm\omega[t_2 - (x/v_0)]} \tag{98}$$

which is an infinite series involving Bessel's functions whose arguments are based on $\omega(xv_1/v_0^2)$, which is called the bunching parameter.[1] Actually this equation is more general than indicated by the derivation since it can be shown to be valid for values of $\omega(xv_1/v_0^2) > 1$.

If $\omega(xv_1/v_0^2)$ is very small, we need not resort to the full Fourier-series formulation. From (94), we see that

$$i_0 = i(t_2)\,\frac{dt_2}{dt_1} \tag{99}$$

Differentiating t_2, as given by (86), with respect to t_1 and substituting the result into (99), we get

$$i_0 = i(t_2)\left(1 - \frac{\omega x v_1}{v_0^2}\cos\omega t_1\right) \tag{100}$$

or

$$i(t_2) = \frac{i_0}{1 - \omega(xv_1/v_0^2)\cos\omega t_1} \tag{101}$$

$$\cong i_0\left(1 + \frac{\omega x v_1}{v_0^2}\cos\omega t_1\right) \tag{102}$$

provided that $\omega(xv_1/v_0^2) \ll 1$. This pair of terms is easily deduced from the general equation (98) for $\omega(xv_1/v_0^2) \ll 1$.

PROBLEMS

1. Calculate g_m, $\partial g_m/\partial E$, and $\partial^2 g_m/\partial E^2$ for a vacuum tube whose dynamic characteristic is similar to that pictured in Fig. 1 for the case when a sinusoidal voltage with a peak value of 2.6 volts is applied to the grid, yielding a peak value of plate current of 5 ma with 5.5 per cent second harmonic distortion. (Assume a large value of plate resistance.)

2. Is it possible to adjust the operating point on the dynamic-characteristic curve of a vacuum tube so that the third harmonic distortion term vanishes? Explain.

3. If a sinusoidal voltage $e_g = 3.2 \sin 377t$ is impressed on the grid of a vacuum tube which is operating at an operating point where $g_m = 2{,}000$ μmhos, $\partial g_m/\partial E = 5 \times 10^{-4}$, and $\partial^2 g_m/\partial E^2 = 0.5 \times 10^{-6}$, deduce the nature of the output current.

4. Let a wave $e_g = 3.2 \sin 377t + 1.4 \sin 1{,}034t$ be applied to the grid of the vacuum tube in Prob. 3 under the operating conditions described there. What is the output current?

5. Obtain a set of characteristic curves of an RCA 6L6 electron tube. Using the limited Fourier-series method, calculate the magnitudes of the first and second harmonics for values of E_c in the range $-25 < E_c < 0$ and $e_g = 10 \sin \omega t$ for the case when the tube is operating into an 8,000-ohm load with a battery potential of 350 volts.

[1] For a detailed discussion of klystrons and the nature of the bunching parameter, see Chap. 9, due to D. R. Hamilton, of Hamilton, Knipp, and Horner Kuper, "Klystrons and Microwave Triodes," McGraw-Hill Book Company, Inc., New York, 1948.

6. Can the limited Fourier-series method be applied to the general problem of the performance of class C amplifiers? Explain.

7. Deduce the output wave appearing across the load of a vacuum tube operating class A when

a. e_g is a square wave occurring 1,000 times a second, $\mu = 20$, $r_p = 10{,}000$ ohms, and $Z_L = 5{,}000$ ohms.

b. Repeat Part *a* for the case where Z_L is a 10,000-ohm resistor in series with an inductance of 75 mh. Diagram an approximate representation of the output.

8. Calculate the amplitudes of the first five harmonics of output voltage of a class C amplifier operating into a resistance load, $R_L = 10{,}000$ ohms, when the output current is a loop of unit amplitude with $\theta_c = 60°$ if

a. The dynamic characteristic is linear.

b. The dynamic characteristic obeys a square law.

9. Derive the Fourier-series representation of the output current of a class C amplifier whose dynamic-characteristic curve is a cubic.

10. Determine the performances of a class C amplifier for $\mu = 20$ and

a. $E_b = 5{,}000$ volts
$E_p = 3{,}500$ volts
$\theta_c = 72°$
$e_{g_{max}} = 1{,}000$ volts

b. $E_b = 500$ volts
$E_p = 1{,}500$ volts
$\theta_c = 72°$
$e_{g_{max}} = 300$ volts

11. An RCA 207 is operating as a frequency doubler such that $E_b = 7{,}000$ volts, $E_c = -400$ volts, $e_{gm} = 550$ volts at 7.5 Mc and $e_{pm} = 700$ volts at 15 Mc. Find the power input, power output, and effective tank impedance.

12. Discuss the problem of feedback in a grounded-base transistor as a function of base area as derived from the equivalent circuit in Fig. 22*a*. If a complex wave, represented by a complex Fourier series, is impressed at the input, what will be the general effect of this feedback on the output wave?

13. Show that transmission of a complex wave through a grounded-emitter transistor amplifier is performed without change in signal polarity. Is there any shift in the phase of harmonic components?

14. If the magnitude of the bunching parameter of a particular klystron is 0.22, calculate the magnitudes of the first three harmonics for the case when $i_0 = 35$ ma, $x = 12$ cm with a beam voltage of 500 volts. Repeat for $\omega x v_1/v_0^2 = 0.07; 0.11; 0.68$.

CHAPTER 8

GASEOUS-RECTIFIER-TUBE CIRCUITS

COMPLEX WAVES IN GASEOUS-RECTIFIER-TUBE CIRCUITS

1. Two-element Mercury-vapor Rectifier.[1] Because of the ability of the two-element mercury-vapor rectifier to prescribe the direction of flow of the system current while introducing only negligible series resistance, this tube enjoys universal usage, when used with a suitable filter network, for changing a-c voltage to d-c voltage in equipment and systems in every phase of electrical communication.

The sections to follow will discuss the Fourier analysis of single-phase (half-wave), biphase (full-wave), and polyphase rectified waves. Filter networks, through which these waves may be passed in order to produce d-c voltage, will also be discussed in this chapter.

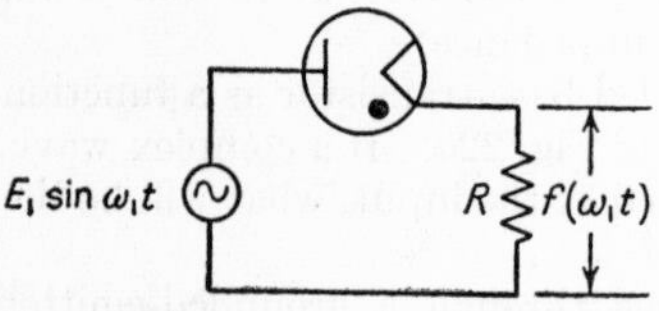

FIG. 1. Half-wave rectifier circuit.

2. Single-phase (Half-wave) Rectification. Consider the circuit which is pictured in Fig. 1. Here an a-c generator, whose peak output voltage and frequencies are E_1 and $\omega_1/2\pi$, respectively, is connected in series with a mercury-vapor rectifier and a resistor R whose magnitude is such that ionization will take place in the rectifier during the periods of current flow. Neglecting the voltage drop across the rectifier, the voltage drop across the resistor is that pictured in Fig. 2*a*. This voltage drop may be expressed mathematically as follows:

$$\begin{aligned} f(\omega_1 t) &= E_1 \sin \omega_1 t \qquad 0 < \omega_1 t < \pi \\ &= 0 \qquad\qquad\quad \pi < \omega_1 t < 2\pi \end{aligned} \tag{1}$$

[1] For a discussion of the electronics of mercury-vapor rectifiers, see W. G. Dow, "Fundamentals of Engineering Electronics," Chap. XXI, John Wiley & Sons, Inc., New York, 1937, or Maxfield and Benedict, "Theory of Gaseous Conduction and Electronics," Chaps. VII–X, McGraw-Hill Book Company, Inc., New York, 1941. For Fourier aspects of rectified waves, see L. B. W. Jolley, "Alternating Current Rectification," Chap. 1, John Wiley & Sons, Inc., New York, 1928.

The trigonometric Fourier-series coefficients may be found as follows:

$$\frac{a_0}{2} = \frac{1}{2\pi}\int_0^{2\pi} f(\omega_1 t)\, d\omega_1 t \tag{2}$$

$$= \frac{E_1}{2\pi}\int_0^{\pi} \sin \omega_1 t\, d\omega_1 t \tag{3}$$

$$= \frac{1}{\pi} \tag{4}$$

This is the average value of the output wave. Continuing with the analysis, we find that

$$a_n = \frac{1}{\pi}\int_0^{2\pi} f(\omega_1 t) \cos n\omega_1 t\, d\omega_1 t \tag{5}$$

$$= \frac{E_1}{\pi}\int_0^{\pi} \sin \omega_1 t \cos n\omega_1 t\, d\omega_1 t \tag{6}$$

$$= \frac{E_1}{\pi}\left[\frac{\cos (n-1)\omega_1 t}{2(n-1)} - \frac{\cos (n+1)\omega_1 t}{2(n+1)}\right] \tag{7}$$

When n is odd,

$$a_n = \frac{E_1}{\pi}\left[\frac{1-1}{2(n-1)} - \frac{1-1}{2(n+1)}\right] = 0 \tag{8}$$

When n is even,

$$a_n = \frac{E_1}{\pi}\left[\frac{-1-1}{2(n-1)} - \frac{-1-1}{2(n+1)}\right] \tag{9}$$

$$= \frac{-2E_1}{\pi(n^2-1)} \tag{10}$$

In like manner, we find for b_n that

$$b_n = \frac{1}{\pi}\int_0^{2\pi} f(\omega_1 t) \sin n\omega_1 t\, d\omega_1 t \tag{11}$$

$$= \frac{E_1}{\pi}\int_0^{\pi} \sin \omega_1 t \sin \omega_1 t\, d\omega_1 t \tag{12}$$

This will be equal to zero for all values of n except $n = 1$. It follows that

$$b_1 = \frac{E_1}{\pi}\int_0^{\pi} \sin^2 \omega_1 t\, d\omega_1 t \tag{13}$$

$$= \frac{E_1}{\pi}\left[\frac{\omega_1 t}{2} - \frac{1}{4}\sin 2\omega_1 t\right]_0^{\pi} \tag{14}$$

$$= \frac{E_1}{2} \tag{15}$$

The Fourier-series representation of $f(\omega_1 t)$ is therefore

$$f(\omega_1 t) = E_1\left(\frac{1}{\pi} + \frac{1}{2}\sin\omega_1 t - \frac{2}{\pi}\sum_{k=1}^{\infty}\frac{\cos 2k\omega_1 t}{4k^2 - 1}\right) \tag{16}$$

where $2k = n$. Written out, (16) becomes

$$f(\omega_1 t) = E_1\left(\frac{1}{\pi} + \frac{1}{2}\sin\omega_1 t - \frac{2}{3\pi}\cos 2\omega_1 t - \frac{2}{15\pi}\cos 4\omega_1 t \cdots\right) \tag{17}$$

The behavior of the first three terms and their sum is shown in Fig. 2b, where it is seen that the half-wave rectified wave form is beginning to take shape.

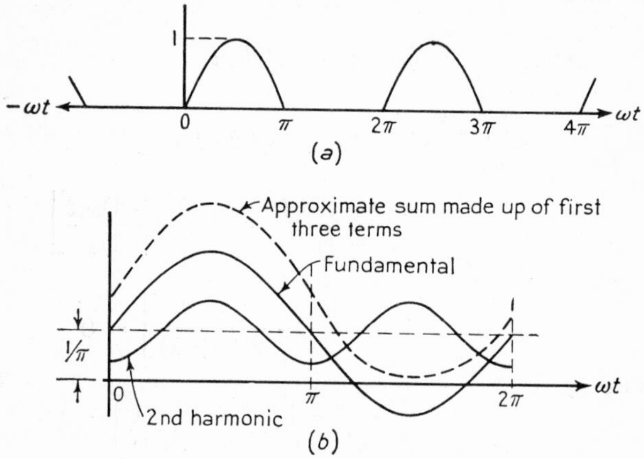

FIG. 2.

3. Single-phase (Half-wave) Rectification (Two-tone). Let us extend the preceding case to include considerations of a two-tone half-wave rectified wave. The circuit producing this wave is pictured in Fig. 3. A double Fourier series will be used to represent the wave appearing across R due to the generator voltages $E_1 \cos \omega_1 t$ and $E_2 \cos \omega_2 t$.

In order to provide a preliminary elementary physical picture of the wave summation which will take place in the circuit in Fig. 3, let the phases of the generators be such that their instantaneous sum will be

$$e(t) = E_1 \cos\omega_1 t + E_2 \cos\omega_2 t \tag{18}$$

$$= f(\omega_1 t, \omega_2 t) \tag{19}$$

where

$$f(\omega_1 t, \omega_2 t) = f(\omega_1 t + 2\pi,\ \omega_2 t) \tag{20}$$

$$= f(\omega_1 t,\ \omega_2 t + 2\pi) \tag{21}$$

$$= f(\omega_1 t + 2\pi,\ \omega_2 t + 2\pi) \tag{22}$$

Thus if the value of $f(\omega_1 t, \omega_2 t)$ is known for every point in the rectangle bounded by $\omega_1 t = \pm\pi$ and $\omega_2 t = \pm\pi$, then it is determined for every point in the entire $\omega_1 t$, $\omega_2 t$ plane. If $e(t)$ is to be passed through a rectifier, then its Fourier components may be determined once the limits of the double integration which yields the amplitude coefficients are determined.

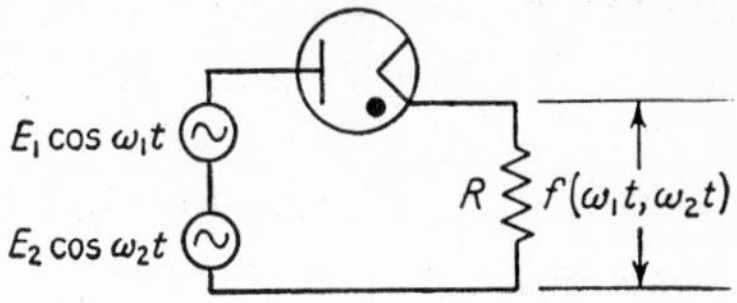

FIG. 3.

In the general analysis of a two-tone rectified wave, due to W. R. Bennet,[1] let us consider the general real two-tone wave

$$e_i(t) = E_1 \cos(\omega_1 t + \varphi_1) + E_2 \cos(\omega_2 t + \varphi_2) \tag{23}$$

where φ_1 and φ_2 are general phase terms. Rectification will cause the *net* negative lobes to be replaced by zero intervals. In this development, let

$$k = \frac{E_2}{E_1} \tag{24}$$

where

$$E_1 > 0 \qquad 0 \leq k \leq 1 \tag{25}$$

and let

$$x = \omega_1 t + \varphi_1 \qquad y = \omega_2 t + \varphi_2 \tag{26}$$

After rectification, we find that

$$\begin{aligned} e_r(t) &= E_1(\cos x + k \cos y) \qquad && \cos x + k \cos y \geq 0 \\ &= 0 && \cos x + k \cos y < 0 \end{aligned} \tag{27}$$

which describes $e_r(t)$ in what is now the xy plane.

The function

$$\cos x + k \cos y = 0 \tag{28}$$

is the boundary on this plane where the wave function goes to zero and is double-valued. On the line $x = 0$ except for the limiting case $k = 1$ [see Eqs. (24) and (25)] the sum $\cos x + k \cos y$ will be greater than zero for all values of y in the interval $-\pi < y < \pi$. For computations made for x and y in the regions approaching $x = \pi$, the phase angle at which $e_r(t)$ will go to zero as a function of x is equal to $\cos^{-1}(-k \cos y)$.

Using the trigonometric double Fourier series, we may write the double cosine series expansion of $e_r(t)$ as follows:

$$e_r(t) = \sum_{m=0}^{\infty} \sum_{n=0}^{\infty} a_{\pm mn} \cos(n\omega_1 \pm m\omega_2)t \tag{29}$$

[1] W. R. Bennet, New Results in the Calculation of Modulation Products, *Bell System Tech. J.*, vol. 12, pp. 228–243, April, 1933.

and

$$a_{\pm mn} = \frac{4}{2\pi^2} \int_0^\pi \int_0^\pi f(\omega_1 t, \omega_2 t) \cos (n\omega_1 \pm m\omega_2)t \, d\omega_1 t \, d\omega_2 t \qquad (30)$$

The integration may be carried out over one quadrant and is multiplied by 4 owing to the evenness of $f(\omega_1 t, \omega_2 t)$, which also demands that $b_{\pm mn}$ be equal to zero for all mn.

Substituting (27) into (30), it follows that

$$a_{\pm mn} = \frac{2E_1}{\pi^2} \int_0^\pi \int_0^{\cos^{-1}(-k\cos y)} (\cos x + k \cos y) \cos (nx \pm my) \, dx \, dy \qquad (31)$$

The cosine of the sum of two angles may be expanded trigonometrically, thus yielding

$$a_{\pm mn} = \frac{2E_1}{\pi^2} \int_0^\pi \int_0^{\cos^{-1}(-k\cos y)} (\cos x + k \cos y) \cos nx \cos my \, dx \, dy \qquad (32)$$

It is easier to solve integral (32) for the individual components directly; a sample solution for a_{11} is presented as follows:

Consider the solution for a_{11} which will yield the amplitudes of the components with angular velocities $\omega_1 \pm \omega_2$. Then

$$a_{11} = \frac{2E_1}{\pi^2} \int_0^\pi \int_0^{\cos^{-1}(-k\cos y)} (\cos x + k \cos y) \cos x \cos y \, dx \, dy \qquad (33)$$

Performing the integration with respect to x, we get

$$a_{11} = \frac{E_1}{\pi^2} \int_0^\pi \cos y [\cos^{-1} (-k \cos y) + k \cos y \sqrt{1 - k^2 \cos^2 y}] \, dy \qquad (34)$$

This may be written in the form,

$$a_{11} = \frac{kE_1}{\pi^2} \int_0^\pi \frac{\sin^2 y + \cos^2 y(1 - k^2 \cos^2 y)}{\sqrt{1 - k^2 \cos^2 y}} \, dy \qquad (35)$$

Making the substitution

$$\cos y = z \qquad (36)$$

integral (35) evolves into the elliptic form

$$a_{11} = \frac{2kE_1}{\pi^2} \int_0^1 \frac{1 - k^2 z^4}{\sqrt{(1 - z^2)(1 - k^2 z^2)}} \, dz \qquad (37)$$

This may be written, after some manipulation, as follows:

$$a_{11} = \frac{4E_1}{3\pi^2 k} [(1 + k^2)\mathcal{E} - (1 - k^2)\mathcal{K}] \qquad (38)$$

where $\mathcal{K}$ and $\mathcal{E}$ are elliptic integrals of the first and second kind, respectively.

The numerical solutions of these elliptic integrals may be found tabulated in "Pierce's Short Tables of Integrals." Figure 4 shows a graph of a_{11} versus k, in addition to curves for other components of low order, whose equations which represent appropriate solutions of integral (32) are tabulated in Bennet's paper.

For the case where $k = 0$, only one wave is present, and the axis intercepts in Fig. 4 for $a_{00}/2$, a_{10}, and a_{20} at $k = 0$ are the values which are

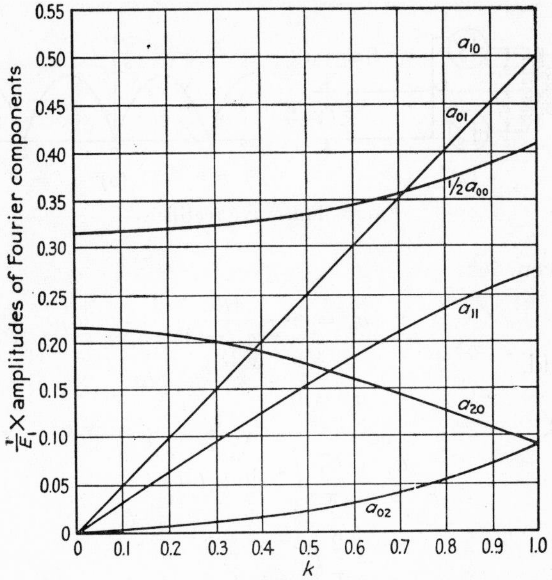

FIG. 4. (*Courtesy of Bell System Technical Journal.*)

obtained from a Fourier-series analysis of a single-tone half-wave rectified wave.

If more than two generators are placed in series with the rectifier and the resistance in Fig. 3, a multiple Fourier series must be used to determine the harmonic content of the output wave. However, the calculations for the coefficients for even a triple Fourier series representing the rectified output due to three series generators become very laborious, the solution being theoretically possible.

4. Biphase (Full-wave) Rectification. Biphase rectification is produced by inverting one-half of a normal sinusoidal wave, using a circuit of the type pictured in Fig. 5*a*, which employs two rectifiers. The output wave as measured across R (neglecting the voltage drop across the rectifiers) is shown in Fig. 5*b* and may be expressed mathematically as follows:

$$\begin{aligned} f(\omega_1 t) &= -E_1 \sin \omega_1 t \qquad -\pi < \omega_1 t < 0 \\ &= E_1 \sin \omega_1 t \qquad 0 < \omega_1 t < \pi \end{aligned} \tag{39}$$

Since the wave in Fig. 5*b* is an even wave, it may be represented by a Fourier cosine series. The amplitudes of this Fourier series are determined as follows:

$$a_n = \frac{2}{\pi}\int_0^{\pi} f(\omega_1 t)\cos n\omega_1 t\, d\omega_1 t \tag{40}$$

$$= \frac{2E_1}{\pi}\int_0^{\pi} \sin \omega_1 t \cos n\omega_1 t\, d\omega_1 t \tag{41}$$

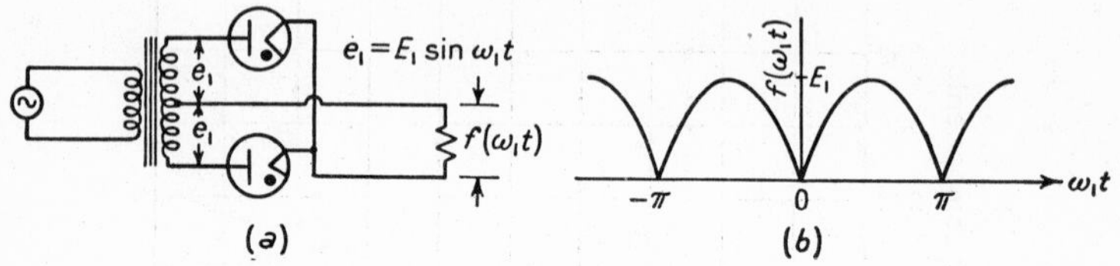

FIG. 5. Full-wave rectifier.

When n is even,

$$a_n = -\frac{4E_1}{\pi(n^2 - 1)} \tag{42}$$

When n is odd,

$$a_n = 0 \tag{43}$$

When $n = 0$,

$$\frac{a_0}{2} = \frac{E_1}{\pi}\int_0^{\pi} \sin \omega_1 t\, d\omega_1 t \tag{44}$$

$$= \frac{2}{\pi}E_1 \tag{45}$$

The Fourier cosine series representing (39) may therefore be written, letting $n = 2r$,

$$f(\omega_1 t) = E_1\left(\frac{2}{\pi} - \frac{4}{\pi}\sum_{r=1}^{\infty}\frac{\cos 2r\omega_1 t}{4r^2 - 1}\right) \tag{46}$$

When written out, Eq. (46) becomes

$$f(\omega_1 t) = \frac{2E_1}{\pi}\left(1 - \frac{2}{1\cdot 3}\cos 2\omega_1 t - \frac{2}{3\cdot 5}\cos 4\omega_1 t - \cdots\right) \tag{47}$$

5. Polyphase Rectification. In high-power high-voltage rectifier installations in which the power is taken from a three-phase line, a polyphase rectifier such as that pictured in Fig. 6*a* enjoys widespread use.

The use of two rectifier tubes with each phase will produce a set of six positive-directed sine voltage loops, each displaced from the adjacent one by a phase angle of 60° as shown in Fig. 6*b*. Because the current will flow from any one-anode circuit only when the voltage of that circuit exceeds that of the instantaneous value of any of the others, the voltage which will appear across R will be the dark line in Fig. 6b formed by the crests of the waves and not by the total instantaneous sum of the waves. Since the wave is even and periodic, we may express it mathematically as

$$\begin{aligned} f(3\omega_1 t) &= -E_1 \sin(\omega_1 t - 60°) \qquad -\pi < 3\omega_1 t < 0 \\ &= E_1 \sin(\omega_1 t + 60°) \qquad 0 < 3\omega_1 t < \pi \end{aligned} \tag{48}$$

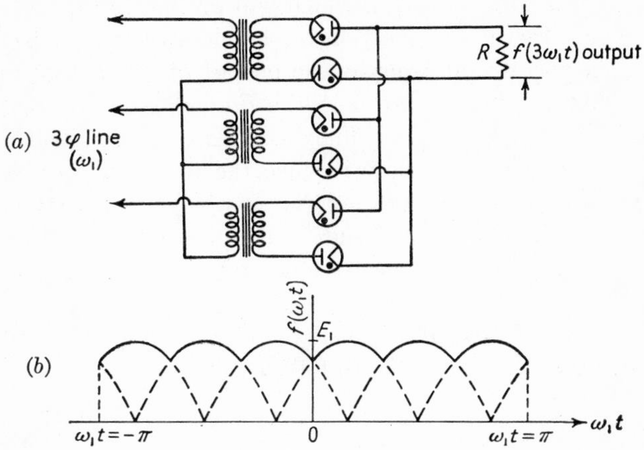

FIG. 6. Polyphase rectifier.

Using a Fourier cosine series for the interval $-\pi/3 < \omega_1 t < \pi/3$, it follows that

$$a_n = \frac{2E_1}{\pi} \int_0^{\pi} 0 \cdot 5 \sin \omega_1 t \cos 3n\omega_1 t \; d3\omega_1 t \tag{49}$$

When $n = 0$, we get

$$\frac{a_0}{2} = \frac{3}{\pi} E_1 \tag{50}$$

When $n \neq 1$, we get

$$a_n = \frac{E_1}{\pi} \left[-\frac{\cos (1 - 3n)3\omega_1 t}{2(1 - 3n)} - \frac{\cos (1 + 3n)3\omega_1 t}{2(1 + 3n)} \right]_0^{\pi} \tag{51}$$

$$= \frac{E_1}{\pi} \frac{6}{1 - 9n^2} \tag{52}$$

The Fourier-series representation of (48) is thus found to be

$$f(3\omega_1 t) = \frac{3E_1}{\pi} \left(1 + 2 \sum_{n=1}^{\infty} \frac{\cos 3n\omega_1 t}{1 - 9n^2} \right) \tag{53}$$

Note that the average value of the wave across R is 0.955 E_1, showing that by using polyphase rectification we have closely approached the attainment of a constant-voltage output without the use of filters.

RECTIFIER FILTERS

6. Rectifiers and Filters. In order to avoid the use of batteries as a source of d-c voltage, it is customary in communication systems to start with a-c line voltage, step it up or down to an appropriate level, rectify the transformed voltage, and then pass the resulting complex current through a suitable filter network, which will produce a virtually constant output voltage. In the first portion of the chapter, the Fourier analysis of the complex waves appearing at the output of the rectifier tubes was discussed. We shall investigate here the fundamentals of rectifier-filter-circuit action, using the Fourier analysis. This analysis will differ from other types of filter-circuit analysis since the firing time of the gaseous rectifiers and hence the shape of the input complex wave will be a function of the parameters of the filter circuit.[1] This will be demonstrated in the sections to follow, using an approach and a point of view due to M. B. Stout.[2]

7. Rectifier Filter Networks. Since the full-wave type of rectifier enjoys very extensive use, the discussion to follow will be in terms of it. A four-

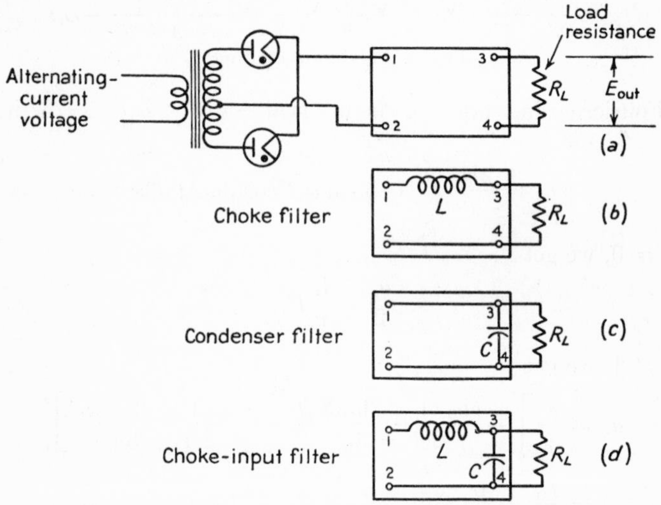

FIG. 7. Various elementary filter networks in a full-wave rectifier circuit.

terminal general representation of a filter in a full-wave rectifier circuit is shown in Fig. 7*a*. Figure 7*b*, *c*, and *d* pictures the schematic diagrams of the choke filter, capacitor filter, and choke input filter, respectively,

[1] P. T. Chin, Gaseous Rectifier Circuits, *Electronics*, vol. 18, Part I, pp. 138–143, April, 1945, Part II, pp. 132–137, May, 1945.

[2] M. B. Stout, Analysis of Rectifier Filter Circuits, *Elec. Eng.*, vol. 54, No. 9, pp. 977–986, September, 1935.

which will be dealt with in this section. There are, of course, other types of filter circuits, but the analysis of those circuits illustrated in Fig. 7 will permit us to illustrate the general Fourier-analysis approach.

8. Per Cent Ripple. The output of a rectifier filter is not absolutely constant and contains some periodic variations. Owing to these periodic variations, it is convenient to describe the quality of the filter output in terms of a ripple factor which will be referred to as *per cent ripple*.

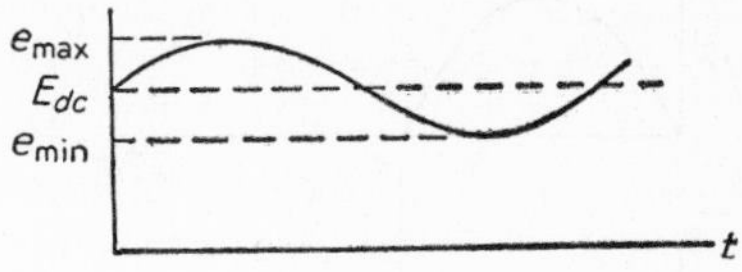

FIG. 8.

There are two ways in which we may describe this ripple factor:

1. We may describe per cent ripple in terms of the maximum, minimum, and mean values of the output voltage (see Fig. 8) as follows:

$$\text{Per cent ripple} = \frac{e_{max} - e_{min}}{E_{dc}} \times 100 \tag{54}$$

2. Per cent ripple may also be described in terms of the most prominent harmonic of the output voltage. If the second harmonic voltage across the output is the most prominent one,[1] then the per cent second harmonic ripple may be defined as

$$\text{Per cent second harmonic ripple} = \frac{2E_2}{E_{dc}} \times 100 \tag{55}$$

where E_2 is the maximum value of the second harmonic voltage appearing across the load.

In most practical applications involving full-wave rectification, except for extreme or unusual loading conditions, the result as calculated, using either (54) or (55), will be virtually the same. The amount of per cent ripple which can be tolerated depends on the application. Many amplifier and transmitter power supplies operate satisfactorily with a ripple factor of around 5 per cent, although a high-fidelity sound-reproduction installation or a continuous-wave magnetron power supply may demand a ripple factor of less than 1 per cent.

9. Full-wave Rectifier and a Choke Filter. Consider the case when the output of a rectifier is passed through the choke filter which is illustrated

[1] Note that although the angular velocity of a full-wave voltage applied to the rectifiers is ω, the first harmonic of the Fourier series is at 2ω. This is due to the fact that the inversion of one loop of the sine wave to produce the voltage pictured in Fig. 5*b* results in a complex wave whose frequency is twice that of the line voltage. Thus, for example, if the line voltage is 60 cycles, the first harmonic to appear across the load has a frequency of 120 cycles. This is, of course, true only of full-wave rectification and does not hold for half-wave or polyphase rectification.

in Fig. 7b. The basic effect of the presence of the choke in the circuit is to cause a delay in current flow and to discourage current discontinuities. As is shown in Fig. 9 for the case when a half-wave rectified voltage is impressed on the choke filter, the current through the RL circuit will not rise as quickly as will the impressed voltage. The rate of change of current

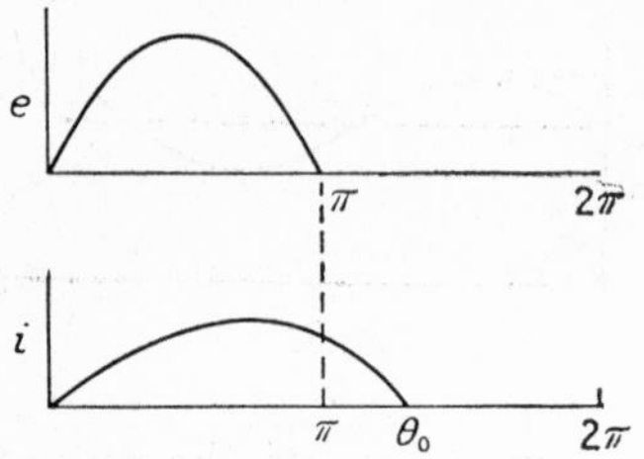

FIG. 9.

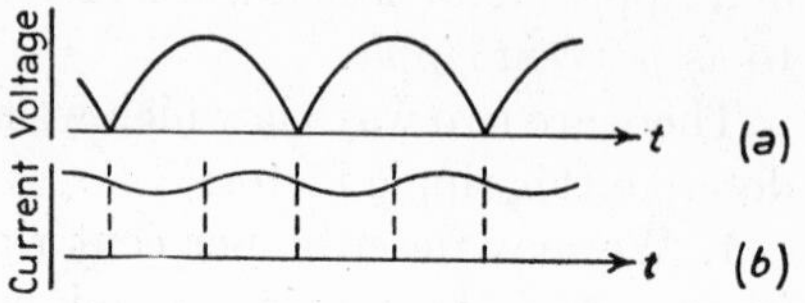

FIG. 10.

will lag that of the voltage, and although the voltage goes to zero at the phase angle π, the current will not come to zero until some angle θ_0, where $\pi < \theta_0 < 2\pi$.

When a full-wave rectified voltage is applied to the choke filter, the current variation will be similar to that illustrated in Fig. 10b. The current does not go to zero at any time during a cycle, and a fair degree of constancy of the d-c voltage output is achieved.

Analytically, we may solve for the output voltage across the output load by using the Fourier analysis as follows:

Since the impedance of the series RL circuit is

$$Z_s(\omega) = R + j\omega L \tag{56}$$

it follows that the current through the circuit due to the impressed full-wave rectified voltage is [recalling from (47) that n is even]

$$i = \frac{2E}{\pi}\left[\frac{1}{R} - \frac{2}{3}\frac{1}{\sqrt{R^2 + (2\omega L)^2}}\cos\left(2\omega t - \tan^{-1}\frac{2\omega L}{R}\right) - \cdots \right.$$
$$\left. - \frac{2}{n^2 - 1}\frac{1}{\sqrt{R^2 + (n\omega L)^2}}\cos\left(n\omega t - \tan^{-1}\frac{n\omega L}{R}\right) - \cdots\right] \tag{57}$$

The voltage e_0 across the load resistance is

$$e_0 = \frac{2E}{\pi}\left[1 - \frac{2}{3}\frac{R}{\sqrt{R^2 + (2\omega L)^2}}\cos\left(2\omega t - \tan^{-1}\frac{2\omega L}{R}\right) - \cdots \right.$$
$$\left. - \frac{2}{n^2 - 1}\frac{R}{\sqrt{R^2 + (n\omega L)^2}}\cos\left(n\omega t - \tan^{-1}\frac{n\omega L}{R}\right) - \cdots\right] \tag{58}$$

By using harmonic summation of the type which was illustrated in Sec. 9 of Chap. 6, the output waveform for various values of R and L

may be deduced. The current waveform shown in Fig. 10*b* is approximately that which will be yielded by $R = 2{,}000$ ohms and $L = 10$ henrys, and the output voltage waveform will, of course, be identical.

10. The Capacitor Filter. When a capacitor filter, such as that pictured in Fig. 7*c*, is installed between a rectifier and a resistive load, the rectifier tubes do not conduct for a large portion of each cycle of operation, and the problem must be first approached from the circuit-analysis standpoint.

When the parallel RC circuit in Fig. 11*a* is charged to some peak voltage

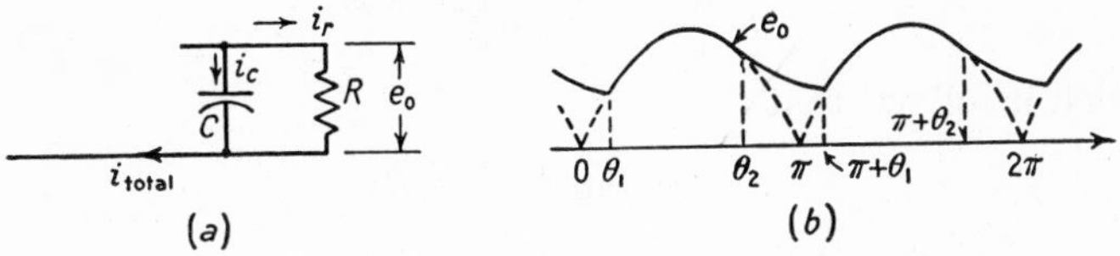

FIG. 11.

and then disconnected from the charging source, the capacitor will discharge exponentially through the resistance and a voltage will appear across the parallel RC circuit which is described by the relationship

$$e_0 = E_0 e^{-t/RC} \tag{59}$$

where E_0 is the voltage which appears across the circuit at the instant the discharge begins and RC is the time constant of the circuit.

When a sine-wave voltage is impressed on the series circuit consisting of the rectifier and the RC circuit, the voltage will charge the capacitor as the voltage increases. During this time, the rectifier conducts. When the voltage passes its maximum value and starts to decrease, the capacitor starts to discharge through the resistor. At some phase angle θ_2 (see Fig. 11*b*), the rate of change of the decrease of the sine voltage will equal the rate of change of the capacitor voltage, and the rectifier will cease to conduct from that point on until the phase angle $\theta_1 + \pi$, at which point the capacitor voltage will equal the rectifier plate voltage, and the tube will fire. After $\theta_1 + \pi$, the sine-wave voltage again rises above the voltage to which the capacitor has discharged, and conduction again takes place.

The general behavior of the output voltage for full-wave rectification is shown in Fig. 11*b*, and we may deduce its behavior analytically as follows:

The rectifier conducts from θ_1 to θ_2 and from $\theta_1 + \pi$ to $\theta_2 + \pi$. During the conduction time, the voltage across the capacitor (and therefore the output voltage) e_0 is

$$e_0 = E \sin \omega t \qquad \theta_1 < \omega t < \theta_2 \tag{60}$$

and the capacitor current and resistor current are, respectively,

$$i_c = C\frac{de_0}{dt} \tag{61}$$

$$= \omega CE \cos \omega t \qquad \theta_1 < \omega t < \theta_2 \tag{62}$$

$$i_r = \frac{E}{R}\sin \omega t \qquad \theta_1 < \omega t < \theta_2 \tag{63}$$

At $\omega t = \theta_2$,

$$\frac{E}{R}\sin \omega t = \omega CE \cos \omega t \tag{64}$$

from which it follows that

$$\theta_2 = \tan^{-1}(-\omega CR) \tag{65}$$

where the minus sign indicates that θ_2 is in the second quadrant.

After θ_2, the RC circuit is independent of the rectifier voltage since the rectifier has ceased to conduct. Therefore,

$$e_0 = E \sin \theta_2 \exp\left[-\frac{1}{\omega CR}(\omega t - \theta_2)\right] \tag{66}$$

$$= \frac{\omega CRE}{\sqrt{1 + (\omega CR)^2}} \exp\left[-\frac{1}{\omega CR}(\omega t - \theta_2)\right] \qquad \theta_2 < \omega t < \theta_1 + \pi \tag{67}$$

whereupon

$$i_c = -\frac{\omega CE}{\sqrt{1 + (\omega CR)^2}} \exp\left[-\frac{1}{\omega CR}(\omega t - \theta_2)\right] \qquad \theta_2 < \omega t < \theta_1 + \pi \tag{68}$$

$$i_r = \frac{\omega CE}{\sqrt{1 + (\omega CR)^2}} \exp\left[-\frac{1}{\omega CR}(\omega t - \theta_2)\right] \qquad \theta_2 < \omega t < \theta_1 + \pi \tag{69}$$

Note that when the rectifier is not conducting, i_c and i_r are equal in magnitude but opposite in sign.

We may deduce the value of phase angle $\theta_1 + \pi$ at which the rectifier again conducts by finding the value of θ_1 which satisfies the relationship,

$$\sin \theta_1 = \left[\frac{\omega CR}{\sqrt{1 + (\omega CR)^2}} e^{-(1/\omega CR)(\pi - \theta_2)}\right] e^{-\theta_1/\omega CR} \tag{70}$$

Since θ_2 is readily found, we may determine θ_1 from (70) by trial and error.

The extent to which the output voltage e_0 approaches a constant value is dependent on the time constant RC of the choke and load circuit. If the circuit is lightly loaded, the per cent ripple will be negligible. If the circuit is heavily loaded, however, the ripple may be very great. The exact shape of e_0 is easily determined by computing the waveform once

θ_1 and θ_2 are known; the per cent ripple (54) is quickly found from the graph of the waveform.

11. Numerical Example of *RC* Filter. For the filter pictured in Fig. 11*a*, let $C = 4\mu f$, and let $R = 2{,}000$ ohms. If a full-wave rectified voltage of maximum amplitude 250 volts, whose basic frequency is 60 cycles before rectification, is impressed at the filter input, it follows that

$$\theta_2 = \tan^{-1}(-377 \times 4 \times 10^{-6} \times 2{,}000) \tag{71}$$

$$= \tan^{-1}(-3.016) = 1.891 \text{ radians} \tag{72}$$

$$\sin \theta_1 = \left[\frac{3.016}{\sqrt{1 + (3.016)^2}} e^{-(\pi - 1.891)/3.016}\right] e^{-\theta_1/3.016} \tag{73}$$

By trial and error, we find

$$\theta_1 = 31.5° \tag{74}$$

Substituting (72) and (74) into (62), (63), (68), and (69), we may plot i_c and i_r for a full cycle of operation as shown in Fig. 12. Also included in

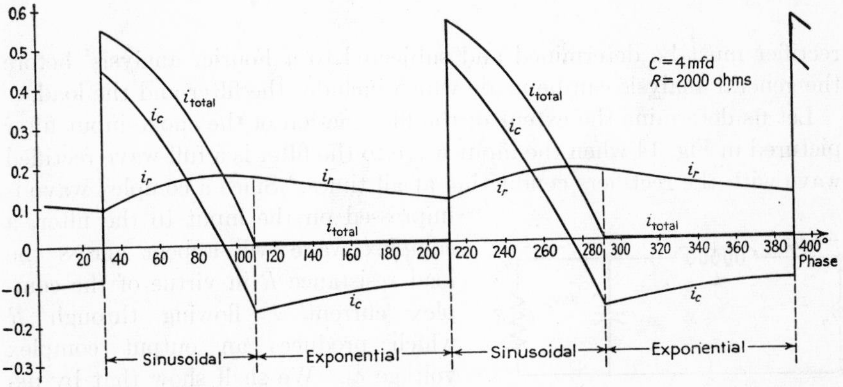

FIG. 12. Currents in the *RC* filter in Fig. 11*a* when $C = 4$ μf and $R = 2{,}000$ ohms.

Fig. 12 is the total current, which is the current delivered by the rectifier and which is described as

$$i_{total} = i_r + i_c \tag{75}$$

12. The Choke-input Filter. Consider the case of the choke-input filter which is pictured in Fig. 7*d*. This commonly used filter combines the features of both the choke filter and the capacitor filter. Figure 13*a* shows the current from the rectifier into the capacitor filter as discussed in the preceding section. As inductance is added, as shown in Fig. 13*b* and *c*, the conducting region of the rectifier increases until, for a large enough value of L, the rectifier will conduct at all portions of the cycle of operation. If an analysis of the choke-input filter is made when the current does not flow during the entire cycle, the exact shape of the voltage as produced by both the conducting and nonconducting regions of the

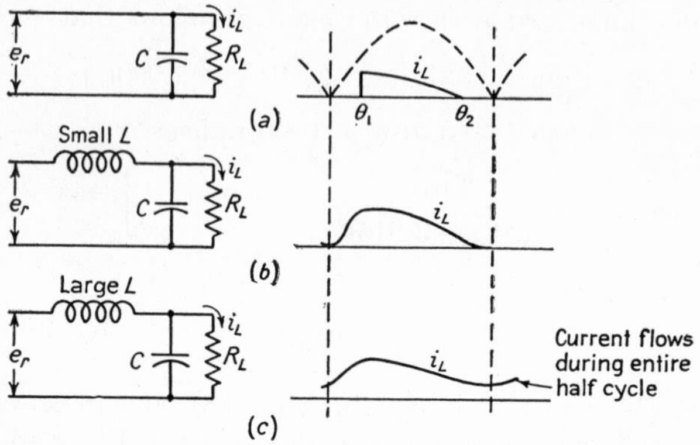

FIG. 13. Behavior of the load-current flow in a choke-input filter as a function of the choke inductance.

rectifier must be determined and subjected to a Fourier analysis[1] before the general analysis can be made which includes the filter and the load.

Let us determine the extent of the filter action of the choke-input filter pictured in Fig. 14 when the input wave to the filter is a full-wave rectified wave with the rectifiers conducting at all times. Since a complex wave is impressed on the input to the filter, a complex wave will appear across the load resistance R in virtue of the complex current i_r flowing through R which produces an output complex voltage e_0. We shall show that by using proper circuit parameters the harmonic content of e_0 will be negligible, the average value being the only significant term in the Fourier-series expansion.

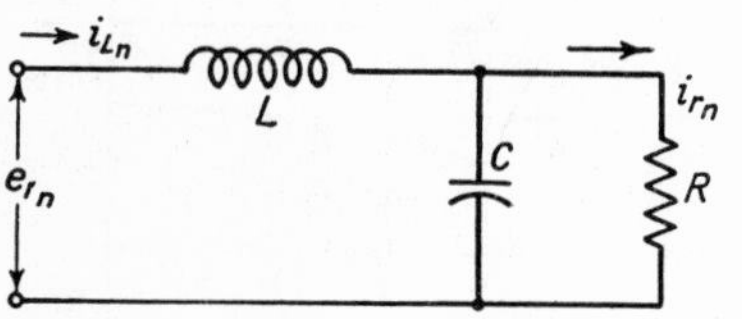

FIG. 14.

The network analysis to determine i_r is developed as follows:

It is evident from Fig. 14, that for some simple harmonic impressed voltage $e_{1,n}$, whose angular velocity is $n\omega$, we get the output voltage

$$e_{0,n} = i_{L,n} \frac{R}{1 + jn\omega RC} \tag{76}$$

[1] See M. B. Stout, Analysis of Rectifier Filter Circuits, *Elec. Eng.*, vol. 54, No. 9, pp. 977–986, September, 1935.

The currents flowing in the circuit due to $e_{1,n}$ are described as follows:

$$i_{r,n} = \frac{e_{0,n}}{R} \tag{77}$$

$$i_{c,n} = j\omega Ce_{0,n} \tag{78}$$

$$i_{L,n} = i_{r,n} + i_{c,n} = e_{0,n}\frac{1 + jn\omega RC}{R} \tag{79}$$

The impressed voltage $e_{1,n}$ may be written as the sum of the output voltage $e_{0,n}$ and the voltage drop across the inductance, as follows:

$$e_{1,n} = jn\omega Li_{L,n} + i_{L,n}\frac{R}{1 + jn\omega RC} \tag{80}$$

$$= i_{L,n}\frac{R(1 - n^2\omega^2LC) + jn\omega L}{1 + jn\omega RC} \tag{81}$$

Since

$$e_{0,n} = e_{1,n}\frac{R}{R(1 - n^2\omega^2LC) + jn\omega L} \tag{82}$$

we get, for the current through the load resistance R,

$$i_{r,n} = e_{1,n}\frac{1}{R(1 - n^2\omega^2LC) + jn\omega L} \tag{83}$$

Rationalizing (83), it follows that

$$i_{r,n} = e_{1,n}\left[\frac{R(1 - n^2\omega^2LC)}{R^2(1 - n^2\omega^2LC)^2 + (n\omega L)^2} - j\frac{n\omega L}{R^2(1 - n^2\omega^2LC)^2 + (n\omega L)^2}\right] \tag{84}$$

which is of the form,

$$i_{r,n} = e_{1,n}[G(n\omega) + jB(n\omega)] \tag{85}$$

Since the output voltage $e_{0,n}$ may be determined from the relationship

$$e_{0,n} = i_{r,n}R \tag{86}$$

we get

$$e_{0,n} = e_{1,n}R[G(n\omega) + jB(n\omega)] \tag{87}$$

which is the nth harmonic of the output voltage. The total output voltage may be determined by the point-to-point summation of the significant harmonics.

13. Numerical Illustration of (87). As a numerical illustration, consider the case when $L = 10$ henrys, $R = 2{,}000$ ohms, $C = 4\ \mu f$, and $f = 60$

cycles. Let the output of the full-wave rectifier be

$$e_r = 225 - 150 \cos 2\omega t - 30 \cos 4\omega t - \cdots \tag{88}$$

Substituting the values of the circuit parameters into (87), it can be shown that

$$e_0 = 225 - (1.2 + j6.6) \cos 2\omega t - j0.3 \cos 4\omega t - \cdots \tag{89}$$

The important term is the average value of 225 volts. For all practical purposes the other harmonics may be neglected. Note that the per cent second harmonic ripple is

$$\text{Per cent second harmonic ripple} = \frac{2\,|E_2|}{E_{dc}} \times 100 \tag{90}$$

$$= \frac{2 \times 6.68}{225} \times 100 \tag{91}$$

$$= 0.596 \text{ per cent} \tag{92}$$

which is well below 1 per cent.

PROBLEMS

1. Calculate the amplitudes of the first five harmonics of voltage appearing across the resistor R in Fig. 1, if the drop across the rectifier is 20 volts and $E_1 = 375$ volts.

2. If a half-wave rectified current whose peak amplitude is 150 ma is passed through a resistor $R = 10^4$ ohms, calculate the amplitudes of the first three voltage harmonics appearing across that resistor.

3. Show that it follows from Eq. (31) that

$$a_{11} = \frac{4E_1}{3\pi^2 k} [(1 + k^2)\,\mathcal{E} - (1 - k^2)\mathcal{K}]$$

4. Calculate the amplitudes of the first five harmonics of the voltage appearing across R in Fig. 5 if the primary voltage is 110 volts rms at 60 cycles, the step-up ratio of the transformer is 8, and the voltage drop across each tube is 10 volts. What is the frequency of the fundamental?

5. Calculate the amplitudes of the first five harmonics and the d-c component of a polyphase rectified wave when 12 loops of peak voltage 500 occur in the interval $-\pi < \omega_1 t < \pi$.

6. Deduce θ_1 for the filter circuit in Fig. 11*a* when
a. $C = 8\ \mu\text{f}$, $R = 5{,}000$ ohms
b. $C = 8\ \mu\text{f}$, $R = 500$ ohms

7. *a*. Verify the numerical values listed in Eq. (89).
b. Solve for the cases when $C = 8\ \mu\text{f}$ and $R = 1{,}000$ ohms. Compare the per cent ripple for this case with (92).

8. Discuss the general effect of adding another filter section to the choke-input filter from the Fourier harmonic standpoint.

CHAPTER 9

HARMONICS AND TRANSIENTS IN FILTER NETWORKS

HARMONIC CONSIDERATIONS IN FILTER NETWORKS

1. Introduction. A filter network[1] is one which permits only those waves existing in certain pass bands to pass through them. They are widely used in communication networks, and the section to follow will discuss the frequency-selective characteristics of constant-k filters, which can be designed to be frequency-discriminatory within desired limits. In addition, filters may be made to have impedance and transient characteristics which will make them useful as load impedances in amplifiers or pulse-forming artificial lines in pulser systems.

2. Pass-band Characteristics of Constant-k Filters.[2] In Fig. 1a and b, single T- and π-section filters are illustrated. The circuit parameters $Z_1/2$, Z_2, and Z_1, $2Z_2$ for the T and π sections, respectively, are so chosen that they may be cascaded as shown in Fig. 1c to form identical transmission networks (assuming that the terminations are correctly made).

In these filters, let Z_1 and Z_2 satisfy the criterion

$$Z_1Z_2 = k^2 \tag{1}$$

where k is a real number. Note, for example, that if Z_1 is a pure inductance reactance $j\omega L$ and if Z_2 is a pure capacitive reactance $1/j\omega C$, then

$$Z_1Z_2 = j\omega L \frac{1}{j\omega C} \tag{2}$$

$$= \frac{L}{C} = k^2 \tag{3}$$

In the networks to be discussed, Z_1 and Z_2 are pure reactances and therefore absorb no power themselves, all the power absorbed by the networks being transmitted to the load Z_0.

[1] For an extensive discussion of filter networks which will be of considerable practical interest to the engineer, see F. E. Terman, Network Theory, Filters and Equalizers, *Proc. IRE*, vol. 31, 1943, Part I, pp. 164–175, April, Part II, pp. 233–240, May, Part III, pp. 288–302, June.

[2] O. J. Zobel, Theory and Design of Uniform and Composite Electric Wave Filters, *Bell System Tech. J.*, January, 1923.

Let us now consider the input impedance of the T network in Fig. 1a. This network is terminated by an impedance Z_0 which, in general, will be

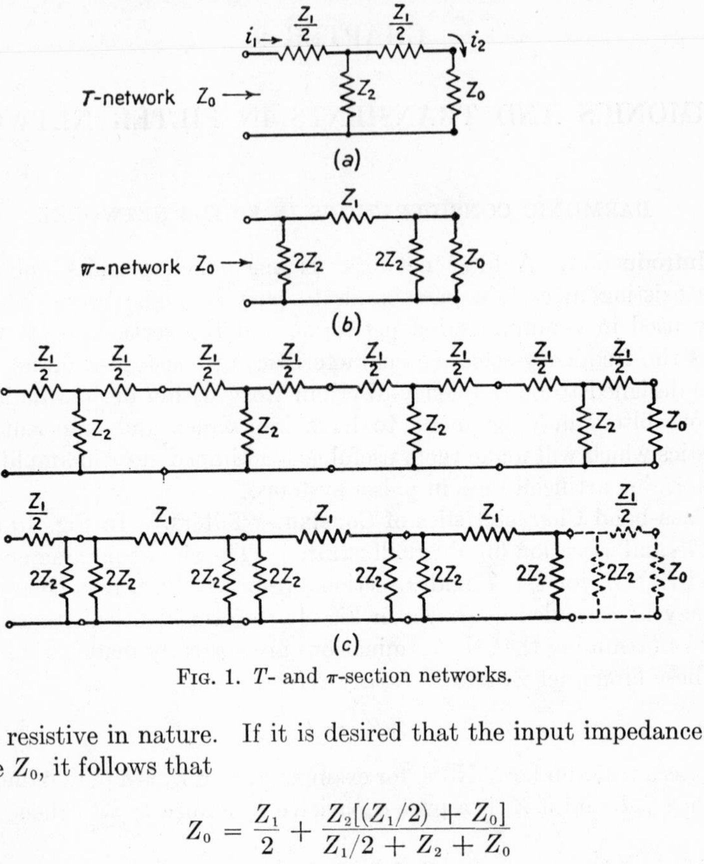

FIG. 1. T- and π-section networks.

purely resistive in nature. If it is desired that the input impedance shall also be Z_0, it follows that

$$Z_0 = \frac{Z_1}{2} + \frac{Z_2[(Z_1/2) + Z_0]}{Z_1/2 + Z_2 + Z_0} \tag{4}$$

or

$$\frac{Z_1Z_0}{2} + Z_0Z_2 + Z_0^2 = \frac{Z_1^2}{4} + \frac{Z_1Z_2}{2} + \frac{Z_1Z_0}{2} + \frac{Z_1Z_2}{2} + Z_0Z_2 \tag{5}$$

This becomes

$$Z_0^2 = \frac{Z_1^2}{4} + Z_1Z_2 \tag{6}$$

or

$$Z_{0T} = \sqrt{Z_1Z_2 + \frac{Z_1^2}{4}} \tag{7}$$

where the subscript T refers to the T section. Let us now perform the same manipulation on the π network, requiring that the input impedance be Z_0 for a termination of Z_0. Therefore

$$Z_0 = \frac{2Z_2\{Z_1 + [2Z_2Z_0/(2Z_2 + Z_0)]\}}{2Z_2 + Z_1 + [2Z_2Z_0/(2Z_2 + Z_0)]} \tag{8}$$

After some algebraic manipulation, we get

$$Z_0^2 = \frac{Z_1^2Z_2^2}{Z_1Z_2 + (Z_1^2/4)} \tag{9}$$

or

$$Z_{0\pi} = \frac{Z_1Z_2}{\sqrt{Z_1Z_2 + (Z_1^2/4)}} = \frac{Z_1Z_2}{Z_{0T}} \tag{10}$$

where the subscript π refers to a π section.

Note that both Z_{0T} and $Z_{0\pi}$ contain the term $\sqrt{Z_1Z_2 + (Z_1^2/4)}$ which can be written

$$\sqrt{Z_1Z_2 + \frac{Z_1^2}{4}} = \sqrt{Z_1Z_2}\sqrt{1 + \frac{Z_1}{4Z_2}} \tag{11}$$

Since Z_1 and Z_2 are reactances and cannot absorb power, then the terminating resistance will receive power only when the input impedance Z_{0T} or $Z_{0\pi}$ is a pure resistance (the case of Z_{0T} or $Z_{0\pi}$ having both a resistance and reactive component does not arise). This can be true only if the term $\sqrt{1 + (Z_1/4Z_2)}$ is real and not imaginary, the former being true only for the following ranges of value of $Z_1/4Z_2$,

$$-1 \leq \frac{Z_1}{4Z_2} \leq 0 \tag{12}$$

since it can be shown that if (1) is adhered to, the quotient of Z_1 and Z_2 will be a negative quantity. It is evident then that a constant-k T or π network which is terminated in Z_0 will pass only those waves whose frequencies lie in the pass band bounded by the values

$$\frac{Z_1}{4Z_2} = 0 \qquad \frac{Z_1}{4Z_2} = -1 \tag{13}$$

The frequency which is the boundary between the passband and the band in which no transmission takes place is called the cutoff frequency.

Consider the cutoff frequency when

$$Z_1 = j\omega L \qquad Z_2 = \frac{1}{j\omega C} \tag{14}$$

Then, denoting f_c as the cutoff frequency, we get

$$\frac{Z_1}{4Z_2} = \frac{2\pi^{-2}f_c^2LC}{4} = 0,\ -1 \tag{15}$$

which yields the values

$$f_c = 0 \tag{16}$$

$$f_c = \frac{1}{\pi\sqrt{LC}} \tag{17}$$

These represent the extremities of the pass band of the low-pass filter which is illustrated in Fig. 2*a*, and it is seen in Fig. 2*b* that all waves of frequency $f_c < f < \infty$ are attenuated, power in this range not appearing across R_0.

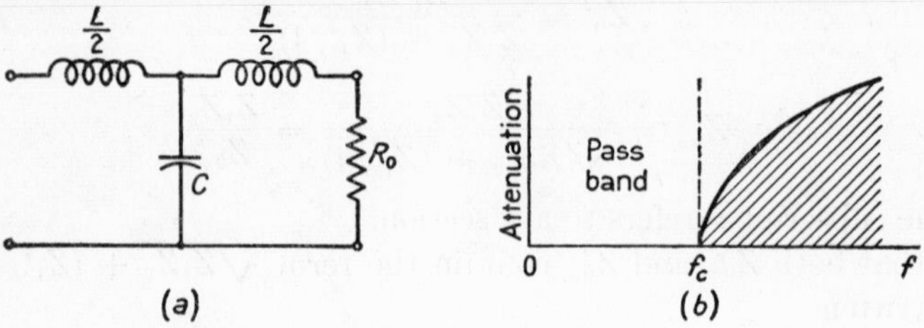

FIG. 2. Low-pass filter.

Consider now the cutoff frequencies when

$$Z_1 = \frac{1}{j\omega C} \qquad Z_2 = j\omega L \tag{18}$$

Then

$$\frac{Z_1}{4Z_2} = -\frac{1}{4(2\pi f_c)^2 LC} = 0, \ -1 \tag{19}$$

and

$$f_c = \infty \tag{20}$$

$$f_c = \frac{1}{4\pi\sqrt{LC}} \tag{21}$$

These equations describe the extremities of the pass band of the *high-pass* filter, which is illustrated in Fig. 3*a*. Its pass band, which extends from $f = f_c$ to $f = \infty$, is illustrated in Fig. 3*b*.

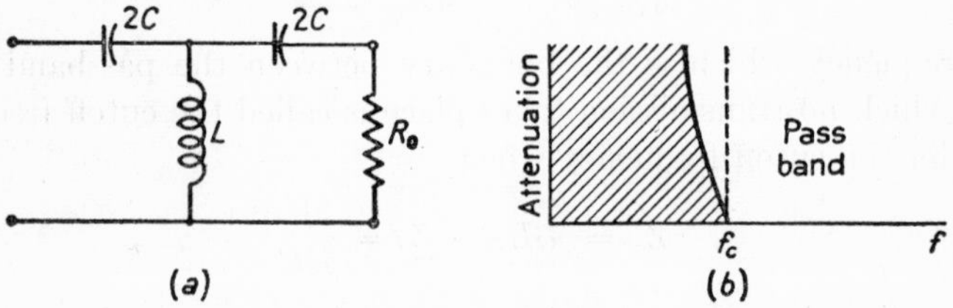

FIG. 3. High-pass filter.

Note in both Figs. 2*a* and 3*a* that the series parameters are $L/2$ and $2C$, respectively. This is due to the fact that we have described these parameters for a T network in terms of $Z_1/2$ so as to facilitate the transformation from a T to a π network.

When the transformation is from a T network to a π network, then the shunt-arm impedance Z_2 must be doubled to $2Z_2$ as is shown in Fig. 1*b*.

It is important to realize that, for such constant-*k* filters, the input impedance over the pass band is not constant. We may show for a low-pass T-network filter, in which $Z_1 = j\omega L$ and $Z_2 = 1/j\omega C$,

$$Z_{0T} = \sqrt{Z_1 Z_2 + \frac{Z_1^2}{4}} \tag{22}$$

$$= \sqrt{\frac{L}{C}\left[1 - \frac{\omega^2 LC}{4}\right]} \tag{23}$$

Substituting

$$f_c^2 = \frac{1}{\pi^2 LC} \tag{24}$$

into (23), we get

$$Z_{0T} = \sqrt{\frac{L}{C}\left(1 - \frac{f^2}{f_c^2}\right)} \tag{25}$$

In like manner, we may show that, for a high-pass filter in which $Z_1 = 1/j\omega C$ and $Z_2 = j\omega L$,

$$Z_{0T} = \sqrt{\frac{L}{C}\left(1 - \frac{f_c^2}{f^2}\right)} \tag{26}$$

which differs from (25) by the inversion of f/f_c. By plotting (25) and (26) as is shown in Fig. 4, we see that the input impedance Z_{0T} for either the high- or the low-pass filter varies from

$$Z_{0T} = \sqrt{\frac{L}{C}} \tag{27}$$

to zero, the latter value occurring at the cutoff frequency. The value $\sqrt{L/C}$ is actually the characteristic impedance of almost any dissipationless-filter network using inverse networks, thus leading to the use of the value

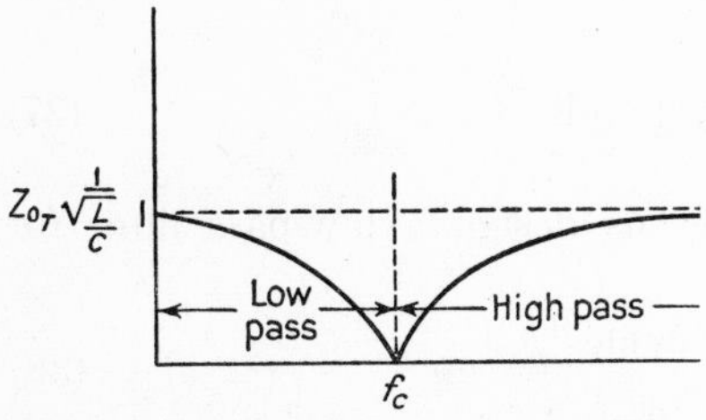

FIG. 4. Input impedance of the low-pass and high-pass filters.

$$Z_0 = \sqrt{\frac{L}{C}} \tag{28}$$

as the optimum terminating resistance, which is seen to be identical to k; that is,

$$Z_0 = \sqrt{\frac{L}{C}} = k \tag{29}$$

3. Design Equations for Constant-k Low-pass and High-pass Filters. We may relate the filter-network parameters L and C to the terminating resistance R_0 and the cutoff frequency f_c, as follows:

Low-pass Filter. For a low-pass filter,

$$R_0 = Z_0 = \sqrt{\frac{L}{C}} \tag{30}$$

$$f_c = \frac{1}{\pi\sqrt{LC}} \tag{31}$$

Solving these two equations simultaneously for L and C, we get

$$L = \frac{R_0}{\pi f_c} \qquad \text{henrys} \tag{32}$$

$$C = \frac{1}{\pi f_c R_0} \qquad \text{farads} \tag{33}$$

High-pass Filter. For a high-pass filter,

$$R_0 = Z_0 = \sqrt{\frac{L}{C}} \tag{34}$$

$$f_c = \frac{1}{4\pi\sqrt{LC}} \tag{35}$$

Solving these two equations for L and C, we get

$$L = \frac{1}{4\pi f_c R_0} \qquad \text{henrys} \tag{36}$$

$$C = \frac{R_0}{4\pi f_c} \qquad \text{farads} \tag{37}$$

4. Design of a Low-pass Filter. Let us design a low-pass filter for which

$$\begin{aligned} f_c &= 1{,}000 \text{ cycles} \\ R_0 &= 1{,}000 \text{ ohms} \end{aligned} \tag{38}$$

It follows then that

$$L = \frac{1{,}000}{\pi \times 1{,}000} = \frac{1}{\pi} \text{ henry} \tag{39}$$

$$C = \frac{1}{\pi \times 10^3 \times 10^3} = \frac{1}{\pi}\ \mu f \tag{40}$$

5. Bandpass Filter. It can be shown that the bandpass-filter circuit pictured in Fig. 5*a* will have a pass band at $f_{1c} < f < f_{2c}$ as depicted in Fig. 5*b* when

$$\begin{aligned} L_1 &= \frac{R_0}{\pi(f_{2c} - f_{1c})} \qquad & L_2 &= \frac{(f_{2c} - f_{1c})R_0}{4\pi f_{2c} f_{1c}} \\ C_1 &= \frac{f_{2c} - f_{1c}}{4\pi f_{1c} f_{2c} R_0} \qquad & C_2 &= \frac{1}{\pi(f_{2c} - f_{1c})R_0} \end{aligned} \tag{41}$$

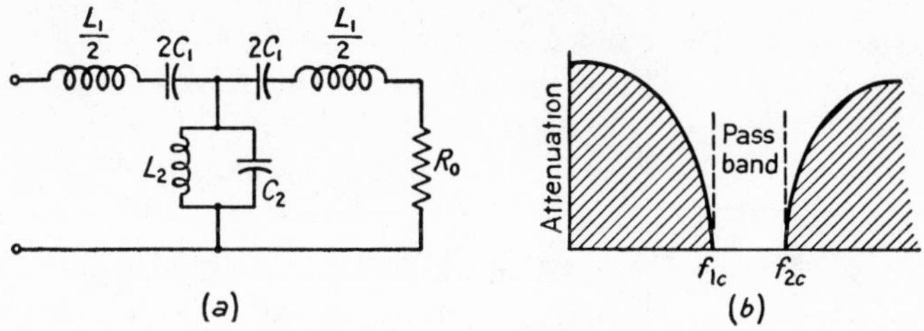

FIG. 5. Bandpass filter.

6. Propagation Characteristics of a Filter Network. Consider the ratio of the currents i_2 and i_1 in the T network pictured in Fig. 1a. This ratio may be written as follows:

$$\frac{i_1}{i_2} = \frac{(Z_1/2) + Z_0 + Z_2}{Z_2} \tag{42}$$

$$= 1 + \frac{Z_1}{2Z_2} + \sqrt{\frac{Z_1}{Z_2}}\sqrt{1 + \frac{Z_1}{4Z_2}} \tag{43}$$

This may be written in the form

$$\frac{i_1}{i_2} = e^{\Gamma} \tag{44}$$

$$= e^{\alpha + j\beta} \tag{45}$$

where Γ is the propagation constant, α being the attenuation constant and β the phase constant; α describes the amount of change in the absolute value of the current, and β describes the change in its phase.

Equation (43) is actually rather cumbersome for calculations of phase shift and attenuation in simple filter networks; of more interest is the following derivable expression [see (65)]:

$$\cosh \Gamma = 1 + \frac{Z_1}{2Z_2} \tag{46}$$

As an illustration of the use of Eq. (46) consider the case of a low-pass filter where

$$Z_1 = j\omega L \qquad Z_2 = \frac{1}{j\omega C} \tag{47}$$

Then

$$\cosh \Gamma = 1 - \frac{\omega^2 LC}{2} \tag{48}$$

We may write

$$\cosh \Gamma = \cosh \alpha \cos \beta + j \sinh \alpha \sin \beta$$

However, since the pass band exists for $-1 \leq Z_1/4Z_2 \leq 0$, then $\cosh \Gamma$ will vary from $+1$ to -1 and will be real in this range. Therefore

$$\cosh \alpha \cos \beta = 1 - \frac{\omega^2 LC}{2} \tag{49}$$

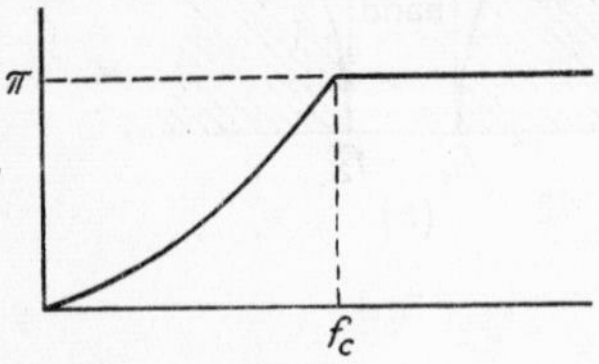

FIG. 6.

or, finally, since $\alpha = 0$ in the pass band,

$$\cos \beta = 1 - \frac{\omega^2 LC}{2} \tag{50}$$

$$\beta = \cos^{-1}\left(1 - \frac{\omega^2 LC}{2}\right) \tag{51}$$

The general shape of β versus f is shown in Fig. 6, where we see that $\beta = 0$ at $f = 0$ and increases almost linearly to a value of $\beta = \pi$ at $f = f_c$, at which value it remains for $f_c < f < \infty$.[1]

THE LAPLACE-TRANSFORM ANALYSIS OF TRANSIENTS IN FILTER NETWORKS

7. Transients in a Cascaded T-network Filter Network. Consider a filter network or an artificial transmission line which is made up of a set of m identical T sections in cascade and which is terminated in Z_r. The $(n + 1)$th section of this network is illustrated in Fig. 7 and is seen to

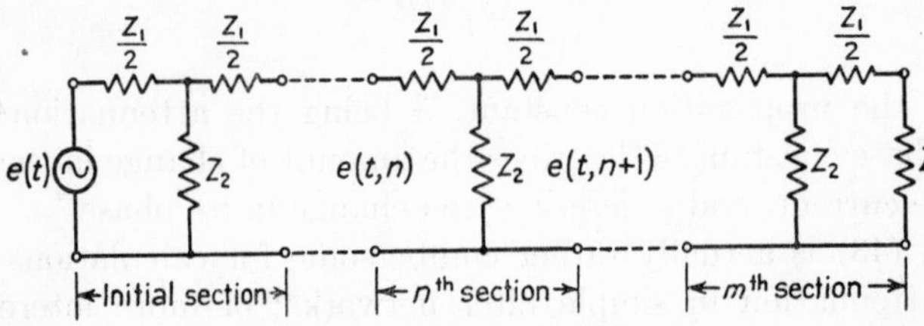

FIG. 7. Artificial transmission line.

be made up of two series sections $Z_1/2$ and a shunt section Z_2, the input and output voltages being $e(t,n)$ and $e(t, n + 1)$, respectively.

The equations describing the currents in the first, next to last, and last meshes in Fig. 7 are

$$\left(\frac{Z_1}{2} + Z_2\right)i(t,0) - Z_2 i(t,1) = e(t) \tag{52}$$

$$Z_2 i(t, m - 2) - (2Z_2 + Z_1)i(t, m - 1) + Z_2 i(t,m) = 0 \tag{53}$$

$$\left(Z_2 + \frac{Z_1}{2} + Z_r\right)i(t,m) - Z_2 i(t, m - 1) = 0 \tag{54}$$

[1] Compare Fig. 6 here with Fig. 2b in Chap. 20, which represents the phase characteristic of an idealized filter.

The Laplace transforms of these equations may be written as follows:

$$\left(\frac{Z_1}{2} + Z_2\right)i(s,0) - Z_2 i(s,1) = e(s) \tag{55}$$

$$Z_2 i(s, m-2) - (2Z_2 + Z_1)i(s, m-1) + Z_2 i(s,m) = 0 \tag{56}$$

$$\left(Z_2 + \frac{Z_1}{2} + Z_r\right)i(s,m) - Z_2 i(s, m-1) = 0 \tag{57}$$

The equation linking the $(m-1)$th mesh with the mth and $(m-2)$th meshes (with the exception of the end section) is

$$Z_2 i(s,m) - (2Z_2 + Z_1)i(s, m-1) + Z_2(s, m-2) = 0 \tag{58}$$

Equation (58) is a difference equation[1] which yields the characteristic equation

$$a^2 - 2\left(1 + \frac{Z_1}{2Z_2}\right)a + 1 = 0 \tag{59}$$

Let us assume the value $a = e^{\pm\Gamma}$. It follows that

$$e^{2\Gamma} - 2\left(1 + \frac{Z_1}{2Z_2}\right)e^{\Gamma} + 1 = 0 \tag{60}$$

which is satisfied by the roots

$$e^{\Gamma} = \lambda + \sqrt{\lambda^2 - 1} \tag{61}$$

$$e^{-\Gamma} = \lambda - \sqrt{\lambda^2 - 1} \tag{62}$$

where

$$\lambda = 1 + \frac{Z_1}{2Z_2} \tag{63}$$

Note that if we add (61) and (62) together and divide by 2, that is,

$$\frac{e^{\Gamma} + e^{-\Gamma}}{2} = \frac{\lambda + \lambda}{2} = \lambda \tag{64}$$

we get the familiar T network artificial-line relationship

$$\cosh \Gamma = 1 + \frac{Z_1}{2Z_2} \tag{65}$$

In like manner, we may show that

$$\sinh \Gamma = \sqrt{\lambda^2 - 1} \tag{66}$$

[1] For a treatment of the general properties of difference equations as solved by the Laplace transform, see Gardner and Barnes, "Transients in Linear Systems," Chap. IX, John Wiley & Sons, Inc., New York, 1942.

Let us solve for the Laplace-transformed current in the nth mesh of the m-mesh filter by assuming the solution

$$i(s,n) = Ae^{n\Gamma} + Be^{-n\Gamma} \tag{67}$$

where A and B are arbitrary constants. Substituting (67) into (55) and (57), we get

$$A\left(\frac{Z_1}{2} + Z_2 - Z_2e^{\Gamma}\right) + B\left(\frac{Z_1}{2} + Z_2 - Z_2e^{-\Gamma}\right) = e(s) \tag{68}$$

$$Ae^{m\Gamma}\left(\frac{Z_1}{2} + Z_2 - Z_2e^{-\Gamma} + Z_r\right) + Be^{-m\Gamma}\left(\frac{Z_1}{2} + Z_2 - Z_2e^{\Gamma} + Z_r\right) = 0 \tag{69}$$

Using (65) and (66) in (68) and (69), we get

$$-A \sinh \Gamma + B \sinh \Gamma = \frac{e(s)}{Z_2} \tag{70}$$

$$Ae^{m\Gamma}\left(\sinh \Gamma + \frac{Z_r}{Z_2}\right) + Be^{-m\Gamma}\left(-\sinh \Gamma + \frac{Z_r}{Z_2}\right) = 0 \tag{71}$$

Solving these equations for A and B and substituting the result into (67) yields

$$i(s,n) = e(s) \frac{\sinh \Gamma \cosh (m-n)\Gamma + (Z_r/Z_2) \sinh (m-n)\Gamma}{Z_2 \sinh \Gamma[\sinh m\Gamma \sinh \Gamma + (Z_r/Z_2) \cosh m\Gamma]} \tag{72}$$

$i(t,n)$ may be recovered from (72) by taking the inverse Laplace transform

$$i(t,n) = \frac{1}{2\pi j} \int_{\alpha - j\infty}^{\alpha + j\infty} i(s,n)e^{st}\, ds \tag{73}$$

8. Semiinfinite Low-pass Filter.[1] A filter network starting with a first section and having an infinite number of sections ($m \to \infty$) is referred to as a semiinfinite line. In such a line, the terminating impedance may be considered to be short-circuited, and reflections do not enter into the analysis. If we substitute $Z_r = 0$ into Eq. (72), we get

$$i(s,n) = \frac{e(s)}{Z_2 \sinh \Gamma} \frac{\cosh (m-n)\Gamma}{\sinh m\Gamma} \tag{74}$$

If $m \to \infty$, then it is easy to show that

$$\lim_{m\to\infty} \frac{\cosh (m-n)\Gamma}{\sinh m\Gamma} = \lim_{m\to\infty} \frac{e^{-n\Gamma} + e^{-(2m-n)\Gamma}}{1 - e^{-2m\Gamma}} \tag{75}$$

$$= e^{-n\Gamma} \tag{76}$$

[1] For an extensive discussion of the transient response of filters using the Fourier integral, see M. S. Corrington, Transient Response in Filters, *RCA Rev.*, vol. 10, pp. 397–429.

whereupon we see that

$$i(s,n) = \frac{e(s)}{Z_2 \sinh \Gamma} e^{-n\Gamma} \tag{77}$$

It is evident that the propagation factor Γ determines the progress of the wave through the network.

If the filter network is a low-pass filter such that $Z_1/2 = s(L/2)$ and $Z_2 = 1/sC$, we see that

$$Z_2 \sin \Gamma = \frac{L}{2} \sqrt{s^2 + \omega_c^2} \tag{78}$$

$$e^{-n\Gamma} = \frac{1}{(\lambda + \sqrt{\lambda^2 - 1})^n} = \frac{\omega_c^{2n}}{(\sqrt{s^2 + \omega_c^2} + s)^{2n}} \tag{79}$$

where

$$\omega_c = \frac{2}{\sqrt{LC}} = 2\pi f_c \tag{80}$$

and is recognized as the cutoff frequency of the low-pass filter [see Eq. (17)].

If a unit step voltage is impressed on the network such that $e(s) = 1/s$

$$i(t,n) = \frac{1}{2\pi j} \int_{\alpha - j\infty}^{\alpha + j\infty} \frac{2\omega_c^{2n} e^{st}\, ds}{sL \sqrt{s^2 + \omega_c^2}(\sqrt{s^2 + \omega_c^2} + s)^{2n}} \tag{81}$$

which yields the solution

$$i(t,n) = \frac{2}{L} \int_0^t J_{2n}(\omega_c t)\, dt \tag{82}$$

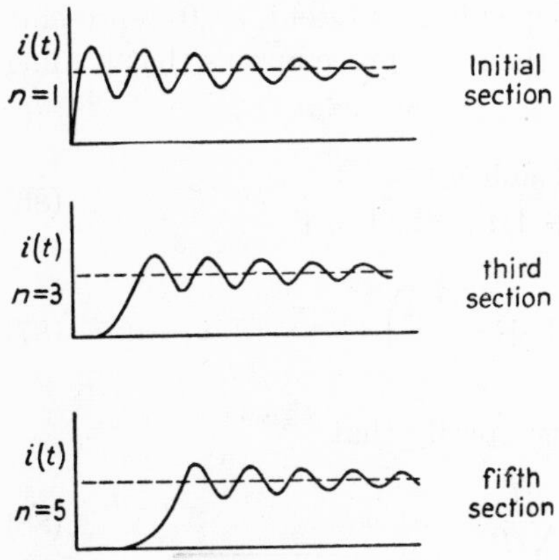

Fig. 8.

The progress of the step-function voltage down the semiinfinite filter is illustrated by the transient waves occurring in the first, third, and fifth sections, these waves being pictured in Fig. 8. The time delay, as imposed by the successive sections of the network, is obvious from a comparison of the transient waves in these sections.[1]

9. Pulse-forming Artificial Line. Consider a semiinfinite artificial line composed of low-pass filter sections which will be shown[2] to have pulse-forming qualities. The series elements are lumped inductances of inductance L, and the shunt elements are capacitances with capacity C.

[1] Carson and Zobel, Transient Oscillations in Electric Wave Filters, *Bell System Tech. J.*, July, 1923. [Eq. (81) is solved in Gardner and Barnes, *loc. cit.*]

[2] Glasoe and Lebacqz, "Pulse Generators," Sec. 6–2, McGraw-Hill Book Company, Inc., New York, 1948.

The input mesh consists of a battery in series with a switch and a series load resistance R_s, across which the pulse is to appear, and the first series and shunt elements. The difference equation describing the transformed current in the nth mesh is

$$-\frac{i(s,n-1)}{sC} + \left(sL + \frac{2}{sC}\right)i(s,n) - \frac{i(s,n+1)}{sC} = 0 \tag{83}$$

Its solution is

$$i(s,n) = Ae^{n\Gamma} + Be^{-n\Gamma} \tag{84}$$

If the switch is closed at $t = 0$, an initial voltage E representing the ratio of the initial charge due to the battery to the total storage capacitance of the filter will be produced across this capacitance; we get for the total input impedance

$$Z_{ab}(s) = R_s + \frac{q_0}{sC_S}\frac{1}{i(s,0)} = R_s + \frac{E}{si(s,0)} \tag{85}$$

$i(s,0)$ is the input mesh current evaluated for $R_s = 0$, q_0 and C_S represent the initial charge and the total storage capacitance, respectively. Let us specify for the artificial line, the circuit pictured in Fig. 7 in which $Z_1 = sL$, $Z_2 = 1/sC$, $Z_r = sL/2 + 1/sC$ and the first series member is sL. Since transients can only arise if dissipative elements are present, $i(s,0)$ represents the steady state condition. Following the same procedure as that leading to (72), it is readily verified that

$$i(s,0) = E\frac{C \sinh m\Gamma}{\sinh (m+1)\Gamma - \sinh m\Gamma} \tag{86}$$

where

$$\Gamma = \cosh^{-1}\left(1 + \frac{LC}{2}s^2\right) \tag{87}$$

For proper match with the line, we must specify that

$$R_s = \sqrt{\frac{L}{C}} \tag{88}$$

Substituting (86) and (88) into (85), we get

$$Z_{ab}(s) = \sqrt{\frac{L}{C}} + \frac{1}{sC}\left[\frac{\sinh (m+1)\Gamma}{\sinh m\Gamma} - 1\right] \tag{89}$$

It then follows that

$$i_1(s) = \frac{E}{s\sqrt{\frac{L}{C}} + \frac{1}{C}\left[\frac{\sinh (m+1)\Gamma}{\sinh m\Gamma} - 1\right]} \tag{90}$$

Let m approach infinity in such a way that the total distributed capacitance C_T and the total distributed inductance L_T remain fixed. Then, since

$$\cosh \Gamma = 1 + \frac{L_T C_T}{2m^2} s^2 \tag{91}$$

$$\sinh \Gamma = s \frac{\sqrt{L_T C_T}}{m} \sqrt{1 + \frac{L_T C_T s^2}{4m^2}} \tag{92}$$

$$m\Gamma = 2m \sinh^{-1} \frac{\sqrt{L_T C_T}}{2m} s \tag{93}$$

we see that

$$\lim_{m\to\infty} i_1(s) = \lim_{m\to\infty} \frac{E}{s\sqrt{\dfrac{L_T}{C_T}} + \dfrac{1}{C_T}(\cosh \Gamma + \coth (m\Gamma) \sinh \Gamma - 1)} \tag{94}$$

$$= \frac{E}{\sqrt{\dfrac{L_T}{C_T}}\,(s + \coth s\sqrt{L_T C_T})} \tag{95}$$

$$\approx \frac{E}{2s\sqrt{L_T/C_T}}\left(1 - e^{-2\sqrt{L_T C_T}\, s}\right) \tag{96}$$

Let us now digress for the moment and consider a current pulse of amplitude I and duration time $0 < t < \tau$, where

$$I = \frac{E}{2\sqrt{L_T/C_T}} \tag{97}$$

$$\tau = 2\sqrt{L_T C_T} \tag{98}$$

Its Laplace transform is found as follows:

$$i(s) = I \int_0^\tau e^{-st}\, dt \tag{99}$$

$$= \frac{I}{s}(1 - e^{-s\tau}) \tag{100}$$

Substituting (97) and (98) into (100), we get

$$i(s) = \frac{E}{2s\sqrt{L_T/C_T}}(1 - e^{-2\sqrt{L_T C_T}\, s}) \tag{101}$$

which is identical to Eq. (96) and shows that since the current $i_1(t)$ is a pulse, the voltage appearing across R_s will also be a pulse[1] of amplitude $i_1(t)R_s$ and duration $0 < t < \tau$.

[1] Compare the solution with that demonstrating the pulse-forming qualities of a suitably connected transmission line in Chap. 21, Sec. 20.

PROBLEMS

1. Design a constant-k-type low-pass filter with a cutoff frequency at 15,000 cycles and a characteristic impedance of $Z_0 = 100$ ohms at $f = 0$. Chart the variation of impedance as a function of frequency in the range $0 < f < f_c$.

2. Find the characteristic impedance of a low-pass constant-k-type filter when $C = 0.1$ μf and $L = 0.05$ henry.

3. Design a constant-k-type high-pass filter with a cutoff frequency at 5,000 cycles and a characteristic impedance of $Z_0 = 50$ ohms at $f = \infty$. Chart the variation of impedance as a function of frequency in the range $0 < f < f_c$.

4. Design a bandpass filter with the following characteristics:

$$z_0 = R_0 = 50 \text{ ohms}$$

$$f_{1c} = 1{,}000 \text{ cycles}$$

$$f_{2c} = 2{,}000 \text{ cycles}$$

5. Discuss and formulate the conditions whereby the difference equation (56) is capable of being solved, assuming the rotating-vector solution $a = e^{\pm j\theta}$ of the characteristic equation.

6. Show that the voltage term $e(t,n)$ for a low-pass filter whose current term $i(t,n)$ is given by (29) is

$$e(t,n) = 2n \int_0^t \frac{J_{2n}(\omega_c t)}{t}\, dt \qquad 0 \le t$$

7. Formulate the contour integral describing $e(t,n)$ and $i(t,n)$ for a high-pass filter.

8. Consider an m-section artificial line, short-circuited at the termination, for the case where $Z_1 = R_1$ and $Z_2 = R_2 + sL$. If a unit step function is applied to its input, show that the current in the nth section is (after Carslaw and Jaeger[1])

$$i(n,t) = \frac{1}{mR_2}\left(1 - e^{-(R_2/L)t}\right) + \frac{(-1)^n[1 - e^{-(4R_1+R_2)t/L}]}{m(4R_1 + R_2)}$$

$$+ \frac{2}{Lm} \sum_{\nu=1}^{m-1} \frac{L}{Q_\nu} \cos \frac{n\nu\pi}{m} \left(1 - e^{-Q_\nu t}\right)$$

where

$$Q_\nu = \frac{2R_1[1 - \cos(\nu\pi/m)] + R_L}{L}$$

9. Discuss from the practical standpoint of a communications-design engineer, the statement frequently encountered in artificial-filter-network analysis: Let the number of sections go to infinity. Is it possible to realize an infinite-section artificial line whose terminating impedance is zero?

[1] Carslaw and Jaeger, "Operational Methods in Applied Mathematics," Chap. II, Oxford University Press, New York, 1941.

CHAPTER 10

HARMONICS AND TRANSIENTS IN AMPLIFIERS

HARMONICS IN CLASS A AMPLIFIERS

1. Introduction. The single-stage wide-band (or video) amplifier is used to amplify the entire significant spectrum of a television signal before modulation or after demodulation and has many other applications in communication systems. It is important, in general, that wide-band communication networks of this type be able to reproduce or amplify the impressed complex wave with fidelity, thus necessitating an operating-system bandwidth for the apparatus such that all significant Fourier components are treated in proper fashion. The following will discuss fidelity in amplifiers from the harmonic standpoint.

2. Elementary Amplifier Theory.[1] Consider the resistance-coupled amplifier which is pictured in Fig. 1*a*. Its low-frequency (l-f) equivalent circuit is shown in Fig. 1*b*, in which the vacuum tube is replaced by a

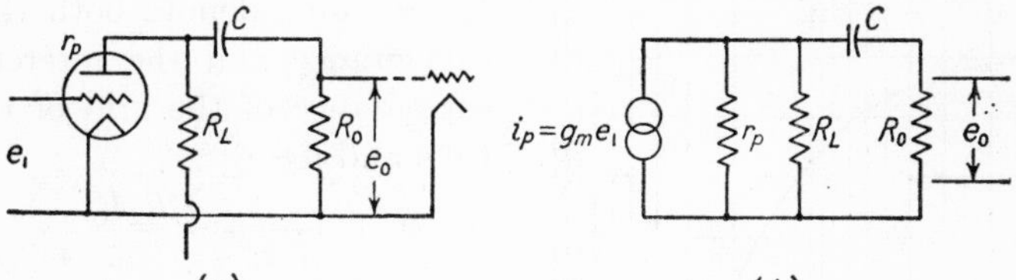

FIG. 1. Resistance-coupled amplifier.

constant-current generator which is shunted by the plate resistance. We may express the output voltage e_0 in terms of the plate current $g_m e_1$ as follows:

$$e_0 = g_m e_1 \frac{R_0[R_L r_p/(R_L + r_p)]}{[R_L r_p/(R_L + r_p)] + R_0 + (1/j\omega C)} \tag{1}$$

From this, it follows that the amplifier gain is

$$\frac{e_0}{e_1} = g_m \frac{j\omega R_L r_p R_0 C}{R_L + r_p + j\omega C(R_L r_p + R_0 R_L + R_0 r_p)} \tag{2}$$

[1] See, for example, F. E. Terman, "Radio Engineering," Chap. 6, McGraw-Hill Book Company, Inc., New York, 1947.

When the values of the plate resistance r_p, the grid resistor R_0, and the capacitor reactance $1/\omega C$ are such that these parameters may be neglected in Eq. (2), we get

$$\frac{e_0}{e_1} \cong g_m R_L \tag{3}$$

showing that, under these conditions, the gain and phase are independent of frequency.

Equation (3) ensures adequate response at low frequencies (except at the very low frequencies), but if the convergence of the Fourier-series representation of the complex wave applied to the grid is not rapid, stray

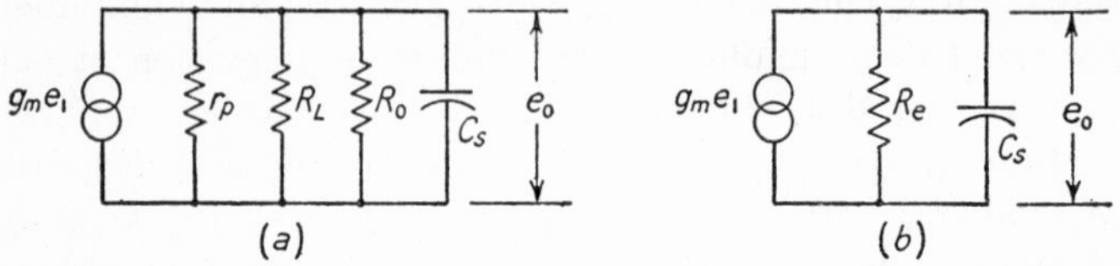

FIG. 2. (a) High-frequency equivalent circuit of a resistance-coupled amplifier. (b) Simplification of equivalent circuit.

and interelectrode capacitances must be included in the circuit considerations in dealing with the gain of the amplifier for the higher harmonics.

At very high frequencies, the equivalent circuit of the resistance-coupled amplifier is that pictured in Fig. 2a. If we let C_s denote both the stray capacitance and the interelectrode capacitance of the grid of the next tube and if

$$R_e = \frac{r_p R_L R_0}{R_L r_p + R_L R_0 + r_p R_0} \tag{4}$$

then the equivalent circuit is that shown in Fig. 2b and it follows that

$$\frac{e_0}{e_1} = \frac{g_m R_e}{1 + j\omega R_e C_s} \tag{5}$$

This expression can be described as follows:

$$\left|\frac{e_0}{e_1}\right| = \frac{g_m R_e}{\sqrt{1 + (f/f_s)^2}} \tag{6}$$

$$\theta = -\tan^{-1}\frac{f}{f_s} \tag{7}$$

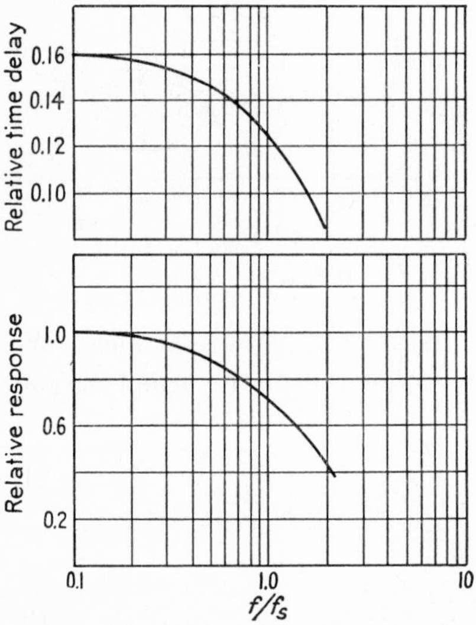

FIG. 3.

where $f_s = 1/2\pi R_e C_s$; θ is the phase shift. A frequency-response curve of the amplifier based on Eqs. (6) and (7) is shown in Fig. 3.

f_s is defined as the *critical frequency*; it determines the highest frequency which can be transmitted through the amplifier and the shape of the response-versus-frequency curve.

For an impressed voltage on the grid which is described by the Fourier series

$$e_g = \sum_{n=0}^{\infty} (a_n \cos n\omega t + b_n \sin n\omega t) \tag{8}$$

it is evident that at the output of the amplifier, using (2) and (5), we get

$$e_0 = \sum_{n=0}^{n\cong n_c} g_m \frac{R_L r_p R_0}{R_L r_p + R_0(R_L + r_p) - j(R_L + r_p)/\omega C} \cdot (a_n \cos n\omega t + b_n \sin n\omega t)$$
$$+ \sum_{n\sim n_c}^{\infty} g_m \frac{R_e}{1 + j\omega R_e C_s} (a_n \cos n\omega t + b_n \sin n\omega t) \tag{9}$$

where n_c represents the harmonic number at which the transition from l-f to h-f analysis must be made.

3. The Shunt-compensated Video Amplifier. It was seen in Chap. 5 that a band from 20 cycles to about 5 Mc is necessary to include the spectrum of a high-definition television picture. It is therefore necessary that any amplifier which is to amplify this television signal have a response curve which will accommodate this frequency range.

A commonly used method of extending the response curve of a resistance-coupled amplifier so as to make it suitable for television-signal amplification is the method of inductively shunt compensating the basic

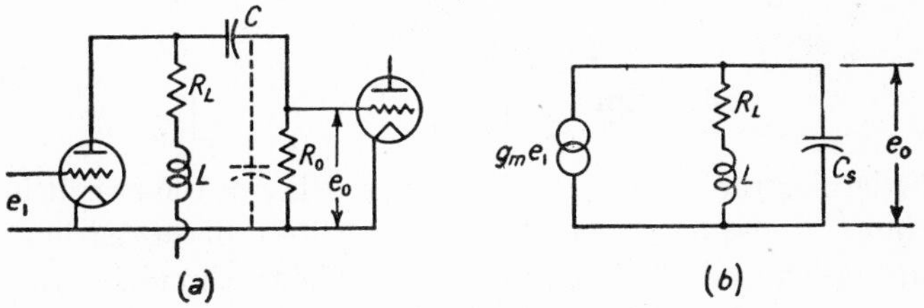

FIG. 4. Shunt-compensated video amplifier.

amplifier circuit which was discussed in the preceding section. The shunt-compensated circuit is shown in Fig. 4*a*. In practice, the value of inductance is generally chosen as

$$L = 0.5\, C_s R_L^2 \tag{10}$$

Figure 4*b* shows the equivalent circuit of the shunt-compensated video amplifier to consist of a parallel resonant circuit whose impedance characteristics are such that the amplifier response curve is flat out to the desired frequency. The flatness of the response curve may be verified as follows:

Equation (3) may be written in the form

$$\mathcal{G} = \left|\frac{e_0}{e_g}\right| = g_m|Z| \tag{11}$$

It follows that

$$\mathcal{G} = \frac{g_m\sqrt{\dfrac{R_L}{4\pi^2f^2C_s^{\,2}} + \left(\dfrac{L}{C_s} - 4\pi f^2L^2 - R_L^{\,2}\right)}}{2\pi fC_s\left[R_L^{\,2} + \left(2\pi fL - \dfrac{1}{2\pi fC_s}\right)^2\right]} \tag{12}$$

The phase angle is given by

$$\theta = \tan^{-1}\frac{(L/C_s) - 4\pi^2f^2L^2 - R_L^{\,2}}{R_L/2\pi fC_s} \tag{13}$$

If we write the gain at low frequencies as

$$\mathcal{G}_L = g_mR_L \tag{14}$$

and

$$f_s = \frac{1}{2\pi R_LC_s} \qquad f_0 = \frac{1}{2\pi\sqrt{LC_s}} \tag{15}$$

$$\kappa = \frac{L}{C_sR_L^{\,2}} = \left(\frac{f_s}{f_0}\right)^2 \tag{16}$$

then,

$$\frac{\mathcal{G}}{\mathcal{G}_L} = \sqrt{\frac{\kappa^2(f/f_s)^2 + 1}{\kappa^2(f/f_s)^4 - (2\kappa - 1)(f/f_s)^2 + 1}} \tag{17}$$

and

$$\theta = \tan^{-1}\frac{f}{f_s}\left[(\kappa - 1) - \kappa^2\frac{f^2}{f_s^{\,2}}\right] \tag{18}$$

Figure 5 pictures the response and the time delay of the circuit in Fig. 4*a*.

The transient response of this amplifier will be discussed in Sec. 11.

4. More Advanced Forms of Video-amplifier Circuits. In order to achieve wider bandwidth and more suitable characteristics for television transmission, it is often convenient to employ more elaborate types of load impedance than the circuit shown in Fig. 4*a*, for example. Because of its impedance properties, the low-pass filter network in various forms and using various systems of connection and termination has been used widely. A method of obtaining a low-pass coupling impedance—due to H. A. Wheeler[1]— is pictured in Fig. 6.

[1] H. A. Wheeler, Wide-band Amplifiers for Television, *Proc. IRE*, vol. 27, No. 7, pp. 429–438, July, 1939.

5. Principle of Conservation of Bandwidth. Note that according to Eqs. (3) and (14),

$$\mathcal{G} \cong g_m R_L \tag{19}$$

$$f_s \approx \frac{1}{2\pi R_L C_s} \tag{20}$$

where f_s is the critical frequency. If we multiply $\mathcal{G}$ and f_s together, we get

$$\mathcal{G} f_s = \frac{g_m}{2\pi C_s} \tag{21}$$

$$= F \tag{22}$$

where F is a constant which does not contain R_L.

In general, the principle of conservation of bandwidth states that the product of voltage amplification in numerical ratio and the bandwidth in cycles is a constant which is independent of R_L. This constant is proportional to the transconductance of the tube and is inversely proportional to the total shunt capacitance.

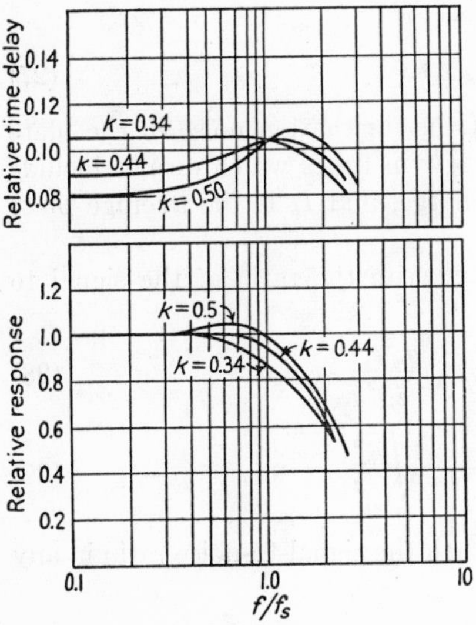

FIG. 5.

6. Noise Bandwidth and Signal-to-noise Ratio. In general we may write that the output power of a communication amplifier, due to a signal, is

$$\text{Signal output power} = \mathcal{P}_s \mathcal{G}^2(f_1) \tag{23}$$

where f_1 is the frequency of the signal and $\mathcal{P}_s$ is a measure of the signal input power. Since noise is distributed over all frequencies, we may write the total noise power output as

$$\text{Noise power} = \mathcal{P}_n \int_0^\infty \mathcal{G}^2(f)\, df \tag{24}$$

where $\mathcal{P}_n$ is a measure of the noise input power per unit of bandwidth.

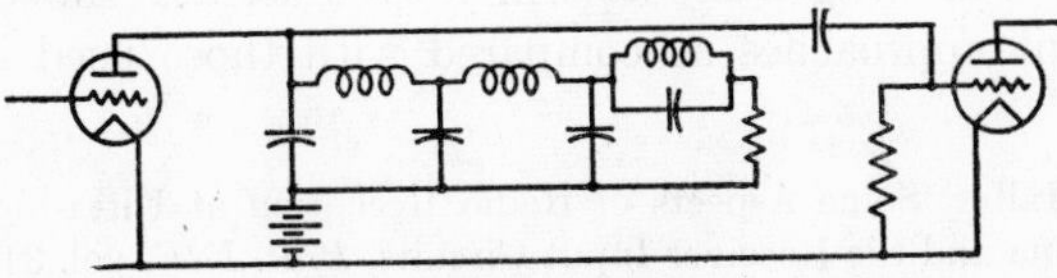

FIG. 6. Low-pass-filter coupling impedance.

We may then write

$$\frac{\text{Noise power}}{\text{Signal power}} = \frac{\mathcal{P}_n}{\mathcal{P}_s} \frac{\int_0^\infty \mathcal{G}^2(f)\, df}{\mathcal{G}^2(f_1)} \tag{25}$$

$$= \frac{\mathcal{P}_n}{\mathcal{P}_s} \Delta f' \tag{26}$$

where $\Delta f'$ is defined as the noise bandwidth.[1] It differs from circuit bandwidth in that it is a function of the signal frequency. It can be shown that tube noise, for example, is expressible as

$$\bar{i}_{pn}^{\,2} = \mathcal{P}_n \, \Delta f' \tag{27}$$

where $\bar{i}_{pn}^{\,2}$ is the mean-square value of the fluctuation noise in the plate current. $\mathcal{P}_n$ has a maximum value of $2eI_b$ in tubes which do not include secondary emitters; e is the electron charge, and I_b is the average plate current.

In a vacuum-tube amplifier, we may write the ratio of the signal to the noise as

$$\frac{\text{Signal}}{\text{Noise}} = \frac{S}{N} = \sqrt{\frac{g_m^2 e_g^2}{\bar{i}_{pn}^{\,2}}} \tag{28}$$

$$= e_g \sqrt{\frac{g_m^2}{\bar{i}_{pn}^{\,2}}} \tag{29}$$

In general, if e_n is the noise voltage, then the signal-to-noise ratio in any communication system is

$$\frac{S}{N} = \frac{e_s}{e_n} \tag{30}$$

where e_s is the signal voltage and in a vacuum tube, for example,

$$e_n = \sqrt{\frac{\bar{i}_{pn}^{\,2}}{g_m^2}} \tag{31}$$

LAPLACE-TRANSFORM ANALYSIS OF THE RESPONSE OF AMPLIFIERS

7. Introduction. The following sections will discuss the amplifier circuits described earlier in this chapter from the standpoint of transient analysis. In addition to yielding important applications of the Laplace transform, analyses of the following systems will also illustrate the difference in equivalent-circuit approaches as compared with those used in harmonic analysis.

[1] Herold and Malter, Some Aspects of Radio Reception at Ultra-high Frequency, Part 1, The Antenna and the Receiver Input Circuits, *Proc. IRE*, vol. 31, pp. 423–438, August, 1943.

8. Response of a Single-stage Resistance-coupled Amplifier. Let us consider the Laplace-transform solution for the response of the simplest type of vacuum-tube amplifier—the single-stage resistance-coupled amplifier, which is pictured in Fig. 1*a*—to an impressed unit step-function voltage. The tube is presumed to be a pentode so that the input is effectively shielded from the output. The *transient* equivalent-circuit representation of the circuit in Fig. 1*a* is shown in Fig. 7*a*.

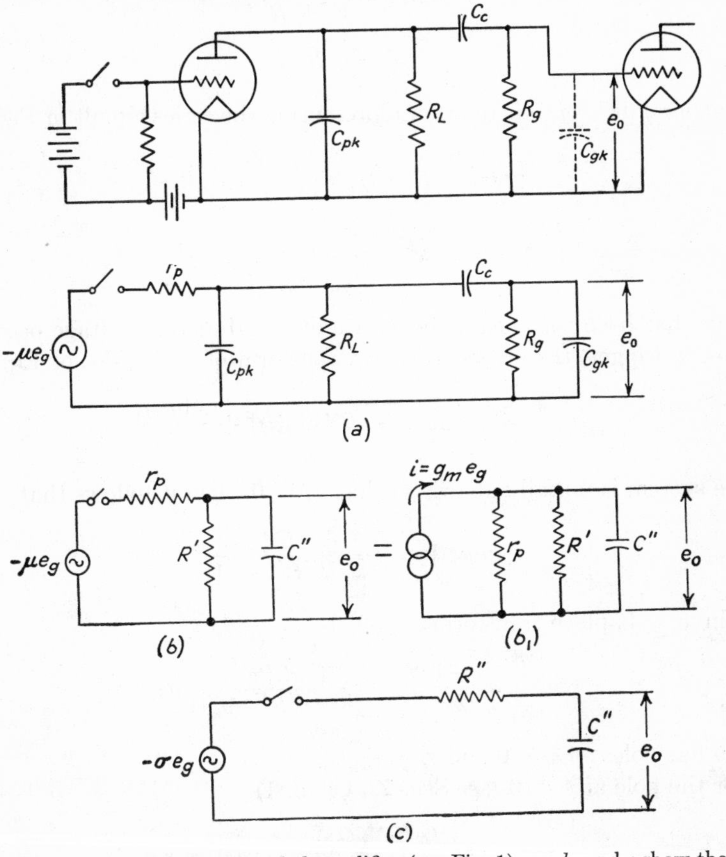

FIG. 7. Single-stage resistance-coupled amplifier (see Fig. 1). *a*, *b*, and *c* show the *transient* equivalent circuit in various stages of transformation into a circuit which may be used for determining the rise time.

For the analysis of the initial behavior of the output response, we may simplify this circuit by considering the coupling capacitor C_C to be initially shorted from the transient standpoint since its value of capacitance is generally large. The equivalent circuit in Fig. 7*a* may then be reduced to that shown in Fig. 7*b*, where

$$R' = \frac{R_L R_g}{R_L + R_g} \tag{32}$$

$$C'' = C_{pk} + C_{gk} \tag{33}$$

This may be further reduced to the final series-circuit form shown in Fig. 7c, where

$$R'' = \frac{r_p R'}{r_p + R'} \tag{34}$$

$$\sigma = g_m R'' \tag{35}$$

The general differential equation representing the series circuit in Fig. 7c is

$$-\sigma e_g = R'' i(t) + \frac{1}{C''} \int i(t)\, dt \tag{36}$$

$$= R'' \frac{dq(t)}{dt} + \frac{q(t)}{C''} \tag{37}$$

Since e_g has been specified as being a unit step-function voltage occurring at $t = 0$, we get, taking the Laplace transform of both sides of Eq. (37),

$$\frac{\sigma}{s} = -q_0 R'' + sR'' \mathfrak{L}[q(t)] + \frac{\mathfrak{L}[q(t)]}{C''} \tag{38}$$

If the system is initially at rest so that $q_0 = 0$, then it follows that

$$\mathfrak{L}[q(t)] = -\frac{\sigma C''}{s(sR''C'' + 1)} \tag{39}$$

The inverse Laplace transform of (39) is

$$q(t) = \frac{-1}{2\pi j} \int_{\alpha - j\infty}^{\alpha + j\infty} \frac{\sigma C'' e^{st}}{s(sC''R'' + 1)}\, ds \tag{40}$$

which has poles at $s = 0$ and $s = -1/R''C''$.

For the pole at $s = 0$ (see Sec. 22, Chap. 1)

$$w(s) = \frac{(\sigma/R'')e^{st}}{s + (1/R''C'')} \qquad g(s) = s \tag{41}$$

whereupon we get

$$\text{res}_1 = \frac{\omega(0)}{g'(0)} = \sigma C'' \tag{42}$$

For the pole at $s = -1/R''C''$, let

$$w(s) = \frac{\sigma}{R''} \frac{e^{st}}{s} \qquad g(s) = s + \frac{1}{R''C''} \tag{43}$$

Then

$$\text{res}_2 = \frac{\omega(-1/R''C'')}{g'(-1/R''C'')} = -\sigma C''e^{-t/R''C''} \tag{44}$$

and we see that

$$q(t) = -(\text{res}_1 + \text{res}_2) = -\sigma C''(1 - e^{-t/R''C''}) \tag{45}$$

which is the expected exponential relationship relating the rise time of the response to R'' and C''. The output voltage e_0 is found as follows: Since

$$e_0 = \frac{q}{C''} \tag{46}$$

then

$$e_0 = -\sigma(1 - e^{-t/R''C''}) \tag{47}$$

This equation shows that the output wave e_0 will rise exponentially to its maximum value. The rate of rise is actually a measure of the h-f response of this amplifier.

After some time following the application of the step function to the grid, the coupling capacitor can no longer be considered to be shorted. The presence of this capacitor will cause the output response to the step-function voltage to decay. We may therefore complete the analysis for the output response by considering the equivalent circuit pictured in Fig.

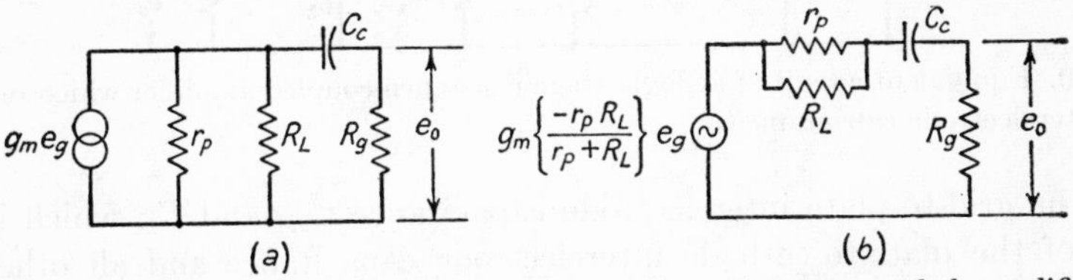

FIG. 8. *Transient* equivalent circuit of a single-stage resistance-coupled amplifier for determining the nature of the decay period of the output voltage.

8*a*, which is equivalent to that circuit pictured in Fig. 7*a* except for the fact that the shunt capacitors are not included and that a constant-current generator is used. This equivalent circuit may be evolved into the series form shown in Fig. 8*b*; the differential equation describing its behavior is

$$-g_m e_g \frac{R_L r_p}{R_L + r_p} = R''' \frac{dq}{dt} + \frac{q}{C_c} \tag{48}$$

where

$$R''' = R_g + \frac{R_L r_p}{R_L + r_p} \tag{49}$$

The solution of (48) for the case where e_g is a step-function voltage follows from that of Eq. (37); it can be shown that

$$R_g \frac{dq}{dt} = e_0 = -\sigma e^{-t/R'''C_c} \tag{50}$$

which shows that, for $t \gg 0$, the output response to the step-function voltage will return to zero. Actually this result is related to the l-f response of the circuit in that the longer the circuit is able to maintain the output voltage due to the step-function voltage, the better is its l-f response.

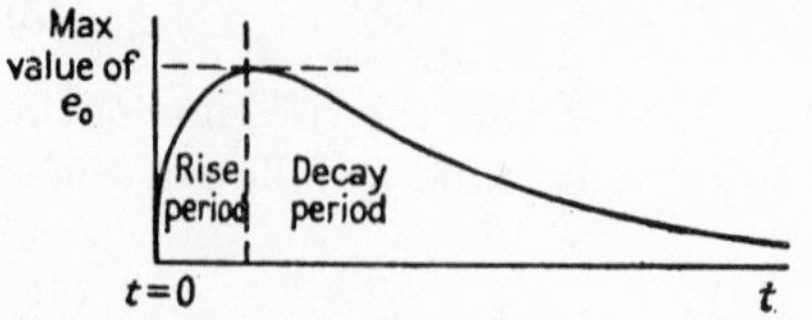

FIG. 9. Response of a single-stage resistance-coupled amplifier to a step voltage.

The general output-wave behavior from $t = 0$ and on due to an impressed step-function voltage is illustrated in Fig. 9, where the rise period [Eq. (47)] and the decay period [Eq. (50)] are shown, which describe the behavior of the output wave from start to end.

9. Considerations of Interelectrode Capacitances in Amplifiers. Consider the analysis of the response of a single-step resistance-coupled amplifier using a triode in which the shielding is such that the interelectrode capacitances must be taken into consideration. The equivalent circuit is shown in Fig. 10 and is seen to include the grid-to-cathode capacitance

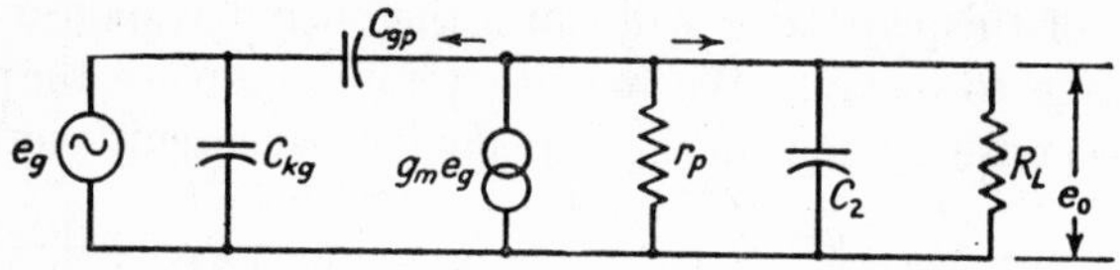

FIG. 10. Equivalent circuit of a single-stage resistance-coupled amplifier which includes the interelectrode capacitances.

C_{kg}, the grid-to-plate interelectrode capacitance C_{gp}, and C_2, which is the sum of the plate-to-cathode interelectrode capacitance and all other capacitances appearing from plate to cathode. The nodal equation is

$$C_2 \frac{de_0}{dt} + C_{gp} \frac{d}{dt}(e_0 - e_g) + e_0\left(\frac{1}{R_L} + \frac{1}{r_p}\right) = -g_m e_g \tag{51}$$

or

$$(C_2 + C_{gp}) \frac{de_0}{dt} + \left(\frac{1}{R_L} + \frac{1}{r_p}\right)e_0 = C_{gp} \frac{de_g}{dt} - g_m e_g \tag{52}$$

Let the impressed voltage e_g be a unit step-function voltage applied at $t = 0$, and let the system be initially at rest. Taking the Laplace transform of both sides of Eq. (52), we get

$$\mathfrak{L}(e_0)\left[(C_2 + C_{gp})s + \left(\frac{1}{R_L} + \frac{1}{r_p}\right)\right] = C_{gp} - \frac{g_m}{s} \tag{53}$$

Then

$$\mathfrak{L}(e_0) = \frac{C_{gp}}{C_2 + C_{gp}} \frac{s - g_m/C_{gp}}{s\left[s + \dfrac{1/r_p + 1/R_L}{C_2 + C_{gp}}\right]} \tag{54}$$

The solution of the inverse Laplace transform of (54) is very similar to that leading to Eq. (47), and it follows that (letting $g_m r_p = \mu$)

$$e_0 = -\mu \frac{R_L}{R_L + r_p} + \left(\frac{C_{gk}}{C_2 + C_{gk}} + \mu \frac{R_L}{R_L + r_p}\right) \exp\left[-\frac{R_L + r_p}{r_p R_L(C_2 + C_{gp})} t\right] \tag{55}$$

10. Cascaded Resistance-coupled Amplifiers. Consider the response of the two-stage resistance-coupled amplifier pictured in Fig. 11 to a step-

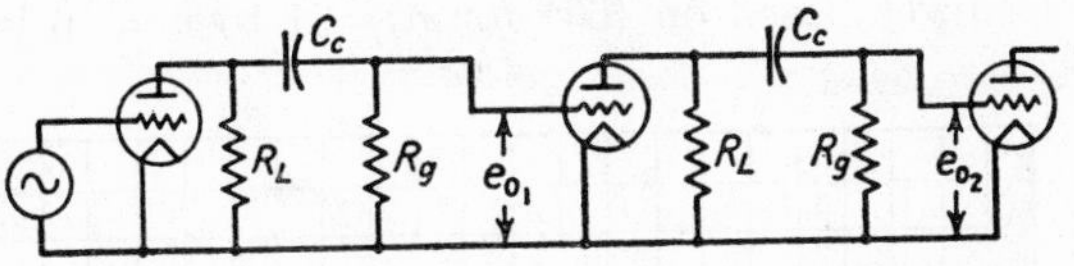

FIG. 11. Two-stage resistance-coupled amplifier.

function voltage occurring at $t = 0$. We have seen that the response e_{o_1} due to the impressed step-function voltage at the input of the first stage is, according to Eq. (50),[1]

$$e_{o_1} = -\sigma e^{-t/\tau} \tag{56}$$

where

$$\tau = C_C R''' \tag{57}$$

We may deduce the output voltage e_{o_2} of the second stage by considering this stage alone with e_{o_1} as its input voltage. For this development, let us use the superposition-integral theorem. Since

$$e_{o_1}(0) = -\sigma$$
$$e_{o_1}(\lambda) = -\sigma e^{-\lambda/\tau} \tag{58}$$

then

$$e_{o_2} = -\sigma(-\sigma e^{-t/\tau}) + \int_0^t (-\sigma e^{-(t-\lambda)/\tau}) \frac{d}{d\lambda}(-\sigma e^{-\lambda/\tau})\, d\lambda \tag{59}$$

$$= \sigma^2 e^{-t/\tau} - \frac{\sigma^2}{\tau}\int_0^t e^{-t/\tau}\, d\lambda \tag{60}$$

$$= \sigma^2 e^{-t/\tau}\left(1 - \frac{1}{\tau}\int_0^t d\lambda\right) \tag{61}$$

$$= \sigma^2(1 - \Phi)e^{-\Phi} \tag{62}$$

where

$$\Phi = \frac{t}{\tau} \tag{63}$$

[1] We shall assume an instantaneous rise of the output voltage in this illustration.

This treatment may be extended to yield the response of $n + 1$ stages; this will yield the normalized expression

$$\frac{e_{0_{n+1}}(t)}{\sigma^{n+1}} = \left\{1 - n\Phi + \frac{n(n-1)}{(2!)^2}\Phi^2 - \cdots + (-1)^k \frac{n(n-1)(n-2)\cdots(n-k+1)}{(k!)^2}\Phi^k - \cdots + (-1)^{n-1}\frac{1}{[(n-1)!]^2}\Phi^{n-1}\right\}e^{-\Phi} \tag{64}$$

A family of curves based on (64) for $n = 1$ to $n = 6$ is illustrated in Fig. 12.

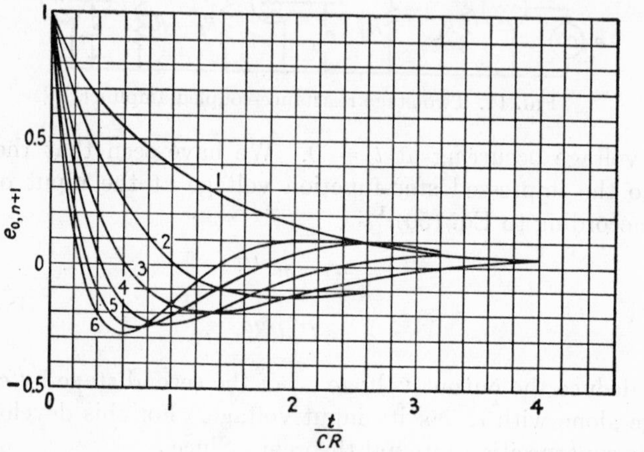

FIG. 12.

11. Shunt-compensated Video Amplifier.[1] Let us consider the solution, due to N. MacLachlan, of the step-function voltage response of the shunt-inductance-compensated video amplifier which was discussed in Sec. 3. The *transient* equivalent circuit of the circuit is shown in Fig. 13, where C_3 is the shunt capacitance as seen from the plate terminal to ground, L is the inductance, and C_C is the coupling capacitor. The output voltage e_0 appears across the grid resistor R_g.

We may write, in terms of the currents i, i_1, i_2, and i_3, at the junction a the following nodal equations:

$$\mu e_g - ir_p = \frac{1}{C_3}\int i_1\,dt = i_2R_L + L\frac{di_2}{dt} = i_3R_g + \frac{1}{C_C}\int i_3\,dt \tag{65}$$

[1] N. W. MacLachlan, "Complex Variable and Operational Calculus," Sec. 12,72, Cambridge University Press, London, 1942.

Bedford and Fredendall, Transient Response of Multistage Video-frequency Amplifiers, *Proc. IRE*, vol. 27, pp. 277–284, April, 1939.

If e_g is assumed to be a unit step-function voltage occurring at $t = 0$ and if the system is considered to be initially at rest, the Laplace transform of (65) is found to be

$$\frac{\mu}{s} - \mathfrak{L}(i)r_p = \frac{\mathfrak{L}(i_1)}{C_3} = \mathfrak{L}(i_2)(R_L + sL) = \mathfrak{L}(i_3)\left(R_g + \frac{1}{sC_C}\right) \qquad (66)$$

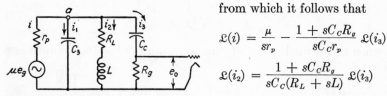

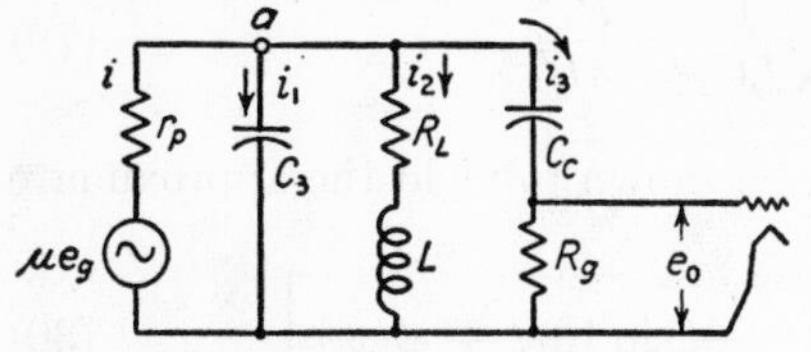

FIG. 13. *Transient* equivalent circuit of the shunt-compensated video amplifier.

from which it follows that

$$\mathfrak{L}(i) = \frac{\mu}{sr_p} - \frac{1 + sC_CR_g}{sC_Cr_p}\mathfrak{L}(i_3) \qquad (67)$$

$$\mathfrak{L}(i_2) = \frac{1 + sC_CR_g}{sC_C(R_L + sL)}\mathfrak{L}(i_3) \qquad (68)$$

$$\mathfrak{L}(i_1) = (1 + sC_CR_g)\frac{C_3}{C_C}\mathfrak{L}(i_3) \qquad (69)$$

Since the output voltage e_0 is i_3R_g, we may combine Eqs. (67), (68), and (69) in accordance with Kirchhoff's first law; this yields for $\mathfrak{L}(i_3)$,

$$\mathfrak{L}(i_3) = \frac{\mu}{LC_3R_gr_p}\frac{(R_L + sL)}{s^3 + as^2 + bs + c} \qquad (70)$$

where

$$a = \frac{R_L}{L} + \frac{1}{C_3r_p} + \frac{1}{R_g}\left(\frac{1}{C_C} + \frac{1}{C_3}\right) \qquad (71)$$

$$b = \frac{1}{LC_3}\left(1 + \frac{R_L}{r_p} + \frac{R_L}{R_g}\right) + \frac{1}{C_CR_g}\left(\frac{R_L}{L} + \frac{1}{C_3r_p}\right) \qquad (72)$$

$$c = \frac{R_L + r_p}{LC_3C_CR_gr_p} \qquad (73)$$

The output voltage may then be represented by the inverse Laplace transform

$$e_0 = i_3R_g = \frac{\mu}{LC_3r_p}\frac{1}{2\pi j}\int_{\alpha - j\infty}^{\alpha + j\infty}\frac{(R_L + sL)e^{st}\,ds}{(s + s_1)(s + s_2)(s + s_3)} \qquad (74)$$

where s_1, s_2, and s_3 are roots of the cubic equation

$$s^3 + as^2 + bs + c = 0 \qquad (75)$$

The general form of e_0 in terms of the residues at s_1, s_2, and s_3 is

$$e_0 = \frac{\mu}{LC_3r_p}\left[\frac{(R_L - s_1L)e^{-s_1t}}{(s_2 - s_1)(s_3 - s_1)} + \frac{(R_L - s_2L)e^{-s_2t}}{(s_1 - s_2)(s_3 - s_2)} + \frac{(R_L - s_3L)e^{-s_3t}}{(s_1 - s_3)(s_2 - s_3)}\right] \qquad (76)$$

If $a \ll b \ll c$, we may show that

$$s_1 = \frac{1}{R_g C_C} \tag{77}$$

$$s_2 = \frac{R_L}{2L} + j\sqrt{\frac{1}{LC_3} - \frac{R_L^2}{4L^2}} \tag{78}$$

$$s_3 = \frac{R_L}{2L} - j\sqrt{\frac{1}{LC_3} - \frac{R_L^2}{4L^2}} \tag{79}$$

which, when substituted into (76), can be shown to yield the approximate equation

$$e_0 = \frac{\mu R_L}{r_p}\left[1 - \frac{e^{-\pi f_0 k t}}{k\sqrt{1 - (k^2/4)}} \sin\,[Mt + \psi(\omega)]\right] \tag{80}$$

where

$$f_0 = \frac{1}{2\pi\sqrt{LC}} \qquad M = 2\pi f_0 \sqrt{1 - \frac{k^2}{4}}$$

$$r_p \gg R_L \qquad \psi(\omega) = \tan^{-1} \frac{k\sqrt{1 - k^2/4}}{(k^2/2) - 1} \tag{81}$$

$$k = 2\pi f_0 R_L C = \frac{f_0}{f_s}$$

The response curves calculated from Eq. (80) are plotted in Fig. 14 for values of k from unity to infinity. It is seen that the response starts

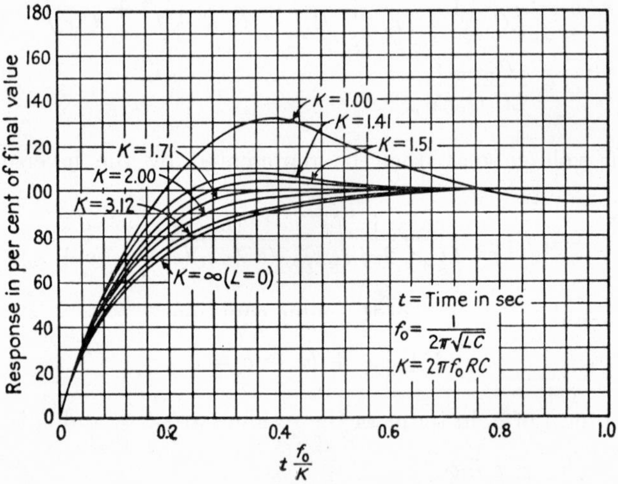

Fig. 14.

immediately with a slope independent of k but exhibits an oscillatory nature at the top of the rise for low values of k.

For an extension of this case which includes multistage-amplifier response, see Sec. 7, Chap. 20.

12. General Aspects of Single-stage Amplifiers. In general, more advanced forms of amplifier circuits, such as the shunt-compensated amplifier, which was described in the preceding section, may be represented by the general circuit pictured in Fig. 15. In this circuit, the amplifier tube is replaced by a constant-current generator which drives the input of a four-terminal transfer network whose output is connected to the grid of the next stage, this network including the various interelectrode and stray capacitances which are present. It is evident, then, that radio- and video-amplifier response for a single stage is determined by the characteristics of the transfer network which exists between the plate of the amplifier tube and the grid of the next stage.[1] In fact, if the tube-anode impedance may be neglected, these transfer characteristics alone describe the amplifier behavior.

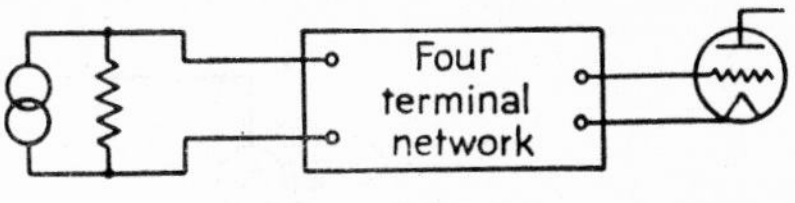

FIG. 15.

PROBLEMS

1. Consider the amplifier circuit shown in the figure. If the load is a pure inductance, derive an expression for gain as a function of frequency. Plot the result. What is the gain at $f = 0$?

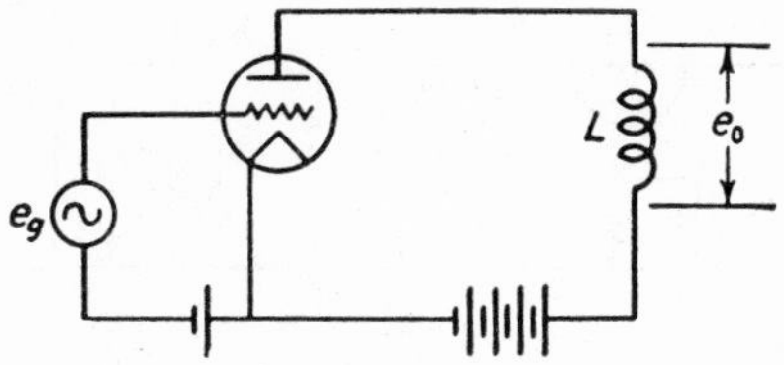

PROB. 1.

2. Neglecting C_s, C_c, and R_g in the figure, show that the gain of the amplifier is

$$g_m R \frac{a}{a + j[(f/f_0) - (f_0/f)]}$$

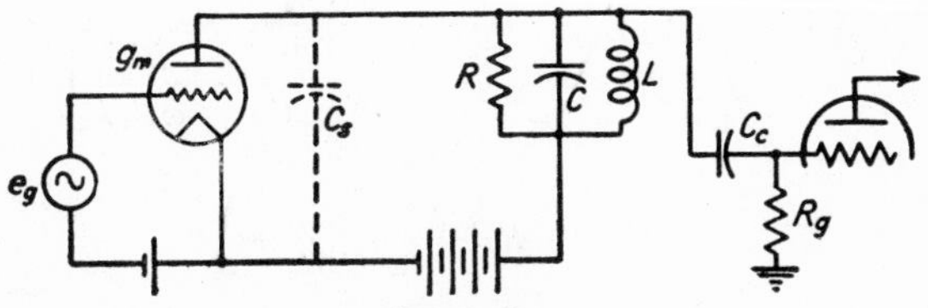

PROB. 2.

[1] See Kallmann and Spencer, Transient Response, *Proc. IRE*, vol. 33, No. 3, pp. 169–195, March, 1945.

where

$$a = \frac{1}{R}\sqrt{\frac{L}{C}} \qquad f_0 = \frac{1}{2\pi\sqrt{LC}}$$

What is the gain at $f = f_0$?

3. The circuit shown in the figure is known as a cathode follower; it is widely

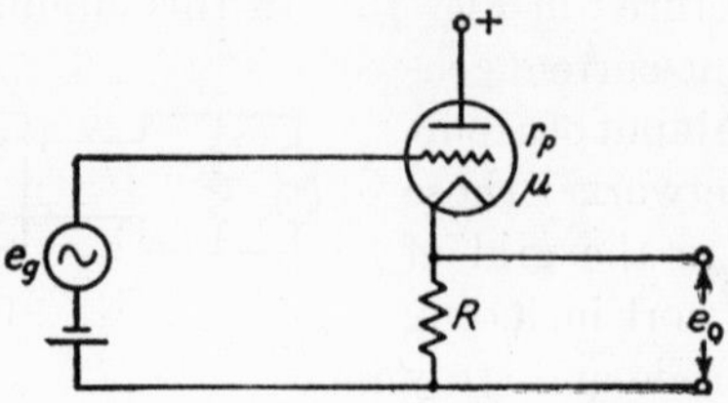

PROB. 3.

used in video amplifiers because it has low amplitude distortion and exhibits good response characteristics at the high frequencies.

a. Show that

$$\frac{e_0}{e_g} = \frac{\mu}{\mu + 1}\frac{R}{R + [r_p/(\mu + 1)]}$$

b. Discuss the fact that this circuit exhibits relatively low equivalent-plate resistance.

4. The l-f range of a resistance-coupled amplifier can be compensated for at low

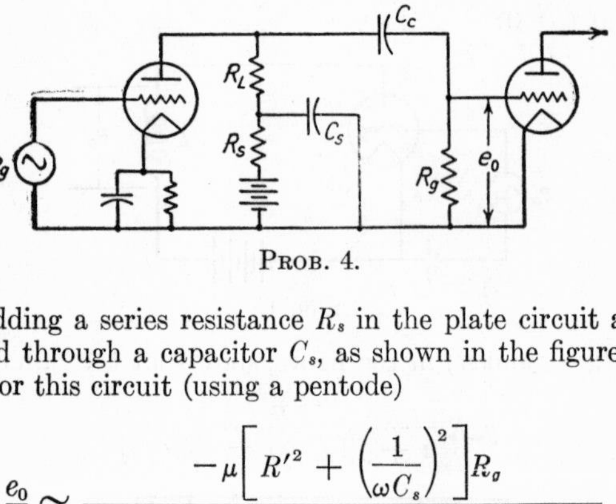

PROB. 4.

frequencies by adding a series resistance R_s in the plate circuit and shunting the resistor to ground through a capacitor C_s, as shown in the figure.

a. Show that for this circuit (using a pentode)

$$\frac{e_0}{e_g} \cong \frac{-\mu\left[R'^2 + \left(\frac{1}{\omega C_s}\right)^2\right]R_g}{r_p\left[R_gR' + \frac{1}{\omega^2 C_s C_c} + j\left(\frac{R_g}{\omega C_s} - \frac{R'}{\omega C_c}\right)\right]}$$

where

$$R' = R_L + \frac{1}{\omega^2 C_s^2 R_s}$$

b. Derive an expression for phase shift, and show that the phase shift is completely compensated for when $R_gC_c = R_LC_s$, provided that $R_g \gg R_L$.

5. Deduce the response of the circuit pictured in Fig. 7 to a unit step function for the case where $\mu = 20$, $r_p = 8{,}000$ ohms, $R_L = 10{,}000$ ohms, $C_C = 0.05\ \mu f$, $R_g = 500{,}000$ ohms, and $C_{pk} = 15\ \mu\mu f$. If C_C is changed to $0.0025\ \mu f$, how will the response be changed? (Ignore C_{gk})

6. Determine the response of the circuit in Fig. 1*a* to the modulating wave $M \cos \omega_1 t$ which starts at $t = 0$, where $M < 1$.

7. Determine the response of the l-f compensated amplifier pictured in the figure of Prob. 4 to a unit step function. Study the rise time and the decay time separately as was done in connection with the circuit in Fig. 7*a*.

8. Deduce the response of the circuit in Fig. 7*a* to a unit step function for the case when the load resistance R_L is replaced by an inductance. Let C_{pk} be so small in magnitude that it can be ignored.

9. Determine the response of the amplifier in Fig. 7, using the parameters listed in Prob. 5 when the interelectrode capacitances are included in the analysis. Let $C_{gk} = 8\ \mu\mu f$, $C_{pk} = 2.7\ \mu\mu f$, and $g_m = 5 \times 10^{-3}$ mho.

10. Derive Eq. (64), using Laplace-transform formulation throughout.

11. Deduce the response of a set of cascaded identical amplifiers to a step function if the output of the first stage is given by Eq. (47).

12. Formulate and discuss the solution for the response of an amplifier using inverse feedback. (See, for example, Mulligan and Mautner, The Steady-State and Transient Analysis of a Feedback Video Amplifier, *Proc. IRE*, vol. 36, pp. 595–610, May, 1948).

CHAPTER 11

INTEGRATING, DIFFERENTIATING, AND SCANNING SYSTEMS FOR TELEVISION

1. Introduction. Integrating, differentiating, and scanning circuits are among the most highly specialized and also the most useful circuits in television. The approach to the analysis of these circuits is somewhat different from that for ordinary linear networks; both the Fourier implications and the basic principles of operation of representative circuits will be discussed in this chapter.

INTEGRATING AND DIFFERENTIATING CIRCUITS

2. Integrating Circuits.[1] Integrating circuits are used in television systems, pulsers, and computing systems. An important integrating circuit (see Sec. 6 for another) is the RC circuit which is pictured in Fig. 1*a*.

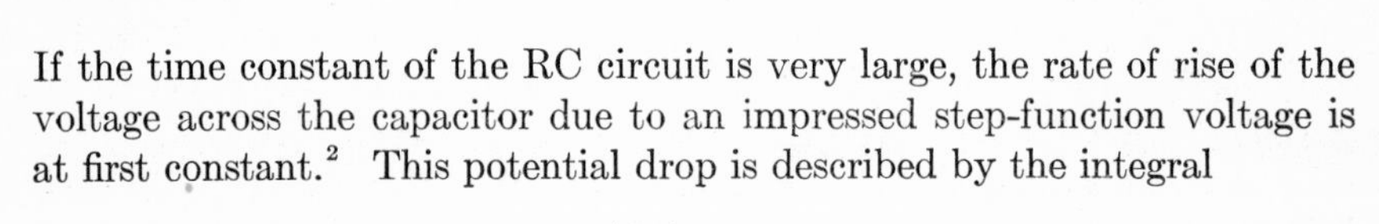

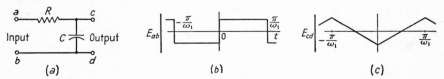

FIG. 1. (*a*) Integrating circuit. (*b*) Periodic square wave. (*c*) Response of an integrating circuit to a periodic square wave.

If the time constant of the RC circuit is very large, the rate of rise of the voltage across the capacitor due to an impressed step-function voltage is at first constant.[2] This potential drop is described by the integral

$$\frac{1}{C}\int i(t)\,dt \tag{1}$$

where $i(t)$ is the current through the capacitor C.

It is well known that if a square wave such as that pictured in Fig. 1*b*

[1] For some additional mathematical aspects of integrating and differentiating circuits, see S. Goldman, "Transformation Calculus and Electrical Transients," Chap. 12, Prentice-Hall, Inc., New York, 1949.

[2] See the discussion relating to Eq. (11), Sec. 5.

is impressed across a, b, the triangular wave which is pictured in Fig. 1c will appear across c, d provided that the time constant RC is large. This may be verified as follows:

The complex Fourier-series representation of the square wave in Fig. 1b is

$$e(t) = j \sum_{n=-\infty}^{\infty} \frac{(-1)^n - 1}{\pi n} e^{jn\omega_1 t} \tag{2}$$

Integrating (2) with respect to time, we get

$$\int e(t)\, dt = \sum_{n=-\infty}^{\infty} \frac{(-1)^n - 1}{\pi n^2 \omega_1} e^{jn\omega_1 t} \tag{3}$$

which is the Fourier-series expansion of an even triangular wave of amplitude $\pi/2\omega_1$, thus verifying the integration properties of the circuit.

3. Differentiating Circuits. A differentiating circuit of the type used in television applications and in many other triggering and timing circuits is

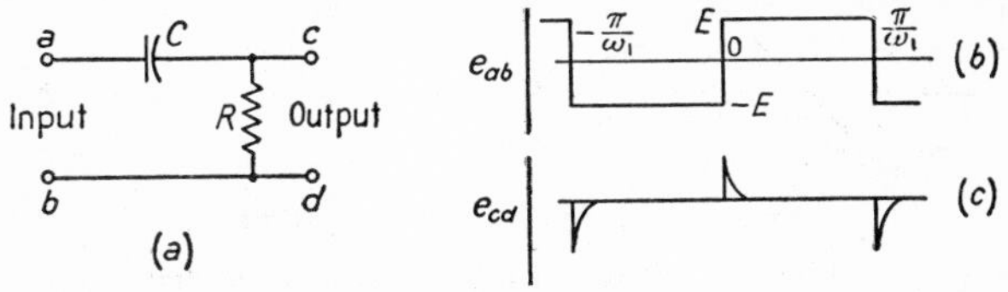

FIG. 2. (a) Differentiating circuit. (b) Periodic square wave. (c) Response of the differentiating circuit to a periodic square wave.

shown in Fig. 2a. If a step-function voltage of amplitude E at $t = 0$ is impressed across the terminals a, b, the voltage across the capacitor will be described by the equation

$$e(t) = Ee^{-t/RC} \qquad t \geq 0 \tag{4}$$

If RC is very small, the voltage drop across the resistance which was equal in value to E at the instant $t = 0$ will immediately return to zero after this instant.

If the square wave pictured in Fig. 2b is impressed across a, b, the series of pips which are pictured in Fig. 2c will result if $RC \ll \pi/\omega_1$. The characteristics of the pips and the spacing between them will be a function of the amplitude, the repetition rate of the impressed square wave, and the time constant RC of the differentiator.

The term *differentiator* as far as the mathematical implications when a square wave or a pulse is concerned is a misnomer since a differentiation of the Fourier-series representation of the square wave in Fig. 2b is not valid owing to the fact that the resulting series will not converge. This is seen to be the case by inspection of the square waveform from which it is evident that the derivative of the flat section of the square wave is equal to zero and that the jumps are points of indeterminacy as far as the differentiation is concerned.

Practically speaking, the term differentiator implies that the circuit responds with maximum amplitude to sudden changes in the applied voltage but that when a constant voltage is applied, the output is zero.

SCANNING SYSTEMS

4. Fourier Analysis of a Scanning Wave. In a cathode-ray oscilloscope, an electron beam may be made to move with linear velocity across a screen by applying a saw-tooth voltage to an electrostatic deflection system or a saw-tooth current to a magnetic deflection system. In a television-image tube or kinescope, by using two mutually perpendicular deflection systems, the electron beam may be made to scan a particular area.

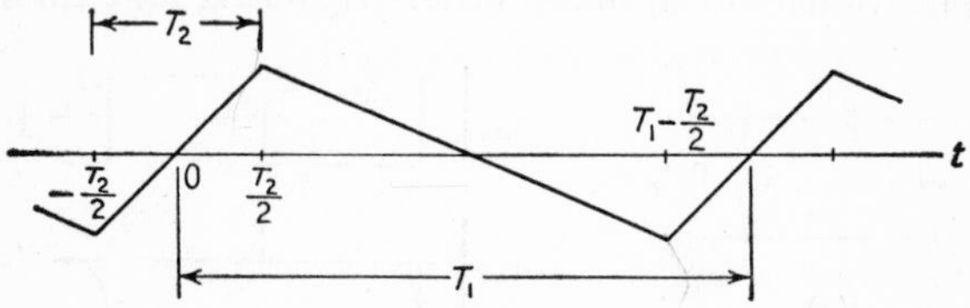

FIG. 3. Unit-amplitude saw-tooth voltage.

Consider the saw-tooth voltage pictured in Fig. 3. The main deflection takes place during the interval $T_2/2 < t < T_1 - (T_2/2)$. From $-T_2/2 < t < T_2/2$, the beam returns to its initial position. In practice, the beam current is turned off during this return time.

We may represent the wave in Fig. 3 by a Fourier series as follows: The wave in Fig. 3 may be expressed mathematically as

$$\begin{aligned} f(t) &= 2\frac{E_1}{T_2}t & -\frac{T_2}{2} < t < \frac{T_2}{2} \\ &= \frac{E_1(T_1 - 2t)}{T_1 - T_2} & \frac{T_2}{2} < t < T_1 - \frac{T_2}{2} \end{aligned} \tag{5}$$

Since this wave is odd, it will yield a Fourier sine series. It follows that

$$b_n = \frac{2}{T_1}\int_0^{T_1} f(t)\sin\frac{2\pi nt}{T_1}\,dt \tag{6}$$

$$= E_1\frac{2T_1^2}{\pi^2 n^2 T_2(T_1 - T_2)}\sin\pi n\frac{T_2}{T_1} \tag{7}$$

and

$$f(t) = E_1\sum_{n=1}^{\infty}\frac{2T_1^2}{\pi^2 n^2 T_2(T_1 - T_2)}\sin\pi n\frac{T_2}{T_1}\sin\frac{2\pi nt}{T_1} \tag{8}$$

If, as an illustration of a typical case, we let $T_2 = 0.15\ T_1$, then we may write out (8) as follows:

$$f(t) = 0.721E_1 \sin \omega_1 t + 0.32E_1 \sin 2\omega_1 t + 0.174E_1 \sin 3\omega_1 t + 0.094E_1 \sin 4\omega_1 t + \cdots \quad (9)$$

5. Grid-controlled Rectifier Scanning Circuit. There are many ways of producing the saw-tooth wave pictured in Fig. 3. Let us consider, for example, the elementary grid-controlled[1] rectifier tube circuit which is

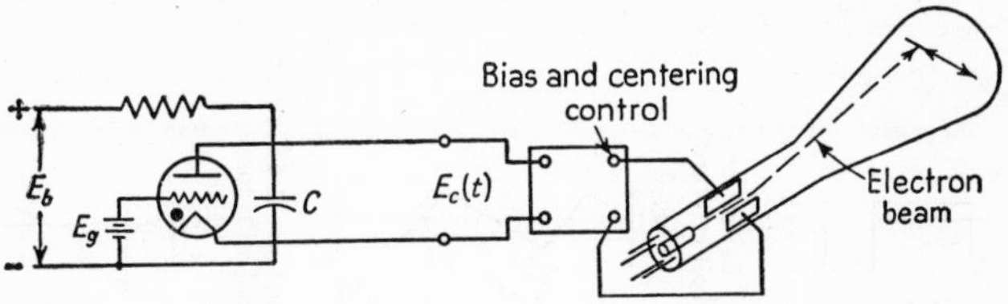

FIG. 4. Elementary deflection circuit.

pictured in Fig. 4. The grid voltage E_g is adjusted to such a potential that when the plate-to-cathode potential reaches the value E_a the tube will fire. The voltage across the capacitor may be written

$$E_c(t) = E_b(1 - e^{-t/RC}) \quad (10)$$

which can be written in the following power-series form:

$$E_c(t) = E_b\left[\frac{t}{RC} - \frac{1}{2!}\left(\frac{t}{RC}\right)^2 + \frac{1}{3!}\left(\frac{t}{RC}\right)^3 + \cdots\right] \quad (11)$$

If $t/RC < 1$, the voltage will build up across C linearly until it reaches the value E_a, at which point the tube fires and remains conducting until the capacitor discharges and the tube ceases conducting; then the cycle starts again.

6. Magnetic Deflection. If magnetic-deflecting coils are used with a picture kinescope, a saw-tooth-wave current must be passed through the coils in order to obtain linear electron deflection. If the resistance of coils is equal to zero, then

$$e(t) = L\frac{di(t)}{dt} \quad (12)$$

where $e(t)$ is the time-varying voltage which will produce $i(t)$.

[1] This grid permits control of the potential between anode and cathode at which ionization takes place. It is important to understand that once the tube has fired, the grid has no control and the only way by which the tube can be cut off is for the cathode-to-anode voltage to drop below the ionization potential of the mercury vapor. As in two-element mercury-vapor tubes, the current through the tube is determined by the load and voltage in the circuit in which it is placed.

Note that we may rewrite (12) as follows,

$$L\,di(t) = e(t)\,dt \tag{13}$$

or

$$i(t) = \frac{1}{L}\int e(t)\,dt + \text{constant} \tag{14}$$

which shows the pure inductance to be an integrating device. Thus if the pulse wave pictured in Fig. 5*a* is impressed across the pure-inductance deflection coil, the saw-tooth-wave current pictured in Fig. 5*b* will flow.

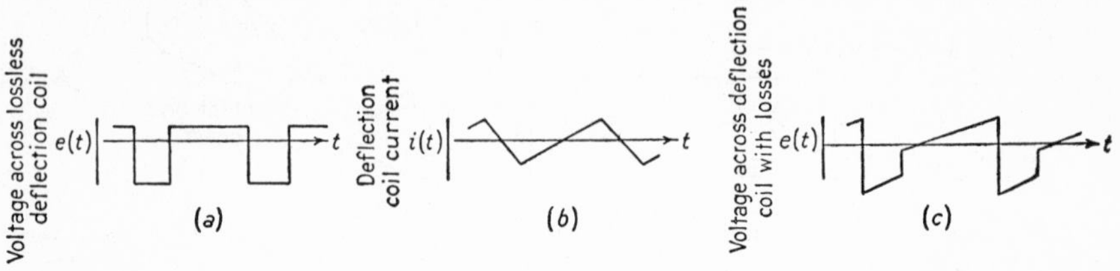

FIG. 5.

In practice, the deflection coils do have resistance, thus leading to the circuit equation

$$e(t) = Ri(t) + L\frac{di(t)}{dt} \tag{15}$$

where R is the total resistance. The voltage shape which must be impressed across this deflection system containing R in order to achieve a saw-tooth-wave current is somewhat like that pictured in Fig. 5*c*.

7. Cyclic-scanning System. Consider the circuit pictured in Fig. 6*a*, in which L and R represent the inductance and resistance of a set of de-

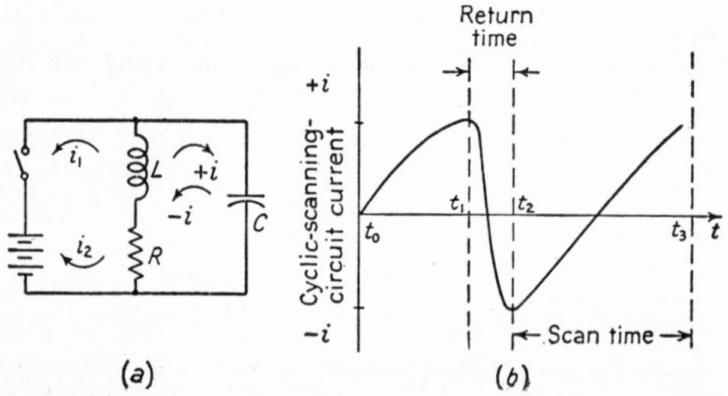

FIG. 6. Basic cyclic-scanning circuit.

flection coils, respectively, C is the lumped stray capacitance present, and the switch represents some suitable vacuum-tube mechanism. This circuit produces what is called *cyclic scanning.*[1] The chief advantage of such a system is that an ideal cyclic-scanning system requires only wattless power as compared, for example, with the 50 watts necessary to produce full deflection of the beam with a deflection angle of 50° at 10 kv, using circuits such as those used in television receivers prior to World War II. This is an important commercial consideration.

Let the switch be closed at $t = t_0$. The current will rise linearly through the inductance at a rate prescribed by the time constant of the RL circuit. This rise is pictured in Fig. 6*b* for the time interval $t_0 < t < t_1$. At $t = t_1$, let the switch be opened. Because of the presence of the RLC circuit, the stored energy in the coil will be converted into potential energy in the capacitor and back to magnetic-field energy in substantially one-half cycle of oscillation of this circuit. The return time (retrace time) $t_1 < t < t_2$ is evidently equal to

$$t_2 - t_1 \approx \pi \sqrt{LC} \tag{16}$$

If the switch is opened at $t = t_2$, the current will go from i_{min} to zero at a rate approximately equal to (letting E be the battery potential)

$$\frac{di}{dt} = \frac{E}{L} \tag{17}$$

from which point on it will rise again as it did at $t = 0$. At $t = t_3$, the switch is opened, and the process begins again, repeating the waveform pictured between $t_1 < t < t_3$.

In the actual television system, the scanning circuit must be designed to yield a linear trace approximately 63 μsec long. If the cyclic-scanning system is used, the RLC circuit must be designed to have a half period of 10 μsec. However, as it stands, the linearity of the sweep current which the basic circuit yields leaves much to be desired. Consider then the practical refinement of this system as illustrated by the horizontal output and reaction scanning circuit pictured in Fig. 7. Its operation is described as follows:

During the latter part of the horizontal trace, the output tube conducts very heavily and builds up a strong magnetic field in the deflection coil and output transformer. When the negative pulse from the horizontal discharge tube is applied to the output-tube grid, its plate current is suddenly cut off and the magnetic field in the transformer and deflection coil begins to collapse at a rate determined by the resonant frequency of the system. If the coil were not damped, it would continue to oscillate at its natural frequency. To prevent this oscillation from occurring, a reaction scanning tube, which is incorporated into a modified damper circuit, is

[1] See O. H. Schade, Characteristics of High-definition Deflection and High Voltage Systems for Kinescopes, *RCA Rev.*, vol. 11, pp. 5–37, March, 1950.

connected across the deflecting coil. When the voltage on the reaction-scanning-tube plate becomes positive with respect to its cathode, it begins to conduct heavily and the field begins to decay at a rate permitted by the load which the reaction scanning tube has placed on the coil. The circuit constants are such that this decay is linear and at a rate suitable for the visible trace.

If no additional energy were fed into the coil, the field would fall to

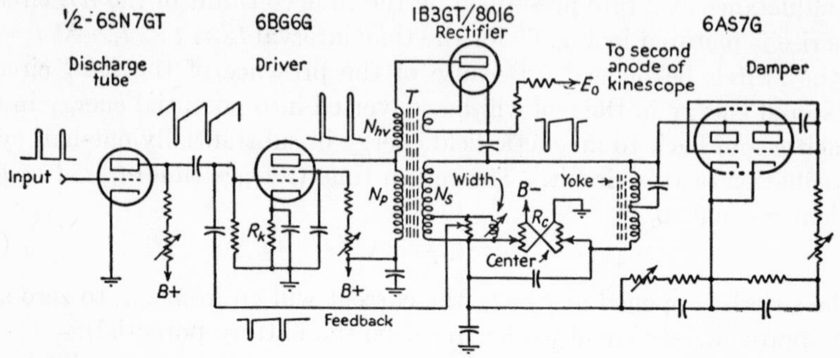

FIG. 7. Horizontal television scanning circuit including a cyclic-scanning circuit and an r-f high-voltage supply for the picture tube. (*Courtesy of RCA Review.*)

zero and the kinescope beam would come to rest in the center of the tube, the deflection coil current approaching its final value asymptotically. It is therefore necessary to have the output tube begin to supply power to the deflection coil before energy in the coil is completely dissipated. Although the currents supplied by the output tube and by the decaying field are curved at the cross point, together they produce a current that is linear.

By the time the beam has reached the right side of the kinescope, the output tube is conducting heavily and has built up a strong field in the transformer and coil. At this point, the output tube is again suddenly cut off and the process is repeated.

8. Radio-frequency Power Supply. The picture-tube high-voltage-supply power is obtained from the energy stored in the deflection inductances during each horizontal scan. When the plate current is cut off by the incoming signal, a positive pulse appears in the transformer primary due to the collapsing field in the deflection coil. This pulse of voltage is stepped up, rectified, filtered, and applied to the second anode of the kinescope. Since the frequency of the supply voltage is high (15,750), relatively little filter capacity is necessary. A typical circuit[1] is included in Fig. 7.

[1] For a detailed discussion of this circuit, see A. W. Friend, Television Deflection Circuits, Part II—Theory and Design of Combined Low-loss Horizontal Deflecting and

PROBLEMS

1. Show that the circuit in the figure is an integrating circuit and that the output is

$$e_0 = \frac{g_m}{C} \int e_g \, dt$$

provided that $iR \gg (1/C) \int i \, dt$.

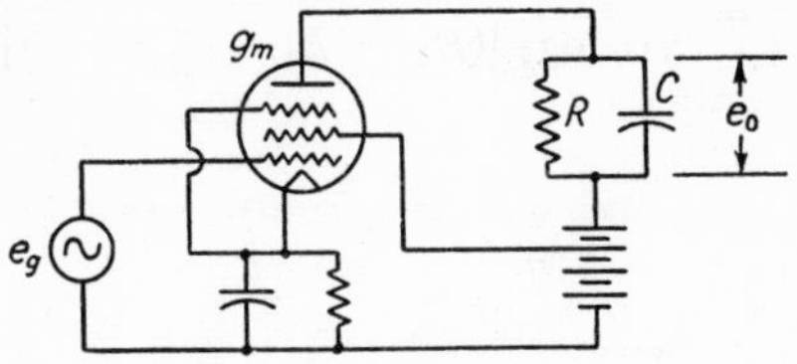

PROB. 1.

2. Show that the circuit in the figure is a differentiating circuit and that the output is

$$e_0 = g_m L \frac{de_g}{dt}$$

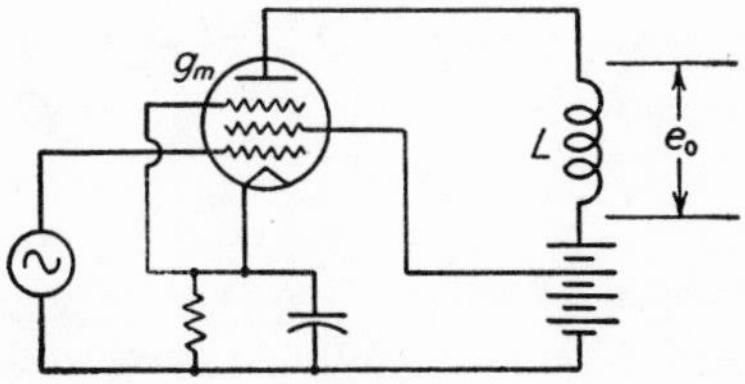

PROB. 2.

3. *a.* Deduce the integrating properties of the circuit shown in the figure.
b. What is the response of this circuit to a set of 6 pulses, each 2.5 μsec long and spaced 32 μsec apart?

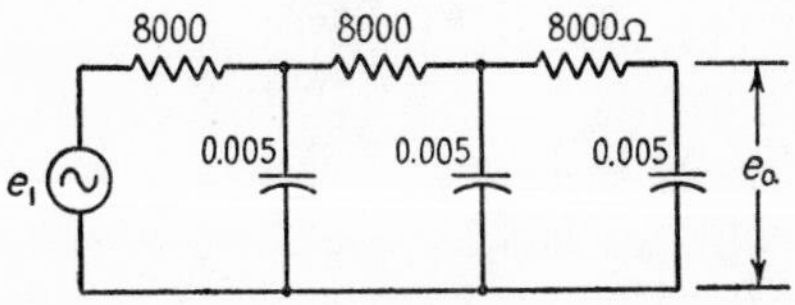

PROB. 3.

High Voltage Power Supply Systems, *RCA Rev.*, vol. 8, pp. 115–138, March, 1947.

For more general aspects of r-f power supplies, see O. H. Schade, Radio-frequency Operated High Voltage Supplies for Cathode-ray Tubes, *Proc. IRE*, vol. 31, pp. 158–163, April, 1943, or Mautner and Schade, Television High Voltage RF Power Supplies, *RCA Rev.*, vol. 8, pp. 43–81, March, 1947.

4. Calculate the amplitudes of the first five harmonics in the output of the sawtooth-wave generator for the case where

a. $E_1 = 100$ volts, $T_2 = 0.05\ T_1$
b. $E_1 = 25$ volts, $T_2 = 0.25\ T_1$
c. $E_1 = 25$ volts, $T_2 = 0.5\ T_1$

5. Consider the circuit in Fig. 4. Show that, if the ionization voltage of the gas tube is E_1 and if E_2 is the firing voltage of the tube corresponding to some particular E_g, the frequency of oscillation is

$$f = \frac{1}{RC \log_e [(E_b - E_1)/(E_b - E_2)]}$$

CHAPTER 12

REACTANCE TUBES, FREQUENCY STABILIZATION, AND PHASE SYNCHRONIZATION

REACTANCE TUBES

1. Basic Theory of Reactance Tubes.[1] Reactance tubes and variable-impedance circuit parameters are used in communication systems for frequency changing or for frequency modulation.

Consider the reactance-tube circuit which is illustrated in Fig. 1*a*. The tube is so biased that it operates class A. In this circuit, a resistance is

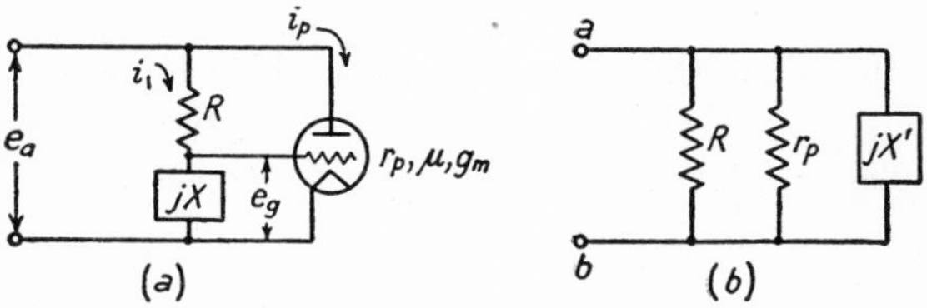

FIG. 1. Basic reactance-tube circuit.

connected from the plate to the grid, and a pure reactance is connected from the grid to the cathode. If the circuit is excited by a rotating-vector voltage generator of output $e_a = E_a e^{j\omega t}$ then we may write

$$i = i_1 + i_p \tag{1}$$

$$i_1 = \frac{e_a}{R + jX} \tag{2}$$

$$e_g = e_a \frac{jX}{R + jX} \tag{3}$$

$$i_p = g_m e_g + \frac{e_a}{r_p} \tag{4}$$

[1] For a more complete discussion of reactance-tube theory, see F. von Vilbig, Blindwiderstände mit negativem induktivem oder kapazitivem Widerstandsverlauf, *Hochfrequenztech. Elektroakustik*, vol. 55, pp. 120–132, April, 1940, or H. J. Reich, The Use of Vacuum Tubes as Variable Impedance Elements, *Proc. IRE*, vol. 30, No. 6, pp. 277–288, June, 1942. For some aspects of reactance-tube applications, see August Hund, "Frequency Modulation," pp. 155–182, McGraw-Hill Book Company, Inc., New York, 1942; also C. L. Cuccia, Certain Aspects of Reactance-tube Performance for Frequency Modulation at Ultra-high Frequencies, *RCA Rev.*, vol. 10, pp. 74–98, March, 1949.

The self-admittance at the input terminals is

$$Y_s(\omega) = \frac{i}{e_a} \tag{5}$$

$$= \frac{g_m e_g + (e_a/r_p) + [e_a/(R + jX)]}{e_a} \tag{6}$$

$$= \frac{g_m X^2 + R}{R^2 + X^2} + \frac{1}{r_p} + j\,\frac{X(g_m R - 1)}{R^2 + X^2} \tag{7}$$

When $R \gg X$ and when $i_1 \ll i_p$, we may write Eq. (7) as follows,

$$Y_s(\omega) = \frac{1}{R} + \frac{1}{r_p} + j\,\frac{g_m X}{R} \tag{8}$$

$$= \frac{1}{R'} + j\,\frac{1}{X'} \tag{9}$$

where

$$R' = \frac{R r_p}{R + r_p} \tag{10}$$

Equation (9) describes the circuit shown in Fig. 1*b*, which has two resistances R and r_p in shunt with an effective reactance $X' = R/g_m X$.

Inductance Tube. If X is a capacitive reactance such that

$$X = \frac{1}{\omega C} \tag{11}$$

then

$$X' = \omega\,\frac{RC}{g_m} \tag{12}$$

showing that the reactance tube appears as an effective inductance L', where

$$L' = \frac{RC}{g_m} \tag{13}$$

which is in shunt with R and r_p.

Capacitance Tube. If X is an inductive reactance such that

$$X = \omega L \tag{14}$$

then the reactance tube appears to be the capacitance[1] C', where

$$C' = \frac{g_m L}{R} \tag{15}$$

[1] Another important variable-capacitance device is the barium titanate–strontium titanate reactor, a semiconductor which, when used in the interplate region of a capacitor, presents a dielectric constant which is a function of the electric-field strength across the semiconductor. See H. Donley, Effect of Field Strength on Dielectric Properties of Barium–Strontium Titanate, *RCA Rev.*, vol. 8, pp. 539–553, September, 1947.

2. Numerical Example. Consider the effective inductance of a 2C43 disk-seal tube when $g_m = 5 \times 10^{-3}$ mho, $R = 10{,}000$ ohms, and $C = 2.8 \times 10^{-12}$ farad. Substituting these values into (13), we get

$$L' = \frac{10{,}000 \times 2.8 \times 10^{-12}}{5 \times 10^{-3}} \tag{16}$$

$$= 5.6\ \mu h \tag{17}$$

3. A Reactance-tube System. A capacitive-reactance tube shunted across the resonant circuit of an electron-coupled oscillator is pictured in Fig. 2. The capacitors marked C_s are by-pass capacitors. Since the

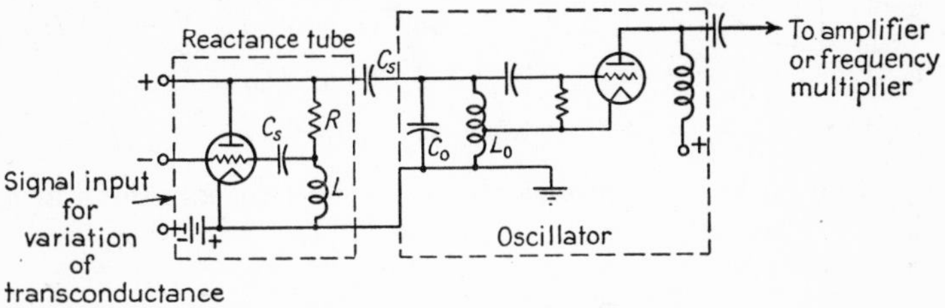

FIG. 2. Oscillator reactance-tube circuit.

capacitance due to the reactance tube shunts the capacitance C_0 of the oscillator circuit, the resonant frequency of the entire circuit is described as

$$f = \frac{1}{2\pi\sqrt{\left[C_0 + \frac{g_m(t)}{R} L\right] L_0}} \tag{18}$$

$g_m(t)$ is the transconductance variation due to the signal which is applied to the transconductance-control circuit.

4. Frequency Modulation by Electron Beams in Ultra-high-frequency (u-h-f) Tubes.[1] At the ultra-high frequencies, electron beams may be used to produce either frequency variation or loading owing to their exhibiting the properties of a reactance or a resistance under certain conditions. An analysis of the electronic system and the conditions under which these reactive or resistive effects are produced is presented as follows:

[1] Smith and Shulman, Frequency Modulation and Control by Electron Beams, *Proc. IRE*, vol. 35, pp. 644–657, July, 1947.

Kilgore, Shulman, and Kurshan, A Frequency Modulated Magnetron for Super-high Frequencies, *Proc. IRE*, vol. 35, pp. 657–664.

Donal, Bush, Cuccia, and Hegbar, A 1-kilowatt Frequency-modulated Magnetron for 900 Megacycles, *Proc. IRE*, vol. 35, pp. 664–669, July, 1947.

Consider the electron-beam system pictured in Fig. 3; it consists of a pair of parallel plates between which exists an electric field $E_x e^{j\omega t}$, due to a generator, which produces an a-c voltage $Ve^{j\omega t}$; the plates are spaced apart by a distance d. An electron beam passes through the plates with velocity v_0 in the z direction, the electric field being in the x direction and transverse to the path of the electrons. A magnetic field of intensity H is parallel to the path of the electrons.

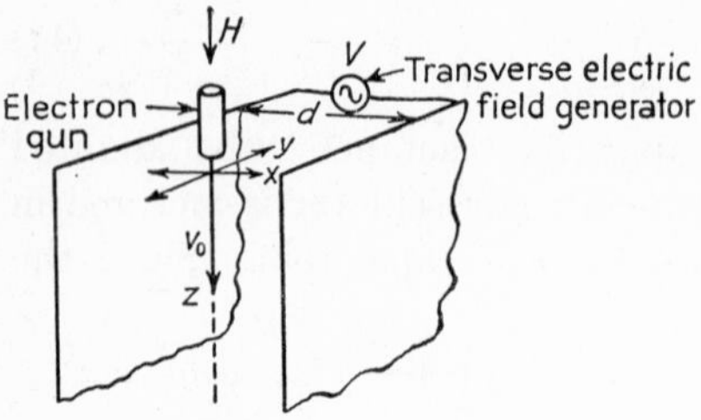

FIG. 3.

If no fringe fields are present, we may write the equations of the electron motion as follows:

$$m\ddot{x} = -|e|\, E_x e^{j\omega t} - |e|\, H\dot{y} \tag{19}$$

$$m\ddot{y} = |e|\, H\dot{x} \tag{20}$$

$$m\ddot{z} = 0 \tag{21}$$

These equations may be combined to form the two equations in v_x and v_y; that is,

$$\ddot{v}_x + \omega_0^2 v_x = -\frac{|e|}{m}\frac{d}{dt} E_x e^{j\omega t} \tag{22}$$

$$\ddot{v}_y + \omega_0^2 v_y = -\omega_0 E_x e^{j\omega t}\frac{|e|}{m} \tag{23}$$

where

$$v_x = \frac{dx}{dt} \tag{24}$$

$$v_y = \frac{dy}{dt} \tag{25}$$

$$\omega_0 = \frac{|e|}{m} H \tag{26}$$

$\omega_0/2\pi$ is a characteristic frequency of the magnetic field and is known as the cyclotron frequency.

Consider the Laplace-transform solution of Eq. (22) subject to the following initial conditions: The electron shall enter the field region at $t = 0$, at which time

$$v_x = v_y = 0 \tag{27}$$

$$\frac{dv_x}{dt} = \frac{dv_y}{dt} = 0 \tag{28}$$

Taking the Laplace transform of both sides of (22), we get

$$\int_0^\infty e^{-st}\frac{d^2v_x}{dt^2}\,dt + \omega_0^2\int_0^\infty e^{-st}v_x\,dt = A\int_0^\infty e^{-(s-j\omega)t}\,dt \tag{29}$$

$$= \frac{A}{s - j\omega} \tag{30}$$

where

$$A = j\omega \frac{|e|}{m} E_x \tag{31}$$

Consider the first integral on the left-hand side of (29). It follows, using integration by parts, that

$$\int_0^\infty e^{-st} \frac{d^2v_x}{dt^2} dt = \int_0^\infty e^{-st} d\frac{dv_x}{dt} = e^{-st}\frac{dv_x}{dt}\Big|_0^\infty + s\int_0^\infty e^{-st}\frac{dv_x}{dt} dt \tag{32}$$

$$= s\int_0^\infty e^{-st}\frac{dv_x}{dt} dt \tag{33}$$

because of (28) provided that $e^{-st}\, dv_x/dt = 0$ at $t = 0$. Integrating (33) by parts, we get

$$\int_0^\infty e^{-st} \frac{d^2v_x}{dt^2} dt = s\left(e^{-st}v_x\Big|_0^\infty\right) + s^2\int_0^\infty e^{-st}v_x\, dt \tag{34}$$

$$= s^2\int_0^\infty e^{-st}v_x\, dt \tag{35}$$

The Laplace transform of (22) may then be written as follows:

$$(s^2 + \omega_0^2)\mathcal{L}(v_x) = \frac{A}{s - j\omega} \tag{36}$$

or

$$\mathcal{L}(v_x) = \frac{A}{(s^2 + \omega_0^2)(s - j\omega)} \tag{37}$$

Then

$$v_x = \frac{A}{2\pi j}\int_{\alpha - j\infty}^{\alpha + j\infty} \frac{e^{st}}{(s + j\omega_0)(s - j\omega_0)(s - j\omega)} ds \tag{38}$$

Because (38) has simple poles at $s = \pm j\omega_0$ and $s = j\omega$, it follows from Eq. (127), Chap. 1, that

$$v_x = A\left[\frac{e^{j\omega t}}{\omega_0^2 + \omega^2} + \frac{e^{j\omega_0 t}}{2j\omega_0(j\omega_0 - j\omega)} + \frac{e^{-j\omega_0 t}}{2j\omega_0(j\omega_0 + j\omega)}\right] \tag{39}$$

Multiplying and dividing (39) through by $e^{-j\omega t}$, we get, for the case when $\omega \approx \omega_0$,

$$v_x = -j\frac{|e|}{m}\frac{E_x}{2}\frac{e^{j(\omega_0 - \omega)t} - 1}{\omega - \omega_0} e^{j\omega t} \tag{40}$$

which is the same as the expression obtained by L. P. Smith and C. I. Shulman in a solution,[1] involving a more classical method, using the

[1] See Eq. (6), Smith and Shulman, Frequency Modulation and Control by Electron Beams, *Proc. IRE*, vol. 35, No. 7, pp. 644–657, July, 1947.

boundary conditions $x = y = v_x = v_y = 0$ at $t = 0$. The Laplace transform would have been difficult to use with these boundary conditions because one of the initial conditions involves an integration rather than a derivative of v_x. It is evident, however, that either set of boundary conditions for this particular problem adequately[1] represent the *entering behavior* of the electron.

If we ignore the effect of space charge, we may describe the current induced in the plates[2] due to the oscillating charge with velocity v_x as

$$dIe^{j\omega t} = \frac{dq}{d} v_x = -\frac{|I_0|}{v_0} \frac{v_x}{d} dz \tag{41}$$

where I_0 is the beam current and dz is a differential distance in the z direction. Substituting (40) into (41) and replacing t by z/v_0 in the resulting expression, we get, for the total current induced in the plates for a traveled distance L,

$$Ie^{j\omega t} = \left[\frac{E_x}{2d} \frac{|e|}{m} \frac{|I_0|}{v_0} \frac{j}{\omega - \omega_0} \int_0^L (e^{j(\omega_0 - \omega)(z/v_0)} - 1)\, dz\right] e^{j\omega t} \tag{42}$$

Performing the integration, we get

$$Ie^{j\omega t} = E_x \frac{L^2 I_0}{4dV_b} \left(\frac{1 - \cos \Theta}{\Theta^2} + j\frac{\Theta - \sin \Theta}{\Theta^2}\right) e^{j\omega t} \tag{43}$$

where

$$\Theta = (\omega - \omega_0)\tau \qquad \tau = \frac{L}{v_0} \qquad V_b = \frac{1}{2}\frac{m}{e} v_0^2 \quad \text{esu} \tag{44}$$

τ and Θ are the electron transit time (seconds) and transit angle (radians) for the distance L (centimeters), respectively, and V_b is the beam voltage (esu) which determines the electron velocity v_0. If I_0 is measured in amperes and V_b in volts, (43) will yield a result in practical units.

The admittance Y_e presented by the electron beam is

$$Y_e = \frac{I}{d \cdot E_x} = \frac{L^2 I_0}{4d^2 V_b} \left(\frac{1 - \cos \Theta}{\Theta^2} + j\frac{\Theta - \sin \Theta}{\Theta^2}\right) \tag{45}$$

$$= G_e + jB_e \tag{46}$$

A plot of $(1 - \cos \Theta)/\Theta^2$ and $(1 - \sin \Theta)/\Theta^2$ is pictured in Fig. 4, where we see that when $\omega = \omega_0$, such that $(\omega_0 - \omega)\tau = 0$, the electron beam presents a pure conductance G_e to the generator. When

$$(\omega_0 - \omega)\tau = 2\pi, 4\pi, \ldots \tag{47}$$

[1] Actually the boundary conditions used by Smith and Shulman are more correct. Equation (28), as a consequence of (19), demands that E_x be zero at $t = 0$.

[2] See Eq. (28), Chap. 5.

it is evident from Fig. 4 that $G_e = 0$ and the electron beam presents a pure susceptance B_e to the generator.

When the beam displays the properties of a pure reactance, the beam configuration is a spiral which increases in spiral radius to some maximum value which represents the absorption of a certain amount of energy and then reduces in spiral radius back to zero, which represents the return of the spiral energy to the system.

5. Frequency Deviation in a Spiral Beam System. Consider the frequency deviation produced when a spiral-reactance beam is incorporated into the structure of a cavity magnetron. If the susceptance of the magnetron cavity system is B_M, then the total susceptance presented by one spiral-reactance beam is

$$B = B_M + B_e \tag{48}$$

$$= \omega C_M\left[1 - \left(\frac{\omega_M}{\omega}\right)^2\right] + \frac{L^2 I_0}{4d^2 V_b}\frac{\Theta - \sin\Theta}{\Theta^2} \tag{49}$$

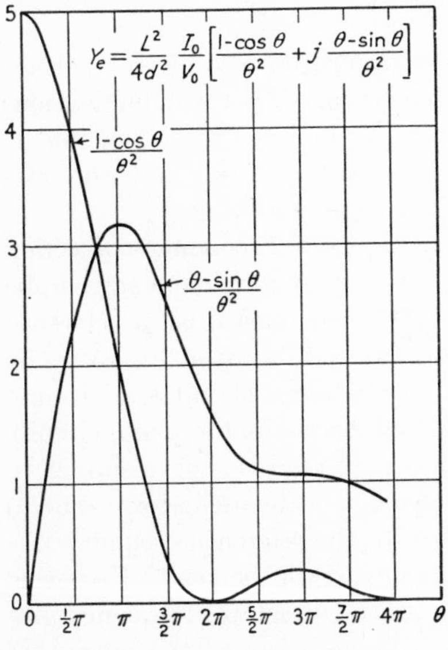

FIG. 4. (*Courtesy of Institute of Radio Engineers.*)

where $\omega_M{}^2 = 1/L_M C_M$ describes the resonant frequency of the magnetron before the beams are introduced, L_M and C_M being the equivalent inductance and capacitance of the magnetron's resonant system. If we let $\omega = \omega_M + \Delta\omega$, where $\Delta\omega/2\pi$ is a small change in frequency,[1] and if $\Delta\omega \ll \omega_0 - \omega_M$, it follows that

$$\Delta\omega = \frac{L^2 I_0}{8d^2 V_b C_M}\frac{\sin\Theta - \Theta}{\Theta^2} \tag{50}$$

where

$$(\omega_0 - \omega)\tau \cong (\omega_0 - \omega_M)\tau = \Theta$$
$$\Delta\omega \ll \omega_M \tag{51}$$
$$B_M \cong 2C_M\Delta\omega$$

The reactance presented by the reactance beam is controlled by varying the beam current I_0.

[1] In a 1-kw, 12-cavity magnetron operating in the 850- to 900-Mc range, about 0.8 Mc per beam was obtained using a beam current of 100 ma and a beam voltage of 300 volts (L = 1.84 in.). See Donal, Bush, Cuccia, and Hegbar, A 1-kilowatt Frequency-modulated Magnetron for 900 Megacycles, *Proc. IRE*, vol. 35, pp. 664–669, July, 1947.

FREQUENCY STABILIZATION AND PHASE SYNCHRONIZATION

6. Introduction to Frequency Stabilization and Phase Synchronization of Oscillators. In the practical design of oscillators and power sources, it is often desirable to stabilize the frequency or adjust the phase within a certain range of specifications or requirements.

If the signal source is to be a piezocrystal oscillator, for example, the inherent frequency stability of this device may make it unnecessary to add a frequency-stabilization system. However, if the signal source is to be a simple oscillator of a type which is not sufficiently stable, the heating up of circuit elements alone in the oscillator may be sufficient to produce an undesired drift in frequency. The desirability of frequency stabilization extends into the realm of FM signal sources, in which devices center-frequency stabilization often becomes necessary.

In many of the circuits used in television and radar, it is necessary to synchronize the phase of some signal source with respect to the phase of some reference signal. This may also involve frequency stabilization to some extent since the signal source may have to be "pulled" to the frequency of the reference system before it can be locked into phase.

Frequency stabilization and phase synchronization are often so interrelated that a separation of the two cannot be made in a communications system. The discussion to follow will present the basic principles underlying the operation of frequency-stabilization networks and the elementary theory of phase synchronization and phase locking.

7. Frequency Control of an Oscillator Using a Frequency-correction System. The frequency of an oscillator of relatively low frequency can be stabilized to a specified frequency by using a reactance tube, a reference frequency source, and a frequency comparator, as shown in Fig. 5. The frequency comparator (discriminator) is an electronic circuit (which may consist of a frequency mixer and a frequency discriminator; these circuits will be described in Chap. 22) which has a characteristic curve similar to that shown in Fig. 6. A sample of the frequency of the oscillator is sent to the comparator. If this frequency is equal to the reference oscillator frequency f_0, the output voltage of the comparator will be zero. However, if a small difference in frequency exists between the sample frequency and the reference oscillator frequency, a d-c voltage exists at the output of the comparator which is proportional to the frequency difference.

The basic operation of the frequency-stabilization circuit pictured in Fig. 5 is described as follows: As the oscillator output is transmitted to the load, a sample portion of this output is sent to the terminals of the frequency comparator, into which is also sent a reference signal of frequency f_0. The output of the comparator goes to a reactance tube which controls the frequency of the oscillator. If the oscillator frequency deviates from f_0, a d-c voltage, of correct polarity and proportional to the deviation, appears at the control grid of the reactance tube, causing the return of the frequency of the oscillator to f_0.

Actually, such a system may be used to stabilize the center frequency of an FM transmitter;[1] by using a phase comparator rather than a frequency comparator, the system may be adapted to applications requiring phase control.[2]

At the ultra-high frequencies and the microwaves,[3] it is very difficult to obtain a stable reference signal source such as that provided by a piezoelectric crystal. R. V. Pound[4] has devised a frequency stabilizer using a

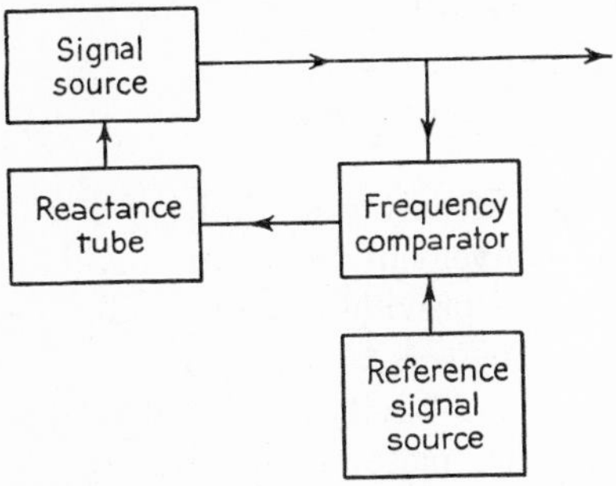

FIG. 5. Frequency-stabilization circuit.

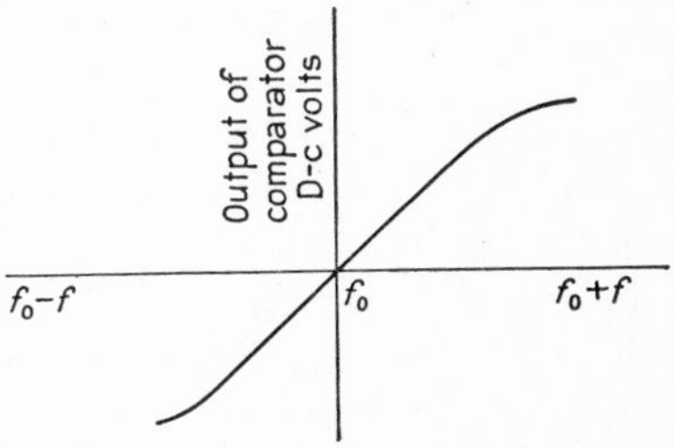

FIG. 6. Frequency-comparator characteristic curve.

high-Q resonant cavity and a special circuit, known as an r-f discriminator, which delivers a voltage which is a measure of difference between the frequency of the cavity and the frequency of the oscillator to be stabilized. The basic circuit is shown in Fig. 7; the output of the oscillator is sampled by the r-f discriminator, which sends a correcting voltage through an amplifier to a frequency-correcting parameter of the oscillator,[5] thus adjusting the oscillator frequency to that of the cavity.

[1] See Chap. 13 or A. Hund, "Frequency Modulation," Chap. III, McGraw-Hill Book Company, Inc., New York, 1942.

[2] For a description of the use of a phase-control system in a television receiver see Sec. 22, Chap. 22, or see Wendt and Fredendall, Automatic Frequency and Phase Control of Synchronization in Television Receivers, *Proc. IRE*, vol. 31, pp. 7–15, January, 1943. For a brief description of a phase-controlled magnetron transmitter see footnote to Sec. 5, Chap. 13.

[3] Absorption lines of gases at reduced pressures exhibit Q's of 100,000 in the 24,000-Mc range. For a description of the stabilization of a K-band klystron using the 23,870.1 Mc line of ammonia, see Hershberger and Norton, Frequency Stabilization with Microwave Spectral Lines, *RCA Rev.*, vol. 9, No. 1, pp. 38–49, March, 1948.

[4] See R. V. Pound, Frequency Stabilization of Microwave Oscillators, *Proc. IRE*, vol. 35, pp. 1405–1415, December, 1947.

[5] Although reactance elements such as spiral electron beams may be incorporated

8. Frequency Stabilization Using an Auxiliary Resonant Cavity. In many communication systems, it is not necessary to achieve the high degree of frequency stabilization which is possible using a reactance tube,

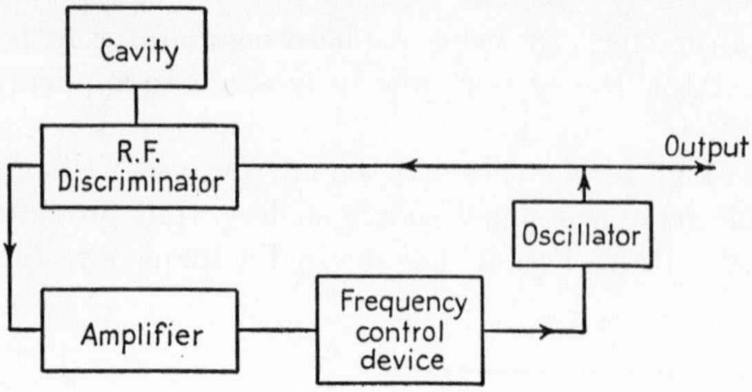

FIG. 7. Basic Pound frequency-stabilizer circuit.

comparator network, or the Pound system. If only a minimizing of the frequency drift is desired, it is sometimes convenient to use an auxiliary resonant cavity,[1] which may be employed to provide certain oscillating systems with a certain amount of frequency *stiffness*.[2]

One of the outstanding examples of a resonant-cavity-stabilized system is the stabilized magnetron-oscillator network pictured in Fig. 8*a*. If considerations of the line-length, coupled-circuit, and mode phenomena are excluded from the considerations of stabilization which are to be discussed, it can be shown that the oscillator-stabilizing resonator system

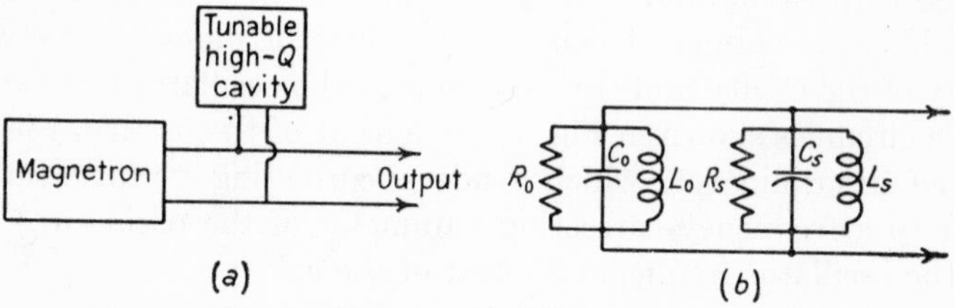

FIG. 8. Magnetron-stabilizer circuit.

may be represented by the circuit pictured in Fig. 8*b*. What is desired of this circuit is that the frequency of the entire resonant system shall adhere closely to the frequency of the stabilizing resonator over a wide range of

into a u-h-f power source, many microwave oscillators such as klystrons may be adjusted in frequency by changing appropriate tube voltages and do not require additional circuit elements.

[1] Not to be confused with the Pound system.

[2] Transit time in an electron tube can also be utilized to minimize frequency drift. See J. Kurshan, The Transitrol, An Experimental Automatic-frequency Control Tube, *RCA Rev.*, vol. 9, pp. 687–703, December, 1948.

parameters, which would normally cause frequency shifts were the stabilizing resonator to be removed from the circuit.

A rewarding approach to the study of the problem is one based on stored energy and a stabilization factor S, which is defined as follows:

$$S = \frac{\text{total stored energy in system}}{\text{stored energy in oscillator}}$$

This factor describes the ratio of the stored energy in the oscillator plus stabilizing resonator plus any attendant lines to the stored energy in the oscillator alone.

The significance of the stabilization factor S may be stated qualitatively as follows:

The greater the proportion of the total-system stored energy which is found in the stabilizing resonator, the greater will be the frequency stiffness of the oscillator.

A mathematical demonstration of the proof of this statement is beyond the scope of this volume. However, a better understanding of it can be obtained by considering the tuning rates of a typical oscillator–stabilizing-resonator system. If ω_i, ω_o, and ω_s represent angular velocities of the entire system, the oscillator alone, and the stabilizing resonator, respectively, the behavior of ω_i as a function of changes in either ω_o or ω_s is described by the differentials $\Delta\omega_i/\Delta\omega_o$ and $\Delta\omega_i/\Delta\omega_s$. It can be shown[1] that

$$\frac{\Delta\omega_i}{\Delta\omega_o} = \frac{1}{S} \tag{52}$$

$$\frac{\Delta\omega_i}{\Delta\omega_s} = \frac{S - 1}{S} \tag{53}$$

It is evident that as S is increased in magnitude, the shift in system frequency, as a function of a shift in oscillator frequency, decreases. At the same time, the shift in system frequency as a function of the stabilizing-resonator frequency may be made virtually a function of the stabilizing-resonator frequency alone. (In practical systems, it is necessary to specify that $S < 2$ in order to prevent frequency instabilities during oscillation.)

The stabilization factor and the stored energies of a stabilized system may be deduced using the following equation, which has been derived by E. A. Guillemin,[2]

$$\frac{dB}{d\omega} = \frac{4}{E_1^2} (\mathcal{E}_e + \mathcal{E}_m) \tag{54}$$

[1] See F. F. Rieke in G. B. Collins, "Microwave Magnetrons," Chap. 16, McGraw-Hill Book Company, Inc., New York, 1948.

[2] E. A. Guillemin, "Communication Networks," vol. II, p. 229, John Wiley & Sons, Inc., New York, 1935.

where B is the driving-point susceptance of the network. E_1 is the voltage across that network, and $\mathcal{E}_e$ and $\mathcal{E}_m$ are the stored energies in the electric field and magnetic field, respectively. It follows from (54) that S may be described in the following way,

$$S = \frac{(\mathcal{E}_e + \mathcal{E}_m)_{\text{tot}}}{(\mathcal{E}_e + \mathcal{E}_m)_{\text{osc}}} = \frac{\left.\frac{dB}{d\omega}\right|_{\text{tot}}}{\left.\frac{dB}{d\omega}\right|_{\text{osc}}} \tag{55}$$

provided that the voltage E_1 is maintained constant with and without the stabilizing resonator in the circuit.

Consider an illustration[1] of the use of Eq. (55) in which it is applied to the circuit in Fig. 8b. For the oscillator circuit alone,

$$B_o = \omega C_o - \frac{1}{\omega L_o} = \sqrt{\frac{C_o}{L_o}}\left(\frac{\omega}{\omega_o} - \frac{\omega_o}{\omega}\right) \tag{56}$$

$$\approx 2\sqrt{\frac{C_o}{L_o}}\,\frac{\omega_o - \omega}{\omega} \tag{57}$$

where $\omega_o = 1/\sqrt{L_o C_o}$ and $\omega \approx \omega_o$. Using (57), it follows that

$$\frac{dB_o}{d\omega} = \sqrt{\frac{C_o}{L_o}}\,\frac{\omega_o}{\omega^2} \tag{58}$$

In like manner, we may show that, for the oscillator plus stabilizing-resonator circuit in Fig. 8b,

$$\frac{dB_{o+s}}{d\omega} = \left(\sqrt{\frac{C_o}{L_o}} + \sqrt{\frac{C_s}{L_s}}\right)\frac{\omega_o}{\omega^2} \tag{59}$$

and we get, substituting (58) and (59) into (55),

$$S = 1 + \sqrt{\frac{C_s}{C_o}}\sqrt{\frac{L_o}{L_s}} \tag{60}$$

which shows that, with the oscillator parameters fixed, the stabilization factor may be adjusted by appropriate variations of C_s and L_s.

9. Synchronization of Oscillators. By injecting a reference signal into an appropriate section of a free-running oscillator, the frequency of the oscillator may be pulled to the frequency of the reference-signal source, and the phases of these signals may be synchronized. · The injection may be performed in any of a number of different ways; in the sample system oscillator using a tuned-plate tuned-grid circuit, shown in Fig. 10, the reference signal is injected into the grid circuit. Actually, in many appli-

[1] See Donal, Cuccia, Brown, Vogel, and Dodds, Stabilized Magnetron for Beacon Service, *RCA Rev.*, vol. 3, pp. 352–372, June, 1947.

cations, it is sufficient to inject the reference signal having proper characteristics at some position between the oscillator output and the load, using suitable decoupling devices so that the signal from the main oscillator does not effect the reference-signal source.

Consider the case when a free-running oscillator applies a voltage $E_1e^{j\omega_1 t}$ at the terminals a, b in Fig. 9, thus causing a current $I_1e^{j\omega_1 t}$ to flow. In addition, let a signal injection source produce the voltage

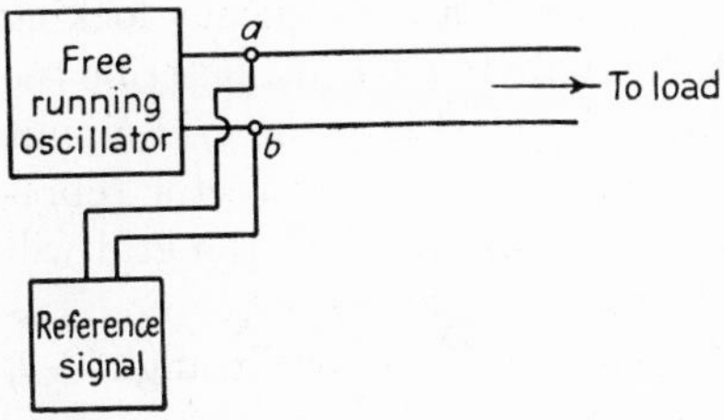

FIG. 9. Basic injection-lock system (the oscillator signal must not react back on the reference-signal source).

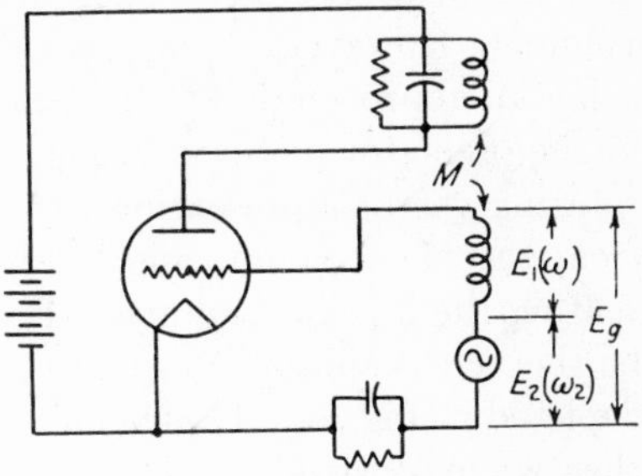

FIG. 10. Injection-locked oscillator.

$E_2e^{j\omega_2 t}$ and the current $I_2e^{j\omega_2 t}$ at the terminals a, b. The admittance presented at a, b may be written in the following way:

$$Y_{ab} = \frac{I_1e^{j\omega_1 t} + I_2e^{j\omega_2 t}}{E_1e^{j\omega_1 t} + E_2e^{j\omega_2 t}} \tag{61}$$

$$= \frac{1}{E_1}\frac{1 + (I_2/I_1)e^{j(\omega_2-\omega_1)t}}{1 + (E_2/E_1)e^{j(\omega_2-\omega_1)t}} \tag{62}$$

If I_2/I_1 and E_2/E_1 are small, as will be the case in a practical injection-synchronization system,

$$Y_{ab} = G + jB + xe^{j(\omega_2-\omega_1)t} \tag{63}$$

where

$$G + jB = \frac{I_1}{E_1} \tag{64}$$

$$x = (G + jB)\left(\frac{I_2}{I_1} - \frac{E_2}{E_1}\right) \tag{65}$$

Equation (63) is an important result which has considerable general significance. It reveals that the admittance has a time-dependent component which is a function of the beat frequency $(1/2\pi)(\omega_2 - \omega_1)$. Under proper conditions for the case when $\omega_2 - \omega_1$ is small, the free-running oscillator will be pulled in frequency toward ω_1 and will rapidly be locked into phase with the injected signal. If $\omega_2 - \omega_1$ is not small, then either frequency or phase locking cannot be accomplished or if it can, the frequency of the free-running oscillator will drift toward the injection-signal frequency, inducing harmonics into the system before the lock eventually takes place. These harmonics are produced by the uneven rotation of the vector admittance function $xe^{j(\omega_2-\omega_1)t}$ even though its rotation is periodic with the frequency $(1/2\pi)(\omega_2 - \omega_1)$.

A complete discussion of frequency locking is beyond the scope of this volume. However, it is convenient and highly instructive to investigate, using an approach due to R. Adler,[1] the phenomenon of frequency locking in the oscillator pictured in Fig. 10. In this circuit let $E_1(\omega)$ describe the rotating vector representing the grid voltage induced into the grid circuit from the plate circuit, and let $E_2(\omega_2)$ describe the rotating vector representing the injected voltage. The total voltage appearing at the grid will be the vector sum of $E_1(\omega)$ and $E_2(\omega_2)$, which constitutes the vector E_g as depicted in Fig. 11. If $E_1(\omega)$ and $E_2(\omega_2)$ are out of phase by the angle $-\theta$, then we may write

$$\omega - \omega_2 = \frac{d\theta}{dt} \tag{66}$$

which represents the instantaneous angular beat frequency as referred to the injected signal.

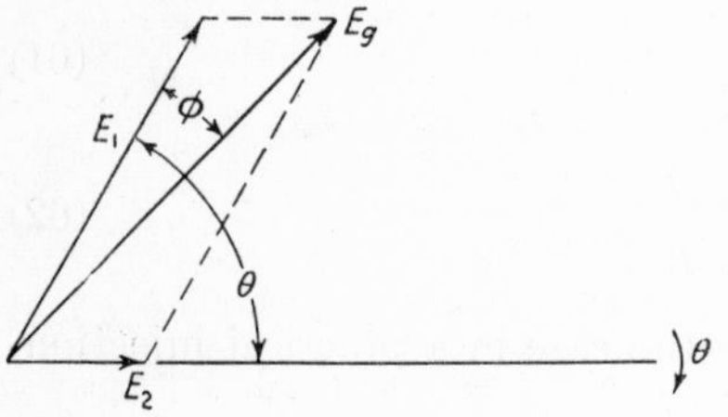

FIG. 11.

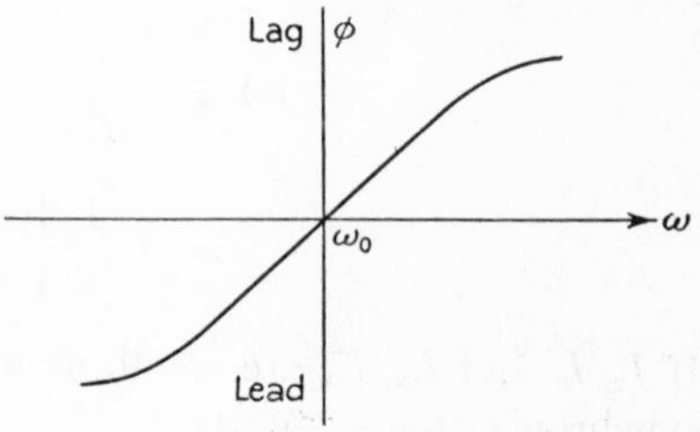

FIG. 12.

Let us digress for a moment to consider the curve pictured in Fig. 12, which describes the phase relationship between E_g and E_1. If the oscillator is running at ω_0, the phase shift is zero, the phases of the two coinciding at the free-running frequency. At other than ω_0, a phase angle will be introduced between E_g and E_1 in virtue of the resonant qualities of the plate load. Ignoring any changes in the amplitudes of E_2 and E_g which may accompany a shift in frequency, it is evident that if the vector sum $E_g(\omega)$ is suddenly produced owing to an injected signal, the voltage E_1

[1] R. A. Adler, A Study of Locking Phenomena in Oscillators, *Proc. IRE*, vol. 34, pp. 351–357, June, 1946.

which is returned to the grid circuit by the feedback system will differ in phase from the grid voltage E_g by the angle ϕ. If $E_2 \ll E_1$, ϕ may be related to E_1, E_2, and θ by the expression

$$\phi = -\frac{E_2}{E_1} \sin \theta \tag{67}$$

If we limit our use of the curve in Fig. 12 only to the linear portion near $\omega = \omega_0$, we may describe the slope A of this curve as follows:

$$A = \frac{d\phi}{d\omega} \tag{68}$$

It therefore follows from (68) that

$$\phi = A(\omega - \omega_0) \tag{69}$$

$$= A[(\omega - \omega_2) - (\omega_0 - \omega_2)] \tag{70}$$

Substituting the expression for $(\omega - \omega_2)$, as given by (66), into (70), we get

$$\phi = A\left[\frac{d\theta}{dt} - (\omega_0 - \omega_2)\right] \tag{71}$$

Combining (67) and (71), we get[1]

$$\frac{d\theta}{dt} + \frac{E_2}{E_1}\frac{1}{A} \sin \theta = \omega_0 - \omega_2 \tag{72}$$

which is an elementary differential equation describing the behavior of the oscillator frequency and phase during injection locking.

Illustration. As a simple illustration of the use of (72), consider the case when the injected-signal frequency is identical to the free-running frequency of the oscillator; that is, $\omega_2 = \omega_0$. If θ is small, (72) becomes

$$\frac{d\theta}{dt} = \left(-\frac{E_2}{E_1}\frac{1}{A}\right)\theta \tag{73}$$

which yields the solution

$$\theta = \Theta_0 e^{-(E_2/E_1A)t} \tag{74}$$

where Θ_0 is the initial phase difference. It is evident that the phase of the free-running oscillator will gradually go to the phase of the injected signal.

[1] For the derivation of an equation which is similar to (72) but which is somewhat broader in scope, see Huntoon and Weiss, Synchronization of Oscillators, *Proc. IRE*, vol. 35, No. 12, pp. 1415–1423, December, 1947. For a derivation of (72) based on the operating characteristics of a magnetron, see J. C. Slater, "Microwave Electronics," Sec. 9.5, D. Van Nostrand Company, Inc., New York, 1950.

Consider a more general solution of (72). Let

$$k = (\omega_2 - \omega_0) \frac{E_1}{E_2} A \tag{75}$$

(72) may then be written in the form

$$\frac{d\theta}{dt} + \frac{E_2}{E_1} \frac{1}{A} [\sin \theta - k] = 0 \tag{76}$$

Multiplying (76) through by dt and integrating, we get, after some manipulating,

$$\theta = 2 \tan^{-1} \left[\frac{1}{k} + \frac{\sqrt{k^2 - 1}}{k} \tan \frac{(E_2/E_1A)(t - t_0)}{2} \sqrt{k^2 - 1} \right] \tag{77}$$

where t_0 is an integration constant. If $|k| < 1$, phase synchronization may be achieved.

PROBLEMS

1. Plot the effective inductance of a 2C43 disk-seal tube used as a reactance tube if g_m is varied from $g_m = 0$ to $g_m = 8 \times 10^{-3}$ mho when $R = 1{,}000$ ohms and $C = 2.8 \times 10^{-12}$ farad.

2. If $X = \omega L$ in Fig. 1, calculate the amount of effective capacitance presented by the reactance tube when $g_m = 5 \times 10^{-3}$ mho, $R = 5{,}000$ ohms, and $L = 90\ \mu$h.

3. Show that if an inductance is placed across the capacitor in a reactance-tube circuit utilizing a capacitance from grid to cathode and a resistance from plate to grid (by-passed), the susceptance presented by the circuit is approximately

$$B \cong \frac{g_m}{\omega RC} + \omega C_{gp} \frac{\Delta f}{f_1}$$

where C_{gp} is the interelectrode capacitance from grid to plate, f_1 is the frequency of the resonant circuit consisting of C and the inductance, and Δf is the frequency deviation from f_1.

4. Using the chart evolved in Prob. 1, plot the resonant frequency of a tank circuit utilizing this reactance tube when the tank inductance is 50 μh and the tank capacitance is 25 $\mu\mu$f.

5. Using Laplace-transform analysis, solve for the admittance presented by an electron beam in a spiral beam tube for the case when $\omega = \omega_0$. Show that the apparent resistance represented by the beam is

$$R_e = 8 \frac{V_b}{I_0} \left(\frac{d}{l}\right)^2$$

where R_e is expressed in practical units. Calculate R_e for the case where $V_b = 500$ volts, $I_0 = 100$ ma, and $d/l = 6$.

6. Calculate the frequency deviation possible in a cavity magnetron when $\Theta = 2\pi$, $I = 50$ ma, $l/d = 0.3$, $V_b = 500$ volts, and $C_M = 50\ \mu\mu$f. If $l = 2$ cm, discuss limitations in frequency deviation due to electron grazing.

7. Design a reactance-tube-controlled oscillator circuit for use at 50 Mc, using a reactance tube in which $0 < g_m < 5 \times 10^{-3}$. The capacitance of the tank circuit is 15 $\mu\mu$f, and the grid circuit of the reactance tube must be capable of accepting a control voltage which will vary the system frequency 100 kc (when the reactance tube is biased off, the system frequency will be at its minimum value). What is the compensating-voltage versus frequency curve which must be characteristic of a frequency-comparator circuit in order to assure frequency stabilization of the oscillator circuit?

8. If a phase-synchronization system is to be used to frequency-stabilize an AM transmitter, discuss the demands which must be made on the phase-synchronization system for it to operate satisfactorily as a frequency stabilizer.

9. Consider a single tuned circuit whose characteristics are described by the expression

$$\tan \theta = 2Q \frac{\omega - \omega_0}{\omega_0}$$

Show that the condition of synchronization, as deduced from (72), is

$$\frac{E_2}{E_1} > 2Q \left| \frac{\omega_0 - \omega_2}{\omega_0} \right|$$

CHAPTER 13

MODULATION SYSTEMS IN ELECTRICAL COMMUNICATIONS

1. Modulation Spectra and Spectral Bandwidth. If intelligence is to be transmitted using a carrier wave whose form is the rotating-vector expression,

$$i = Ie^{j\theta_0} = Ie^{j\omega_0 t}$$

then the intelligence may be represented by the modulation of the amplitude, phase, or frequency of the rotating vector. Carrier modulation is used as a means of transmitting intelligence because it utilizes the propagation properties of h-f and u-h-f electromagnetic waves and because the intelligence may be recovered from the modulated wave.

When a carrier is modulated with respect to amplitude, frequency, or phase, spectral components which are called side frequencies[1] appear in the vicinity of the carrier. The group of side frequencies above and below the carrier are called the upper and lower sidebands, respectively. These side frequencies, which may or may not undergo a change in amplitude and phase, are propagated with the carrier to the receiver, where, using a suitable circuit, demodulation of the proper type takes place. The general form of modulated-wave spectra is pictured in Fig. 1*a* and *b*,

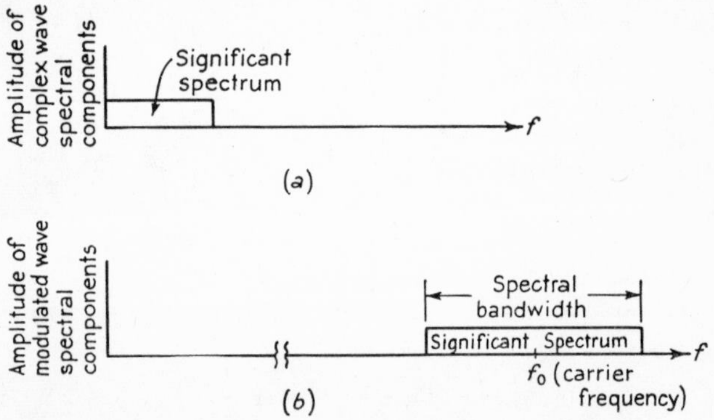

FIG. 1.

[1] Side frequencies are often improperly referred to as sidebands. This usage of the term *sideband* is correct only when just one pair of side frequencies is present.

which illustrate two basic quantities—spectral bandwidth and the significant spectrum of both the modulating wave and the modulated wave. Resemblance of the *modulated*-wave spectrum to the *modulating*-wave spectrum is encountered only during amplitude modulation. The modulation analysis, which will be dealt with in considerable detail in the chapters to follow, is primarily intended to establish the spectral properties of any modulated-wave spectrum so that spectral bandwidth and sideband energy distribution can be determined and used in computing or predicting over-all transmission-system performance.

We may acquire a preliminary basic concept associated with spectral bandwidth by noting that the more intelligence there is to be transmitted, the more rapid will be the variations in the modulating wave. This will result in a wider significant spectrum of the modulating wave, with the result that the modulated-wave spectrum will also broaden, this spectrum being, in general, centered at the frequency of the carrier.

2. Commercial Modulation Systems. The five most widely used modulation systems in electrical communications may be listed as follows:

1. Amplitude modulation (double sideband)
2. Amplitude modulation (single sideband)[1]
3. Frequency modulation
4. Pulse modulation
5. Multiplex systems

Phase modulation[2] is not listed because it has very limited application in broadcasting and communications. Television broadcasting, on the other hand, uses two modulation systems for its transmission—single-sideband amplitude modulation for the video and frequency modulation for the sound.

In commercial sound and television transmission, the following maximum spectral bandwidths are assigned:

A. Sound broadcasting
   1. Amplitude modulation—10 kc
   2. Frequency modulation—150 kc for commercial frequency modulation, 50 kc for television

B. Television broadcasting
   Video—single-sideband amplitude modulation } 6 Mc
   Sound—frequency modulation }

3. Wavelength and Frequency. Wavelength and frequency are related by the expression

$$f\lambda = c \tag{1}$$

[1] Also termed *vestigial-sideband amplitude modulation* since complete elimination of one sideband cannot be achieved.

[2] For some practical aspects of phase modulation, see M. G. Crosby, Communication by Phase Modulation, *Proc. IRE*, vol. 27, pp. 126–136, February, 1939.

where c is the velocity of light (3×10^8 m per sec), f is the frequency in cycles, and λ is the wavelength in meters. A chart of frequency and wavelength is shown in Fig. 2. The bands assigned for commercial broadcasting, short waves, frequency modulation and television, experimental color television, radar, and radio relay are indicated.

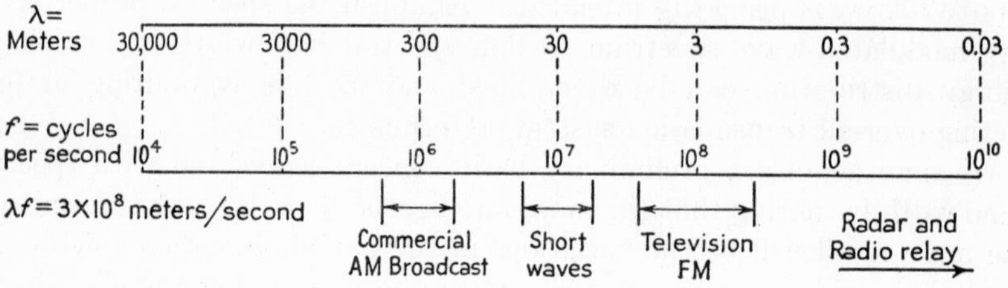

FIG. 2.

4. Circuit Bandwidth and Spectral Bandwidth. In considerations of modulated-wave transmission, circuit bandwidth and spectral bandwidth play very important roles. Circuit bandwidth is related to the Q of the circuit by the relationship

$$\Delta f' = \frac{f_0}{Q} \tag{2}$$

where $\Delta f'$ is the spacing measured in frequency, between half power points (3 db down) of the circuit, and f_0 is the center frequency of the circuit.

We see in Fig. 2 that as the amount of intelligence is increased from 10 kc for AM transmission to 6 Mc for television the bands assigned for these transmissions are found to occur at higher and higher frequencies. The reason for this is quickly understood by considering both the spectral and circuit bandwidths involved. Obviously, television transmission, which, with single-sideband transmission requires a spectral bandwidth of 6 Mc, could not occur in the commercial broadcast band from 500 to 1,500 kc because this entire band could contain only a sixth of the television modulation spectrum.

As a simple demonstration of the application of the concept of circuit bandwidth note that for $f_0 = 100$ kc and $\Delta f' > 6$ Mc, the Q of the circuits involved must have a value of at least

$$Q < \frac{10^5}{6 \times 10^6} \tag{3}$$

$$< 0.0125 \tag{4}$$

which, of course, is absurd. However, for a carrier frequency of 120 Mc, we see that

$$Q = \frac{1.2 \times 10^8}{6 \times 10^6} \qquad (5)$$

$$= 20 \qquad (6)$$

which is a value readily obtained in practical communication circuits.

It is therefore evident that as the amount of intelligence to be transmitted is increased, thus increasing the spectral bandwidth, the frequency of the carrier must be increased to a region commensurate with both the adjacent channel transmission and the circuit and spectral bandwidths involved.

5. Aspects of AM Systems. It can be shown that, by impressing a modulating wave ω_1 and a carrier wave ω_0 on a nonlinear circuit, waves with the frequencies $\omega_0/2\pi$, $(1/2\pi)(\omega_0 + \omega_1)$, and $(1/2\pi)(\omega_0 - \omega_1)$ will be evolved which will be seen in the next chapter to correspond to those waves produced during single-tone amplitude modulation. However, owing to the nature of the nonlinear circuit, distortion components will also be produced, which are undesirable in commercial transmission. It is therefore more appropriate to resort to other methods of amplitude modulation.

The most widely used system for AM transmission at broadcast and short waves is the plate modulation system due to R. V. L. Hartley. A block diagram of such a system is shown in Fig. 3, where it is seen that

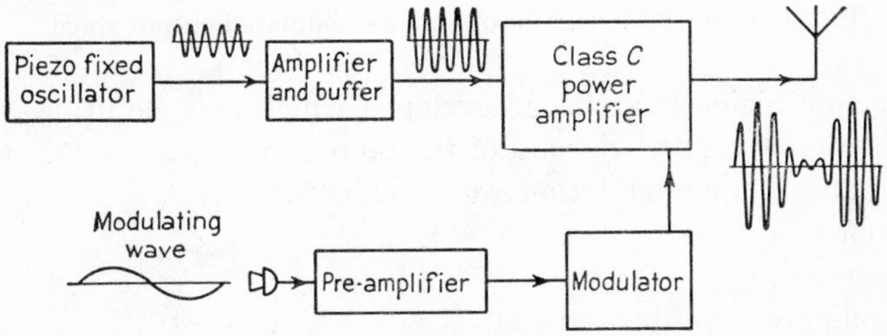

FIG. 3. Plate-modulated transmitter.

the carrier signal originates in a crystal-controlled oscillator, is raised to full power level, using amplifiers, and is modulated in the final stage of power amplification, which operates class C.

A typical plate modulator circuit is pictured in Fig. 4, where it is seen that the modulating voltage is introduced in the plate-voltage supply line and adds to or subtracts from the plate supply voltage in accordance with a rate and magnitude determined by the modulating signal and the modulator output. Since the load is fixed, then, as the voltage level changes because of the modulation, the tank voltage swing, the plate-current operating angle, and the current-pulse form and amplitude change so that the d-c plate voltage varies linearly with respect to the square root of the power output. This is a highly desirable operating characteristic in that it permits distortionless amplitude modulation although considerable modulation power is required.[1]

Other types of AM schemes occasionally used at low and high frequencies are grid modulation, cathode modulation, and absorption modulation.

At the ultra-high frequencies, triode and tetrode systems are very difficult to design for high power with usable efficiency because of transit-time and other effects. However, new types of tubes and systems native to

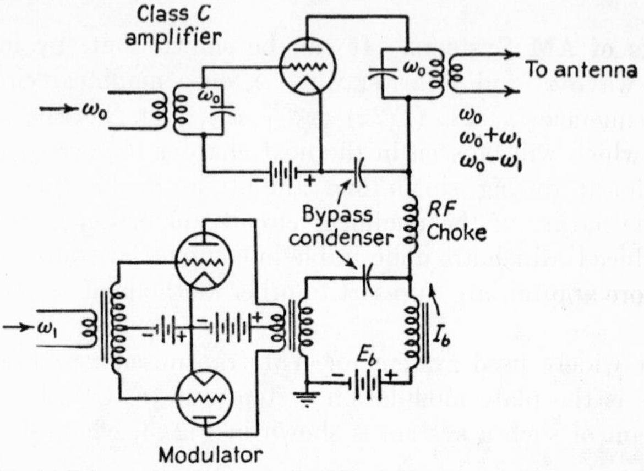

FIG. 4. Schematic diagram of a plate-modulated output stage.

this frequency region have been developed which may be utilized in AM communication systems. Several of the more important u-h-f systems for producing amplitude modulation are listed as follows:

1. Resnatrons[2]
2. Klystrons[3]
3. Traveling-wave tube systems[4]
4. Magnetrons utilizing a spiral beam absorption tube[5]
5. Magnetron-electron coupler systems[6]

[1] At 100 per cent modulation, the modulator must supply power equal to one-half of the unmodulated carrier power.

[2] Radio Research Laboratory Staff (Harvard), "Very High Frequency Techniques," vol. I, Chaps. 13–32, McGraw-Hill Book Company, Inc., New York, 1947.

[3] A. F. Harvey, "High Frequency Thermionic Tubes," John Wiley & Sons, Inc., New York, 1943.

[4] L. M. Field, Recent Developments in Traveling-wave Tubes, *Electronics*, vol. 23, pp. 100–104, January, 1950.

[5] Donal and Bush, A Spiral Beam Method for the Amplitude Modulation of Magnetrons, *Proc. IRE*, vol. 37, p. 375, April, 1949.

[6] Cuccia and Donal, The Electron Coupler, *Electronics*, vol. 23, pp. 80–85, March, 1950.

6. Crystal-controlled magnetron systems[1]
7. Injection-lock magnetron systems[2]

6. Aspects of FM Transmitting Systems. Although several systems for producing FM waves are in use, it is instructive to consider some aspects of the *direct* FM transmitter whose block diagram is pictured in Fig. 5. Here we see an oscillator whose frequency is controlled by a reactance

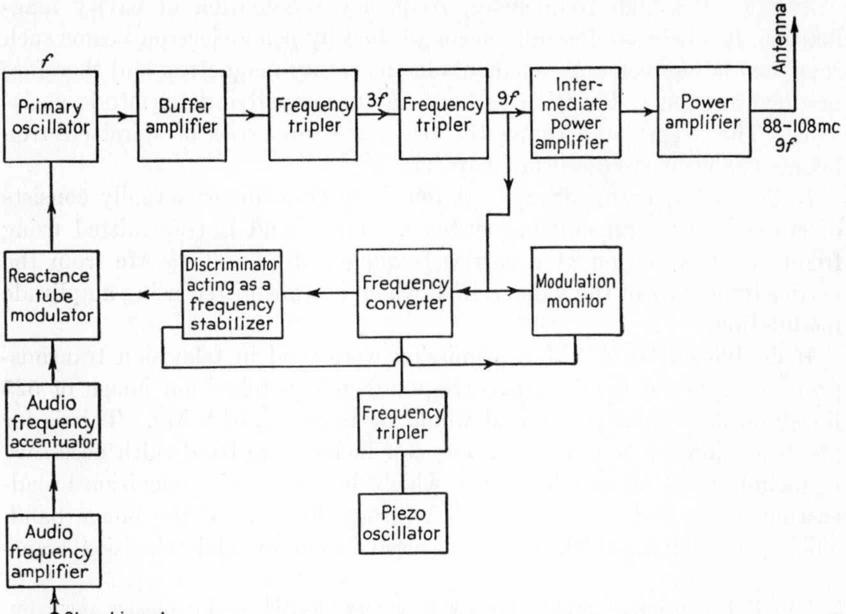

FIG. 5. Direct FM transmitter.

tube. The oscillator output frequency is multiplied nine times; the resulting wave is impressed on the input of a class C power amplifier which feeds into the antenna. The main problem here is one of center-frequency stabilization,[3] and, as is shown in Fig. 5, the problem of monitoring is

[1] A description of an experimental AM transmitter employing a crystal-controlled magnetron was given by D. S. Bond and J. S. Donal, Jr., of the RCA Laboratories before the New England Radio Engineering Meeting at Boston, Massachusetts, on Apr. 15, 1950. In this system a magnetron is frequency-stabilized during modulation by phase comparison with a harmonic of a crystal oscillator. The output signal of the magnetron is sampled and compared with the reference harmonic, using a phase-comparison circuit, which in turn impresses appropriate compensating signals on the grids of the electron guns which control the spiral electron reactance beams located in the interior of the magnetron.

[2] J. C. Slater, "Microwave Electronics," Sec. 9.5, D. Van Nostrand Company, Inc., New York, 1950.

[3] See, for example, E. S. Winlund, Drift Analysis of the Crosby Frequency Modulated Transmitter Circuit, *Proc. IRE*, vol. 29, pp. 390–398, July, 1941.

solved by beating a sample of the output signal against a reference signal from a piezo fixed-frequency standard; any center-frequency drift[1] is impressed at the input of a frequency discriminator (see Chap. 22). The discriminator yields a control voltage, which is a function of the center-frequency drift. This voltage is impressed with suitable polarity into the modulating reactance-tube circuit to compensate for this drift.

At the ultra-high frequencies, frequency modulation of cavity magnetrons[2] has been successfully accomplished by using electron beams such that they act as reactance elements in the cavity magnetron and therefore produce frequency deviation without any accompanying amplitude variation. The theory underlying the reactance properties of spiral electron beams has been discussed in Chap. 12.

7. Television Transmitters.[3] A television transmitter actually consists of two separate transmitting systems. The sound is transmitted using frequency modulation at a carrier frequency displaced $4\frac{1}{2}$ Mc from the carrier frequency of the video signal, which is transmitted using amplitude modulation.

If double-sideband AM transmission were used in television transmission, the spectral bandwidth corresponding to a television image of 525 lines and 30 frames per second would be in excess of 8 Mc. This is for the television image alone and does not include the bandwidth necessary to include the FM sound channel, which, in commercial television broadcasting, is located about $\frac{1}{4}$ Mc away from the edge of the image band. This spectral bandwidth cannot be used in commercial television trans-

[1] An FM transmitter which starts with a piezoelectric fixed-frequency oscillator, thus eliminating the necessity for center-frequency stabilization, is discussed in Chap. 17. For still another system, see Bailey and Thomas, Phasitron F-M Transmitter, *Electronics*, October, 1946, pp. 108–112. For an FM transmitter which uses phase control for frequency stabilization, see Ostlund, Vallarino, and Silber, Center-frequency-stabilized Frequency-modulation System, *Proc. IRE*, vol. 35, pp. 1144–1149, October, 1947. For a general discussion of FM transmitters, see Hund, "Frequency Modulation," Chaps. II, III, McGraw-Hill Book Company, Inc., New York, 1942.

[2] For an extensive discussion of spiral beam frequency modulation see Smith and Shulman, Frequency Modulation and Control by Electron Beams, *Proc. IRE*, vol. 35, No. 7, pp. 644–657, July, 1947; Kilgore, Shulman, and Kurshan, A Frequency Modulated Magnetron for Super-high Frequencies, *Proc. IRE*, vol. 35, No. 7, pp. 657–644, July, 1947; Donal, Bush, Cuccia, and Hegbar, A 1-Kilowatt Frequency-modulated Magnetron for 900 Megacycles, *Proc. IRE*, vol. 35, No. 7, pp. 664–669, July, 1947; G. B. Collins, "Microwave Magnetrons," Chap. 15, McGraw-Hill Book Company, Inc., New York, 1948.

[3] See D. G. Fink, "Principles of Television Engineering," Chap. IX, McGraw-Hill Book Company, Inc., New York, 1940, or F. E. Terman, "Radio Engineering," Chap. 17, McGraw-Hill Book Company, Inc., New York, 1947. For a review of modern RCA, Du Mont, and General Electric television transmitters, see, Design Trends in Television Transmitters, *Electronics*, vol. 21, pp. 76–82.

mission since the Federal Communications Commission has specified that assignments for television channels be based on a total channel width of 6 Mc. By using vestigial-sideband transmission this specification can be adhered to, and satisfactory reproduction, using a linear detector, can be obtained. The complete signal channel, which includes both video and

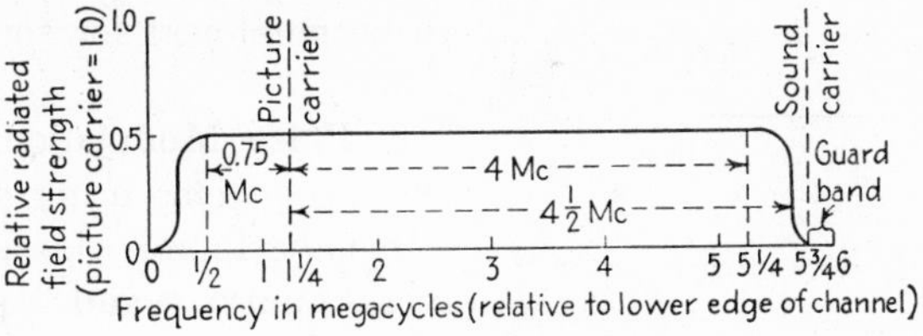

FIG. 6. Video signal channel.

sound, is shown in Fig. 6, where we see that the channel extends from 1.5 Mc below the carrier to 4.75 Mc above the carrier and includes guard bands in between the edge of the video channel and the sound channel and in between the sound channel and the edge of the specified total channel.

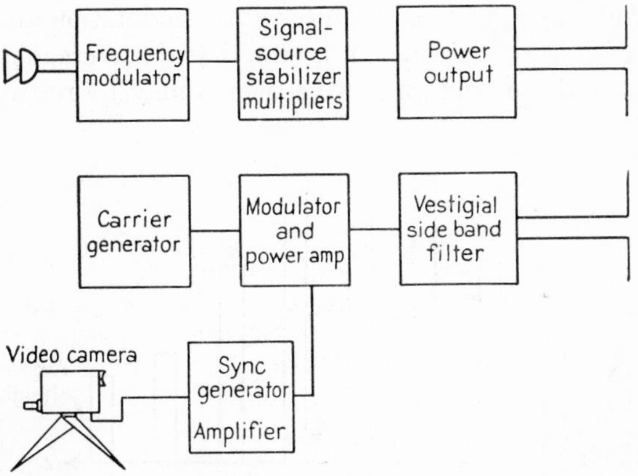

FIG. 7. Television transmitter consisting of an AM video transmitter and an FM sound transmitter.

A block diagram of a typical television transmitter, together with the vestigial-sideband filter[1] which is included in the antenna circuit of the transmitter, is pictured in Fig. 7. Typical transmission characteristics of a vestigial-sideband filter designed to operate with a transmitter pro-

[1] For details of vestigial-sideband filters, see Zworykin and Morton, "Television," Chap. XVI, John Wiley & Sons, Inc., New York, 1940, or H. Salinger, A Coaxial Filter for Vestigial Side Band Transmission in Television, *Proc. IRE*, vol. 29, pp. 115–120, March, 1941.

ducing a carrier at f_0 are illustrated in Fig. 8. It will be shown in Chap. 22 that the elimination of virtually an entire sideband does not impair the quality of the television image although distortion resulting from this method of transmission could not be tolerated were this method to be employed for sound transmission.

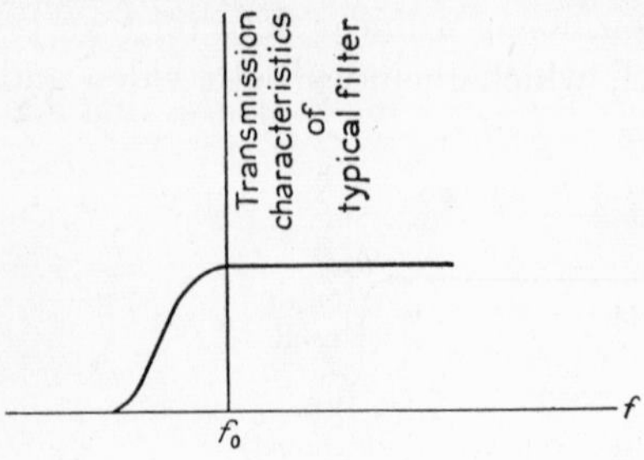

FIG. 8.

8. Pulse Modulation. Communications systems using pulse modulation have found wide application in cross-country and point-to-point microwave-relay circuits, in many cases replacing wire and cable circuits. There are four general kinds of pulse modulation:

1. Pulse-amplitude modulation (PAM)
2. Pulse-width modulation (PWM)
3. Pulse-numbers modulation (PNM)
4. Pulse-phase modulation (PPM)

Pulse-amplitude modulation and pulse-width modulation are illustrated in Fig. 9*a* and *b*, respectively, where it is seen that the average power involved is a function of the modulating wave, which may be recovered from the

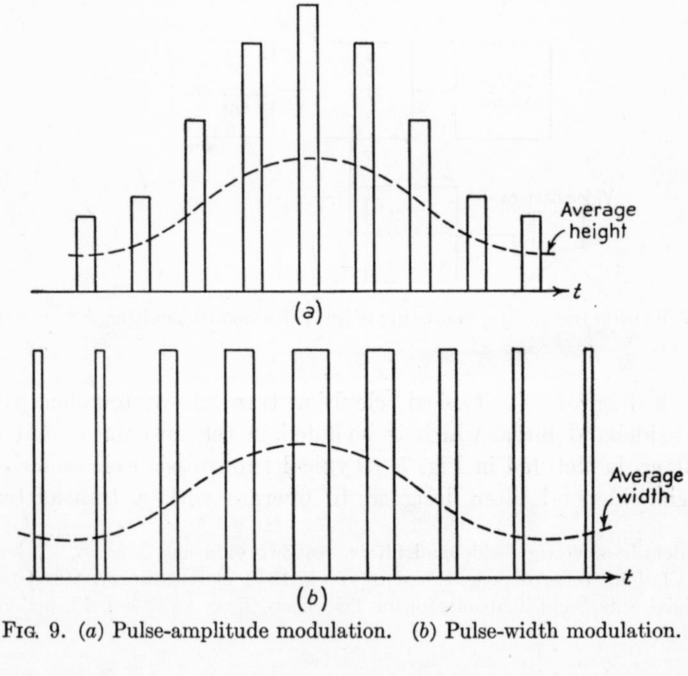

FIG. 9. (*a*) Pulse-amplitude modulation. (*b*) Pulse-width modulation.

pulse-modulated wave by suitable means of demodulation. Actually more than 40 methods of pulse modulation, combinations of the above kinds, are used as subcarriers, with either AM- or FM-wave main carriers.

There are several excellent reasons for employing pulse-modulation systems. As a result of radar research, for example, tubes such as magnetrons and klystrons are available which are capable of high peak power. Since the average power involved is equal to the product of the peak power, the pulse duration time, and the pulse repetition frequency, it is evident that by proper choice of operating parameters the average power demands made by the pulse-modulation transmitter on its power supply may be caused to be relatively small, resulting in economy of equipment, size, and weight.

9. Multiplexing Systems.[1] Multiplexing is the technique of impressing two or more communication channels on a single circuit so that each can be operated simultaneously without interference with the others. There are two methods of multiplexing, time-division multiplexing and frequency-division multiplexing.

Time-division multiplexing[2] is performed using a system with subcarriers, each of which consists of a series of d-c pulses; each pulse subcarrier has the same frequency, but the pulses are spaced in carrier angle so that they do not overlap although interleaved, thus resulting in a series of pulses. Each pulse subcarrier may be amplitude-modulated, phase-modulated, width-modulated, or numbers-modulated and then used to modulate a carrier.

A frequency-division system[3] is one using a separate subcarrier for each channel with spaced subcarrier frequencies. Subcarriers may be amplitude-modulated, frequency-modulated, or single-sideband-modulated, and a group of subcarriers may be used to modulate a higher frequency carrier.

10. Transmission in Radar Systems.[4] Radar transmission apparatus differs from conventional broadcasting apparatus in that the transmitter and receiver are located together or in the same locality, with suitable

[1] See W. R. Bennet, Time Division Multiplex Systems, *Bell System Tech. J.*, vol. 20, pp. 199–221, April, 1941, and V. D. Landon, Theoretical Analysis of Various Systems of Multiplex Transmission, *RCA Rev.*, first part, vol. 9, No. 2, pp. 287–351, June, 1948, concluding part, vol. 9, No. 3, pp. 433–482, September, 1948.

[2] For an application of time-division multiplexing to color television, see An Analysis of the Sampling Principle of the Dot-sequential Color Television System, *RCA Rev.*, vol. 11, No. 2, pp. 225–286, June, 1950.

[3] For an application of frequency-division multiplexing to color television, see R. B. Dome, Frequency-interlace Color-television, *Electronics*, vol. 33, pp. 70–75, September, 1950.

[4] See L. N. Ridenour, "Radar System Engineering," Radiation Laboratory Series, McGraw-Hill Book Company, Inc., New York, 1947.

isolation of the two, so that the outgoing signal will not block out the receiver or render the returning signal unintelligible.

Most pulse radar systems use the same antenna for both transmission and reception. The pulse transmitter and the receiver are connected or disconnected from the mutual antenna by fast-acting gas-tube switches known as TR (transmit-receive) or ATR tubes, which are located in the transmission lines from the transmitter and the receiver, these lines combining at a T junction, forming the single transmission line to the antenna. Essentially speaking, the leading edge of the pulse from the transmitter immediately breaks down the gas tube in the transmission line from the receiver, thus shorting the receiver input terminals, preventing damage to the receiver. The line lengths are such that this short circuit does not interfere with the pulse wave traveling toward the antenna. At the end of the pulse, the gas tube deionizes, ceasing to act as a short circuit, and the receiver is ready to receive echoes.

CHAPTER 14

AMPLITUDE-MODULATED WAVES

1. Introduction and Basic Concepts. The "carrier," or basic wave, with constant angular velocity ω_0 may be represented mathematically, when there is no modulation or variation of its amplitude or phase, by the rotating vector

$$i = Ie^{j\omega_0 t} \tag{1}$$

where I is the magnitude of the rotating vector and $e^{j\omega_0 t}$ represents the periodic component of the wave with period $2\pi/\omega_0 = T_0$. Any variation or modulation of the amplitude of $Ie^{j\omega_0 t}$ must be imposed upon the rotating-vector *magnitude* I and must not affect the exponential. We may then represent a pure AM wave as follows,

$$i = \mathfrak{M}_A(t)Ie^{j\omega_0 t} \tag{2}$$

where $\mathfrak{M}_A(t)$ is the general amplitude-modulating function which varies the rotating-vector amplitude I and will be seen to be made up of one or more simple harmonic modulating waves.

The modulating waves to be discussed in this chapter (and in succeeding chapters) will be *real*. This is due to the fact (as was pointed out in Chap. 1) that if a plurality of waves are beat together, waves with both sum and difference angular velocities will result only if certain beating waves are real. In modulation analysis, these sum and difference angular-velocity waves are seen to be the upper and lower side frequencies.[1]

SINGLE-TONE AMPLITUDE MODULATION

2. Introduction. The analysis of single-tone amplitude modulation will not only serve to demonstrate the basic concepts and behavior in amplitude modulation; it will also serve as an introduction to the general Fourier analysis of amplitude modulation since the pair of sidebands[2] which will be produced by single-tone amplitude modulation will actually be one of

[1] J. R. Carson, Notes on the Theory of Modulation, *Proc. IRE*, vol. 10, pp. 57–64, February, 1922.

[2] When only one upper and one lower side frequency is present, each side frequency is a sideband.

an infinite number of pairs of side frequencies which will be described by the Fourier analysis.

3. Single-tone Cosinusoidal Amplitude Modulation. Consider the AM wave described by (2). For single-tone cosinusoidal amplitude modulation,

$$\mathfrak{M}_A(t) = 1 + M \cos \omega_1 t \tag{3}$$

In this discussion, M is assumed to be limited to the range, $M \leq 1$. The behavior of the AM wave for the case when $M > 1$ will be discussed on pages 249 and 250.

Equation (3) may be written in the form

$$\mathfrak{M}_A(t) = 1 + \mathcal{N}_A(t) \tag{4}$$

where, for this case

$$\mathcal{N}_A(t) = M \cos \omega_1 t \tag{5}$$

Figure 1*a* pictures the modulating function $\mathcal{N}_A(t)$. Equations (2) and (3) are depicted in Fig. 1*b* for a modulation cycle. This diagram shows

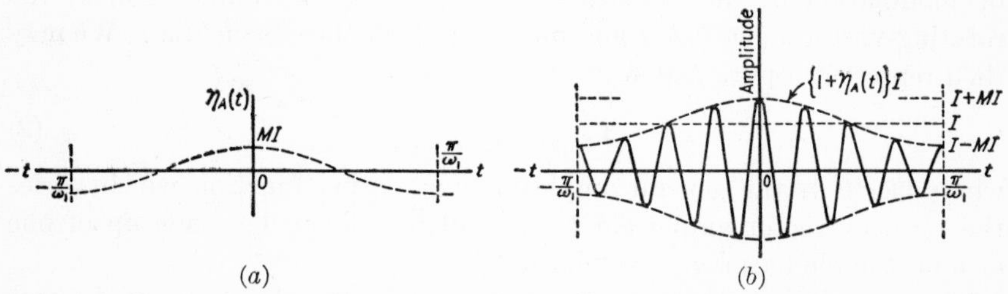

FIG. 1. (*a*) Single-tone amplitude-*modulating* wave. (*b*) Single-tone amplitude-*modulated* wave.

the real part of the resultant single-tone AM wave with its envelope, which is described by $[1 + \mathcal{N}_A(t)]I$. Note that at no time has the fundamental period $T_0 = 2\pi/\omega_0$ of the modulated wave been changed.

Equations (2), (4), and (5) may be combined to yield the equation

$$i = Ie^{j\omega_0 t} + \frac{MI}{2}(e^{j\omega_1 t} - e^{-j\omega_1 t})e^{j\omega_0 t} \tag{6}$$

$$= Ie^{j\omega_0 t} + \frac{MI}{2}e^{j(\omega_0+\omega_1)t} + \frac{MI}{2}e^{j(\omega_0-\omega_1)t} \tag{7}$$

The real part of (7) is

$$i = I \cos \omega_0 t + \frac{MI}{2}\cos(\omega_0 + \omega_1)t + \frac{MI}{2}\cos(\omega_0 - \omega_1)t \tag{8}$$

Equation (7) shows that the result is the vector sum of three rotating vectors (a carrier and a pair of sidebands) whose amplitudes are I, $MI/2$, and $MI/2$ and whose angular velocities in the counterclockwise direction are ω_0, $\omega_0 + \omega_1$, and $\omega_0 - \omega_1$, respectively.

4. Verification of Eq. (7). The terms in Eq. (7) may be shown to satisfy the Fourier formulation. This may be demonstrated by considering, for example, the upper sideband,

$$i_{\text{usb}} = \frac{MI}{2} e^{j\omega_1 t} e^{j\omega_0 t} \tag{9}$$

This may be written in terms of an illustrative Fourier series as follows:

$$i_{\text{usb}} = I\left(\sum_{n=-\infty}^{\infty} C_n' e^{jn\omega_0 t}\right) e^{j\omega_0 t} \tag{10}$$

It follows that

$$C_n' = \frac{\omega_1}{2\pi} \int_{-\pi/\omega_1}^{\pi/\omega_1} \left(\frac{M}{2} e^{j\omega_1 t}\right) e^{-jn\omega_1 t}\, dt \tag{11}$$

$$= \frac{\omega_1 M}{4\pi} \int_{-\pi/\omega_1}^{\pi/\omega_1} e^{-j(n-1)\omega_1 t}\, dt \tag{12}$$

This integral will integrate to yield zero for all values of n except $n = 1$. For this value,

$$C_{n=1} = \frac{M\omega_1}{4\pi} \int_{-\pi/\omega_1}^{\pi/\omega_1} dt \tag{13}$$

$$= \frac{M}{2} \tag{14}$$

Thus. Eq. (9) may validly be written

$$i_{\text{usb}} = i_{n=1} = \frac{MI}{2} e^{j(\omega_0 + \omega_1)t} \tag{15}$$

5. Factor M in Terms of Per Cent Modulation. The AM function containing the factor M has been seen to be

$$\mathfrak{M}_A(t) = 1 + M \cos \omega_1 t \tag{3}$$

As a result of this modulation, the wave rotating-vector amplitude fluctuates between $I + MI$ and $I - MI$. When $M = 1$, the wave amplitude goes to zero at the envelope trough and the wave is said to be subjected to 100 per cent modulation. Per cent modulation relates the unmodulated and modulated wave amplitudes and may be expressed in per cent as follows:

$$\begin{aligned} \text{Per cent modulation} &= M \times 100 \\ &= \frac{\text{maximum value of modulating wave} \times 100 \text{ per cent}}{\text{amplitude of carrier rotating vector}} \end{aligned} \tag{16}$$

When the per cent modulation exceeds 100 per cent, the single-tone problem becomes a problem in general AM analysis.

6. Vector-diagram Representation of Eq. (7). The three rotating vectors given by Eq. (7) are

$$\begin{aligned} \text{Upper sideband} &= \frac{MI}{2} e^{j(\omega_0+\omega_1)t} \\ \text{Carrier} &= Ie^{j\omega_0 t} \\ \text{Lower sideband} &= \frac{MI}{2} e^{j(\omega_0-\omega_1)t} \end{aligned} \tag{17}$$

If it is assumed that the axis of reference rotates with angular velocity ω_0 in the counterclockwise direction, then the three vectors can be repre-

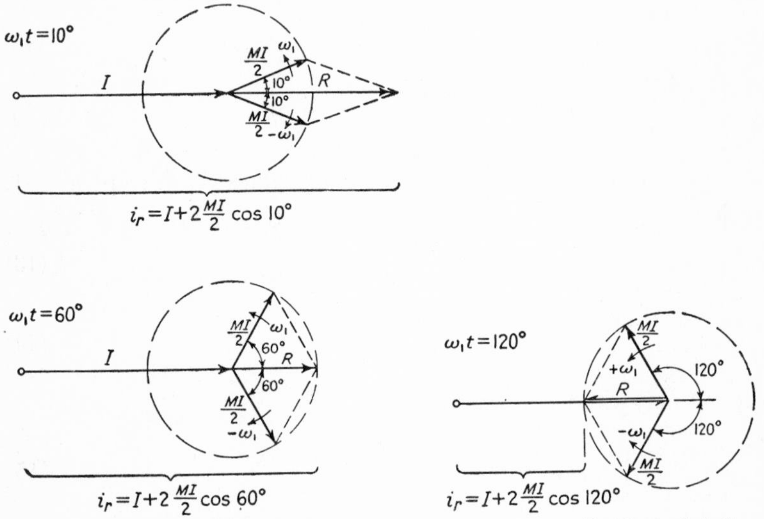

FIG. 2. Vector diagrams describing single-tone amplitude modulation.

sented as shown in Fig. 2. As is seen, the lower sideband appears to be rotating in the opposite direction with respect to the upper sideband since it rotates with less angular velocity than the carrier. These three vectors are added vectorially at any instant in time to yield the resultant vector i_r. The positions of the three rotating vectors at the phase angles $\omega_1 t = 10°, 60°, 120°$ and their vector summations appear as shown in Fig. 2, where R is the vector sum of the upper and lower sidebands and its magnitude at any phase angle is determined by $MI \cos \omega_1 t$.

7. The Amplitude Spectrum Corresponding to Eq. (7). The amplitude spectrum corresponding to Eq. (7) is pictured in Fig. 3. Both sidebands are positive and real and are symmetric with respect to the carrier, being separated from the carrier by the angular velocity of the modulating wave.

8. Numerical Example of Cosinusoidal Amplitude Modulation. Consider the numerical result when a carrier wave of amplitude 20, whose frequency is 1,000,000 cycles, is amplitude-modulated by a wave whose frequency is 10,000 cycles, with 50 per cent modulation.

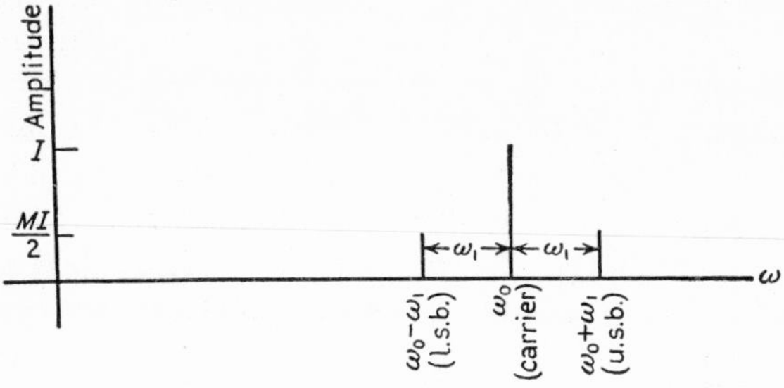

Fig. 3.

It follows from (8) that

$$i = 20 \cos 2\pi \times 10^6 t + \frac{0.5}{2} \times 20 \cos 2\pi(10^6 + 10^4)t + \frac{0.5}{2} \times 20 \cos 2\pi(10^6 - 10^4)t \qquad (18)$$

or, finally,

$$i = 20 \cos 2\pi \times 10^6 t + 5 \cos 2\pi \times 1{,}010{,}000t + 5 \cos 2\pi \times 990{,}000t \qquad (19)$$

The sidebands of amplitude 5 are located at the frequencies 1,010,000 and 990,000 cycles, respectively.

FOURIER-SERIES ANALYSIS OF COMPLEX-WAVE AMPLITUDE MODULATION

9. General Fourier-series Representation of Complex-wave Amplitude Modulation. Consider the AM wave shown in Fig. 4*a*, where the amplitude-modulating function is complex.[1] If $\omega_0 \gg \omega_1$, we may show the amplitude-modulating function $\mathfrak{M}_A(t)$ as pictured in Fig. 4*b*. This function $\mathfrak{M}_A(t)$ may be represented in the interval $-\pi/\omega_1 < t < \pi/\omega_1$ by the complex Fourier series

$$\mathfrak{M}_A(t) = \sum_{n=-\infty}^{\infty} C_n e^{in\omega_1 t} \qquad (20)$$

where

$$C_n = \frac{\omega_1}{2\pi} \int_{-\pi/\omega_1}^{\pi/\omega_1} \mathfrak{M}_A(t) e^{-in\omega_1 t}\, dt \qquad (21)$$

[1] Not simple harmonic.

The choice of the complex form over the trigonometric form of the Fourier series was made so that $\mathfrak{M}_A(t)$ would be expressed in rotating-vector form. The original unmodulated wave, which is described by Eq. (1), is now seen to be modulated by an infinite number of rotating vectors. The magnitude of each modulating rotating vector is given by C_n, which is determined by the integral in Eq. (3) from the amplitude-modulating function $\mathfrak{M}_A(t)$. The Fourier-series expansion of an AM wave is thus expressible as

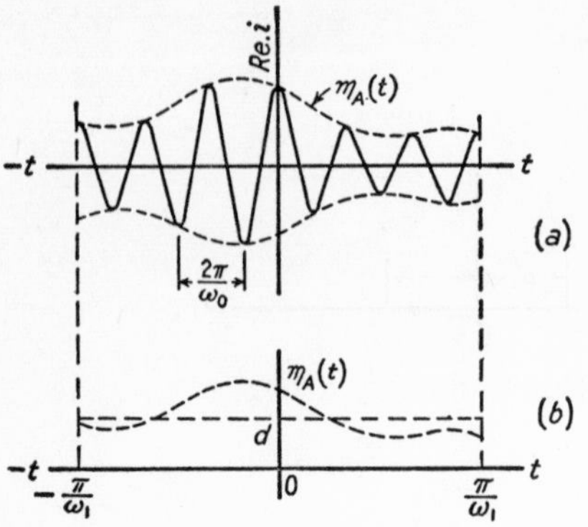

FIG. 4.

$$i = I\left(\sum_{n=-\infty}^{\infty} C_n e^{jn\omega_1 t}\right)e^{j\omega_0 t} \tag{22}$$

which becomes

$$i = I \sum_{n=-\infty}^{\infty} C_n e^{j(\omega_0 + n\omega_1)t} \tag{23}$$

10. Nature of Eq. (23). Whereas, in complex wave formulation, the Fourier series took the form of a fundamental wave plus integral multiples or harmonics of this wave, in amplitude modulation the rotating vectors listed in Eq. (23), which are produced by beating the rotating vectors representing the modulating wave with the carrier rotating vector, comprise a set in which the carrier (at its original angular velocity) is now flanked by an infinite number of side frequencies. These side frequencies are located on each side of the carrier and spaced from the carrier by the angular velocity of the particular component of the modulating wave being considered.

The amplitude spectrum of Eq. (23) is shown in Fig. 5. The amplitudes

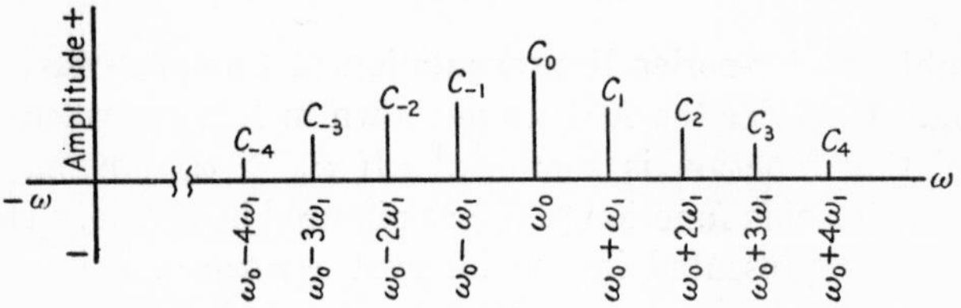

FIG. 5.

of the side frequencies and carrier may be determined by evaluating Eq. (21).

An interesting observation that we may make from Fig. 5 is, as is indicated by Eq. (23), that all frequency components in the Fourier expansion are separated by the modulating-wave angular velocity. Since in a complex Fourier series, the nth components will always have the same *absolute* magnitude, the absolute spectrum of the AM wave will be a symmetrical spectrum centered about the carrier angular velocity.

Equation (23) may be written out as follows:

$$
\begin{aligned}
i = \quad & C_0Ie^{j\omega_0 t} && \text{carrier frequency wave} \\
& + C_1Ie^{j(\omega_0+\omega_1)t} && \text{1st upper side frequency} \\
& + C_{-1}Ie^{j(\omega_0-\omega_1)t} && \text{1st lower side frequency} \\
& + C_2Ie^{j(\omega_0+2\omega_1)t} && \text{2d upper side frequency} \\
& + C_{-2}Ie^{j(\omega_0-2\omega_1)t} && \text{2d lower side frequency} \\
& + C_3Ie^{j(\omega_0+3\omega_1)t} && \text{3d upper side frequency} \\
& + C_{-3}Ie^{j(\omega_0-3\omega_1)t} && \text{3d lower side frequency} \\
& \cdots\cdots\cdots\cdots\cdots \\
& + C_nIe^{j(\omega_0+n\omega_1)t} && n\text{th upper side frequency} \\
& + C_{-n}Ie^{j(\omega_0-n\omega_1)t} && n\text{th lower side frequency} \\
& + \cdots
\end{aligned} \tag{24}
$$

The side frequencies listed in (24) occur in pairs. The h-f and l-f members are referred to as the upper and lower side frequencies, respectively. Although these two side frequencies are located at different frequencies, their amplitudes are always identical. If this were not so, amplitude modulation alone would not be possible.

In Sec. 3, we considered the first pair of side frequencies; it is obvious that any number of pairs of side frequencies may be combined to produce

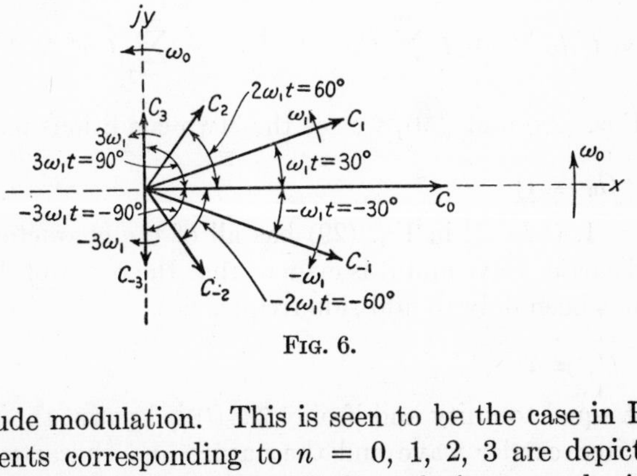

FIG. 6.

only amplitude modulation. This is seen to be the case in Fig. 6, where the components corresponding to $n = 0, 1, 2, 3$ are depicted with the frame of reference rotating with angular velocity ω_0 and with the phase angle $\omega_1 t$ equal to 30°. All of the side-frequency resultant vectors are seen to lie in the real axis.

Thus we see the validity of writing the amplitude-modulating function as a Fourier series in terms of an infinite sum of pairs of side frequencies. When the modulating signal is a simple harmonic wave whose angular velocity is ω_1, n will be found equal to unity and all other amplitudes will be of zero magnitude.

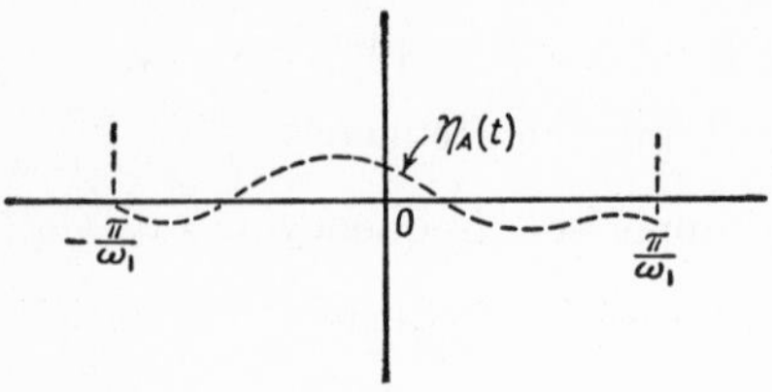

FIG. 7.

11. The Nature of C_0 in Eq. (24). Consider the amplitude-modulating function pictured in Fig. 4b. The height d represents its average value. The varying portion of $\mathfrak{M}_A(t)$ may be separated from its average value and is pictured in Fig. 7, where it is identified as $\mathcal{N}_A(t)$. Thus, by superposition, we see (referring to Fig. 4b) that

$$\mathfrak{M}_A(t) = d + \mathcal{N}_A(t) \tag{25}$$

Let us consider the case when d is made equal to unity in Eq. (25); *i.e.*,

$$\mathfrak{M}_A(t) = 1 + \mathcal{N}_A(t) \tag{26}$$

We may investigate the significance of Eq. (26) by substituting it into Eq. (2) as follows:

$$i = [1 + \mathcal{N}_A(t)]Ie^{j\omega_0 t} \tag{27}$$

$$= Ie^{j\omega_0 t} + \mathcal{N}_A(t)Ie^{j\omega_0 t} \tag{28}$$

Let us now write (23) in the following way:

$$i = C_0 Ie^{j\omega_0 t} + I\sum_{1}^{\infty} C_n e^{j(\omega_0 + n\omega_1)t} + \sum_{n=-1}^{-\infty} C_n e^{j(\omega_0 + n\omega_1)t} \tag{29}$$

Comparing Eqs. (28) and (29), we see that two conditions may arise:

Condition 1. $C_0 = 1$:

When $C_0 = 1$, $C_0 Ie^{j\omega_0 t}$ in Eq. (29) has all of the characteristics of the unmodulated carrier wave and it is evident that the result of the amplitude modulation has been only to add side frequencies.

Condition 2. $C_0 \neq 1$:

If C_0 is not equal to unity and if only $\mathfrak{M}_A(t)$ is known, the amplitude of the unmodulated carrier wave and the nature and characteristics of the modulating wave cannot be completely deduced from Eq. (23).

12. Discussion of Conditions 1 and 2. To illustrate conditions 1 and 2, let us consider an extension of the case where $\mathfrak{M}_A(t) = 1 + M \cos \omega_1 t$. This case has been previously discussed for the special case where $M \leq 1$. Substituting this amplitude-modulating function into Eq. (2), we get

$$i = (1 + M \cos \omega_1 t) I e^{j\omega_0 t} \tag{30}$$

Let us discuss the cases where $M = 0.35, 1, 1.5, 2.5$. These cases are diagramed in terms of the real portion of Eq. (30) in Fig. 8*a*, 8*b*, 8*c*, and 8*d*, respectively. In Fig. 8*a* and *b*, the amplitude of the envelope of the modulating wave is seen to vary cosinusoidally to an extent determined by the magnitude of M. In Fig. 8*c* and *d*, however, the envelope of the

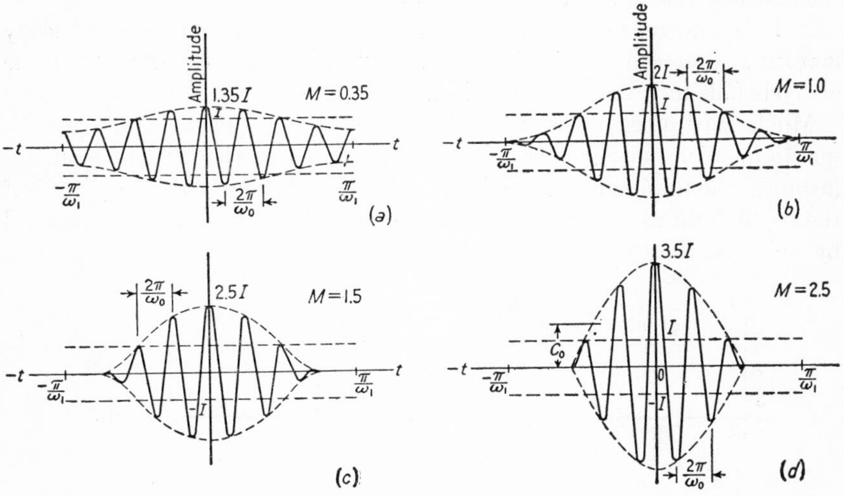

FIG. 8. Single-tone amplitude-modulated wave for the cases where (*a*) $M = 0.35$, (*b*) $M = 1$, (*c*) $M = 1.5$, (*d*) $M = 2.5$.

modulated wave is no longer a true cosinusoid since the magnitude of a large portion of the modulated wave in the intervals $-\pi/\omega_1 < t < -\pi/2\omega_1$ and $\pi/2\omega_1 < t < \pi/\omega_1$ is equal to zero. As M becomes larger, as is seen in Fig. 8*d*, the modulated-wave amplitude is equal to zero for still larger portions of these intervals, and as the magnitude of M increases still further, the wave amplitude goes to zero for the entire intervals $-\pi/\omega_1 < t < -\pi/2\omega_1$ and $\pi/\omega_1 < t < \pi/2\omega_1$.

In Fig. 8*a* and *b*, for the case where $M \leq 1$, the magnitude of C_0 may be found by use of the expression

$$C_0 = \frac{\omega_1}{2\pi} \int_{-\pi/\omega_1}^{\pi/\omega_1} \mathfrak{M}_A(t)\, dt \tag{31}$$

to equal unity.

As M increases, C_0 will increase. It is evident that if the wave pictured in Fig. 8*d* had been subjected to a Fourier analysis without any previous knowledge of the unmodulated-wave amplitude, we could not have deduced this information from C_0I, and therefore we see that Fig. 8*c* and *d* represents cases which fall into the category of condition 2, while condition 1 is satisfied by the waves pictured in Fig. 8*a* and *b*.

13. Criteria for Conditions 1 and 2. In AM analysis, we may specify the following criteria:

1. If the magnitude of the envelope, during a modulation cycle, either is at all times greater than zero or goes to zero for intervals of very small duration compared with the duration time of the modulation cycle, then the AM analysis falls into the category of condition 1.
2. If the magnitude of the envelope goes to zero for intervals of fairly large duration compared with the modulation-cycle duration, then the analysis falls into the category of condition 2.

Much may often be learned directly from the specific AM waves in question. For pulse- or *square*-wave modulated carrier transmission, for instance, the unmodulated-carrier amplitude is obviously the amplitude of the wave train although a calculation of C_0 will find it to be determined by the pulse duration.

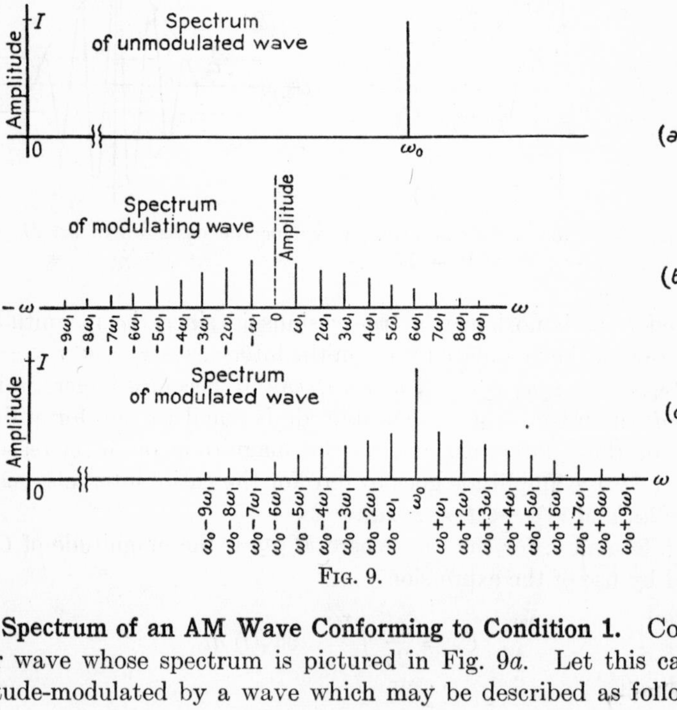

FIG. 9.

14. Spectrum of an AM Wave Conforming to Condition 1. Consider a carrier wave whose spectrum is pictured in Fig. 9*a*. Let this carrier be amplitude-modulated by a wave which may be described as follows:

$$\mathcal{N}_A(t) = \sum_{n=1}^{\infty} C_n e^{jn\omega_1 t} + \sum_{n=-1}^{-\infty} C_n e^{jn\omega_1 t} \tag{32}$$

This representation is pictured for both negative and positive angular velocities in Fig. 9*b*.

If condition 1 is satisfied, then the product of the carrier [Eq. (1)] and the complex modulating wave [Eq. (32)] transfers the spectrum of the complex Fourier series representing the modulating wave to a position where it is symmetric with respect to $\omega = \omega_0$. No amplitudes are changed, and the spacing between components remains the same. This is pictured in Fig. 9*c*, which should be compared with Fig. 9*b*, in which the amplitude spectrum of the modulating wave prior to modulation is shown.

The carrier remains unchanged in both amplitude and angular velocity. This is a criterion on which condition 1 is based. Physically speaking, the energy in a carrier remains the same whether modulated or unmodulated. The modulation energy will appear entirely in the sidebands.

15. Amplitude Modulation Conforming to Condition 2. Consider the wave, represented by Eq. (1) with angular velocity ω_0 and amplitude I, which is amplitude-modulated by the amplitude-modulating function

$$\begin{aligned} \mathfrak{M}_A(t) &= 0 & -\frac{\pi}{\omega_1} < t < -\frac{\pi}{2\omega_1} \\ &= \cos\omega_1 t & -\frac{\pi}{2\omega_1} < t < \frac{\pi}{2\omega_1} \\ &= 0 & \frac{\pi}{2\omega_1} < t < \frac{\pi}{\omega_1} \end{aligned} \tag{33}$$

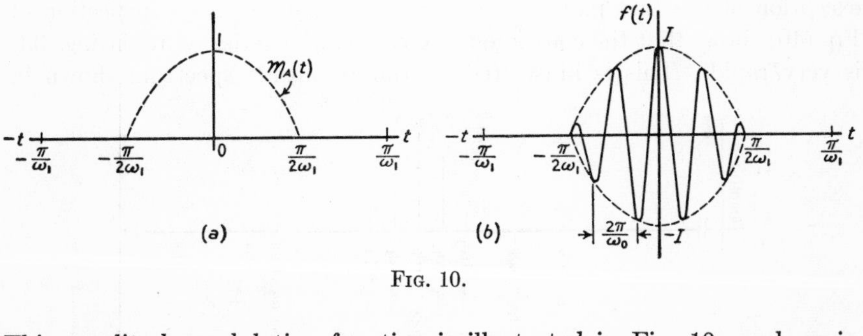

FIG. 10.

This amplitude-modulating function is illustrated in Fig. 10*a* and, as is shown in Fig. 10*b*, represents the envelope of the modulated wave. Then, from Eq. (23), we see that

$$i = \mathfrak{M}_A(t) I e^{j\omega_0 t} \tag{2}$$

$$= I \sum_{n=-\infty}^{\infty} C_n e^{j(\omega_0 + n\omega_1)t} \tag{34}$$

Substituting (33) into (21), we get

$$C_n = \frac{\omega_1}{2\pi} \int_{-\pi/2\omega_1}^{\pi/2\omega_1} \cos \omega_1 t e^{-jn\omega_1 t}\, dt \tag{35}$$

$$= \frac{1}{2\pi} \left[\frac{\sin (1 - n)(\pi/2)}{1 - n} + \frac{\sin (1 + n)(\pi/2)}{1 + n} \right] \tag{36}$$

$$= \frac{1}{\pi} \frac{\cos n(\pi/2)}{1 - n^2} \tag{37}$$

We must solve (35) separately for C_1 and C_{-1}; it follows that

$$C_1 = \tfrac{1}{4} \qquad C_{-1} = \tfrac{1}{4} \tag{38}$$

It follows from (38) and (37) that

$$\mathfrak{M}_A(t) = \frac{1}{\pi} + \frac{1}{2} \cos \omega_1 t - \frac{1}{\pi} \sum_{n=2}^{\infty} \frac{\cos n(\pi/2)}{n^2 - 1} e^{jn\omega_1 t} \tag{39}$$

Substituting (39) into Eq. (2), we get for the spectrum equation representing the AM wave pictured in Fig. 17*b*

$$i = \frac{I}{\pi} e^{j\omega_0 t} + \frac{I}{4} (e^{j(\omega_0+\omega_1)t} + e^{j(\omega_0-\omega_1)t})$$

$$- \frac{1}{\pi} \sum_{n=-\infty}^{\infty} \frac{\cos (n\pi/2)}{n^2 - 1} e^{j(\omega_0+n\omega_1)t} \qquad n = \pm 2, \pm 4, \ldots \tag{40}$$

We see from Eq. (40) that all odd-numbered side frequencies with the exception of the first pair have amplitudes equal to zero. Inspection of Eq. (40) shows that the convergence of the Fourier series representing (33) is very rapid. This is illustrated by the amplitude spectrum shown in

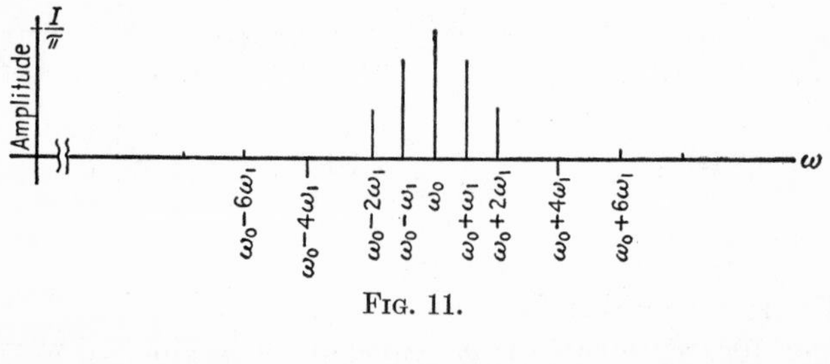

FIG. 11.

Fig. 11. It is obvious that the bulk of the energy representing the modulated wave is in the carrier and the first two pairs of side frequencies.

16. Fourier Analysis of Pulse-amplitude-modulated Waves. In the AM waves discussed previously in this chapter, the unmodulated carrier was a single rotating vector $Ee^{j\omega_0 t}$. In pulse-amplitude modulation, the unmodulated carrier is a repeated pulse whose Fourier-series representation has been shown in Chap. 3, Sec. 5, to be

$$i = \frac{I}{\pi} \sum_{-\infty}^{\infty} \frac{\sin km\pi}{m} e^{jm\omega_0 t} \tag{41}$$

where $\omega_0/2\pi$ is the repetition frequency and k is the ratio of pulse width to the periodic-wave period $2\pi/\omega_0$.

If this complex-wave carrier is amplitude-modulated by some modulating function $\mathfrak{M}_A(t)$, the resulting expression will be

$$i = \frac{I}{\pi} \mathfrak{M}_A(t) \sum_{m=-\infty}^{\infty} \frac{\sin km\pi}{m} e^{jm\omega_0 t} \tag{42}$$

To illustrate the nature of this equation, let

$$\mathfrak{M}_A(t) = 1 + M \sin \omega_1 t = 1 + \frac{M}{2j} (e^{j\omega_1 t} - e^{-j\omega_1 t}) \tag{43}$$

where $\omega_1 \ll \omega_0$. Substituting (43) into (42), we get

$$i = kMI \sin \omega_1 t + \frac{I}{\pi} \sum_{-\infty}^{\infty} \frac{\sin km\pi}{m} e^{jm\omega_0 t}$$
$$+ \frac{MI}{2\pi j} \left[\sum_{\substack{m=1,2,\ldots \\ =-1,-2,\ldots}} \frac{\sin km\pi}{m} (e^{j(m\omega_0+\omega_1)t} - e^{j(m\omega_0-\omega_1)t}) \right] \tag{44}$$

The first term is the modulating wave diminished by k, the second is the unmodulated pulse carrier, and the third describes the sidebands produced by the modulation.

If $\omega_1 < \omega_0/2$ and if k is very small,[1] then by passing (44) through a low-pass filter having a cutoff frequency less than $\omega_0/2$ the output wave will be the modulating wave without distortion due to side frequencies.

PROBLEMS

1. Compute the frequencies and amplitudes of the side frequencies produced when a carrier $Ie^{j2\pi\times10^6 t}$ is amplitude-modulated by each of the following waves:

a. $0.5I \cos 2\pi \times 1{,}000t$

b. $0.15I \cos 2\pi \times 29{,}850t + 0.17I \sin 2\pi \times 3{,}400t$

c. $0.65I \sin 2\pi \times 1{,}800t$

2. Determine the ratio of the energy in each side frequency to the energy in the unmodulated carrier for each part of Prob. 1.

3. Discuss the case where the carrier $Ie^{j2\pi\times10^6 t}$ is amplitude-modulated by the

[1] For applications of pulse-amplitude modulation in television, see Fredendall, Schlesinger, and Schroeder, Transmission of Television Sound on the Picture Carrier, *Proc. IRE*, vol. 34, pp. 49–61, February, 1946.

wave $0.4I\dot{e}^{j2\pi\times 10^7 t}$. What is the physical significance of the amplitude-modulating function $\mathfrak{M}_A(t)$ in this case?

4. Calculate C_0 for single-tone amplitude modulation for the case when $M = 1.7$. Check the results graphically.

5. Discuss the difference in vector-diagram representation of

$$i = (1 + 0.7 \cos \omega_1 t)Ie^{j\omega_0 t}$$

and

$$i = (1 + 0.7 \sin \omega_1 t)Ie^{j\omega_0 t}$$

6. Derive expressions for and discuss the case when a carrier is simultaneously amplitude-modulated by a square wave and a triangular wave whose maximum combined amplitude excursion does not exceed the amplitude of the unmodulated carrier and whose fundamental periods are not identical.

CHAPTER 15

SINGLE-TONE FREQUENCY MODULATION

1. Fundamental Considerations. In single-tone frequency modulation, the angular velocity $\omega_0 = 2\pi f_0$ of a carrier rotating vector will be varied by a periodic sinusoidal or cosinusoidal modulating wave whose frequency is $\omega_1/2\pi$. The variation of angular velocity as a function of time is illustrated in Fig. 1*b* with the corresponding variation in the period of each individual cycle of the FM wave illustrated in Fig. 1*a*. The amplitude of the modulating wave is such that the angular velocity varies between $\omega_0 + \Delta\omega$ and $\omega_0 - \Delta\omega$. In commercial FM transmission in the United States, f_0 is located in the band 88 to 108 Mc, $\Delta\omega/2\pi$ is limited to 75 kc maximum, and the modulating frequencies are those in the range

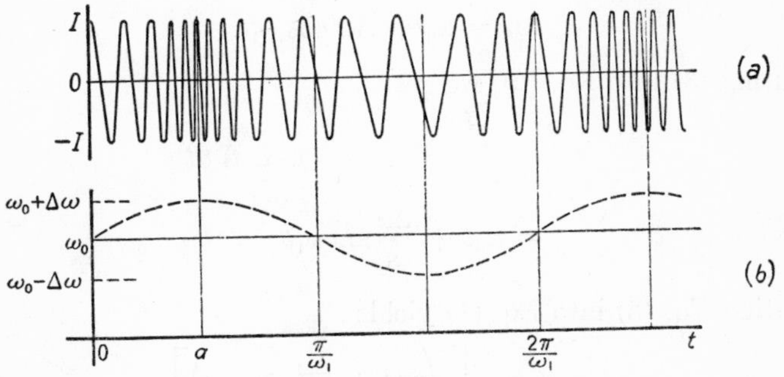

FIG. 1. Single-tone frequency-modulated wave.

$0 < f_1 < 15$ kc. For the sound signal in television transmission, see Sec. 2, Chap. 13.

It will be seen that the Fourier analysis will result in an expression summing an infinite number of side frequencies. It is of interest to note at this point that, while during the course of the cyclic variation of angular velocity (see Fig. 1*b*) the rotating vector rotates at every angular velocity between $\omega_0 + \Delta\omega$ and $\omega_0 - \Delta\omega$, the resultant Fourier expansion will not indicate every frequency in this range as being present but will consist of a Fourier series made up of a carrier and an infinite number of side frequencies, each spaced from the adjacent one by the modulating frequency.

2. Modulation Index. In Chap. 1, we have seen that a wave whose rotating-vector magnitude is constant may be represented as follows:

$$i = Ie^{j\Theta_t} \tag{1}$$

where

$$\Theta_t = \int \omega_t \, dt \tag{2}$$

For these expressions,

I = magnitude of rotating vector
ω_t = instantaneous angular velocity
Θ_t = instantaneous phase of rotating vector

When the period of a wave is varied at some rate which is determined by a modulating source, then frequency modulation results. As is seen in Fig. 1*a* and *b*, no changes in peak amplitude occur. It must be noted at this point that for every change in angular velocity (or period) a corresponding change in phase occurs. The full implications of this relationship will be discussed in the next three chapters.

Consider the wave described by Eqs. (1) and (2), whose rotating-vector magnitude I does not vary with time and whose instantaneous angular velocity may be expressed as

$$\omega_t = \omega_0 + \Delta\omega \cos \omega_1 t \tag{3}$$

Substituting (3) into Eq. (2), we get

$$\Theta_t = \int_0^t (\omega_0 + \Delta\omega \cos \omega_1 t) \, dt \tag{4}$$

$$= \omega_0 t + \frac{\Delta\omega}{\omega_1} \sin \omega_1 t \tag{5}$$

Substituting Eq. (5) into Eq. (1) yields

$$i = I \exp\left[j\left(\omega_0 t + \frac{\Delta\omega}{\omega_1} \sin \omega_1 t\right)\right] \tag{6}$$

Equations (5) and (6) introduce the concept of the modulation index; *i.e.*,

$$\text{Modulation index} = \beta = \frac{\Delta\omega}{\omega_1} = \frac{\Delta f}{f_1} \tag{7}$$

The modulation index was first suggested by van der Pol[1] and is seen to relate the maximum frequency deviation to the modulating frequency. It will be of considerable use in all frequency- and phase-modulation analysis. The symbol[2] β is a convenient expression for this ratio.

[1] B. van der Pol, Frequency Modulation, *Proc. IRE*, vol. 18, pp. 1194–1205, July, 1930.

[2] The symbol used to represent the modulation index is the same as that used in A. Hund, "Frequency Modulation," McGraw-Hill Book Company, Inc., New York, 1942.

3. Fourier-series Expansion of Eq. (6)[1]. Consider the Fourier-series expansion of Eq. (6), which may be written, using (7), as follows:

$$i = I(e^{j\beta\sin\omega_1 t})e^{j\omega_0 t} \tag{8}$$

The factor $e^{j\beta\sin\omega_1 t}$ is a modulation factor which modifies the expression for the unperturbed carrier rotating vector. It may be expanded by using a complex Fourier series such that

$$i = I\left(\sum_{n=-\infty}^{\infty} C_n e^{jn\omega_1 t}\right)e^{j\omega_0 t} \tag{9}$$

where, in general,

$$C_n = \frac{\omega_1}{2\pi}\int_{-\pi/\omega_1}^{\pi/\omega_1} f(t)e^{-jn\omega_1 t}\,dt \tag{10}$$

In this case

$$f(t) = e^{j\beta\sin\omega_1 t} \tag{11}$$

which, when substituted into (10), yields

$$C_n = \frac{\omega_1}{2\pi}\int_{-\pi/\omega_1}^{\pi/\omega_1} e^{j(\beta\sin\omega_1 t - n\omega_1 t)}\,dt \tag{12}$$

To facilitate the evaluation of C_n in Eq. (12), let

$$\varphi = \omega_1 t \tag{13}$$

The substitution of (13) into Eq. (12) yields

$$C_n = \frac{1}{2\pi}\int_{-\pi}^{\pi} e^{j(\beta\sin\varphi - n\varphi)}\,d\varphi \tag{14}$$

According to Eq. (90) in Chap. 2

$$C_n = J_n(\beta) \tag{15}$$

Substituting (15) into Eq. (9), we get finally, after combining exponents,

$$i = I\sum_{n=-\infty}^{\infty} J_n(\beta)e^{j(\omega_0 + n\omega_1)t} \tag{16}$$

If we equate the real and the imaginary parts of Eqs. (16) and (6), we get[2]

$$I\cos(\omega_0 t + \beta\sin\omega_1 t) = I\sum_{n=-\infty}^{\infty} J_n(\beta)\cos(\omega_0 + n\omega_1)t \tag{17}$$

$$I\sin(\omega_0 t + \beta\sin\omega_1 t) = I\sum_{n=-\infty}^{\infty} J_n(\beta)\sin(\omega_0 + n\omega_1)t \qquad (18)^{3}$$

These are the real equations for single-tone frequency modulation.

[1] For a Fourier analysis of a single-tone FM wave train of finite duration, see Sec. 9, Chap. 19.

[2] Since, as is shown in the Appendix, $J_{-n}(\beta) = (-1)^n J_n(\beta)$.

[3] It is of historical interest to communication engineers that Lord Rayleigh discussed the solution of this equation, many years before the advent of FM broadcasting, in a memorandum entitled On Approximately Simple Waves, *Phil. Mag.*, pp. 135–139, 1900.

4. The Series-generator Concept of Eq. (18). Let us discuss the significance of the representative equation (18) which may be written out as follows:

$$\begin{aligned} i = {} & I \sin (\omega_0 t + \beta \sin \omega_1 t) \\ = {} & J_0(\beta) I \sin \omega_0 t \\ & + J_1(\beta) I \sin (\omega_0 + \omega_1)t - J_1(\beta) I \sin (\omega_0 - \omega_1)t \\ & + J_2(\beta) I \sin (\omega_0 + 2\omega_1)t + J_2(\beta) I \sin (\omega_0 - 2\omega_1)t \\ & \cdots\cdots\cdots\cdots\cdots\cdots\cdots\cdots \\ & + J_n(\beta) I \sin (\omega_0 + n\omega_1)t + (-1)^n J_n(\beta) I \sin (\omega_0 - n\omega_1)t \\ & + \cdots \end{aligned} \tag{18}$$

The Fourier analysis has shown that although we started out with a system which was made up of an FM-wave generator, as shown in Fig. 2*a*, this system may be replaced by an infinite number of side-frequency generators and a carrier generator in series whose instantaneous total amplitude and instantaneous frequency are identical to those of the original network. This equivalent series circuit is pictured in Fig. 2*b*.

5. FM Equation in Terms of Sidebands. The Fourier-series equation (18) has been seen to be composed of a carrier and an infinite number of pairs of side frequencies. These pairs are so arranged that the nth upper or lower side frequency is separated from the $(n \pm 1)$th upper or lower side frequency by the modulating frequency.

The components of Eq. (18) are identified as follows:

$i =$	$J_0(\beta) I \sin \omega_0 t$	carrier	
$+$	$J_1(\beta) I \sin (\omega_0 + \omega_1)t$	upper side frequency	1st pair
$-$	$J_1(\beta) I \sin (\omega_0 - \omega_1)t$	lower side frequency	
$+$	$J_2(\beta) I \sin (\omega_0 + 2\omega_1)t$	upper side frequency	2d pair
$+$	$J_2(\beta) I \sin (\omega_0 - 2\omega_1)t$	lower side frequency	
$+$	$J_3(\beta) I \sin (\omega_0 + 3\omega_1)t$	upper side frequency	3d pair
$-$	$J_3(\beta) I \sin (\omega_0 - 3\omega_1)t$	lower side frequency	
$\cdots$	$\cdots\cdots$		
$+$	$J_n(\beta) I \sin (\omega_0 + n\omega_1)t$	upper side frequency	nth pair
$+$	$(-1)^n J_n(\beta) I \sin (\omega_0 - n\omega_1)t$	lower side frequency	
$+ \cdots$			

The maximum amplitude of the nth pair of side frequencies is seen to be $J_n(\beta)I$. Thus the magnitude of the original unmodulated-carrier rotating vector I is multiplied by the nth Bessel coefficient to yield the magnitude of the nth component. The Bessel coefficient is, therefore, the carrier- and side-frequency-amplitude factor to be determined and is a function of the modulation index and the side-frequency-pair number alone. At no time do phase or frequency considerations enter into its computation.

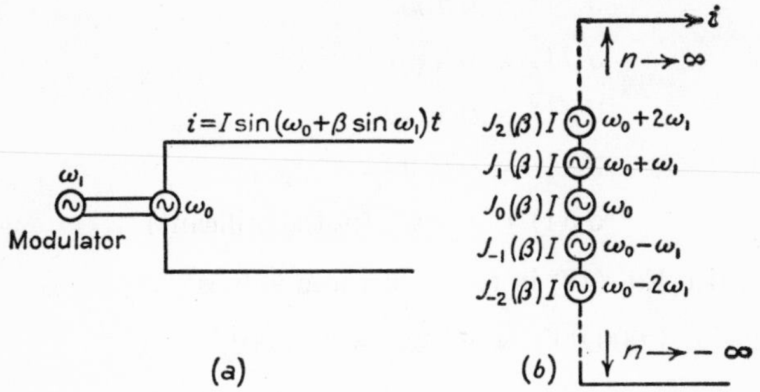

FIG. 2.

The general term of (18) is $J_n(\beta)I \sin (\omega_0 \pm n\omega_1)t$. From this general term, we may identify the angular velocities of the carrier and the upper and lower side frequencies. Once the carrier frequency $f_0 = \omega_0/2\pi$ and the modulating frequency $f_1 = \omega_1/2\pi$ are determined, the sideband frequencies are immediately determined since each component of the first side-frequency pair is separated from the carrier by the modulating frequency. The second upper side frequency is separated from the first upper side frequency by the modulating-wave frequency, etc. The nth side-

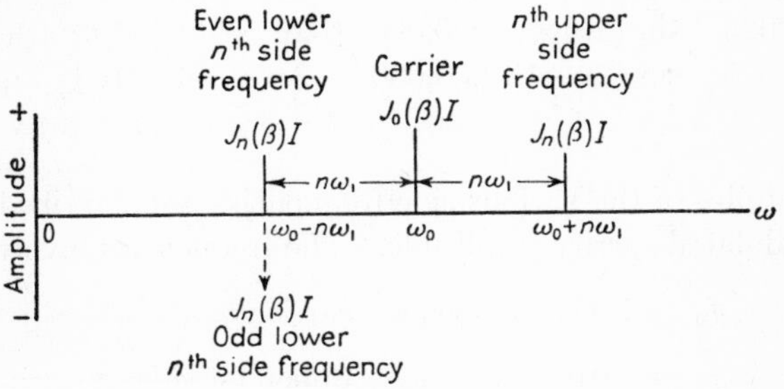

FIG. 3.

frequency pair and the carrier are pictured in Fig. 3, in which only rotating vectors with positive angular velocity are considered.

6. An FM Spectrum for $\beta = 1$. Before discussing the amplitude spectrum in general, let us consider the case where

f_0 = carrier frequency = 10^6 cycles
f_1 = modulating frequency = 10^4 cycles
Δf = maximum frequency deviation = 10^4 cycles

Then the modulation index is

$$\beta = \frac{\Delta f}{f_1} = 1 \tag{19}$$

From a table of Bessel functions, we find that

$$J_0(1) = 0.7652$$
$$J_1(1) = 0.4401$$
$$J_2(1) = 0.1149$$
$$J_3(1) = 0.0196$$
$$J_4(1) = 0.0025 \text{ (not significant)}$$

We may write Eq. (18) in terms of these values

$$i = I \sin (2\pi \times 1{,}000{,}000t + \sin 2\pi \times 10{,}000t) \tag{20}$$

or

$$\begin{aligned}
i = {} & 0.7652\, I \sin 2\pi \times 1{,}000{,}000t && \text{carrier} \\
& \left.\begin{aligned} &+ 0.4401\, I \sin (2\pi \times 1{,}000{,}000 + 2\pi \times 10{,}000)t \\ &- 0.4401\, I \sin (2\pi \times 1{,}000{,}000 - 2\pi \times 10{,}000)t \end{aligned}\right\} && \text{1st side-frequency pair} \\
& \left.\begin{aligned} &+ 0.1149\, I \sin (2\pi \times 1{,}000{,}000 + 2\pi \times 20{,}000)t \\ &+ 0.1149\, I \sin (2\pi \times 1{,}000{,}000 - 2\pi \times 20{,}000)t \end{aligned}\right\} && \text{2d side-frequency pair} \\
& \left.\begin{aligned} &+ 0.0196\, I \sin (2\pi \times 1{,}000{,}000 + 2\pi \times 30{,}000)t \\ &- 0.0196\, I \sin (2\pi \times 1{,}000{,}000 - 2\pi \times 30{,}000)t \end{aligned}\right\} && \text{3d side-frequency pair} \\
& \left.\begin{aligned} &+ 0.0025\, I \sin (2\pi \times 1{,}000{,}000 + 2\pi \times 40{,}000)t \\ &+ 0.0025\, I \sin (2\pi \times 1{,}000{,}000 - 2\pi \times 40{,}000)t \end{aligned}\right\} && \text{4th side-frequency pair} \\
& + \cdots
\end{aligned} \tag{21}$$

The amplitudes of the various side frequencies are described in per cent of the unmodulated-carrier amplitude. The frequencies involved are

$f_0 =$	1,000,000 cycles	carrier
$f_0 + f_1 =$	1,010,000 cycles	upper 1st side frequency
$f_0 - f_1 =$	990,000 cycles	lower 1st side frequency
$f_0 + 2f_1 =$	1,020,000 cycles	upper 2d side frequency
$f_0 - 2f_1 =$	980,000 cycles	lower 2d side frequency
$f_0 + 3f_1 =$	1,030,000 cycles	upper 3d side frequency
$f_0 - 3f_1 =$	970,000 cycles	lower 3d side frequency
$f_0 + 4f_1 =$	1,040,000 cycles	upper 4th side frequency
$f_0 - 4f_1 =$	960,000 cycles	lower 4th side frequency

A plot of the rotating-vector amplitude spectrum of Eq. (21) is shown in Fig. 4, in which only the positive angular-velocity vectors are pictured.

7. Significant Side Frequencies and Bandwidth. In modulation spectra, a significant side frequency is defined as a side frequency whose magnitude is equal to or is in excess of 1 per cent of the magnitude of the unmodulated-carrier rotating vector. In an analysis such as the Fourier analysis in which an infinite number of terms is evolved, the significant-side-frequency

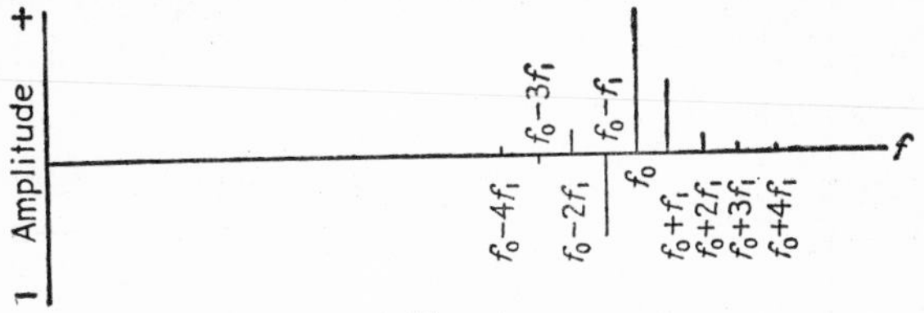

FIG. 4.

concept is an important tool for the practical determination of spectral bandwidth, which, to the communications engineer, is the most important consideration in modulated-wave analysis.

The bandwidth of a modulation spectrum is defined as the spacing between the outermost significant side frequencies. In AM spectra the bandwidth may be obtained from a Fourier expansion of the *modulating* wave, but in frequency modulation the bandwidth may be obtained only from the Fourier expansion of the *modulated* wave.

The identification of the significant side frequencies and of all the side frequencies which are included in the band is a function of modulation index which *alone* determines this consideration. A small modulating frequency and a large one with identical indexes will yield the same significant side frequencies; the spectra will be the same with regard to the amplitudes and signs of these side frequencies. These spectra will not be identical with respect to bandwidth, however, since the spacing between the side frequencies is determined by the modulating wave.

8. Small Modulation Index and Single-tone FM Spectrum. Consider the equation

$$i = I \sin (\omega_0 t + \beta \sin \omega_1 t) \tag{22}$$

This may be expanded trigonometrically into the following equation:

$$i = I[\sin \omega_0 t \cos (\beta \sin \omega_1 t) + \cos \omega_0 t \sin (\beta \sin \omega_1 t)] \tag{23}$$

For small values of β, we may write

$$\cos (\beta \sin \omega_1 t) \approx 1 \qquad \sin (\beta \sin \omega_1 t) \approx \beta \sin \omega_1 t \tag{24}$$

Using these values, we may rewrite Eq. (23) as follows,

$$i = I(\sin \omega_0 t + \beta \cos \omega_0 t \sin \omega_1 t) \tag{25}$$

and this may be expanded by use of a trigonometric identity into

$$i = I \sin \omega_0 t + \frac{\beta I}{2} [\sin (\omega_0 + \omega_1)t - \sin (\omega_0 - \omega_1)t] \tag{26}$$

The positive-vector spectrum corresponding to (26) is shown in Fig. 5. The bandwidth of this spectrum is seen to be equal to twice the modulating frequency.

The validity of Eq. (26) may be checked by comparing the amplitudes

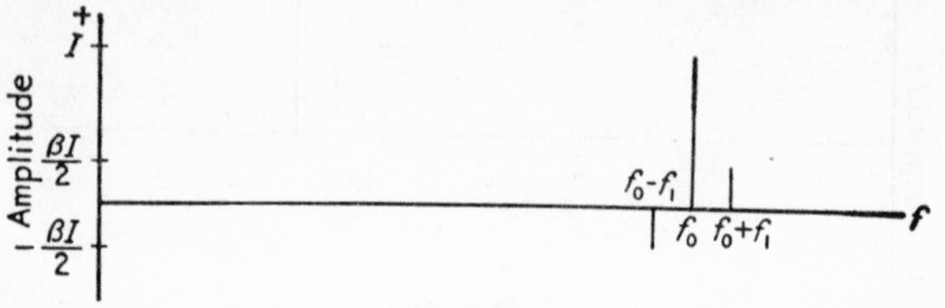

FIG. 5.

of the components with those of the carrier and the first pair of side frequencies from Eq. (18) for $\beta > 0.5$. These amplitudes are tabulated in Table 1 and are expressed in per cent of the unmodulated-carrier level.

TABLE 1

β	Eq. (26)		Eq. (18)	
	I	$\frac{\beta I}{2}$	$J_0(\beta)I$	$J_1(\beta)I$
0	100I	0I	100I	0I
0.01	100I	0.5I	100I	0.5I
0.02	100I	1.0I	99.99I	1.0I
0.03	100I	1.5I	99.98I	1.5I
0.04	100I	2.0I	99.96I	2.0I
0.05	100I	2.5I	99.94I	2.5I
0.1	100I	5.0I	99.75I	4.99I
0.2	100I	10I	99.00I	9.95I
0.3	100I	15I	97.76I	14.83I
0.4	100I	20I	96.04I	19.60I
0.5	100I	25I	93.85I	24.23I

This table shows that for $\beta \leq 0.4$ the carrier amplitude does not change appreciably from its unmodulated value. Values computed from Eq. (26) are seen to agree substantially with the values from (18) as given in Table 1.

9. Large Modulation Index and Single-tone FM Spectrum. Section 8 was concerned with values of β from $\beta = 0$ to $\beta = 0.5$. This section will deal with all values of β equal to or greater than 0.5. We must now consider the general equation (18) and determine which of the infinite number of side frequencies are significant for particular values of β. Once the amplitudes of the side frequencies are known, the amplitude distribution and the bandwidth are easily determined.

The Behavior of the Carrier Amplitude during Single-tone Frequency Modulation. The behavior of the carrier amplitude as a function of modulation index is determined by the zero-order Bessel function, *viz.*,

$$\text{Carrier} = J_0(\beta)Ie^{j\omega_0 t} \tag{27}$$

It has already been shown that for small values of β the carrier amplitude is almost unchanged. A plot of $J_0(\beta)$ versus β which pictures the behavior of the carrier amplitude for values of the modulation index β is shown in Fig. 6. The amplitude coefficient $J_0(\beta)$ is unity for $\beta = 0$. As β exceeds unity, the value of the Bessel function drops off rapidly until at β = 2.404 the amplitude is zero. It becomes negative in sign until $\beta = 5.52$, where it goes to zero again. As is illustrated in Fig. 6, the zero-order

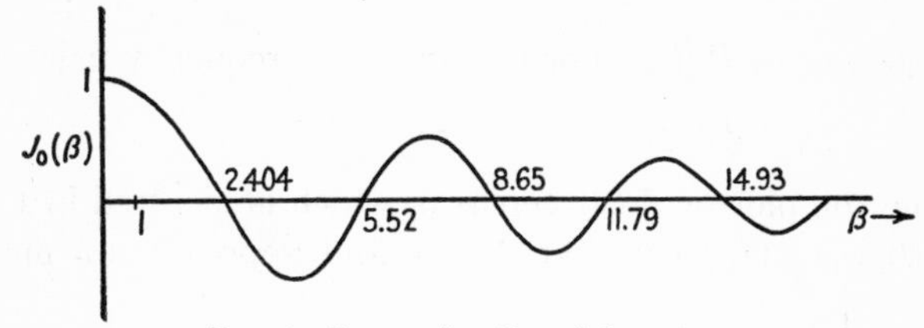

FIG. 6. Zero-order Bessel function.

Bessel function is an oscillatory function with decreasing peak amplitude. The spacing between zeros decreases and asymptotically approaches a constant value at large values of β. Because of this asymptotic behavior, we may write, as an approximation,

$$J_0(\beta) \cong \frac{\cos\,[\beta - (\pi/4)]}{\sqrt{\pi\beta/2}} \tag{28}$$

The fact that the carrier can go to zero in the spectrum representation for single-tone frequency modulation is of interest since the FM wave passes through f_0 as it swings from $f_0 + \Delta f$ to $f_0 - \Delta f$ and back during the modulation cycle. The fact that the carrier amplitude is equal to zero at the Bessel-function zeros means that there is *no* energy at carrier frequency for these values and consequently all of the energy must be present in the sidebands.

The presence of these zeros is quite useful from the experimental point of view since it provides a means of measuring frequency deviation.[1] If

[1] See R. J. Pieracci, A Frequency Modulation Monitoring System, *Proc. IRE*, vol. 28, pp. 374–378, August, 1940.

a selective resonant circuit is tuned to the carrier frequency and if its Q is such that the side frequencies are well away from the peak and from the sides of the resonance curve, then an increase in the maximum frequency deviation by increasing the amplitude of the modulating wave from zero amplitude will produce a point where the selective resonant circuit will not be excited. At this point $\beta = 2.404$. As the amplitude of the modulating wave is increased further, the zeros will be passed through in order. By tabulating the zeros as a function of the amplitude of the modulating wave and by having kept the modulating frequency constant, the maximum frequency deviation at these zeros can be determined. By plotting Δf as a function of the modulating-wave amplitude at these zeros and by using a smooth curve through these points, a chart for all values of β may be obtained.

Figure 6 shows that the peak value of the carrier-frequency rotating vector decreases as β increases, which indicates that as β becomes larger, less and less energy will be found at the carrier frequency in the FM spectrum.

First Side-frequency Pair. For the first side-frequency pair

$$J_1(\beta)I(e^{j(\omega_0+\omega_1)t} - e^{+j(\omega_0-\omega_1)t}) \tag{29}$$

let us examine the plot of $J_1(\beta)$ versus β, which is pictured in Fig. 7. We see that $J_1(\beta)$ is equal to zero at $\beta = 0$ and approaches a maximum at

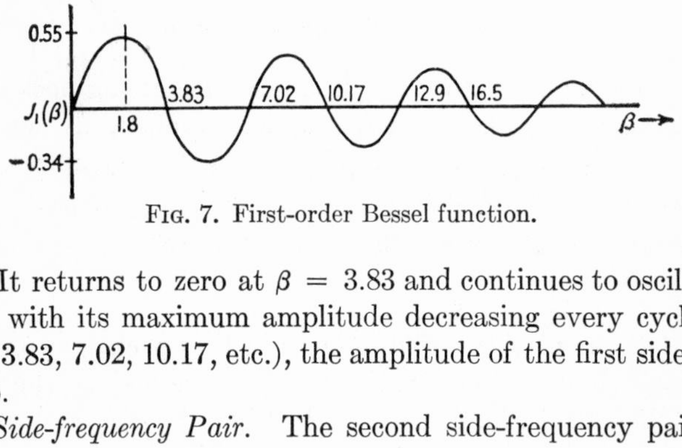

FIG. 7. First-order Bessel function.

$\beta = 1.8$. It returns to zero at $\beta = 3.83$ and continues to oscillate for increasing β, with its maximum amplitude decreasing every cycle. At the zeros ($\beta = 3.83, 7.02, 10.17$, etc.), the amplitude of the first side-frequency pair is zero.

Second Side-frequency Pair. The second side-frequency pair is represented by

$$J_2(\beta)I(e^{j(\omega_0+2\omega_1)t} + e^{j(\omega_0-2\omega_1)t}) \tag{30}$$

The plot of the second-order Bessel function will appear somewhat the same as that of the first-order Bessel function except that it will have smaller peak amplitude and its first maximum will occur at a larger value of β than for the corresponding maximum of the first side-frequency pair.

nth Side-frequency Pair. For the nth side-frequency pair

$$J_n(\beta)I[e^{j(\omega_0+n\omega_1)t} + (-1)^n e^{j(\omega_0+n\omega_1)t}] \tag{31}$$

Let us investigate the general behavior of the Bessel function as a function of modulation index and order. Compare, for example, the plots of $J_1(\beta)$, $J_5(\beta)$, $J_{10}(\beta)$, which are pictured in Fig. 8. We see that a principal difference between the various Bessel-function orders is that the first maximum occurs at larger values of β as the order of the Bessel function increases. All orders of Bessel functions become oscillatory with gradually decreasing maximum amplitudes per cycle.

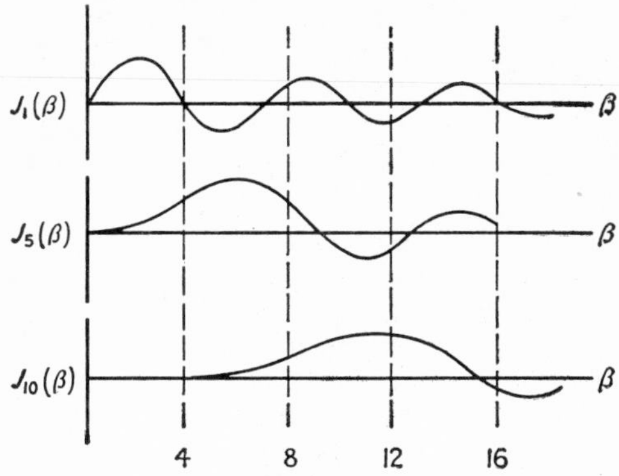

FIG. 8.

10. Significant Side Frequencies, Modulation Index, and Bandwidth. The significant side frequencies and the position and number of the other side frequencies which are included between the last significant side-frequency pair as a function of the modulation index β are tabulated in Table 2, where the carrier-frequency wave amplitude and the successive side-frequency amplitudes are expressed in terms of per cent of the unmodulated-carrier amplitude I. The table also includes the spectral bandwidth, which is equal to twice the distance from the carrier to the last significant side frequency. For the values of β which are tabulated, none of the Bessel functions pass through their zeros, and all of the side frequencies which are contained between the carrier-frequency wave and the last significant side frequencies are significant.

Consider, for example, the case of $\beta = 5$ from Table 2. We see directly that the amplitudes of the various side frequencies may be listed as follows:

	Amplitude
Carrier	$0.1776I$
First side-frequency pair	$0.3276I$
Second side-frequency pair	$0.0466I$
Third side-frequency pair	$0.3648I$
Fourth side-frequency pair	$0.3912I$
Fifth side-frequency pair	$0.2611I$
Sixth side-frequency pair	$0.1310I$
Seventh side-frequency pair	$0.0534I$
Eighth side-frequency pair	$0.0184I$

TABLE 2*

β	Carrier frequency and successive significant side frequencies expressed in percentage of the unmodulated-carrier level	Required bandwidth
0.01	100; 0.5	2*f*
0.02	99.99; 1	2*f*
0.03	99.98; 1.5	2*f*
0.04	99.96; 2	2*f*
0.05	99.94; 2.5	2*f*
0.1	99.75; 4.99	2*f*
0.2	99.00; 9.95	2*f*
0.3	97.76; 14.83	2*f*
0.4	96.04; 19.60	2*f*
0.5	93.85; 24.23; 3.1	4*f*
1.0	76.52; 44.01; 11.49, 1.96	6*f*
2.0	22.39; 57.67; 35.28; 12.89; 3.4	8*f*
3.0	26.01; 33.91; 48.61; 30.91; 13.2, 4.3; 1.14	12*f*
4.0	39.71, 6.6; 36.41; 43.02; 28.11; 13.21; 4.91; 1.52	14*f*
5.0	17.76; 32.76; 4.66; 36.48; 39.12; 26.11; 13.1; 5.34; 1.84	16*f*
6.0	15.06; 27.67; 24.29; 11.48; 35.76; 36.21; 24.58; 12.96; 5.653, 212	18*f*
7.0	30.01; 0.5; 30.14; 16.76; 15.78; 34.79; 33.92; 23.36; 12.90, 5.9; 2.3; 0.8	22*f*
8.0	17.17; 23.46; 11.3; 29.11; 10.54; 18.58; 33.76; 32.06; 22.35, 12.63, 6.1, 2.6; 0.96	24*f*
9.0	9.03; 24.53; 14.48; 18.10; 26.55; 5.5; 20.43; 32.75; 30.51; 21.49; 12.47; 6.2; 2.73; 1.1	26*f*
10.0	24.59; 4.35; 25.46; 5.83; 21.96; 23.41; 1.45; 21.67; 31.79; 29.19; 20.75; 12.31; 6.34; 2.9; 1.2	28*f*
12	4.8; 22.34; 8.5; 19.51; 18.25; 7.3; 24.37; 17.03; 4.5; 23.04; 30.05; 27.04; 19.53; 12.01; 6.5; 3.2; 1.4	32*f*
15	1.4; 20.51; 4.2; 11.92; 19.40; 13.05; 20.61; 3.45; 17.40; 22; 9; 9.99; 23.67; 27.87; 24.64; 18.13; 11.62; 6.6; 3.5; 1.66	38*f*
18	1.34; 18.8; 0.75; 18.63; 6.96; 15.54; 15.6; 5.1; 19.59; 12.28; 7.3; 20.41; 17.62; 3.1; 13.16; 23.56; 26.11; 22.86; 17.06; 11.27; 6.7; 3.7; 1.9; 0.9	46*f*
21	3.7; 17.11; 2.03; 17.50; 2.97; 16.37; 10.76; 10.22; 17.57; 3.2; 14.85; 17.32; 3.3; 13.56; 20.08; 13.21; 1.2; 15.05; 23.16; 24.65; 21.45; 16.21; 10.97; 6.77; 3.86; 2.05; 1	52*f*
24	5.6; 15.4; 4.34; 16.13; 0.3; 16.23; 6.4; 13; 14.04; 3.6; 16.77; 10.33; 7.3; 17.63; 11.8; 3.9; 16.63; 18.31; 9.3; 4.3; 16.19; 22.64; 23.43; 20.31; 15.5; 10.7; 6.8; 3.99; 2.2; 1.1	58*f*

*From A. Hund, "Frequency Modulation," McGraw-Hill Book Company, Inc., New York, 1942.

11. Spectral Behavior as β is Varied; $\Delta\omega$ Constant. Figure 9 illustrates the spectral behavior as β is varied, holding $\Delta\omega$ constant. As β approaches 20, the number of side frequencies increases and the spectral components become more and more confined to the band between $\omega_0 + \Delta\omega$ and $\omega_0 - \Delta\omega$. As β becomes larger than 20, the number of components in the band between $\omega_0 + \Delta\omega$ and $\omega_0 - \Delta\omega$ will increase although the sidebands of greatest magnitude will still be found at the edges of the band. As β becomes extremely large, the large vectors at the band edges will decrease in magnitude to the level of the others in the band until when

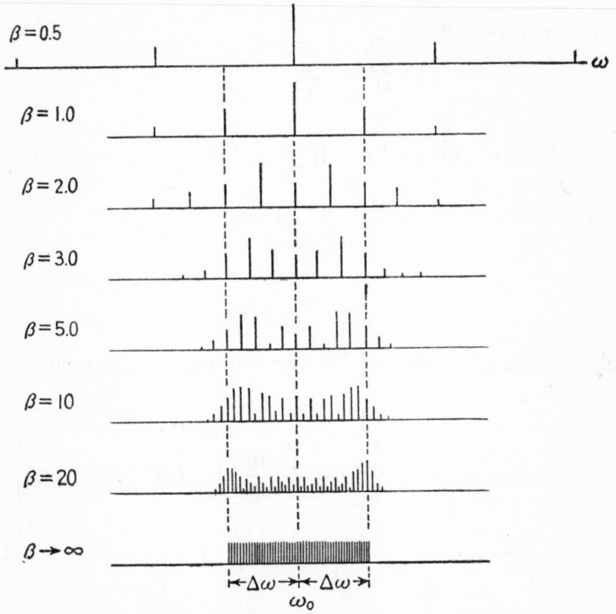

FIG. 9. Behavior of a single-tone FM spectrum as β is varied and $\Delta\omega$ is maintained constant. (*After van der Pol, courtesy of Institute of Radio Engineers.*)

$\beta \to \infty$, a true band spectrum whose energy is confined to a band which is exactly $2\Delta\omega$ wide will result.

12. Simultaneous Amplitude and Frequency Modulation.[1] Consider the case when the wave which is being frequency-modulated by a wave $\Delta\omega \cos \omega_1 t$ is also amplitude-modulated by this wave with a modulation factor M. This is a case commonly met in practical FM communication systems since it is very difficult to produce frequency modulation without

[1] A. Hund, "Frequency Modulation," Chap. 1, McGraw-Hill Book Company, Inc., New York, 1942.

L. J. Giacoletto, Generalized Theory of Multitone Amplitude and Frequency Modulation, *Proc. IRE*, vol. 35, pp. 680–693, July, 1947.

some attendant amplitude modulation, particularly at the ultra-high frequencies.

The expression for single-tone cosinusoidal amplitude plus frequency modulation may be written as follows:

$$i = (1 + M \cos \omega_1 t) I e^{j(\omega_0 t + \beta \sin \omega_1 t)} \tag{32}$$

Writing the AM function in Eq. (32) in exponential form gives

$$i = I e^{j(\omega_0 t + \beta \sin \omega_1 t)} + \frac{MI}{2} e^{j(\omega_0 + \omega_1 + \beta \sin \omega_1)t} + \frac{MI}{2} e^{j(\omega_0 - \omega_1 + \beta \sin \omega_1)t} \tag{33}$$

According to Eq. (90), Chap. 2,

$$e^{j\beta \sin \omega_1 t} = \sum_{n=-\infty}^{\infty} J_n(\beta) e^{jn\omega_1 t} \tag{34}$$

Substituting this into (33) and combining the exponents, we get

$$i = I \sum_{n=-\infty}^{\infty} J_n(\beta) e^{j(\omega_0 + \omega n_1)t} + \frac{MI}{2} \sum_{n=-\infty}^{\infty} J_n(\beta) e^{j[\omega_0 + (n+1)\omega_1]t}$$
$$+ \frac{MI}{2} \sum_{n=-\infty}^{\infty} J_n(\beta) e^{j[\omega_0 + (n-1)\omega_1]t} \tag{35}$$

The sideband equation (35) yields the following term forms:

$$\text{Carrier} = I e^{j\omega_0 t}$$

Upper nth side frequency: $\left\{ J_n(\beta) + \frac{M}{2} [J_{n+1}(\beta) + J_{n-1}(\beta)] \right\} I e^{j(\omega_0 + n\omega_1)t}$

Odd lower side frequency: $\left\{ -J_n(\beta) + \frac{M}{2} [J_{n+1}(\beta) + J_{n-1}(\beta)] \right\} I e^{j(\omega_0 - n\omega_1)t}$

Even, lower, side frequency: $\left\{ J_n(\beta) - \frac{M}{2} [J_{n+1}(\beta) + J_{n-1}(\beta)] \right\} I e^{j(\omega_0 - n\omega_1)t}$

It is evident that

1. The spectrum becomes asymmetrical with respect to the carrier since the amplitudes of the upper side frequencies always increase in magnitude while, in general, the amplitudes of the lower side frequencies may either increase or decrease in magnitude. It must be remembered that the additional energy which is found in the spectrum is contributed by the AM source.
2. The carrier remains unaffected by the amplitude modulation.
3. All upper side frequencies enjoy the same phase as during pure frequency modulation.
4. All lower side frequencies either enjoy the same phase as during pure frequency modulation or become shifted by 180°.

5. It is possible to cancel various lower side frequencies. In fact, there is a value of β and M where the only significant components present are the carrier and the first upper side frequency.

6. It is not possible to cancel an entire upper side frequency at some instant since three Bessel functions of consecutive order cannot go to zero at the same time.

13. Illustrative Example. Consider the case where $M = 0.6$ and $\beta = 3$. Then

$$\begin{aligned} i = I(-0.2601e^{j\omega_0 t} &+ 0.5629e^{j(\omega_0+\omega_1)t} \\ &- 0.1153e^{j(\omega_0-\omega_1)t} \\ &+ 0.6805e^{j(\omega_0+2\omega_1)t} \\ &- 0.2917e^{j(\omega_0-2\omega_1)t} \\ &+ 0.4945e^{j(\omega_0+3\omega_1)t} \\ &- 0.1237e^{j(\omega_0-3\omega_1)t} \\ &+ 0.2376e^{j(\omega_0+4\omega_1)t} \\ &- 0.0264e^{j(\omega_0-4\omega_1)t} \\ &+ 0.077\ e^{j(\omega_0+5\omega_1)t} + \cdots) \end{aligned} \tag{36}$$

Equation (36) is shown in the form of an amplitude spectrum in Fig. 10*b*, where it is shown compared with the amplitude spectrum for pure frequency modulation with the same modulation index which is pictured in

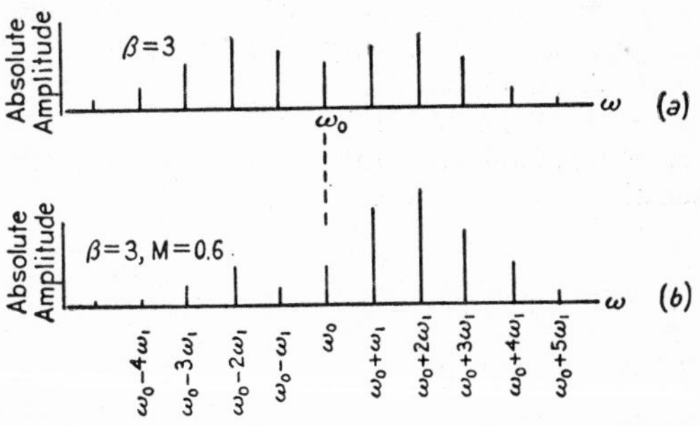

FIG. 10.

Fig. 10*a*. The lack of symmetry in the frequency- plus amplitude-modulation spectrum is immediately apparent since it is seen that the energy is now predominately in the upper sideband. (Note that this spectrum now includes the energy from the AM source.)

PROBLEMS

1. Determine the range of modulation index of an FM wave whose maximum frequency deviation is 7.2 per cent of the carrier frequency, 10^6 cycles, and whose modulating frequency varies from 25 to 15×10^3 cycles.

2. Determine the amplitude spectrum of a carrier $100 \sin 2\pi \times 40 \times 10^6 t$ which is frequency-modulated by the wave $10 \sin 2\pi \times 15 \times 10^3 t$ so that the maximum frequency deviation is 75×10^3 cycles. What is the bandwidth?

3. Repeat Prob. 2 for the following modulating waves and frequency deviations:

a. $10 \sin 2\pi \times 7.5 \times 10^3 t$, $\Delta f = 15 \times 10^3$ cycles

b. $10 \sin 2\pi \times 10^3 t$, $\Delta f = 500$ cycles

c. $10 \sin 2\pi \times 3.02 \times 10^3 t$, $\Delta f = 75 \times 10^3$ cycles

d. $10 \cos 2\pi \times 256t$, $\Delta f = 3{,}910$ cycles

4. If the frequency of the modulating wave in Prob. 2 is changed to 7,500 cycles, determine the change in energy in the carrier and the first 14 side-frequency pairs. If the output of the transmitter is 1 kw, determine the amount of power in each sideband after the change of frequency.

5. Construct the vector-diagram representation of the spectrum of an FM wave for the case when $\beta = 5$ and $\omega_1 t = 15°$. What is the length of the resultant vector if the unmodulated-carrier amplitude is unity? What is the phase displacement from that of the unmodulated carrier?

6. What value of β must an FM wave have for the absolute values of its spectral components to be identical to the absolute values of the spectral components resulting from single-tone amplitude modulation with 25 per cent modulation?

7. Consider a single-tone FM wave which is to be broadcast from a transmitter so that its modulating frequency and unmodulated-carrier frequency are 10^3 and 5×10^6 cycles, respectively. If the modulation index is to be limited to 75, determine the Q of the tank circuit of the transmitter's final stage so that the voltage change during the entire frequency excursion is limited to a maximum value of 1.5 per cent of the voltage level of the unmodulated carrier.

8. Compute and diagram the amplitudes of the spectral components resulting from cosinusoidal amplitude plus frequency modulation when

a. $\beta = 1$ and $M = 0{,}1, 0.35, 0.75, 1.0$

b. $\beta = 5$ and $M = 0.1, 0.35, 0.75, 1.0$

c. $\beta = 10$ and $M = 0.1, 0.35, 0.75, 1.0$

Determine the bandwidth for each case.

CHAPTER 16

SINGLE-TONE PHASE MODULATION

1. Fundamental Concepts of Phase Modulation.[1] In general, any wave of constant amplitude which is represented by a single rotating vector may be expressed as

$$i = Ie^{j\Theta_t} \tag{1}$$

where Θ_t is the instantaneous phase angle of the rotating vector. Any variations in the phase of the wave must be expressed in the exponent of Eq. (1). The instantaneous phase is related to the angular velocity of the rotating vector by the equation

$$\Theta_t = \int \omega_t \, dt \qquad \omega_t = \frac{d\Theta_t}{dt} \tag{2}$$

where ω_t is the instantaneous angular velocity.

Consider the wave represented by Eq. (1), which is phase-modulated by a single-tone sinusoidal wave such that the instantaneous phase Θ_t is written as

$$\Theta_t = \Theta_0 + \Delta\Theta \sin \omega_1 t \tag{3}$$

where

$$\Theta_0 = \omega_0 t \tag{4}$$

Θ_0 is the phase of the unmodulated-carrier vector rotating with angular velocity ω_0 at time t, and $\Delta\Theta$ and ω_1 are the maximum phase deviation of the modulated wave and the angular velocity of the modulating wave, respectively. Equation (3) is pictured in Fig. 1.

The phase variation represented in Eq. (3) is also shown in Fig. 2. Figure 2 shows the function $\Delta\Theta \sin \omega_1 t$, which is the phase variation imposed by the modulating source on the linear phase variation $\omega_0 t$ of the unmodulated wave. At t_0 and t_2, the phase deviation is zero. At t_1 and t_3, owing to the nature of a sinusoid, the phase deviation is at its positive and negative maxima, respectively. The effect of this phase deviation on the real part of Eq. (1) is shown in Fig. 1*a*. At $\pi/2\omega_1$, the advance of the phase of the wave is evident, and by comparing the modulated and

[1] M. G. Crosby, Communication by Phase Modulation, *Proc. IRE*, vol. 27, pp. 126–136, February, 1939.

unmodulated wave in this diagram the behavior of the phase of the wave during the entire modulation cycle is evident.

2. Equivalent Phase and Frequency Modulation.[1] Phase and frequency are related as described by (2). Owing to this interrelationship, it is evident that during the course of any modulation of frequency there will exist a simultaneous or equivalent modulation of phase. Similarly, during the course of phase modulation, there will exist equivalent frequency modulation.

The concepts of equivalent modulation are of particular importance to

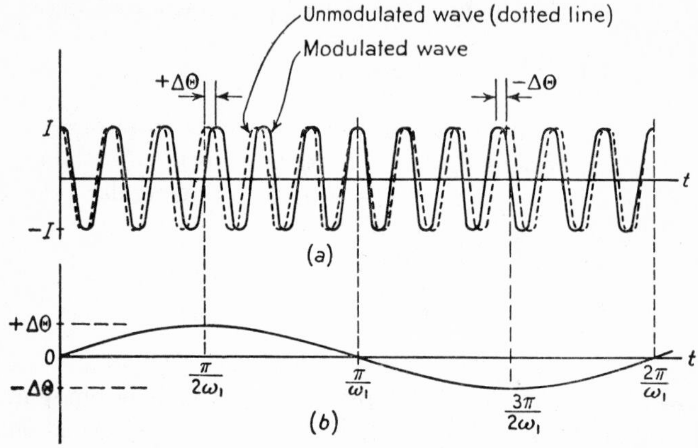

FIG. 1. Single-tone phase-modulated wave.

the communications engineer since, for example, if intelligence is being transmitted by an FM transmitter, a frequency demodulator will recover the intelligence from the signal. However, if the same incoming wave is applied to a phase demodulator, only the equivalent phase modulation will be demodulated.

As a demonstration of the concepts associated with equivalent frequency and phase modulation as derived from (2), consider the case of cosinusoidal frequency modulation with a maximum frequency deviation Δf such that the instantaneous angular velocity ω_t is written

$$\omega_t = \omega_0 + \Delta\omega \cos \omega_1 t \tag{5}$$

The instantaneous phase Θ_t is found, using (2), to be, letting $\Delta\omega/\omega_1 = \Delta\Theta$,

$$\Theta_t = \omega_0 t + \Delta\Theta \sin \omega_1 t \tag{6}$$

[1] A. Hund, "Frequency Modulation," Chap. 1, McGraw-Hill Book Company, Inc., New York, 1942.

A comparison of these expressions demonstrates an important property of phase modulation and its equivalent frequency modulation, *viz.*, the variation in frequency is determined by the rate of change of phase alone. This is illustrated in Fig. 2, where we see diagramed (5) and (6). At $t = t_0$, $\omega_0 t = \omega_0 t_0$. At $t = t_4$, $\omega_0 t = \omega_0 t_4$. At $t = t_0, t_2, t_4$, the frequency has momentarily come to rest, but the phase is experiencing its most

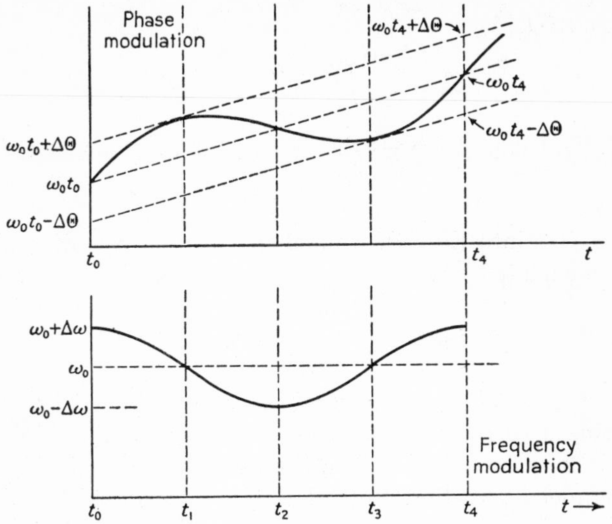

FIG. 2.

rapid rate of change. At $t = t_1$, although the frequency is passing through ω_0, where it is experiencing its greatest rate of change, the phase is momentarily stationary at its maximum value $\omega_0 t + \Delta\Theta$. At $t = t_2$, the frequency passes through its minimum $\omega_0 - \Delta\omega$, at which time it momentarily comes to rest. At this time, the phase experiences its maximum negative rate of change. At $t = t_4$, another cycle begins.

3. Fourier-series Expansion of a Single-tone PM Wave. By substituting Eq. (3) into Eq. (1), the following expression for a single-tone sinusoidally phase-modulated wave results:

$$i = Ie^{j(\omega_0 t + \Delta\Theta \sin \omega_1 t)} \tag{7}$$

Equation (7) may be written in the form

$$i = I(e^{j\Delta\Theta \sin \omega_1 t})e^{j\omega_0 t} \tag{8}$$

where the portion in the parentheses is the varying time function, which can be expanded in series form using the Fourier analysis. Using this analysis, we may represent Eq. (8) by the complex Fourier series

$$i = I\left(\sum_{n=-\infty}^{\infty} C_n e^{jn\omega_1 t}\right)e^{j\omega_0 t} \tag{9}$$

where

$$C_n = \frac{\omega_1}{2\pi} \int_{-\pi/\omega_1}^{\pi/\omega_1} e^{j\Delta\Theta \sin \omega_1 t} e^{-jn\omega_1 t} \, dt \tag{10}$$

By combining exponentials, we get

$$C_n = \frac{\omega_1}{2\pi} \int_{-\pi/\omega_1}^{\pi/\omega_1} e^{j(\Delta\Theta \sin \omega_1 t - n\omega_1 t)} \, dt \tag{11}$$

Let $\varphi = \omega_1 t$; then

$$C_n = \frac{1}{2\pi} \int_{-\pi}^{\pi} e^{j(\Delta\Theta \sin \varphi - n\varphi)} \, d\varphi \tag{12}$$

From Eq. (88), Chap. 2, we see that Eq. (12) may be evaluated to yield

$$C_n = J_n(\Delta\Theta) \tag{13}$$

Substituting (13) into Eq. (9), we find the Fourier expansion of a single-tone phase-modulated wave to be

$$i = I \sum_{n=-\infty}^{\infty} J_n(\Delta\Theta) e^{j(\omega_0 + n\omega_1)t} \tag{14}$$

Thus, for sinusoidal phase modulation, Eq. (6) yields a sideband equation involving a carrier at ω_0 and an infinite number of side-frequency pairs. As in frequency modulation, the amplitude of each side-frequency pair is determined by a Bessel function, the order of which is determined by the pair number. The argument of the Bessel function is the maximum phase deviation.

4. Comparison of Modulation Index in Single-tone Phase and Frequency Modulation. Let us compare the basic equations for single-tone cosinusoidal frequency modulation and single-tone sinusoidal phase modulation; *i.e.*,

Cosinusoidal frequency modulation:

$$I e^{j\int_0^t (\omega_0 + \Delta\omega \cos \omega_1 t) dt} = I \sum_{-\infty}^{\infty} J_n\left(\frac{\Delta\omega}{\omega_1}\right) e^{j(\omega_0 + n\omega_1)t} \tag{15}$$

Sinusoidal phase modulation:

$$I e^{j(\omega_0 + \Delta\Theta \sin \omega_1)t} = I \sum_{-\infty}^{\infty} J_n(\Delta\Theta) e^{j(\omega_0 + n\omega_1)t} \tag{16}$$

It is immediately evident from this comparison that if

$$\frac{\Delta\omega}{\omega_1} = \Delta\Theta = \beta \tag{17}$$

the absolute-amplitude spectrum equations for frequency modulation and phase modulation will be identical.

There is one fundamental way in which the phase-modulation spectrum is different from the FM spectrum, *viz.*, as the maximum phase deviation in phase modulation is kept constant, the modulation index remains constant regardless of the modulating frequency. The behavior of the single-tone phase-modulation spectrum for $\beta = 2$ is pictured in Fig. 3 for three values of modulating frequency. The spectrum amplitudes and distribution remain the same while the modulating frequency is varied, but since the spacing between sidebands decreases as this modulating frequency decreases, the bandwidth becomes smaller for smaller values of ω_1.

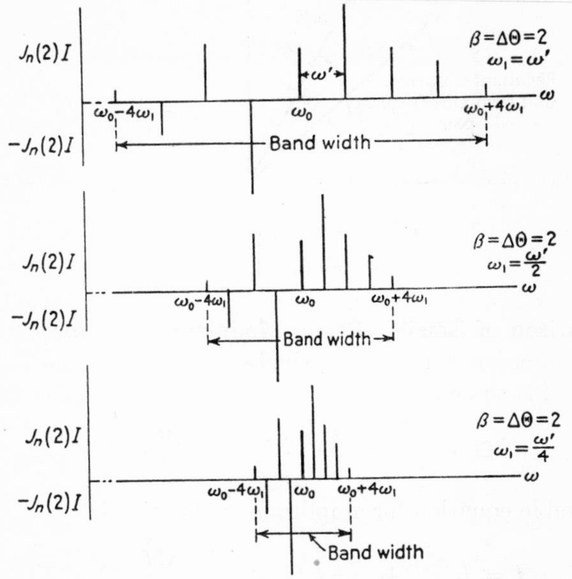

FIG. 3. Variation of a single-tone phase-modulation spectrum for the case when β is constant and ω_1 is varied.

5. Spectrum and Vector Considerations for Small Modulation Index ($0 < \beta < 0.4$). At small values of maximum phase deviation in the range $0 < \beta < 0.4$, the single-tone phase-modulation spectrum will consist of a carrier and the first side-frequency pair, the lower sideband being opposite in sign to the upper sideband; its characteristics are similar to those of small-β frequency modulation as discussed in Sec. 8, Chap. 15, with the exception of considerations of phase deviation and vector relationships, which are illustrated as follows: Consider the vector diagram for the case when $\Delta\Theta = 0.3$. This vector diagram is pictured in Fig. 4. The magnitude of the vector summation of the carrier whose magnitude is $0.9776\ I$ and the sideband resultant whose magnitude is $0.296\ I$ is seen to be approximately equal to I. As long as the final resultant vector has an amplitude which is equal to the unmodulated-carrier vector amplitude, pure phase modulation takes place and no amplitude modulation is realized. The vector summation of the carrier and the two sidebands, which comprise the first pair, for all β in the range $0 < \beta < 0.4$, can be shown to result in a vector whose amplitude is substantially the same as that of the unmodulated vector.

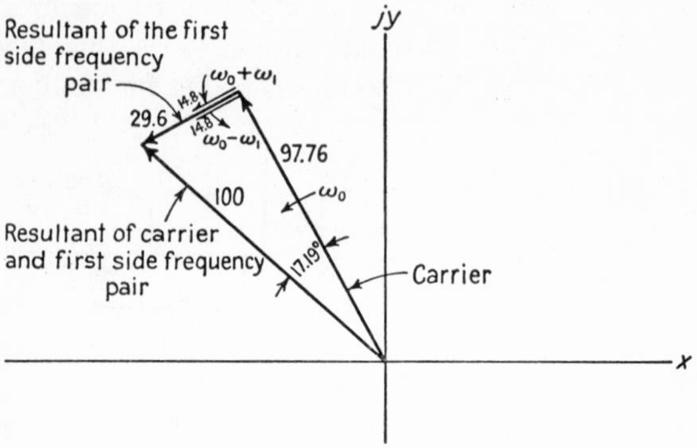

FIG. 4.

6. Comparison of Small-β Phase Modulation and Amplitude Modulation. The equation for small-β single-tone phase modulation may be shown from (14) to be

$$i \cong Ie^{j\omega_0 t} + \frac{\beta I}{2} e^{j(\omega_0+\omega_1)t} - \frac{\beta I}{2} e^{j(\omega_0-\omega_1)t} \tag{18}$$

The comparable equation for amplitude modulation is

$$i = Ie^{j\omega_0 t} + \frac{MI}{2} e^{j(\omega_0+\omega_1)t} + \frac{MI}{2} e^{j(\omega_0-\omega_1)t} \tag{19}$$

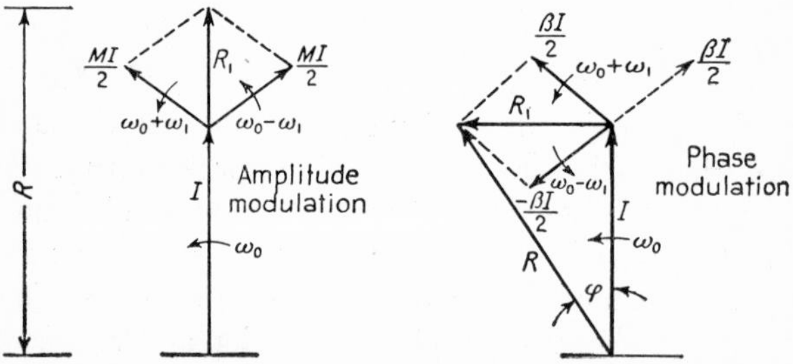

FIG. 5.

It is seen that the fundamental difference between these two equations lies in the sign of the lower sideband. The rotating vectors describing these two cases are drawn in Fig. 5, where we see that, in the case of amplitude modulation, the sideband pair yields a resultant R_1 which adds to the carrier and produces amplitude modulation. It is seen that the change in the sign of the lower sideband is instrumental in shifting the sideband resultant R_1 by 90° so that the new total resultant R is out of phase with respect to the carrier and produces the phase shift whose magnitude is φ. Thus it is possible to take an AM wave and, by means of a suitable network, shift one sideband by 180° (or both sidebands by 90°) and produce phase modulation. This is the basis of the *indirect* FM system.

7. Vector Representation of Large-β Phase Modulation. It was seen in Sec. 5 that the first side-frequency pair produced a vector which was in quadrature with the carrier and thus produced a deviation in phase (see Fig. 4). The vector sum of the carrier and the first side-frequency-pair resultant produced a resultant vector whose amplitude was substantially the same as the unmodulated carrier.

Consider the vector summation of all of the significant side frequencies resulting from the modulation index $\beta = \Delta\Theta = 1$. For such a wave, we find that

	Amplitude
Carrier	$J_0(1)I = 0.7652I$
First pair	$J_1(1)I = 0.4401I$
Second pair	$J_2(1)I = 0.1149I$
Third pair	$J_3(1)I = 0.0196I$

The maximum phase deviation for this wave is 1 radian or 57°.

Let us choose the case where $(\omega_0 + \omega_1)t - \omega_0 t = 90°$. The vector summation corresponding to this case is shown in Fig. 6. As has been

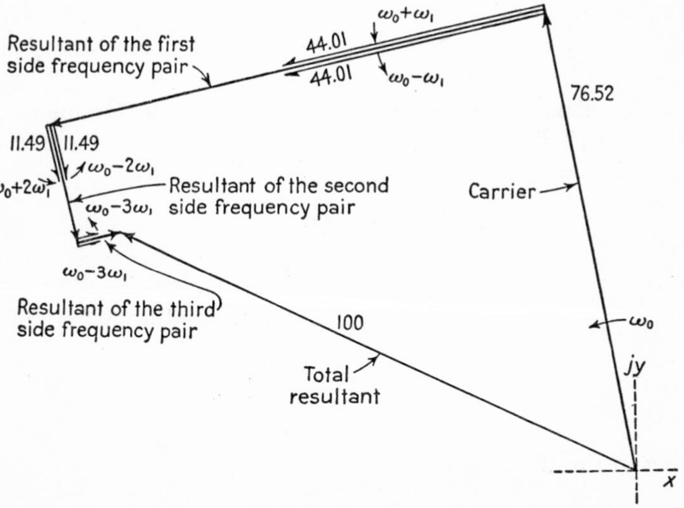

FIG. 6. Vector-diagram representation of a single-tone phase-modulated wave spectrum for the case when $\beta = 1$.

seen in Fig. 4, the resultant of the first side-frequency pair and the carrier produces a vector whose magnitude is 16 per cent greater than that of the unmodulated carrier. Figure 6 shows the addition of the second side-frequency pair, whose resultant vector is 180° out of phase with respect to the carrier. This resultant vector will reduce the amplitude of the resultant of the carrier and the first pair. The third side-frequency pair, which is 270° out of phase with respect to the carrier, will act to decrease the amount of advance in phase. The total resultant vector of the carrier and the three side-frequency pairs is a vector which leads the carrier by 57° and which has the same amplitude as the unmodulated carrier.

The important outgrowth of this development is that we may now identify the various side-frequency pairs with respect to their contributions to the shifts in phase or changes in amplitude, *viz*:

1. The first, third, fifth, etc., side-frequency pairs yield a phase-shifting vector at all times in quadrature with the carrier vector.

2. The second, fourth, sixth, etc., side-frequency pairs yield an amplitude-correcting vector at all times in the same or the opposite direction with respect to the carrier vector.

Thus we see that the odd side-frequency pairs serve to produce a resultant vector which is shifted in phase with respect to the carrier, while the even side-frequency pairs combine to adjust the amplitude of the shifted vector until its amplitude is equal to that of the unmodulated vector. This is, of course, true for both phase and frequency modulation since we may describe the instantaneous phase of an FM rotating vector.

It is easily seen that if an important phase-shifting or amplitude-correcting pair is removed, considerable amplitude distortion may take place although, for large phase deviations, the loss of a phase-shifting pair may not seriously affect the phase.

8. Simultaneous Phase Modulation and Amplitude Modulation. The expression describing simultaneous single-tone cosinusoidal amplitude and phase modulation is

$$i = (1 + M \cos \omega_1 t) I e^{j(\omega_0 t + \Delta\Theta \cos \omega_1 t)} \tag{20}$$

where $\Delta\Theta$ is the maximum phase deviation. By writing the amplitude-modulating function in exponential form we get, letting $\Delta\Theta = \beta$,

$$i = Ie^{j(\omega_0 t + \beta \cos \omega_1 t)} + \frac{MI}{2} e^{j(\omega_0 + \omega_1 + \beta \cos \omega_1)t} + \frac{MI}{2} e^{j(\omega_0 - \omega_1 + \beta \cos \omega_1)t} \tag{21}$$

According to Eq. (92), Chap. 2,

$$e^{j\beta \cos \omega_1 t} = \sum_{-\infty}^{\infty} j^n J_n(\beta) e^{jn\omega_1 t} \tag{22}$$

Substituting (22) into Eq. (21), we get

$$= I \sum_{n=-\infty}^{\infty} j^n J_n(\beta) e^{j(\omega_0 + n\omega_1)t} + \frac{MI}{2} \sum_{n=-\infty}^{\infty} j^n J_n(\beta) e^{j[\omega_0 + (n+1)\omega_1]t}$$
$$+ \frac{MI}{2} \sum_{n=-\infty}^{\infty} j^n J_n(\beta) e^{j[\omega_0 + (n-1)\omega_1]t} \qquad (23)$$

Writing out Eq. (23) and grouping the coefficients of each side frequency, we get

$$\begin{aligned} i = I\Big(&[J_0(\beta) + jMJ_1(\beta)]e^{j\omega_0 t} \\ &+ \left\{\frac{M}{2}[J_0(\beta) - J_2(\beta)] + jJ_1(\beta)\right\}(e^{j(\omega_0+\omega_1)t} + e^{j(\omega_0-\omega_1)t}) \\ &+ \left\{-J_2(\beta) + j\frac{M}{2}[J_1(\beta) - J_3(\beta)]\right\}(e^{j(\omega_0+2\omega_1)t} + e^{j(\omega_0-2\omega_1)t}) \\ &+ \left\{-\frac{M}{2}[J_2(\beta) - J_4(\beta)] - jJ_3(\beta)\right\}(e^{j(\omega_0+3\omega_1)t} + e^{j(\omega_0-3\omega_1)t}) \\ &+ \left\{J_4(\beta) - j\frac{M}{2}[J_3(\beta) - J_5(\beta)]\right\}(e^{j(\omega_0+4\omega_1)t} + e^{j(\omega_0-4\omega_1)t}) \\ &+ \cdots\Big) \end{aligned} \qquad (24)$$

The important characteristics demonstrated by (24) may be listed as follows:

1. During amplitude plus phase modulation, the carrier vector is modified by a quadrature component.
2. The amplitude spectrum remains symmetrical at all times. The result of the simultaneous amplitude modulation is the broadening and the filling in of the spectrum.
3. The amplitudes of the two resultant vectors comprising a side-frequency pair are always the same. Thus, it is not possible to cancel lower side frequencies as in amplitude plus frequency modulation.
4. It is possible to cancel out amplitude variations in the odd-order side frequencies and the frequency flutter in the even-order side frequencies for particular values of β, but it will be impossible for any entire side frequency to go to zero since no three consecutive-order Bessel functions may have zeros at the same time.

9. Numerical Illustration of Amplitude plus Phase Modulation. The broadening and the filling in of the spectrum due to amplitude plus phase modulation is illustrated as follows: Consider the absolute-magnitude amplitude spectrum for $M = 0.6$ and $\beta = 3$. The Bessel coefficients corresponding to $\beta = 3$ may be substituted into Eq. (24) to give

$$|i| = I(0.33e^{j\omega_0 t} + 0.4071e^{j(\omega_0 \pm \omega_1)t} + 0.4861e^{j(\omega_0 \pm 2\omega_1)t} + 0.326e^{j(\omega_0 \pm 3\omega_1)t} + 0.155e^{j(\omega_0 \pm 4\omega_1)t} + \cdots) \quad (25)$$

The amplitude spectrum corresponding to (25) is pictured in Fig. 7*b*. Although the number of significant side frequencies involved is small, the broadening and filling in of the amplitude spectrum in Fig. 7*b* can be

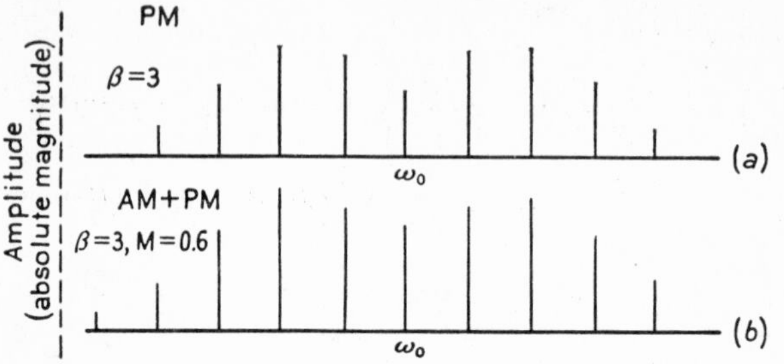

FIG. 7.

noticed when compared with the pure phase-modulation spectrum shown in Fig. 7*a*. The increase in side-frequency amplitudes is due to the addition of energy by the AM source.

PROBLEMS

1. Find the maximum phase deviation $\Delta\Theta$ corresponding to a frequency deviation of 25,000 cycles and a modulating tone frequency of 256 cycles.

2. Determine the amplitude spectrum of a carrier $100 \sin 2\pi \times 40 \times 10^6 t$ which is phase-modulated by a wave of frequency 15,000 cycles, which produces a maximum phase deviation of 8 radians. What is the bandwidth?

3. If the maximum phase deviation in Prob. 2 is changed to 12 radians, determine the new amplitude spectrum and discuss the change in the distribution of sideband energy.

4. If the phase deviation is maintained constant in Prob. 2 and if the frequency of the modulating wave is doubled, what is the new bandwidth?

5. Construct a vector diagram for a single-tone phase-modulated wave for the case where $\Delta\Theta = 3$ radians. Determine the phase shift or amplitude correction provided by each pair of side frequencies.

6. Deduce the spectral equation for simultaneous single-tone amplitude plus phase modulation when the frequencies of the amplitude-modulating wave and of the frequency-modulating wave are so related that

$$i = (1 + M \cos 0.9\,\omega_1 t) I e^{j(\omega_0 + \Delta\omega \cos \omega_1 t)t}$$

Compute and diagram the spectral amplitudes for the case when $M = 0.6$ and $\beta = 3$.

CHAPTER 17

INDIRECT FREQUENCY MODULATION AND WAVE INTERFERENCE

1. Introduction. In this chapter, we shall discuss the fundamentals of the indirect FM system and wave interference, these highly important considerations in commercial transmission furnishing excellent illustrations of concepts and analyses involving basic relationships between frequency and phase.

THE THEORY OF THE INDIRECT FREQUENCY-MODULATION SYSTEM

2. Indirect Frequency Modulation. The *indirect* FM system is used to produce FM waves in many commercial FM transmitters; its operation is based on the shifting in phase of side-frequency components of an AM wave. A careful analysis of this system is particularly instructive because the circuit behavior is more suitably explained in terms of sideband theory and Fourier analysis than in terms of conventional circuit and network theory. In addition, the system operation serves as an excellent demonstration of the fundamental concepts of amplitude, phase, and frequency modulation.

3. The Balanced Modulator.[1] Before discussing the theory of the indirect system, let us first consider the basic operation of an electronic system which is known as a balanced modulator. A typical balanced-modulator circuit is included in Fig. 1. Let a modulating signal $E_1 \cos \omega_1 t$ be applied to the grids of the tubes in push-pull at the same time that a carrier signal $E_0 \sin \omega_0 t$ is applied so that it drives each grid with equal potential.

Thus the grid voltage on tube I is, neglecting the bias voltage,

$$e_{g_1} = E_0 \sin \omega_0 t + E_1 \cos \omega_1 t \tag{1}$$

and on the grid of tube II is

$$e_{g_2} = E_0 \sin \omega_0 t - E_1 \cos \omega_1 t \tag{2}$$

[1] A. Hund, "Frequency Modulation," Chaps. II, III, McGraw-Hill Book Company, Inc., New York, 1942.

The current variation in tube I will be

$$i_{p_1} = I \sin \omega_0 t + 0.5MI[\sin (\omega_0 + \omega_1)t + \sin (\omega_0 - \omega_1)t] \tag{3}$$

and in tube II,

$$i_{p_2} = I \sin \omega_0 t - 0.5MI[\sin (\omega_0 + \omega_1)t + \sin (\omega_0 - \omega_1)t] \tag{4}$$

where

$$M = \frac{E_1}{E_0} \tag{5}$$

As i_{p_1} and i_{p_2} are passed through their respective halves of the plate transformer, they are seen to be in opposition and we see that

$$e_0 = ME'[\sin (\omega_0 + \omega_1)t + \sin (\omega_0 - \omega_1)t] \tag{6}$$

$$= 2ME' \cos \omega_1 t \sin \omega_0 t \tag{7}$$

which is the modulation product representing the two sidebands (the prime denotes a transformed voltage). Note that the carrier-frequency wave does not appear.

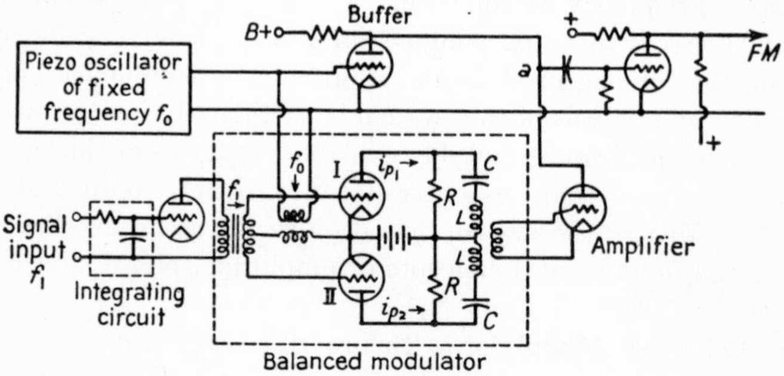

Fig. 1. Basic *indirect* FM circuit.

4. The Indirect FM System. A schematic diagram of a typical circuit for producing frequency modulation using the indirect system is shown in Fig. 1.

A carrier signal from a fixed piezo oscillator is seen to go through a buffer amplifier to the junction a. At the same time, the oscillator output is impressed at the input to the balanced modulator.

Let us at this point follow the modulating-wave voltage, which is impressed at the input terminals, through the circuit. Let this modulating-wave voltage be $E_1 \cos \omega_1 t$. The first circuit that it encounters is the RC integrating circuit. If the time constant RC is large and if the current in this circuit due to $E_1 \cos \omega_1 t$ is denoted as $I_1 \cos \omega_1 t$, the output e_C of the integrating circuit as produced across the capacitor C is

$$e_C = \int X_C I_1 \cos \omega_1 t \, dt \tag{8}$$

where $X_C = 1/\omega C$. If we write $E_C = X_C I_1$, then

$$e_C \cong \frac{E_C}{\omega_1} \sin \omega_1 t \tag{9}$$

The amplitude of e_C is seen to vary inversely with respect to the frequency.

Now let e_C be applied to the proper input terminals of the balanced modulator in addition to the carrier signal, which is applied at its correct terminals as shown. As was pointed out in the preceding section, the carrier does not appear in the output of the balanced modulator—only the sidebands due to the beating together of the carrier signal and the integrated modulating signal. Note that the balanced modulator is so connected that each plate circuit works into a coupled load circuit whose primary has a natural period of $T = 2\pi\sqrt{LC}$. By making the natural period of the secondary short compared with T, the modulation product $\sin \omega_1 t \sin \omega_0 t$ is shifted in phase by 90°, thus yielding the phase-shifted sidebands

$$\frac{kE''}{\omega_1} [\sin (\omega_0 + \omega_1)t - \sin (\omega_0 - \omega_1)t] \tag{10}$$

where k is an absolute amplification factor. These sidebands are then combined at the junction a with the direct carrier-signal voltage to produce the current

$$i_a = I''' \sin \omega_0 t \pm \frac{kI'''}{\omega_1} [\sin (\omega_0 + \omega_1)t - \sin (\omega_0 - \omega_1)t] \tag{11}$$

where the primes indicate appropriate values of current magnitude which may be obtained by suitable amplification. Dropping the primes, it is evident that i_a can be written

$$i_a = I \sin \omega_0 t \pm \frac{2kI}{\omega_1} \sin \omega_1 t \cos \omega_0 t \tag{12}$$

$$= I \sqrt{1 + \left(\frac{2k}{\omega_1} \sin \omega_1 t\right)^2} \sin (\omega_0 t \pm \tan^{-1} \beta \sin \omega_1 t) \tag{13}$$

where

$$\beta = \frac{2k}{\omega_1} \tag{14}$$

When $\beta \sin \omega_1 t$ is small (as will be seen to be the case),

$$i_a = I\sqrt{1 + (\beta \sin \omega_1 t)^2} \sin (\omega_0 t \pm \beta \sin \omega_1 t) \tag{15}$$

which is, of course, the equation of an FM wave which experiences some amplitude modulation depending on the extent of the term $(2k/\omega_1) \sin \omega_1 t$. Note that if the input signal had not been integrated, the factor $1/\omega_1$, which must be contained in the modulation index of an FM wave, would not have appeared and a true FM wave would not have resulted.

5. Distortion in the Indirect FM System. The distortion which is produced by the sideband shifting method may be readily deduced by considering the vector representation of the carrier and sidebands as illustrated in Fig. 2, where it is seen that the sideband resultant shifts the phase and produces some amplitude change.

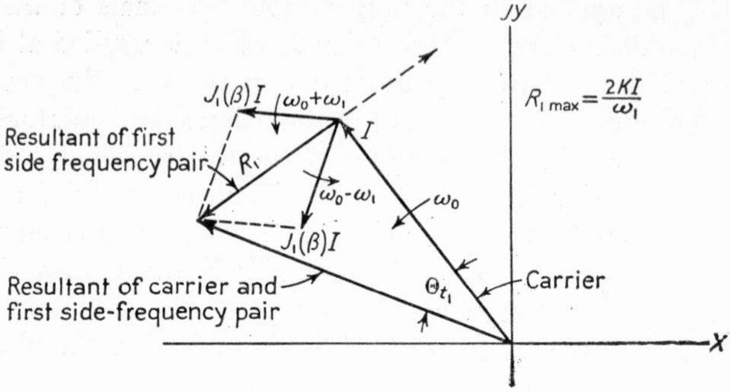

FIG. 2.

It is evident that the instantaneous phase angle Θ_{t_1} in Fig. 2 may be written

$$\Theta_{t_1} = \tan^{-1} \frac{2kI \sin \omega_1 t}{\omega_1 I} \tag{16}$$

But

$$\frac{2kI}{\omega_1 I} = \Delta\Theta \tag{17}$$

where $\Delta\Theta$ is the maximum angle of phase deviation. Therefore

$$\Theta_{t_1} = \tan^{-1} \Delta\Theta \sin \omega_1 t \tag{18}$$

The equivalent frequency modulation resulting from this phase modulation is the time derivative of Eq. (18). Since

$$\frac{d}{dx} \tan^{-1} u = \frac{du/dx}{1 + u^2} \tag{19}$$

we may write

$$\Delta\omega_t = \frac{d\Theta_{t_1}}{dt} = \frac{\omega_1 \Delta\Theta \cos \omega_1 t}{1 + (\Delta\Theta)^2 \sin^2 \omega_1 t} \tag{20}$$

It follows that

$$\omega_t = \omega_0 + \Delta\omega_t = \omega_0 + \frac{\omega_1 \Delta\Theta \cos \omega_1 t}{1 + (\Delta\Theta)^2 \sin^2 \omega_1 t} \tag{21}$$

A calculation, due to D. L. Jaffe,[1] of the amount of harmonic distortion as a function of $\Delta\Theta$ may be made by expanding the second term on the right-hand side of Eq. (21) as a Fourier series. Thus if

$$\Delta\omega_t = \Delta\Theta \frac{\omega_1 \cos \omega_1 t}{1 + (\Delta\Theta)^2 \sin^2 \omega_1 t} \qquad -\pi < \omega_1 t < \pi \tag{22}$$

then, since the function is even,

$$\Delta\omega_t = \sum_{m=1}^{\infty} A_m \cos m\omega_1 t \tag{23}$$

where

$$A_m = \frac{2}{\pi} \int_0^{\pi} \Delta\omega_t \cos m\omega_1 t \, d\omega_1 t \tag{24}$$

$$= \frac{2\Delta\Theta}{\pi} \int_0^{\pi} \frac{\omega_1 \cos \omega_1 t \cos m\omega_1 t}{1 + (\Delta\Theta)^2 \sin^2 \omega_1 t} d\omega_1 t \tag{25}$$

$$= \frac{2\omega_1}{(\Delta\Theta)^m} [\sqrt{1 + (\Delta\Theta)^2} - 1]^m \qquad m \text{ odd} \tag{26}$$

Substituting (26) into (23), which is then substituted into (21), we get

$$\omega_t = \omega_0 \pm \Delta\omega_t$$

$$= \omega_0 \pm \sum_{m=1,3,\ldots}^{\infty} \frac{2\omega_1}{(\Delta\Theta)^m} [\sqrt{1 + (\Delta\Theta)^2} - 1]^m \cos m\omega_1 t \tag{27}$$

This indicates that the wave will have odd-order harmonic distortion which will be a function of $\Delta\Theta$.

Figure 3 pictures the third and fifth harmonic distortion as a function of maximum phase deviation $\Delta\Theta$. It is seen that the third harmonic distortion is the most important contributor to the total harmonic distortion, and it follows that if $\Delta\Theta$ is limited to a maximum value of 30° at 20 cycles, since, in general, $f_1 = \Delta f/\Delta\Theta$, then modulating frequencies in the general audio range will produce negligible distortion.

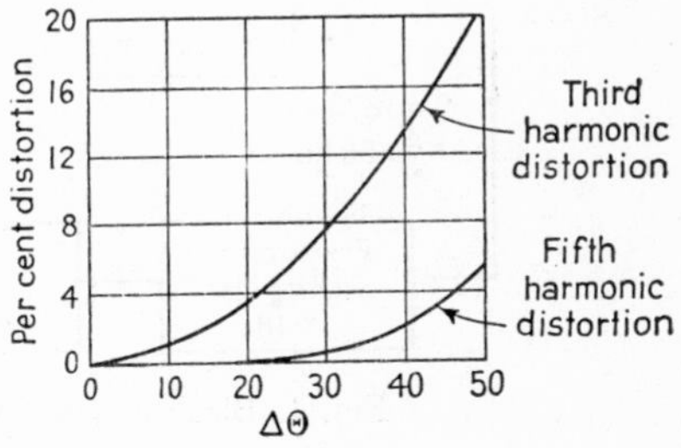

FIG. 3.

6. Some Practical Aspects of the Indirect System.[2] One of the most important features of the indirect system of frequency modulation is that

[1] D. L. Jaffe, Armstrong's Frequency Modulator, *Proc. IRE*, vol. 26, pp. 475–481, April, 1938.

[2] E. A. Armstrong, A Method of Reducing Disturbances in Radio Signaling by a System of Frequency Modulation, *Proc. IRE*, vol. 24, pp. 689–739, May, 1936.

a fixed-frequency piezo oscillator may be used as the carrier-frequency oscillator, thus eliminating complex and elaborate methods of center-frequency stabilization such as were mentioned in connection with the direct FM transmitter described in Chap. 13.

The problem of obtaining suitable frequency deviation, when the phase deviation in the primary stages is limited in magnitude to prevent distortion, is an important one. Note that if $\Delta\Theta = 0.524$ radians at 50 cycles

$$\Delta f = \Delta\Theta \cdot f_1 \tag{28}$$

$$= 0.524 \times 50 = 26.2 \text{ cycles} \tag{29}$$

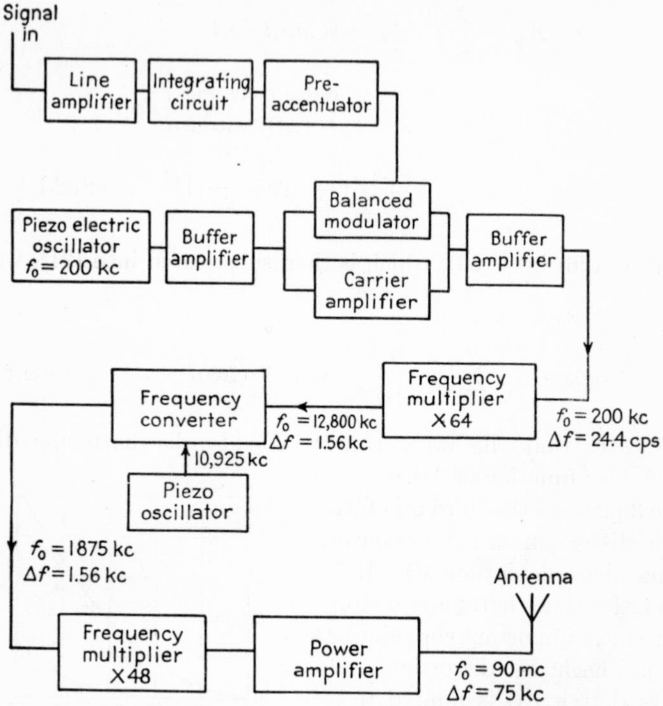

FIG. 4. Block diagram of an *indirect* FM transmitter.

If a carrier with this frequency deviation were to be passed through a series of frequency multipliers to bring the frequency deviation up to the value of $\Delta f = 75{,}000$ cycles, a multiplication factor of 2,860 would be necessary. In addition, if a center frequency of 90 Mc is desired, then the fixed-frequency piezo oscillator would have to oscillate at

$$f_0 = \frac{90{,}000{,}000}{2{,}860} = 31{,}468 \text{ cycles} \tag{30}$$

It is evident that this would not be practical. As an illustration of how the problem was solved by E. A. Armstrong, let us consider the indirect FM transmitter whose block diagram is illustrated in Fig. 4. The primary fixed oscillator puts out a signal at 200 kc. This signal is then multiplied in frequency 64 times up to 12.8 Mc. At this point, an initial maximum frequency deviation of $\Delta f = 24.4$ cycles has also been multiplied 64 times up to $\Delta f = 1.562$ kc. The signal is then beat against the output of a fixed-frequency piezo oscillator whose frequency is 10,925 kc to produce the beat frequency of 1,875 kc with Δf still at $\Delta f = 1.562$ Mc. This signal is multiplied in frequency 48 times and then amplified to deliver to the antenna an output wave with a center frequency at $f_0 = 90$ Mc with $\Delta f = 75$ kc.

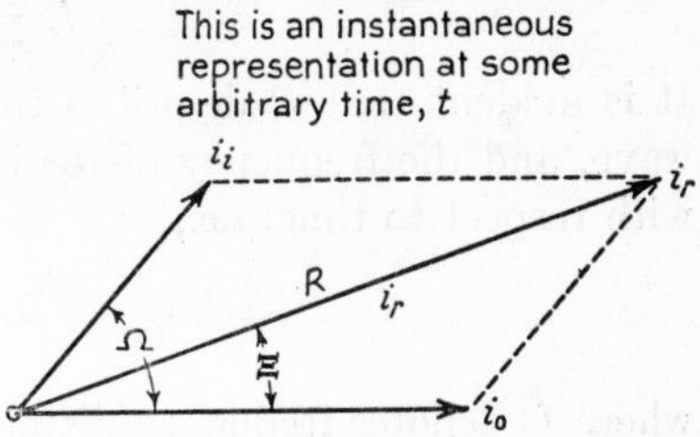

FIG. 5.

FREQUENCY DISTORTION DUE TO WAVE INTERFERENCE IN FM TRANSMISSION

7. Interference between Two Unmodulated Carriers.[1] Consider the general case when the carrier,

$$i_0 = I_0 e^{j\omega_0 t} \tag{31}$$

is interfered with by the wave

$$i_i = I_i e^{j\omega_i t} \tag{32}$$

The vector-diagram representation of the vector resultant i_r of i_0 and i_i is shown in Fig. 5. By using the cosine law, the magnitude R of i_r is found to be

$$R = \sqrt{I_0^2 + I_i^2 + 2I_0 I_i \cos \Omega} \tag{33}$$

where Ω is the angle between i_0 and i_i and is described as follows:

$$\Omega = (\omega_0 - \omega_i)t \tag{34}$$

The angle Ξ between i_r and i_0 is found from the relationship

$$\tan \Xi = \frac{x \sin (\omega_0 - \omega_i)t}{1 + x \cos (\omega_0 - \omega_i)t} \tag{35}$$

[1] M. G. Crosby, Frequency Modulation Noise Characteristics, *Proc. IRE*, vol. 25, pp. 472–514, April, 1937.

M. S. Corrington, Frequency Modulation Distortion Caused by Common and Adjacent Channel Interference, *RCA Rev.*, vol. 7, pp. 522–560, December, 1946.

where

$$x = \frac{I_i}{I_0} \tag{36}$$

Since the resultant wave i_r may be written in the form

$$i_r = Re^{j(\omega_0 t - \Xi)} \tag{37}$$

It is evident that R describes the amplitude distortion[1] in the resultant wave, and the frequency distortion may be obtained by differentiating Ξ with respect to time; *i.e.*,

$$2\pi f_d = \frac{d\Xi}{dt} \tag{38}$$

where f_d denotes frequency distortion.

According to Sec. 9, Chap. 2, Ξ may be represented by the Fourier series,

$$\Xi = x \sin (\omega_0 - \omega_i)t - \frac{x^2}{2} \sin 2(\omega_0 - \omega_i)t + \cdots \tag{39}$$

which, when differentiated, yields the Fourier series[2]

$$2\pi f_d = \frac{d\Xi}{dt} = (\omega_0 - \omega_i) \sum_{m=1}^{\infty} (-1)^{m+1} x^m \cos m(\omega_0 - \omega_i)t \tag{40}$$

which is valid in the limits $-1 < x \leq 1$. f_d is nonsymmetrical in that it is peaked at $\cos m(\omega_0 - \omega_i)t = \pm 1$. At $\cos m(\omega_0 - \omega_i)t = 1$

$$2\pi f_d = (\omega_0 - \omega_i) \sum_{m=1}^{\infty} (-1)^{m+1} x^m = \frac{(\omega_0 - \omega_i)x}{x + 1} \tag{41}$$

At $\cos m(\omega_0 - \omega_i)t = -1$,

$$2\pi f_d = (\omega_0 - \omega_i) \sum_{m=1}^{\infty} x^{m+1} = \frac{(\omega_0 - \omega_i)x}{x - 1} \tag{42}$$

If (35) is substituted directly into (38), we get for all x

$$2\pi f_d = \omega_b - \omega_b \frac{uv + u^2}{1 + u^2 + 2uv} \tag{43}$$

where

$$\omega_b = (\omega_0 - \omega_i), \qquad u = 1/x, \qquad v = \cos \omega_b t \tag{44}$$

The general behavior of $f_d/(\omega_0 - \omega_i)$ as a function of x and $(\omega_0 - \omega_i)t$ is illustrated in Fig. 6*a* and *b*. The curve, as x is varied, behaves somewhat as a delta function, and it is seen that as x approaches $x = 1$ and then passes through it, the polarity of the curve changes. This shows that as

[1] Amplitude distortion in FM transmission is not necessarily detrimental to the transmission since it can be minimized by use of an amplitude limiter (see Sec. 10).

[2] See also I. Plusc, Investigation of Frequency-modulation Signal Interference, *Proc. IRE*, vol. 35, pp. 1054–1059, October, 1947.

long as $I_0 > I_i$, the frequency distortion varies with x, the interfering wave is suppressed, and for all practical purposes

$$2\pi f \cong \omega_0 \text{ plus distortion terms} \tag{45}$$

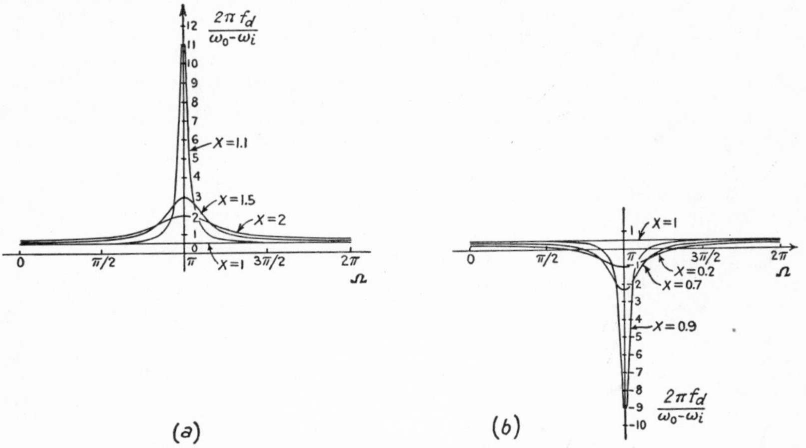

FIG. 6. $2\pi f_d/(\omega_0 - \omega_i)$ versus $(\omega_0 - \omega_i)t$ as a function of x.

However, when $I_i > I_0$,

$$2\pi f \cong \omega_0 - (\omega_0 - \omega_i) \text{ plus distortion terms} \tag{46}$$

$$\cong \omega_i \text{ plus distortion terms} \tag{47}$$

which shows that the interfering wave takes control.

Figure 7 pictures the amplitudes of the first five harmonics which are given by Eq. (40) for values of x in the range $0 \leq x \leq 1$.

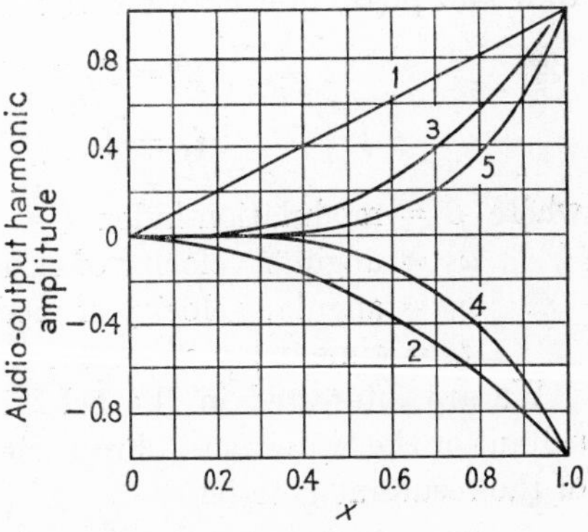

FIG. 7.

8. Phase and Frequency Considerations in Multipath Transmission. An important contribution to distortion in commercial FM transmission is that provided by multipath transmission. In this transmission, the wave, upon leaving the source, follows more than one path to the receiver. Figure 8 illustrates the production of two-path transmission using a reflector such as a metal-frame building or an airplane. The received waves differ only in amplitude and in the time necessary to travel from the source to the receiver. Let us determine the characteristics of the final wave, which is composed of all the waves received at some time, using the Fourier analysis.

As an illustration of the analysis, consider the solution of the two-path case, which is illustrated in Fig. 8, where it is to be understood that the

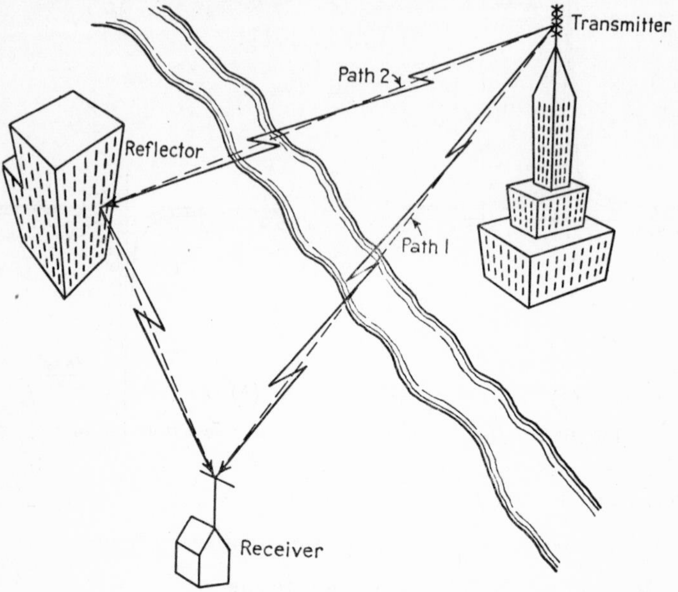

FIG. 8. Two-path transmission.

two path lengths are invariant. The instantaneous values of the amplitude and phase of each wave at the receiver are

$$i_0 = I_0 e^{j(\omega_0 t + \beta \sin \omega_1 t)} \tag{48}$$

$$i_i = I_i e^{j[\omega_0 (t - t_0) + \beta \sin \omega_1 (t - t_0)]} \tag{49}$$

where β = modulation index
ω_0 = angular velocity of carrier
ω_1 = angular velocity of modulating wave
t_0 = time delay of second signal with respect to the first

We are interested in the behavior and in the form of the vector resultant of the two waves. From the cosine law, we may find the amplitude of the resultant i_r to be

$$|R| = \sqrt{I_0^2 + I_i^2 + 2I_0 I_i \cos \Theta} \tag{50}$$

and the angle Θ, which describes the difference in phase between the two vectors i_0 and i_i, is found to be

$$\Theta = \beta \sin \omega_1 t - \beta \sin \omega_1 (t - t_0) + \omega_0 t_0 \tag{51}$$

$$= a \cos \omega_1 \left(t - \frac{t_0}{2}\right) + \omega_0 t_0 \tag{52}$$

where

$$a = 2\beta \sin \omega_1 \frac{t_0}{2} \tag{53}$$

The angle Ξ between i_0 and i_i is found from the relationship

$$\tan \Xi = \frac{x \sin \Theta}{1 + x \cos \Theta} \tag{54}$$

where

$$x = \frac{I_i}{I_0} \tag{55}$$

The instantaneous frequency is

$$f = \frac{\omega_0}{2\pi} + \frac{\Delta\omega}{2\pi} \cos \omega_1 t + f_d \tag{56}$$

where

$$f_d = \frac{1}{2\pi} \frac{d\Xi}{dt} \tag{57}$$

Using a Fourier-series solution of the form given in Sec. 9, Chap. 2, it follows that

$$f_d = \frac{a\omega_1}{2\pi} \sum_{m=1}^{\infty} (-1)^m \sin \omega_1 \left(t - \frac{t_0}{2}\right) \cos \left[ma \cos \omega_1 \left(t - \frac{t_0}{2}\right) + m\omega_0 t_0\right] \tag{58}$$

which may be evolved into the form, due to M. S. Corrington,[1]

$$f_d = \frac{\omega_1}{\pi} \sum_{m=1}^{\infty} \sum_{k=0}^{\infty} \frac{(-1)^k (-x)^m}{m} \cdot \left[(2k+1) J_{2k+1}(ma) \sin (2k+1)\omega_1 \left(t - \frac{t_0}{2}\right) \cos m\omega_0 t_0 + 2k J_{2k}(ma) \sin 2k\omega_1 \left(t - \frac{t_0}{2}\right) \sin m\omega_0 t_0\right] \tag{59}$$

which describes the harmonic distortion due to the multipath transmission.

Multipath interference causes sharp irregularities in the resultant wave. These irregularities, which are produced by the two waves being in and out of phase during modulation, may be illustrated by considering the particular case when Δf = 60,000 cycles, f_1 = 500 cycles, t_0 = 1/30,000

[1] M. S. Corrington, Frequency Modulation Distortion, Caused by Multipath Transmission, *Proc. IRE*, vol. 33, pp. 878–891, December, 1945.

sec, $x = 0.9$, and $\omega_0 t_0 = 2m(180°) + 180°$. The frequency during interference, as a function of $\omega_1 t$, is pictured in Fig. 9.

9. Fundamental Vector Concepts in Wave Interference. In spite of the mathematical complexity inherent in wave-interference analysis, the interference behavior is, in some cases, easily visualized when based on vector concepts. Consider, for example, the two rotating vectors of different angular velocity pictured in Fig. 10. It is evident from this vector diagram that the maximum angle of lead or lag produced by i_i on i_0 is, for $I_i < I_0$, less than 1 radian. If i_0 is an FM wave of large modulation index such that phase variations of from the neighborhood of 15 to 1,000° and more are involved, it follows that the phase *flutter* of less than 2 radians produced by i_i may be negligible, thus resulting in the apparent suppression of i_i. If the modulation index is low, then the phase flutter may cause serious distortion.

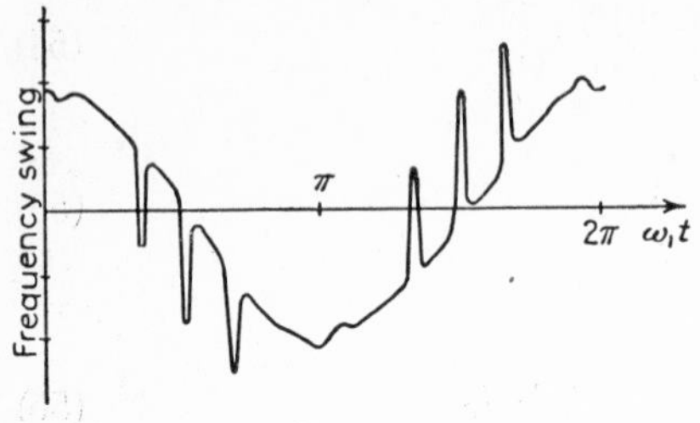

FIG. 9.

Common- and Adjacent-channel Interference. When the interfering signal vector has the same frequency as the desired signal vector, common-channel interference results. When the carriers involved are separated by the width of one channel, adjacent-channel interference results. M. S. Corrington (see footnote 1, page 287) has concisely described the nature of the waves resulting from these types of interference as follows:

Case 1. The simplest case of frequency modulation interference occurs when two modulated carriers, having nearly the same frequency, beat together to produce a resultant signal. As the two voltages alternately reinforce and cancel each other, the result is a heterodyne envelope consisting of a series of broad peaks and sharp dips. Each time the two interfering voltages cancel each other to produce a hole in the envelope, there is a rapid phase shift of the resultant voltage. Since the audio output from a frequency modulation receiver is proportional to the rate of change of the phase of this resultant, the rapid phase shift produces a distorted audio output which becomes more and more like an impulse as the interfering carrier voltage becomes nearly equal to the desired carrier voltage.

Case 2. When the two amplitudes of the interfering voltages are kept constant but the frequency of one is changed, the result is common- or adjacent-channel interference depending upon what range of frequencies the swings of the modulated carrier cover. The beat-note produced by this interference consists of sharp peaks and dips of noise and is imposed on the desired audio output. When the modulation index is increased, these peaks occur more and more rapidly, and the harmonics produced are distributed to higher and higher orders. If the receiver has sufficient bandwidth, with a perfect limiter, and a wide band audio system the signal-to-noise (interference noise) ratio does not depend on the modulation index, but is determined solely by the ratio of the desired signal voltage to the undesired signal voltage.

Note that in the case of multipath distortion (see Sec. 8) the complete incoherence between the rotations of i_0 and i_i is eliminated. i_i closely follows or leads i_0 with a phase angle whose magnitude is determined by the modulating signal and the time delay; the behavior is then very much like that described in case 1, thereby resulting in the irregularities described there and discussed in Sec. 8.

10. Amplitude Limiters. If a pure FM wave is interfered with by another wave, amplitude variation of the first wave will occur, in addition to frequency and phase distortion. In a communication system, this amplitude variation is undesirable. A practical means of eliminating this amplitude variation is to pass the wave which is interfered with through an amplitude-limiting device which will clip the wave at some desired level. This device is known as a *limiter*. Actually, a limiter performs *two* important functions in a communication system using frequency modulation. In addition to eliminating amplitude variations due to interference in a transmitted wave, it also serves to maintain constant the amplitude of any input wave to a receiver demodulator,[1] regardless of the amplitude of the FM wave as it enters the input of the receiver.

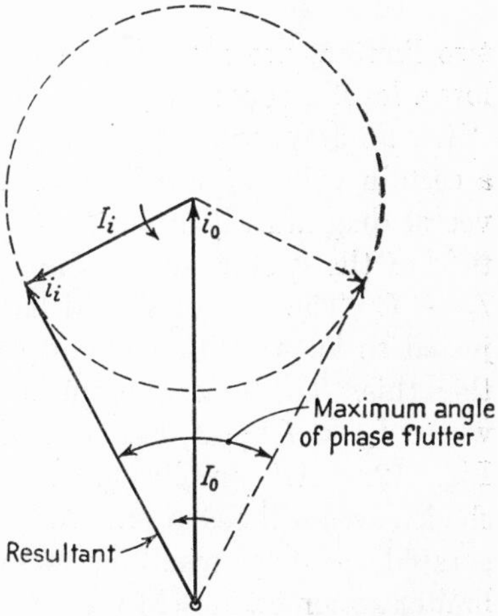

FIG. 10. Phase flutter caused by wave interference.

In order that we may understand more clearly the process of amplitude limiting, let us consider the operation of the vacuum-tube circuit pictured in Fig. 11*a*. The circuit is so adjusted that the 6SJ7 tube will saturate whenever a voltage greater than E_{th}, which is known as the threshold voltage, is impressed across it. The plate-current–impressed-voltage relationship is pictured in Fig. 11*b*. For the limiter to be effective, the im-

[1] In general, a limiter precedes a frequency discriminator in an FM receiver. For a general discussion of limiters, see A. Hund, "Frequency Modulation," Chap. IV, McGraw-Hill Book Company, Inc., New York, 1942. Frequency discriminators are discussed in Chap. 22 of the present volume. Actually, amplitude-limiting action may be incorporated into the discriminator circuit, using any of several different methods. For details of some of the more diverse methods, see, for example,

L. J. Giacoletto, Experimental Tube for FM Detection, *Electronics*, vol. 22, pp. 87–89, November, 1949. W. E. Bradley, Single Stage FM Detector, *Electronics*, vol. 19, p. 88, October, 1946. Robert Adler, A Gated Beam Tube, *Electronics*, vol. 23, pp. 82–85, February, 1950. G. L. Beers, A Frequency-dividing Locked-in Oscillator Frequency Modulation Receiver, *Proc. IRE*, vol. 32, pp. 730–737, December, 1944.

pressed-wave amplitude should be well above the threshold level. This threshold level may vary from as high as 200 μv down to about 10 μv if an 1852 tube is used. It is evident that a high degree of amplification in the amplifier preceding the limiter is desirable, and in many applications,

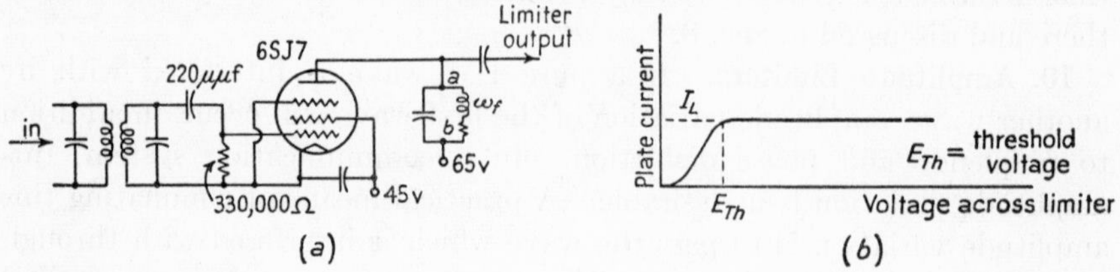

FIG. 11. Amplitude-limiter details.

two limiters are cascaded in order to reduce the threshold voltage to as low a level as possible.

Let an amplitude limiter be adjusted so that no amplitude greater than a certain value I_L will be passed through it. Figure 12 shows a rotating-vector diagram which illustrates this limiter action. The minimum amplitude of the vector sum of the signal of the interfering wave is seen to be $I_1 - I$. The limiter should be adjusted to an amplitude slightly less than this. The limiter amplitude I_L, where $I_L < I_1 - I$, is indicated in Fig. 12. *All* amplitudes in the shaded area will be cut off. An exaggerated waveform resulting from this limiter action on an FM wave is pictured in Fig. 13, this resultant wave being a near-square wave with a varying period and constant amplitude. This clipping action is not enough, however, to complete the action of the limiter; before the clipped wave can be introduced into the input of a demodulator, it must be passed through a resonant circuit, which will separate the fundamental (with varying frequency) from the near-square wave. The intelligence contained in the original modulated wave may then be recovered from the fundamental.

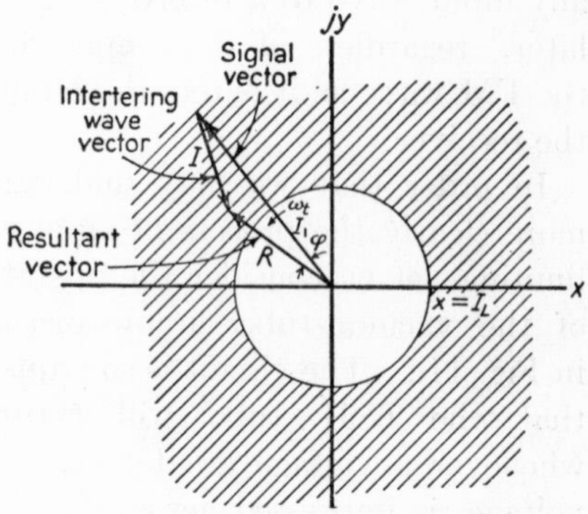

FIG. 12. Amplitude limiter cuts off all portions of the resultant vector appearing in the shaded area.

An involved discussion of the general theory of an amplitude-limiting system is beyond the scope of this volume. However, we may gain an understanding of its over-all behavior by considering further the waveform pictured in Fig. 13. The near-square wave may be approximately represented by the Fourier series

$$i_L = \frac{4}{\pi} I_L \left[\sin \frac{2\pi t}{T(\omega_0,\omega_M)} + \frac{1}{3} \sin 3 \frac{2\pi t}{T(\omega_0,\omega_M)} + \cdots \right] \tag{60}$$

the period T being a function of both the carrier frequency $\omega_0/2\pi$ and the modulating-wave frequency $\omega_M/2\pi$. The fact that (60) is an approximation arises from the fact that the sides of the clipped wave are not perpendicular to the time axis. If we wish to consider only a single period of the wave—see, for example, the period T_f in Fig. 13—the point where

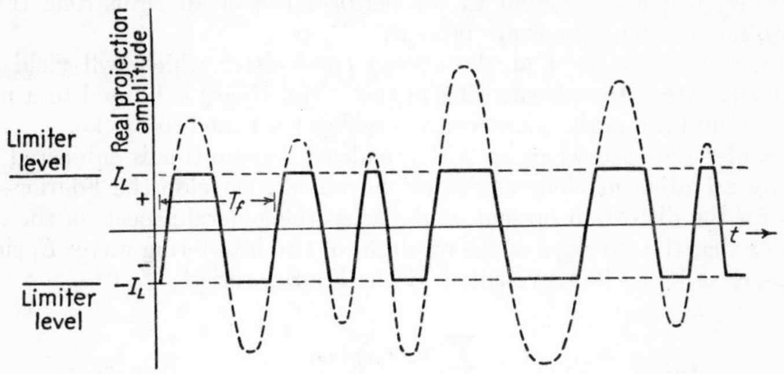

FIG. 13. Limiter action on a frequency-plus-amplitude-modulated wave.

the waveform crosses the axis is not exactly halfway between the start and end of the period, and the suitability of the approximation must be considered even further.

Let us pass the wave which is described by (60) through the selective resonant network shown in the plate circuit in Fig. 11a. If a current having a nonsinusoidal waveform is passed through this network, only the fundamental frequency will cause an appreciable voltage to appear across the terminals a, b. The higher harmonics will go through the capacitor, which will present a path of very low reactance to them and so the resulting voltage across a, b, will be a voltage having the varying fundamental frequency of the near-square wave; the amplitude of this fundamental voltage will be approximately

$$E(\omega_0,\omega_M) \cong 4 \frac{I_L}{\pi} \frac{L}{RC} \tag{61}$$

The variation in period in Fig. 13 is exaggerated for purposes of illustration. In practice, the variation is so small that the maximum excursions in frequency will not ride the crest of the impedance curve of the resonant circuit a sufficient distance to cause appreciable amplitude variation in the magnitude of the voltage appearing across the resonant circuit. This voltage is then introduced into the input of a frequency discriminator.

PROBLEMS

1. Let the waves $0.4 \sin 2\pi \times 40 \times 10^6 t$ and $0.16 \cos 2\pi \times 15 \times 10^3 t$ be applied to the input of a balanced modulator. What frequencies will appear as its output? Discuss briefly the resultant output when each of the vacuum tubes involved is operated in a region of its dynamic-characteristic curve which obeys a square law.

2. Let $\Delta\Theta$ be set at 30° in an Armstrong transmitter during the transmission of a test signal. Deduce and tabulate the harmonic distortion present up to the fifteenth harmonic. Repeat for $\Delta\Theta = 45°, 60°, 120°$.

3. Develop an expression describing the harmonic distortion, due to excessive phase swing, which is inherent in the performance of an Armstrong transmitter when two modulating signals are present.

4. Discuss the design of an Armstrong transmitter which will yield a carrier signal at 76.4 Mc if the phase swing in the initial stages is limited to a maximum value of 30° and the initial piezoelectric oscillator is tuned to 235 kc.

5. Consider the case when an AM broadcast transmitter is subjected to interference by an adjacent channel single-tone wave. Develop the Fourier-series expression for the distortion present, and discuss the general aspects of the case.

6. Show that the envelope of the resultant of two interfering waves $E_1 \sin \omega_0 t$ and $E_2 \sin (\omega_0 + \omega_1)t$ can be represented by the Fourier series[1]

$$\sum_0^\infty a_n \cos n\omega_1 t$$

where

$$a_n = 2(-1)^n \left[\frac{1 \cdot 3 \cdots (2n-1)}{n!}\right] \frac{x^n}{2^n} \left[\frac{-1}{2n-1} + \frac{1}{n+1}\frac{x^2}{2^2} + \sum_{k=2}^{\infty} \frac{1 \cdot 3 \cdots (2k-3)}{k!\, 2^{2k}} \frac{(2n+1)(2n+3) \cdots (2n+2k-3)}{(n+1)(n+2) \cdots (n+k)} x^{2k}\right]$$

and $x = E_2/E_1$.

7. Determine the nature of the distortion present when an AM wave is subjected to interference arising from transmission of the wave over two paths of different length; these lengths are considered to be invariant.

[1] See, for example, E. B. Moullin, The Detection by a Straight Line Rectifier of Modulated and Heterodyne Signals, *Wireless Engr. Exptl. Wireless*, vol. 9, pp. 378–383, July, 1932.

CHAPTER 18

MULTITONE FREQUENCY-MODULATED WAVES AND PULSE-WIDTH MODULATION

1. Introduction. In commercial radio and television transmission, the modulating wave is multitone in nature rather than possessing the single tone which has been used to discuss and illustrate the basic concepts of frequency- and phase-modulation spectra. The term *multitone* implies a group of waves whose frequencies either are unrelated or consist of a fundamental and an infinite number of harmonics as in a complex wave.

This chapter will discuss the Fourier analysis of multitone FM waves, leading to considerations of spectral bandwidth, using the complex Fourier series approach, which results in a vast reduction in the number of terms involved compared with the use of the trigonometric Fourier series; the chapter will conclude with an application of Fourier analysis to pulse-width modulation.

The Fourier analysis of multitone frequency modulation is necessarily a highly involved analysis, yielding complicated spectrum equations. This chapter is dedicated to the proposition that even the most complicated equations prove to be of considerable engineering value when the proper methods of approach and evaluation are employed.

2. Phase-modulating Functions. The analysis of frequency and phase modulation has been concerned to this point with the single-tone case for both types of modulation and has demonstrated both the fundamental concepts of rotating-vector behavior and the fundamental relationships between frequency and phase. We have seen that the rotating-vector representations of cosinusoidal frequency modulation and sinusoidal phase modulation may be expressed mathematically as follows:

$$i = I \exp \left[j \int_0^t (\omega_0 + \Delta\omega \cos \omega_1 t)\, dt \right] \qquad \text{frequency modulation} \qquad (1)$$

$$i = I \exp [j(\omega_0 t + \Delta\Theta \sin \omega_1 t)] \qquad \text{phase modulation} \qquad (2)$$

If the modulation index of one is equal in value to the other and is denoted by the symbol β, we may write the same expression for both types of modulation, *viz.*,

$$i = Ie^{j(\omega_0 t + \beta \sin \omega_1 t)} \qquad (3)$$

The form of this equation suggests immediately the use of a phase-modulating function, *viz.*,

$$i = \mathfrak{M}_P(\omega_1 t) I e^{j\omega_0 t} \tag{4}$$

where

$$\mathfrak{M}_P(\omega_1 t) = e^{j\beta \sin \omega_1 t} \tag{5}$$

$\mathfrak{M}_P(\omega_1 t)$ as described by (5) is the sinusoidal phase-modulating function, with angular velocity ω_1, which will modulate the phase of the carrier rotating vector.

In general, regardless of whether the initial statement of a problem in modulation is in terms of phase modulation or frequency modulation, the mathematical representation of the rotating vector must be reduced to an expression describing the amplitude and the phase of the vector at any instant in time before the Fourier analysis may be used. Thus, the phase-modulating function given by Eq. (5) describes the rotating-vector behavior for phase modulation and the equivalent phase modulation for frequency modulation for the single-tone case where the angular velocity of the modulating wave is ω_1.

In general, two types of phase-modulating functions will be encountered in multitone frequency- and phase-modulation analysis. The first describes the variation of phase of a rotating vector that is modulated by more than one modulating wave. Consider the multitone FM wave

$$i = I \exp\left\{j \int_0^t [\omega_0 + f(\omega_1 t) + f(\omega_2 t) + \cdots + f(\omega_n t)]\, dt\right\} \tag{6}$$

which may be written as follows:

$$i = \left\{\exp\left[j \int_0^t f(\omega_1 t)\, dt\right]\right\}\left\{\exp\left[j \int_0^t f(\omega_2 t)\, dt\right]\right\} \cdots \left\{\exp\left[j \int_0^t f(\omega_n t)\, dt\right]\right\} I e^{(j\omega_0 t)} \tag{7}$$

$$= \left\{\prod_{k=1}^{n} \exp\left[j \int_0^t f(\omega_k t)\, dt\right]\right\} I e^{(j\omega_0 t)} \tag{8}$$

By denoting each individual phase-modulating function as

$$\begin{aligned} \mathfrak{M}_P(\omega_1 t) &= \exp\left[j \int_0^t f(\omega_1 t)\, dt\right] \\ \mathfrak{M}_P(\omega_2 t) &= \exp\left[j \int_0^t f(\omega_2 t)\, dt\right] \\ &\cdots\cdots\cdots\cdots\cdots\cdots \\ \mathfrak{M}_P(\omega_n t) &= \exp\left[j \int_0^t f(\omega_n t)\, dt\right] \end{aligned} \tag{9}$$

Eq. (8) may be rewritten as follows:

$$i = \left[\prod_{k=1}^{n} \mathfrak{M}_P(\omega_k t) \right] I e^{j\omega_0 t} \qquad \textbf{Type I} \tag{10}$$

For each continuous modulating wave, there will exist a phase-modulating function which will shift the phase of the carrier rotating vector. The product of all of the phase-modulating functions which affect the carrier rotating vector will describe its phase behavior.

The second type of phase-modulating function is shown included in the description of the phase- or frequency-modulated wave,

$$i = \mathfrak{M}_P(\Delta\Theta_t) I e^{j\omega_0 t} \qquad \textbf{Type II} \tag{11}$$

where only a single phase-modulating function is seen to be present in the expression. $\Delta\Theta_t$ describes the instantaneous phase deviation of the vector. This type of phase-modulating function is applicable only to phase and frequency modulation resulting from a complex periodic modulating wave.

THE FOURIER ANALYSIS OF MULTITONE FREQUENCY MODULATION

3. Cases to Be Considered. Two cases will be discussed in connection with multitone frequency or phase modulation. They are

Case 1. Simultaneous modulation by independent modulating tones where the instantaneous angular velocity is

$$\omega_t = \omega_0 + \Delta\omega_1 \cos \omega_1 t + \Delta\omega_2 \cos \omega_2 t + \cdots + \Delta\omega_m \cos \omega_m t \tag{12}$$

where $\Delta\omega_m/2\pi$ denotes the frequency deviation produced by the mth modulating tone. Analysis of multitone modulation due to sine terms or to both sine and cosine terms is easily deduced from this case.

Case 2. Modulation by a complex periodic wave which produces an instantaneous angular-velocity modulation whose Fourier expansion is

$$\Delta\omega_t = \Delta\omega_d + \sum_{m=1}^{\infty} (\Delta\omega_{a_m} \cos m\omega_1 t + \Delta\omega_{b_m} \sin m\omega_1 t) \tag{13}$$

where $\Delta\omega_d$ = average value of angular-velocity modulation in the period $T_1 = 2\pi/\omega_1$

ω_1 = angular velocity of fundamental of modulating wave

$$\Delta\omega_{a_m} = \frac{\omega_1}{\pi} \int_{-\pi/\omega_1}^{\pi/\omega_1} \Delta\omega_t \cos m\omega_1 t \, dt = \text{frequency deviation of each cosinusoidal component}$$

$$\Delta\omega_{b_m} = \frac{\omega_1}{\pi} \int_{-\pi/\omega_1}^{\pi/\omega_1} \Delta\omega_t \sin m\omega_1 t \, dt = \text{frequency deviation of each sinusoidal component}$$

4. Considerations of Frequency and Phase Related to Case 2. The equivalent phase variation corresponding to (13) may be obtained by termwise integration of this expression; *i.e.*,

$$\Delta\Theta_t = \int \Delta\omega_t \, dt \tag{14}$$

where $\Delta\Theta_t$ is the phase variation as a function of time. However, in the event that the statement of a FM spectrum problem is made in terms of phase, considerable care must be taken if the equivalent frequency variation corresponding to the phase is to be determined. This is illustrated as follows: For any phase variation, the equivalent frequency variation may be derived, using the expression

$$\omega_t = \frac{d\Theta_t}{dt} \tag{15}$$

However, the differentiation of the Fourier series in Eq. (13) must be performed with great caution since the resulting series expansion for the equivalent frequency modulation may not be convergent. The difficulty grows out of the fact that when Eq. (13) is differentiated, the phase-deviation components will be multiplied by $m\omega_1$; that is,

$$\Delta\omega_t = \frac{d\Delta\Theta_t}{dt} = -\sum_{m=1}^{\infty} m\omega_1(\Delta\Theta_{a_m} \sin m\omega_1 t - \Delta\Theta_{b_m} \cos m\omega_1 t) \tag{16}$$

As long as the differentiation of $\Delta\Theta_t$ produces a convergent series, we may obtain a representation of the complex equivalent frequency-modulating wave by a Fourier series. This may not be possible; we have seen in Chap. 2 that a Fourier series may always be integrated, but there is a definite limit to the number of differentiations (if any) which may be performed on some particular series.

An illustration of our inability to write a valid expression for the equivalent frequency modulation resulting from certain phase-modulated waves is to be had by taking the case of square-wave phase modulation. The actual phase variation is shown in Fig. 1*a* as a function of time. It may be expressed mathematically as

$$\begin{aligned} \Theta_t &= \omega_0 t - \Delta\Theta \qquad 0 < t < \frac{\tau}{2} \\ &= \omega_0 t + \Delta\Theta \qquad \frac{\tau}{2} < t < \tau \end{aligned} \tag{17}$$

If we differentiate (17) directly, we get for the equivalent frequency variation

$$\omega_t \approx \omega_0 \qquad 0 < t < \tau \tag{18}$$

This is obviously not a correct representation since it does not describe the behavior of frequency when the phase jumps from its advanced to its retarded position. Actually the value of frequency at exactly $t = 0$,

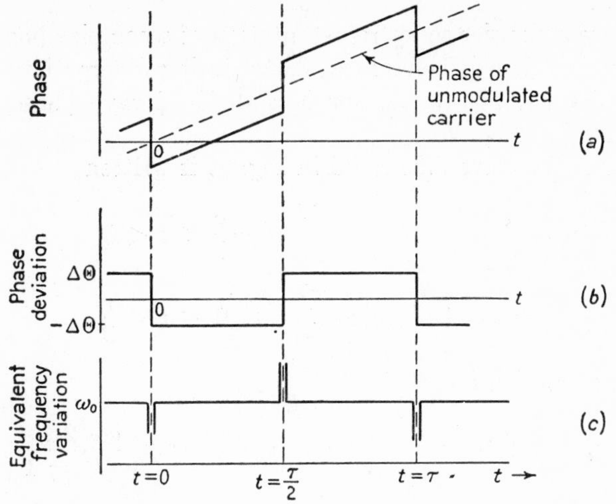

FIG. 1. Square-wave phase-modulated wave.

$\tau/2$, τ, . . . , etc., is indeterminate (see Fig. 1c). To check this mathematically, let us express Eq. (17) as a Fourier series, which is readily found to be

$$\Theta_t = \omega_0 t + \frac{2}{\pi} \Delta\Theta\left(\sin \omega_1 t + \frac{1}{3} \sin 3\omega_1 t + \cdots\right) \tag{19}$$

It follows that

$$\omega_t = \frac{d\Theta_t}{dt} = \omega_0 + \frac{2}{\pi} \Delta\Theta(\omega_1 \cos \omega_1 t + \omega_1 \cos 3\omega_1 t + \cdots) \tag{20}$$

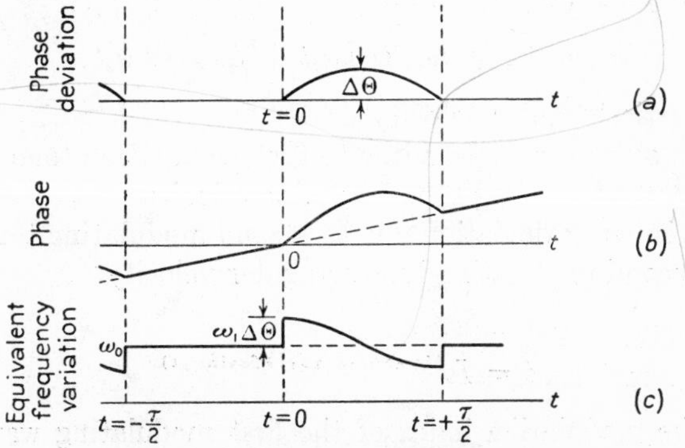

FIG. 2. Half-wave phase-modulated wave.

which does not converge to all values of the equivalent frequency modulation during all portions of the modulation cycle since the term $\omega_1 \cos m\omega_1 t$ does not approach zero as m tends toward infinity. Therefore Eq. (20) is divergent.

To illustrate a Fourier-series representation of a complex phase-modulation function which will behave regularly during differentiation so as to yield an equivalent FM wave, consider the half-wave phase-modulated wave illustrated in Fig. 2*b*.

The phase of the wave illustrated in Fig. 2*b* is written

$$\begin{aligned} \Theta_t &= \omega_0 t & -\frac{\tau}{2} < t < 0 \\ &= \omega_0 t + \Delta\Theta \sin \omega_1 t & 0 < t < \frac{\tau}{2} \end{aligned} \tag{21}$$

The Fourier expansion of (21) is

$$\Theta_t = \omega_0 t + \frac{\Delta\Theta}{\pi} + \frac{\Delta\Theta}{2} \sin \omega_1 t - \frac{2\Delta\Theta}{\pi} \sum_{k=1}^{\infty} \frac{\cos 2k\omega_1 t}{4k^2 - 1} \tag{22}$$

where $k = 2n$. This will converge to zero at all points for $-\tau/2 < t < 0$ and will converge to points on the sinusoidal variation of phase for $0 < t < \tau/2$. The equivalent frequency modulation associated with Eq. (21) is found by differentiating Eq. (22); *i.e.*,

$$\omega_t = \frac{d\Theta_t}{dt} = \omega_0 + \frac{\omega_1 \Delta\Theta}{2} \cos \omega_1 t + \frac{2\Delta\Theta}{\pi} \sum_{k=1}^{\infty} \frac{2k\omega_1 \sin 2k\omega_1 t}{4k^2 - 1} \tag{23}$$

ω_t is plotted in Fig. 2*c*. It converges to ω_0 for $-\tau/2 < t < 0$ and to $\omega_0 + \omega_1 \Delta\Theta \cos \omega_1 t$ for $0 < t < \tau/2$.

5. Two-tone Frequency Modulation. Consider the Fourier analysis of a wave whose frequency or phase is modulated by two tones. Let the instantaneous angular velocity ω_t be

$$\omega_t = \omega_0 + \Delta\omega_1 \cos \omega_1 t + \Delta\omega_2 \cos \omega_2 t \tag{24}$$

where ω_0 = carrier angular velocity
$\Delta\omega_1$ = frequency deviation due to first modulating tone
ω_1 = first modulating tone's angular velocity
$\Delta\omega_2$ = frequency deviation due to second modulating tone
ω_2 = second modulating tone's angular velocity

Then

$$i = Ie^{j(\omega_0 t + \beta_1 \sin \omega_1 t + \beta_2 \sin \omega_2 t)} \tag{25}$$

where β_1 is the modulation index of the first modulating wave and β_2 is the modulation index of the second modulating wave. Equation (25) may be rewritten using a phase-modulating function, as follows:

$$i = \mathfrak{M}_P(\omega_1 t)\mathfrak{M}_p(\omega_2 t) I e^{j\omega_0 t} \tag{26}$$

where

$$\mathfrak{M}_P(\omega_1 t)\mathfrak{M}_P(\omega_2 t) = (e^{j\beta_1 \sin \omega_1 t})(e^{j\beta_2 \sin \omega_2 t}) \tag{27}$$

It follows from Eq. (90), Chap. 2, that

$$i = I\left[\sum_{-\infty}^{\infty} J_n(\beta_1) e^{jn\omega_1 t}\right]\left[\sum_{-\infty}^{\infty} J_m(\beta_2) e^{jm\omega_2 t}\right] e^{j\omega_0 t} \tag{28}$$

which yields a sideband equation of the form

$$i = I \sum_{n,m=-\infty}^{n,m=\infty} C_{n,m} e^{j(\omega_0 + n\omega_1 + m\omega_2)t} \tag{29}$$

Equation (29) yields four types of side-frequency terms: the carrier, a set of side frequencies corresponding to the modulating wave whose frequency is $\omega_1/2\pi$, a second set to the modulating wave whose frequency is $\omega_2/2\pi$, and a third set to the sum and beat frequencies of the two modulating waves. The amplitudes of these term types are listed in Table 1.

TABLE 1

	Term	*Identification*
(1)	$J_0(\beta_1) J_0(\beta_2) I e^{j\omega_0 t}$	Carrier
(2)	$J_0(\beta_1) J_m(\beta_2) I e^{j(\omega_0 \pm m\omega_2)t}$	Side frequencies due to modulating wave at ω_2
(3)	$J_n(\beta_1) J_0(\beta_2) I e^{j(\omega_0 \pm n\omega_1)t}$	Side frequencies due to modulating wave at ω_1
(4)	$J_n(\beta_1) J_m(\beta_2) I e^{j(\omega_0 \pm n\omega_1 \pm m_2\omega_2)t}$	Beat side frequencies at $\omega_0 \pm n\omega_1 \pm m\omega_2$

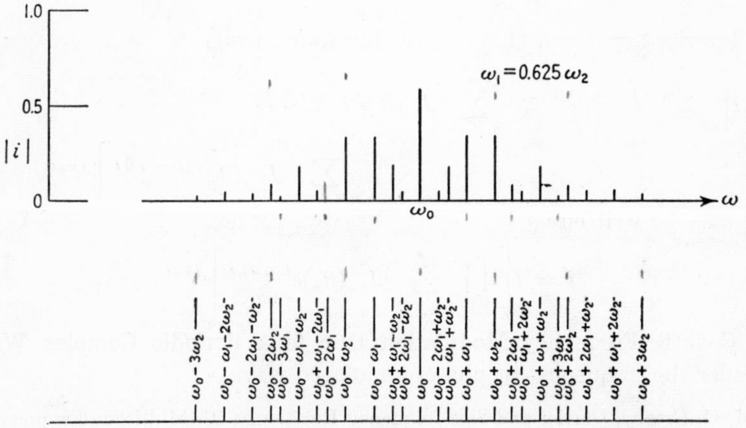

FIG. 3. Two-tone FM spectrum for $\beta_1 = \beta_2 = 1$ with $\omega_1 = 0.625\ \omega_2$.

An amplitude spectrum corresponding to the case $\beta_1 = \beta_2 = 1$ is pictured in Fig. 3. The crowding of the spectrum is illustrated, this crowding being due to the presence of beat-frequency components in addition to the side frequencies due to either of the modulating waves. In general all amplitudes are reduced in amplitude as compared with the case of single-tone frequency modulation with the same modulation index, this being due to the fact that each amplitude is determined by the product of two Bessel functions. Despite the large number of side-frequency components, the bandwidth is actually somewhat smaller than that corresponding to the case of single-tone frequency modulation having a maximum frequency deviation equal to $\Delta\omega_1 + \Delta\omega_2$.[1]

6. The General Case of *m*-tone Frequency or Phase Modulation. We have seen that

$$i = I \exp\left(j \int_0^t \omega_t \, dt\right) = I \exp(j\Theta_t) \tag{30}$$

where, for the *m*-tone case, the instantaneous frequency ω_t is equal to

$$\omega_t = \omega_0 + \Delta\omega_1 \cos \omega_1 t + \Delta\omega_2 \cos \omega_2 t + \cdots + \Delta\omega_M \cos \omega_M t \tag{31}$$

and

$$\Theta_t = \omega_0 t + \beta_1 \sin \omega_1 t + \beta_2 \sin \omega_2 t + \cdots + \beta_M \sin \omega_M t \tag{32}$$

where $\Delta\omega_M$ is the maximum frequency deviation of the *m*th term and β_M is the modulation index of the *m*th term. Then

$$i = I\left[\prod_{m=1}^{M} \mathfrak{M}_P(\omega_m t)\right] e^{j\omega_0 t} \tag{33}$$

where

$$\prod_{m=1}^{M} \mathfrak{M}_P(\omega_m t) = e^{j\beta_1 \sin \omega_1 t} e^{j\beta_2 \sin \omega_2 t} \cdots e^{j\beta_M \sin \omega_M t} \tag{34}$$

The Fourier expansion of this is readily found to be

$$i = I\left[\sum_{n_1=-\infty}^{\infty} J_{n_1}(\beta_1) e^{jn_1\omega_1 t} \sum_{n_2=-\infty}^{\infty} J_{n_2}(\beta_2) e^{jn_2\omega_2 t} \cdots \sum_{n_M=-\infty}^{\infty} J_{n_M}(\beta_M) e^{jn_M\omega_M t}\right] e^{j\omega_0 t} \tag{35}$$

This may be written as

$$i = I\left[\prod_{m=1}^{M} \sum_{n_m=-\infty}^{\infty} J_{n_m}(\beta_m) e^{jn_m\omega_m t}\right] e^{j\omega_0 t} \tag{36}$$

7. Case 2. Frequency Modulation Due to a Periodic Complex Wave. Consider the frequency- or phase-modulated wave

[1] M. G. Crosby, Carrier and Side-frequency Relations with Multitone Frequency or Phase Modulation, *RCA Rev.*, vol. 3, pp. 103–106, July, 1938.

$$i = I \exp\left(j \int_0^t \omega_t \, dt\right) \tag{37}$$

where

$$\omega_t = \omega_0 + \Delta\omega_d + \sum_{m=1}^{\infty} \Delta\omega_{a_m} \cos \omega_1 mt + \sum_{m=1}^{\infty} \Delta\omega_{b_m} \sin m\omega_1 t \tag{38}$$

This is the sum of ω_0 and the Fourier-series expansion of $\Delta\omega_t$ in the period $T_1 = 2\pi/\omega_1$. Note that m is used rather than n so as to avoid confusion between the mth Fourier harmonic and the nth side-frequency term.

Substituting Eq. (38) into Eq. (37), it follows that

$$i = I \exp\left[j\left(\omega_0 t + \Delta\omega_d t + \sum_{m=1}^{\infty} \frac{\Delta\omega_{a_m}}{m\omega_1} \sin m\omega_1 t + \sum_{m=1}^{\infty} \frac{\Delta\omega_{b_m}}{m\omega_1} \cos m\omega_1 t\right)\right] \tag{39}$$

where $\Delta\omega_{a_m}/m\omega_1$, modulation index of the mth sine term $= \beta_{a_m}$
$\Delta\omega_{b_m}/m\omega_1$, modulation index of the mth cosine term $= \beta_{b_m}$

Equation (39) may be written

$$i = Ie^{j(\omega_0 + \Delta\omega_d)t} \exp\left(j \sum_1^{\infty} \beta_{a_m} \sin m\omega_1 t\right) \exp\left(j \sum_1^{\infty} \beta_{b_m} \cos m\omega_1 t\right) \tag{40}$$

It follows from Eqs. (90) and (92), Chap. 2, that

$$\exp\left(j \sum_1^{\infty} \beta_{a_m} \sin m\omega_1 t\right) = \prod_{m=1}^{\infty} \sum_{n=-\infty}^{\infty} J_n(\beta_{a_m}) e^{jnm\omega_1 t} \tag{41}$$

and

$$\exp\left(j \sum_1^{\infty} \beta_{b_m} \cos m\omega_1 t\right) = \prod_{m=1}^{\infty} \sum_{n=-\infty}^{\infty} J_n(\beta_{b_m}) e^{j[nm(\omega_1 t + 3\pi/2)]} \tag{42}$$

Thus

$$i = I\left[\prod_{m=1}^{\infty} \sum_{n=-\infty}^{\infty} J_n(\beta_{a_m}) e^{jnm\omega_1 t}\right] \cdot \left[\prod_{m=1}^{\infty} \sum_{n=-\infty}^{\infty} J_n(\beta_{b_m}) e^{j[nm(\omega_1 t + 3\pi/2)]}\right] e^{j(\omega_0 + \Delta\omega_d)t} \tag{43}$$

Equation (43) is far too involved for direct evaluation of the side frequencies representing i. However, we may deduce two pertinent points from the Fourier analysis leading to Eq. (43). They apply to the carrier and the presence of beat frequencies.

1. Carrier. It is evident from the term $e^{j(\omega_0 + \Delta\omega_0)t}$ that if a carrier with angular velocity ω_0 is modulated by a complex wave producing an

average frequency deviation $\Delta\omega_d$, then the carrier is displaced to a new frequency $(1/2\pi)\ (\omega_0 + \Delta\omega_d)$.

2. Beat frequencies. Since all of the frequencies represented by Eq. (27) are harmonics of the fundamental frequency $\omega_1/2\pi$ which are added to or subtracted from the carrier frequency $\omega_0/2\pi$, no new frequencies, other than these shifted harmonics, will be produced by the beats. This can be seen by considering term type (4) in Table 1. This term is of the form

$$Ae^{j(\omega_0 \pm n_1\omega_1 \pm n_2\omega_2)t}$$

where A is an amplitude coefficient. From the case where the modulating wave is composed of a fundamental ω_1 and its harmonics, consider the two-tone case where the tones involved are ω_1 and $m\omega_1$. Then in term type (5), we replace ω_2 by $m\omega_1$ as follows:

$$Ae^{j(\omega_0 \pm n_1\omega_1 \pm n_2 m\omega_1)t}$$

From this, it follows that

$$Ae^{j[\omega_0 \pm (n_1 \mp mn_2)\omega_1]t}$$

Thus the resulting beat side frequency will still be a harmonic of ω_1 and must be added arithmetically or vectorially to any other side frequencies which are present at its frequency.

8. Bandwidth Considerations in Multitone Frequency Modulation. To solve a multitone FM sideband equation for more than three harmonic modulating-wave terms would be out of the question. If the modulating wave is periodic and complex and if its Fourier series representation may be closely approximated by only a few terms, the use of Eq. (43) might be quite successful. However, despite the complexity encountered in pursuing these formulations, it is possible to derive in simple fashion qualitative considerations of spectral bandwidth and energy distribution which materially contribute to the sideband solutions of multitone FM waves, regardless of how they are derived.

We may deduce the significant-spectrum limits of an FM wave using the principle of stationary phase as follows:[1]

Any FM wave may be described as follows:

$$i = I \exp \left\{ j \left[\omega_0 t + \Delta\omega \int_0^t \Omega(t)\, dt \right] \right\} \tag{44}$$

where the instantaneous frequency is defined as

$$\omega_t = \omega_0 + \Delta\omega\,\Omega(t) \tag{45}$$

with $\Omega(t)$ being a simple harmonic, complex, or multitone function varying between ± 1 [for cosinusoidal single-tone frequency modulation, for ex-

[1] Carson and Fry, Variable Frequency Electric Circuit Theory, *Bell System Tech. J.*, vol. 16, pp. 513–540, October, 1937.

ample, $\Omega(t) = \cos \omega t$]. The instantaneous angular velocity of the rotating vector varies between the limits

$$\omega_0 - \Delta\omega < \omega_t < \omega_0 + \Delta\omega \tag{46}$$

Consider the Fourier transform of the modulation portion of (44) in the epoch $0 < t < T$, where T can be made as great as desired. We may then express $g(\omega)$ as

$$g(\omega) = \int_T \exp\left\{j\left[\Delta\omega \int_0^t \Omega(t)\, dt - \omega t\right]\right\} dt \tag{47}$$

Equation (47) may be written in the form

$$g(\omega) = \int_T \Psi(t) e^{j\Phi(t)}\, dt \tag{48}$$

If $\Psi(t)$ is a slowly varying function while $\Phi(t)$ changes by 2π, the major contributions of the integrand to the integral will be those which take place when $\Phi(t)$ has stationary values; *i.e.*,

$$\frac{d}{dt}[\Phi(t)] = 0 \tag{49}$$

This is known as the principle of stationary phase,[1] which may be stated as follows:

In an integral of the type given by the real part of (48), there is a general cancellation of the positive and negative portions of the integral except for ranges of stationary phase.

Suppose that in the epoch T in integral (47)

$$\left|\Delta\omega \int_0^t \Omega(t)\, dt\right| \gg 2\pi \tag{50}$$

On this assumption, it follows from the principle of stationary phase that, for a fixed value of ω, the important contributions to the integral (48) occur for those values of the integration variable t for which

$$\frac{d}{dt}\left[\Delta\omega \int_0^t \Omega(t)\, dt - \omega t\right] = 0 \tag{51}$$

Performing the differentiation, we find

$$\omega = \Delta\omega\, \Omega(t) \tag{52}$$

Then $g(\omega)$ will have significant amplitudes in the region corresponding to those values of ω in the range

$$\Delta\omega\, \Omega_{max}(t) < \omega < \Delta\omega\, \Omega_{min}(t) \tag{53}$$

and the significant sidebands will be found in the range described by (46).

[1] This principle is generally attributed to Lord Kelvin.

9. Direct Fourier Analysis of FM Waves. Complex-periodic-wave frequency and phase modulation may be analyzed by using what we shall term *direct* Fourier analysis. This will be the preferred procedure only with periodic-wave-modulation analysis since the direct method is not readily adaptable to the multitone analysis where the modulating frequencies are not directly related to each other. In the direct Fourier analysis, we write

$$i = e^{j\Delta\Theta_t} I e^{j\omega_0 t} \tag{54}$$

$$= \mathfrak{M}_P(\Delta\Theta_t) I e^{j\omega_0 t} \tag{55}$$

$\mathfrak{M}_P(\Delta\Theta_t)$ is the Type II phase-modulating function which is described by the phase-deviation rotating vector $e^{j\Delta\Theta_t}$ during a complete modulation cycle and may be expanded into a Fourier series such that

$$i = I \sum_{n=-\infty}^{\infty} C_n e^{j(\omega_0 + n\omega_1)t} \tag{56}$$

where

$$C_n = \frac{\omega_1}{2\pi} \int_{-\pi/\omega_1}^{\pi/\omega_1} \mathfrak{M}_P(\Delta\Theta_t) e^{-jn\omega_1 t}\, dt \tag{57}$$

ω_0 is the angular velocity of the carrier, and $2\pi/\omega_1$ is the period of the modulating wave.

In solving for the Fourier series (56), $e^{j\Delta\Theta_t}$ must be identified for each part of the modulation cycle. For example, referring to Fig. 4 we see a

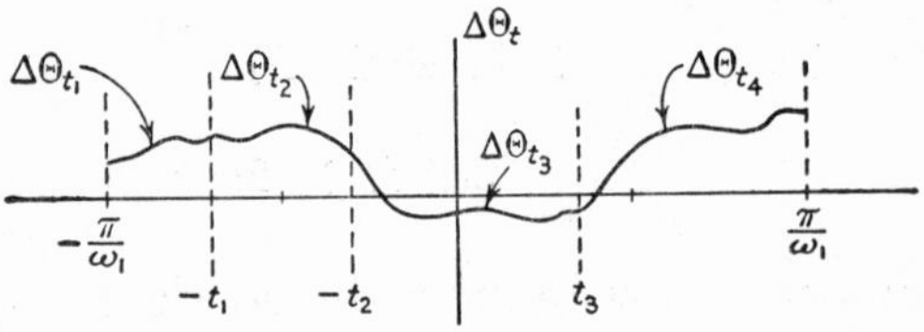

FIG. 4.

particular $\Delta\Theta_t$ which can be separated into four sections in the interval $-\pi/\omega_1 < t < \pi/\omega_1$ such that $\Delta\Theta_t$ is described analytically as $\Delta\Theta_{t_1}$, $\Delta\Theta_{t_2}$, $\Delta\Theta_{t_3}$, and $\Delta\Theta_{t_4}$ in the intervals $-\pi/\omega_1 < t < -t_1$, $-t_1 < t < -t_2$, $-t_2 < t < t_3$, and $t_3 < t < \pi/\omega_1$, respectively. Then we may write C_n as follows:

$$C_n = \frac{\omega_1}{2\pi}\left(\int_{-\pi/\omega_1}^{-t_1} \exp\,[j(\Delta\Theta_{t_1} - n\omega_1 t)]\, dt \right.$$

$$+ \int_{-t_1}^{-t_2} \exp\,[j(\Delta\Theta_{t_2} - n\omega_1 t)]\, dt + \int_{-t_2}^{t_3} \exp\,[j(\Delta\Theta_{t_3} - n\omega_1 t)]\, dt$$

$$\left. + \int_{t_3}^{+\pi/\omega_1} \exp\,[j(\Delta\Theta_{t_4} - n\omega_1 t)]\, dt\right) \tag{58}$$

When (57) is solved for a particular portion of the modulation cycle, it will yield the spectral amplitudes of a frequency- or phase-modulated wave whose period time is $2\pi/\omega_1$ and which has zero amplitude in all portions of the modulation cycle which are not included in the interval being considered. The final spectrum equation (56) will sum the spectral contributions from all portions of the modulation cycle.

10. Spectral Superposition and the Direct Fourier Analysis. We may best illustrate the principle of spectral superposition, which is the basic concept of the direct Fourier analysis, by use of the following example:

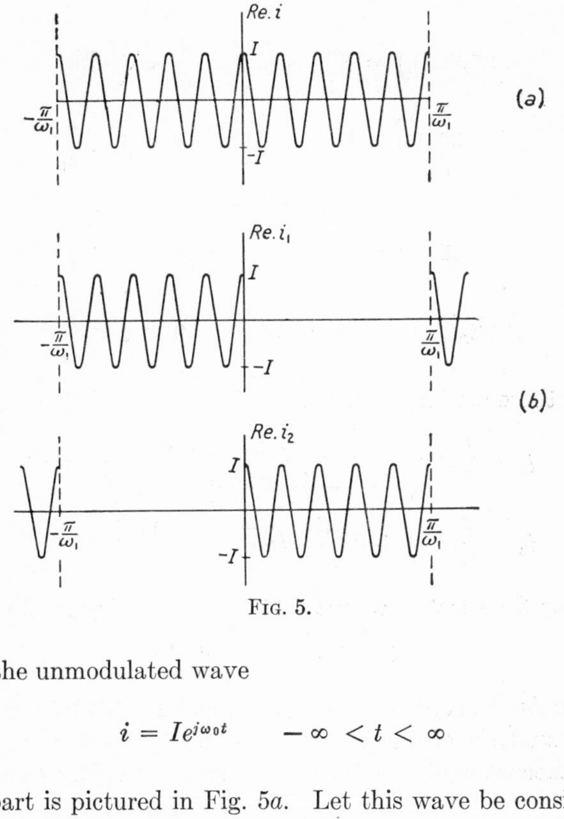

FIG. 5.

Consider the unmodulated wave

$$i = Ie^{j\omega_0 t} \qquad -\infty < t < \infty \tag{59}$$

whose real part is pictured in Fig. 5*a*. Let this wave be considered to be the superposition of two square-wave AM periodic waves i_1 and i_2 which are periodic with a period $2\pi/\omega_1$ and which may be expressed as follows:

$$\begin{aligned} i_1 &= Ie^{j\omega_0 t} \qquad -\frac{\pi}{\omega_1} < t < 0 \\ &= 0 \qquad\qquad 0 < t < \frac{\pi}{\omega_1} \end{aligned} \tag{60}$$

and

$$i_2 = 0 \qquad -\frac{\pi}{\omega_1} < t < 0$$
$$= Ie^{j\omega_0 t} \qquad 0 < t < \frac{\pi}{\omega_1} \tag{61}$$

The real parts of i_1 and i_2 are pictured in Fig. 5*b*. We may describe the modulation of these waves by combining a Type II phase-modulating function and an amplitude-modulating function as follows:

Wave 1:

$$\mathfrak{M}_P(\Delta\Theta_t) = e^{j0} = 1 \qquad -\frac{\pi}{\omega_1} < t < 0$$
$$\mathfrak{M}_A(t) = 0 \qquad 0 < t < \frac{\pi}{\omega_1} \tag{62}$$

Wave 2:

$$\mathfrak{M}_A(t) = 0 \qquad -\frac{\pi}{\omega_1} < t < 0$$
$$\mathfrak{M}_P(\Delta\Theta_t) = e^{j0} = 1 \qquad 0 < t < \frac{\pi}{\omega_1} \tag{63}$$

Substituting these modulating functions into (56) and (57), we get

$$i_1 = \frac{I}{2}e^{j\omega_0 t} + I\sum_{n=-\infty}^{\infty}\frac{j[1-(-1)^n]}{n}e^{j(\omega_0+n\omega_1)t} \tag{64}$$

$$i_2 = \frac{I}{2}e^{j\omega_0 t} + I\sum_{n=-\infty}^{\infty}\frac{j[(-1)^n-1]}{n}e^{j(\omega_0+n\omega_1)t} \tag{65}$$

Superimposing the spectra, we see that the sidebands cancel and that

$$i = i_1 + i_2 = Ie^{j\omega_0 t} \tag{66}$$

11. Fourier Analysis of Square-wave Frequency Modulation. Consider the Fourier analysis of the square-wave FM wave pictured in Fig. 6. The instantaneous angular velocity of the rotating vector representing this wave is

$$\omega_t = \omega_0 - \Delta\omega \qquad -\frac{\pi}{\omega_1} < t < -\frac{\pi}{2\omega_1}$$
$$= \omega_0 + \Delta\omega \qquad -\frac{\pi}{2\omega_1} < t < \frac{\pi}{2\omega_1} \tag{67}$$
$$= \omega_0 - \Delta\omega \qquad \frac{\pi}{2\omega_1} < t < \frac{\pi}{\omega_1}$$

The instantaneous phase corresponding to (67) may be described as

$$\begin{aligned}\Theta_t &= \omega_0 t - \frac{\Delta\omega}{\omega_1}(\pi + \omega_1 t) && -\frac{\pi}{\omega_1} < t < -\frac{\pi}{2\omega_1} \\ &= \omega_0 t + \Delta\omega t && -\frac{\pi}{2\omega_1} < t < \frac{\pi}{2\omega_1} \\ &= \omega_0 t + \frac{\Delta\omega}{\omega_1}(\pi - \omega_1 t) && \frac{\pi}{2\omega_1} < t < \frac{\pi}{\omega_1}\end{aligned} \tag{68}$$

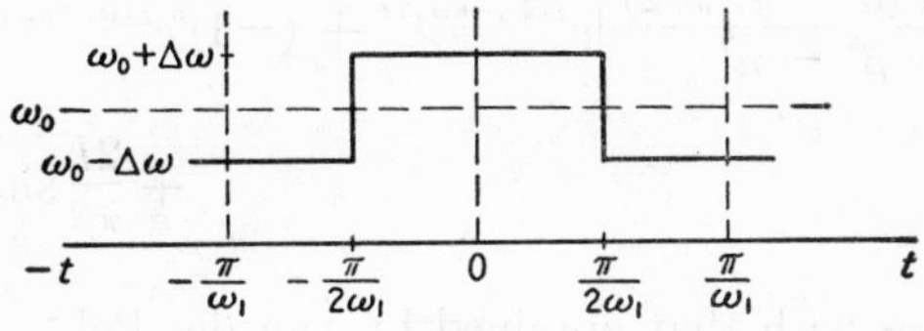

FIG. 6.

Then, using the Type II phase-modulating function, we see that

$$i = \mathfrak{M}_P(\Delta\Theta_t) I e^{j\omega_0 t} \tag{69}$$

where

$$\begin{aligned}\mathfrak{M}_P(\Delta\Theta_t) &= e^{-j\beta(\pi + \omega_1 t)} && -\frac{\pi}{\omega_1} < t < -\frac{\pi}{2\omega_1} \\ &= e^{j\beta t} && -\frac{\pi}{2\omega_1} < t < \frac{\pi}{2\omega_1} \\ &= e^{j\beta(\pi - \omega_1 t)} && \frac{\pi}{2\omega_1} < t < \frac{\pi}{\omega_1}\end{aligned} \tag{70}$$

where

$$\beta = \frac{\Delta\omega}{\omega_1} \tag{71}$$

Since we wish a spectrum equation in the form

$$i = I \sum_{-\infty}^{\infty} C_n e^{j(\omega_0 + n\omega_1)t} \tag{72}$$

we must substitute (70) into Eq. (57) for the evaluation of C_n as follows:

$$C_n = \frac{\omega_1}{2\pi}\left(\int_{-\pi/\omega_1}^{-\pi/2\omega_1} e^{-j\beta\pi} e^{-j(\beta\omega_1 t + n\omega_1 t)}\,dt + \int_{-\pi/2\omega_1}^{\pi/2\omega_1} e^{j(\beta\omega_1 t - n\omega_1 t)}\,dt + \int_{\pi/2\omega_1}^{\pi/\omega_1} e^{j\beta\pi} e^{-j(\beta\omega_1 t + n\omega_1 t)}\,dt\right) \tag{73}$$

Let $\varphi = \omega_1 t$. Making this substitution, we get

$$C_n = \frac{1}{2\pi}\left(e^{-i\beta\pi}\int_{\pi}^{-\pi/2} e^{-i(\beta+n)\varphi}\,d\varphi + \int_{-\pi/2}^{\pi/2} e^{i(\beta-n)\varphi}\,d\varphi + e^{i\beta\pi}\int_{\pi/2}^{\pi} e^{-i(\beta-n)\varphi}\,d\varphi\right) \tag{74}$$

Performing the integration, combining the terms, and substituting the result into Eq. (56), we get finally the Fourier series[1]

$$i = I\sum_{n=1}^{\infty}\frac{2\beta}{\pi}\frac{\sin(\beta-n)(\pi/2)}{\beta^2-n^2}\left[e^{j(\omega_0-n\omega_1)t} + (-1)^n e^{j(\omega_0+n\omega_1)t}\right] + \frac{2I}{\pi\beta}\sin\frac{\pi\beta}{2}\,e^{j\omega_0 t} \tag{75}$$

This result agrees with that obtained by van der Pol.[2] Writing out the first few terms of sideband equation (75), we get

$$\begin{aligned}
i = \frac{2I}{\pi}\Bigg[&\frac{1}{\beta}\sin\frac{\pi\beta}{2}\,e^{j\omega_0 t} && \text{carrier}\\
&+\frac{\beta}{\beta^2-1}\cos\frac{\beta\pi}{2}\left(e^{j(\omega_0-\omega_1)t} - e^{j(\omega_0+\omega_1)t}\right) && \text{1st side-frequency pair}\\
&-\frac{\beta}{\beta^2-4}\sin\frac{\beta\pi}{2}\left(e^{j(\omega_0-2\omega_1)t} + e^{j(\omega_0+2\omega_1)t}\right) && \text{2d side-frequency pair}\\
&-\frac{\beta}{\beta^2-9}\cos\frac{\beta\pi}{2}\left(e^{j(\omega_0-3\omega_1)t} - e^{j(\omega_0+3\omega_1)t}\right) && \text{3d side-frequency pair}\\
&+\frac{\beta}{\beta^2-16}\sin\frac{\beta\pi}{2}\left(e^{j(\omega_0-4\omega_1)t} + e^{j(\omega_0-4\omega_1)t}\right) && \text{4th side-frequency pair}\\
&+\cdots\Bigg]
\end{aligned} \tag{76}$$

From (75), we see that the absolute magnitude of the nth term is

$$|i_n| = \frac{2\beta}{\pi}\frac{\sin(\beta-n)(\pi/2)}{\beta^2-n^2}\,I \tag{77}$$

Certain important aspects of Eq. (77) are immediately ascertained by inspection. They are as follows:

[1] See M. S. Corrington, Variation of Bandwidth with Modulation Index in Frequency Modulation, *Proc. IRE*, vol. 35, pp. 1013–1020, October, 1947.

[2] B. van der Pol, Frequency Modulation, *Proc. IRE*, vol. 18, pp. 1194–1205, July, 1930.

1. When β is an odd integer, the amplitudes of the odd side frequencies are equal to zero.

2. When β is an even integer, the amplitudes of the even side frequencies are equal to zero.

3. When $\beta = n$,

$$|i| = \lim_{\beta \to n} \frac{2\beta}{\pi} \frac{\sin (\beta - n)(\pi/2)}{\beta^2 - n^2} I \tag{78}$$

$$= \frac{\beta}{\beta + n} I \lim_{\beta \to n} \frac{\sin (\beta - n)(\pi/2)}{(\beta - n)(\pi/2)} \rightarrow \frac{I}{2} \tag{79}$$

Then

$$|i_{\beta=n}|^2 = \frac{I^2}{4} \tag{80}$$

indicating that for the special case $\beta = n$, regardless of whether n is even or odd, one-half of the spectral energy is found in the side frequencies which are displaced from the carrier angular velocity by $n\omega_1$.

The more general aspects of (75) are illustrated in Fig. 7, where $\Delta\omega$

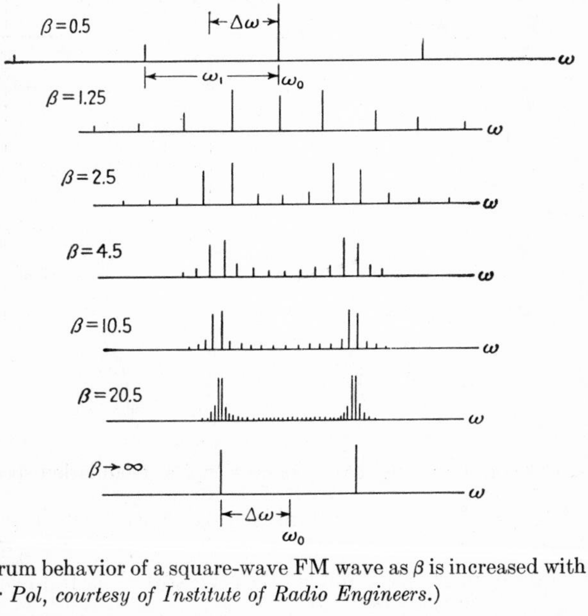

FIG. 7. Spectrum behavior of a square-wave FM wave as β is increased with $\Delta\omega$ constant. (*After van der Pol, courtesy of Institute of Radio Engineers.*)

is kept constant and ω_1 is varied to illustrate the square-wave-spectrum amplitudes for $\beta = 0.5, 1.25, 2.5, 4.5, 10.5, 20.5, \infty$.[1] For low β, corresponding to a value of ω_1 which exceeds $\Delta\omega$ in magnitude, the energy is

[1] B. van der Pol, Frequency Modulation, *Proc. IRE*, vol. 18, pp. 1194–1205, July, 1930.

now distributed among the carrier and the first pair of side frequencies, with a small amount of energy found in the second pair of side frequencies. As β increases toward 2.5, the energy is still spread out, but as $\beta = 2.5$, the square-wave spectrum starts to take shape, the largest spectral amplitudes occurring in the vicinity of $\omega_0 + \Delta\omega$ and $\omega_0 - \Delta\omega$. As β continues to increase, more and more energy is contributed by the side frequencies in the vicinity of these angular velocities. As $\beta \to \infty$, which corresponds to the wave frequency spending an infinitely long half period at $\omega_0 + \Delta\omega$ and an infinitely long half period at $\omega_0 - \Delta\omega$, the energy and amplitude spectra will consist of only two spectral lines, indicating that all energy is at $\omega_0 + \Delta\omega$ and $\omega_0 - \Delta\omega$.

12. Some Practical Aspects of Complex-wave FM Spectra. In working with the complicated mathematical expressions often evolved in complex-

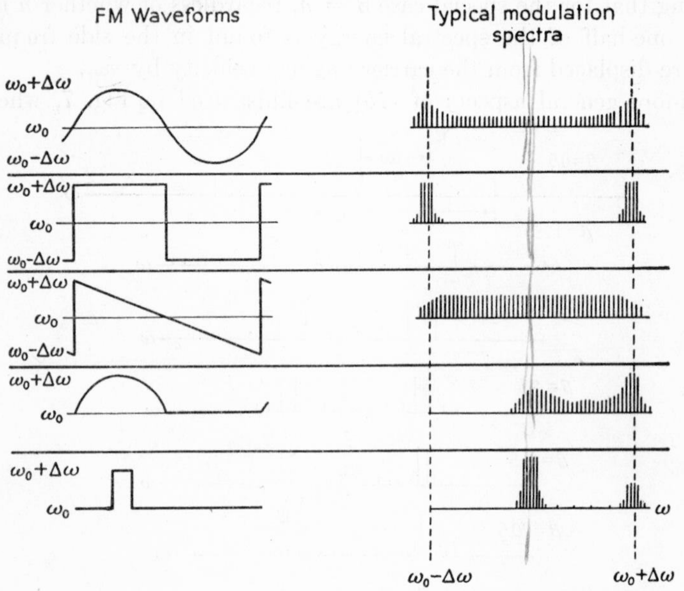

FIG. 8. FM waveforms and corresponding typical modulation spectra.

wave and multitone FM spectrum analysis, it is extremely important that the formulation not become confusing. A very useful rule, which follows from the principle of stationary phase, may be stated as follows:

> The spectral contributions of an FM wave are functions of the rate of change of frequency during the entire cycle; the longer the frequency of an FM wave remains in a certain range of frequencies, the greater will be the spectral contributions in that frequency range.

Several complex-wave FM modulating waveforms are shown in Fig. 8, with typical corresponding spectra resulting from large modulation indexes. These spectra and waveforms serve as excellent illustrations of this rule. It is evident that qualitative predictions of FM spectra can be made once the modulating wave is known, which will serve as a check of the complete Fourier analysis of the FM wave.

PULSE-WIDTH MODULATION

13. Introduction. In the discussion of FM waves in this chapter the unmodulated carrier has been considered to be a single rotating vector whose period is modulated, thus producing frequency modulation. In pulse-width modulation, the unmodulated wave is a repeated pulse whose repetition frequency is maintained constant while the pulse width is varied at some prescribed rate. This is a special case of the general subject of the frequency modulation of complex-wave carriers and will serve as an excellent introduction to the mathematical approach and concepts involved, the general subject being too involved for inclusion in this book.

14. Fourier Analysis of Symmetrical Pulse-width Modulation.[1] Consider the pulse-width-modulated wave in Fig. 9*b*, Chap. 13. If the pulse repetition frequency is $\omega_0/2\pi = 1/T_0$, it follows from Sec. 5, Chap. 3, that each pulse of width T is expressible by the Fourier series

$$e(t) = f_0T + \frac{1}{\pi}\sum_{-\infty}^{\infty}\frac{1}{n}\sin n\omega_0\frac{T}{2}\,e^{jn\omega_0 t} \qquad n \neq 0 \tag{81}$$

Let the width T be modulated cosinusoidally (see Fig. 9*b*, Chap. 13) so that

$$T = \tau(1 + k\cos\omega_1 t) \tag{82}$$

where ω_1 is the angular velocity of the modulating frequency and k is the modulation index; *i.e.*,

$$k = \frac{T_{\max} - T_{\min}}{T_{\max} + T_{\min}} \tag{83}$$

Substituting (82) into (81), we get

$$e(t) = f_0\tau(1 + k\cos\omega_1 t) + \frac{1}{\pi}\sum_{-\infty}^{\infty}\frac{1}{n}\sin\left[\frac{n\omega_0\tau}{2}(1 + k\cos\omega_1 t)\right]e^{jn\omega_0 t} \tag{84}$$

The second term of (84) may be written in the form ($x = n\omega_0\tau k/2$)

$$\frac{1}{2\pi j}\sum_{-\infty}^{\infty}\frac{1}{n}\left(e^{jx\cos\omega_1 t}e^{jn\omega_0(t+\tau/2)} + e^{-jx\cos\omega_1 t}e^{jn\omega_0(t-\tau/2)}\right) \tag{85}$$

[1] See E. R. Kretzmer, Distortion in Pulse-duration Modulation, *Proc. IRE*, vol. 35, pp. 1230–1235, November, 1947, and S. C. Kleene, Analysis of Lengthening of Modulated Repetitive Pulses, *Proc. IRE*, vol. 35, pp. 1049–1053, October, 1947.

Using Eqs. (92) and (93) in Chap. 2, (84) may be easily developed into the following double summation ($n \neq 0$):[1]

$$f(t) = f_0\tau(1 + k \cos \omega_1 t) + \frac{1}{\pi} \sum_{n=-\infty}^{\infty} \sum_{m=-\infty}^{\infty} \frac{1}{n} J_{|m|}\left(\frac{nk\omega_0\tau}{2}\right) \sin\left(\frac{n\omega_0\tau}{2} + \frac{|m|\pi}{2}\right) e^{j(n\omega_0 + m\omega_1)t} \tag{86}$$

Despite the number of components involved, the components of interest are those of frequency $\omega_1/2\pi$—the modulating wave frequency—and such components $\omega_0 \pm m\omega_1$ as are near enough to ω_1 to cause distortion.

Kretzmer has shown that for a television application of pulse-width modulation in which $T/T_0 = 0.03$, $\tau = 0.83$, the ratios of the magnitudes of the components at $\omega_0 - \omega_1$, $\omega_0 - 2\omega_1$, and $\omega_0 - 3\omega_1$ to the magnitude of the component at ω_1 are 1.0, 0.0018, and 0.00024, respectively. It is evident that an appropriate filter must be installed to remove the component at $\omega_0 - \omega_1$ should that lie close to the component at ω_1.

PROBLEMS

1. Compute and diagram the amplitudes of the spectral components listed in Eq. (29) for the case when

a. $\beta_1 = 1, \beta_2 = 5$

b. $\beta_1 = 5, \beta_2 = 5$

Determine the bandwidth for each case.

2. Develop the double Fourier-series expansion for the case of two-tone frequency modulation when

a. $\Delta\omega_t = \Delta\omega_1 \sin \omega_1 t + \Delta\omega_2 \cos \omega_1 t$

b. $\Delta\omega_t = \Delta\omega_1 \sin \omega_1 t + \Delta\omega_2 \sin \omega_2 t$

3. Compute and diagram the amplitudes of the spectral components which result in Prob. 2*a* for the case when $\Delta\omega_1/\omega_1 = \Delta\omega_2/\omega_1 = 1$. Determine the modulation index of the single-tone FM wave whose absolute amplitude spectrum is identical to that which results from this development. Compute the problem for the case when $\Delta\omega_1/\omega_1 = 5$ and $\Delta\omega_2/\omega_1 = 2$. Discuss bandwidth considerations.

4. Develop the Fourier-series expansion, using the direct Fourier analysis, of the FM wave whose frequency variation is described as follows:

$$\begin{aligned} \omega_t &= \omega_0 & -\frac{\pi}{\omega_1} < t < -\frac{T}{2} \\ &= \omega_0 + \Delta\omega \cos \omega_1 t & -\frac{T}{2} < t < \frac{T}{2} \\ &= \omega_0 & \frac{T}{2} < t < \frac{\pi}{\omega_1} \end{aligned}$$

for the general case when $T < 2\pi/\omega_1$.

[1] For a fundamentally different approach in which the spectrum amplitudes and phase of each pulse are considered separately and then summed, see Appendix III of Fredendall, Schlesinger, and Schroeder, Transmission of Television Sound on the Television Carrier, *Proc. IRE*, vol. 34, pp. 49–61, February, 1946.

5. Show that the Fourier-series expansion of a unit-amplitude carrier of frequency $\omega_0/2\pi$, which is frequency-modulated with a rectangular signal so that the frequency deviation is that pictured in the figure, is

$$e = E \sum_{n=-\infty}^{\infty} \frac{\beta}{\pi(\beta - n)(\beta x - nx + n)} \sin \pi x(\beta - n) e^{j(\omega_0 + n\omega_1)t}$$

Show that when $x = \frac{1}{2}$, we get Eq. (75).

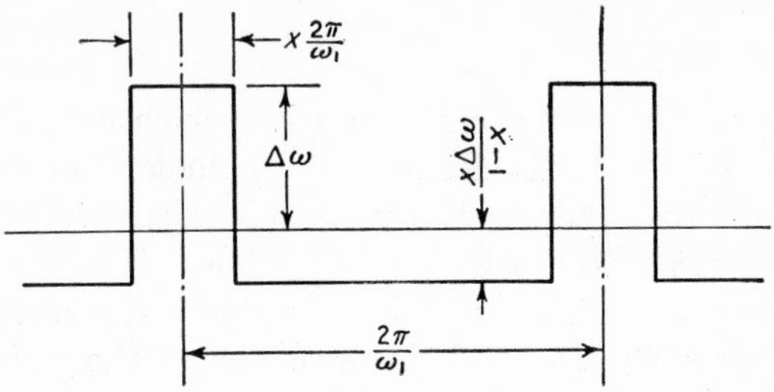

PROB. 5.

6. Compute and diagram the amplitudes of the Fourier series in Prob. 5 for the case when $x = \frac{1}{8}$ and $\beta = 5$. Discuss the problem from the standpoint of considerations of the principle of stationary phase and of bandwidth.

7. Develop the Fourier-series representation of a wave which is simultaneously half-wave amplitude- and frequency-modulated by the same modulating wave.

CHAPTER 19

SPECTRAL ANALYSIS OF FINITE WAVE TRAINS

1. Introduction. A Fourier representation which lists a set of discrete components is realized only in dealing with periodic waves. The tacit assumption is made that the periodic wave has existed from the beginning of time and will continue until the end of time. However, when a nonperiodic wave or a wave train of finite duration is encountered, a Fourier series can no longer be used and the spectrum of the wave must be determined by use of the Fourier or Laplace transform. In using the transform, the status of the perturbing force exciting a system must be identified over all time.

In this chapter, we shall be concerned with the spectrum representation of a nonperiodic wave. By using the Fourier transform, the function of time representing the nonperiodic wave may be expressed as a function of frequency. However, as has been seen in Chap. 3, the concept of individual side frequencies must be supplanted by a concept involving the *distribution* of energy or voltage as a function of frequency. The Fourier transform has been shown in Chap. 3 to be

$$g(\omega) = \int_{t=-\infty}^{\infty} f(t)e^{-i\omega t}\,dt \tag{1}$$

$$= G(\omega)e^{i\Theta(\omega)} \tag{2}$$

where $g(\omega)$ is the spectral function corresponding to $f(t)$, $G(\omega)$ and $\Theta(\omega)$ representing the amplitude and phase spectra, respectively.

Two types of nonperiodic waves will be considered: (1) a wave train whose amplitude is equal to zero for all time with the exception of the interval $-T/2 < t < T/2$; (2) a wave train which exists for all time and which is subjected to an amplitude or angular-velocity change or transient during a finite interval.

The wave train of finite duration is, of course, the wave which is met in practical electrical communications. A mathematical description of the transition from infinite-duration-wave spectra to finite-duration-wave spectra will be discussed in this chapter. The second type of wave train may be exemplified by the wave which is encountered when frequency modulation is used to transmit a video signal. If a rapid change from black to white is the intelligence to be transmitted, the sudden change in frequency which is the difference between the two frequencies representing black and white may be analyzed by the Fourier transform.

FOURIER-TRANSFORM ANALYSIS OF A WAVE TRAIN OF FINITE DURATION

The Fourier Analysis of Simple Harmonic and Complex Wave Trains of Finite Duration

2. Elementary Considerations in Single-tone-wave-train Analysis. Consider the spectral representation of a single-tone wave train of finite duration which may be expressed as

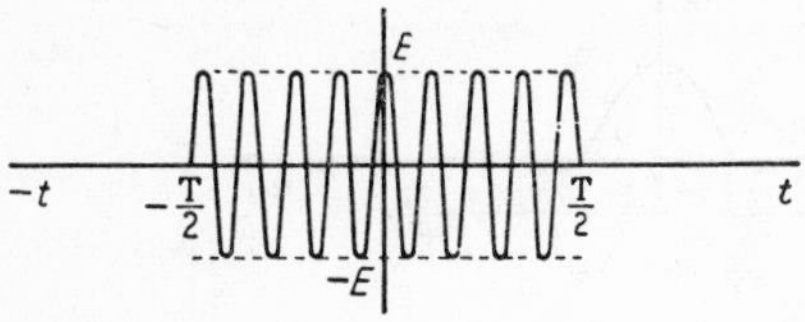

Fig. 1.

$$\begin{aligned} e &= 0 && -\infty < t < -\frac{T}{2} \\ &= Ee^{j\omega_1 t} && -\frac{T}{2} < t < \frac{T}{2} \qquad (3) \\ &= 0 && \frac{T}{2} < t < \infty \end{aligned}$$

The wave train is expressed in rotating-vector form. The real part of (3) may be pictured as shown in Fig. 1.

Substituting Eq. (3) into Eq. (1), we get, by combining exponents,

$$g(\omega) = E \int_{-T/2}^{T/2} e^{j(\omega_1 - \omega)t}\, dt \tag{4}$$

$$= E\,\frac{e^{j(\omega_1-\omega)(T/2)} - e^{-j(\omega_1-\omega)(T/2)}}{j(\omega_1 - \omega)} \tag{5}$$

By multiplying and dividing through by $T/2$, Eq. (5) becomes

$$g(\omega) = ET\,\frac{\sin (\omega_1 - \omega)(T/2)}{(\omega_1 - \omega)(T/2)} \tag{6}$$

Let us compare Eq. (6) with the Fourier transform of a pulse, which may be described as

$$\begin{aligned} f(t) &= 0 && -\infty < t < -\frac{T}{2} \\ &= E && -\frac{T}{2} < t < \frac{T}{2} \qquad (7) \\ &= 0 && \frac{T}{2} < t < \infty \end{aligned}$$

The Fourier transform of this pulse has been shown in Chap. 3 to be

$$g(\omega) = E\int_{-T/2}^{T/2} e^{-j\omega t}\,dt \tag{8}$$

$$= ET\frac{\sin\omega(T/2)}{\omega(T/2)} \tag{9}$$

It is therefore evident that Eq. (6) represents the $(\sin\theta)/\theta$ function contained in (9), displaced from the origin by the wave-train angular velocity as shown in Fig. 2.

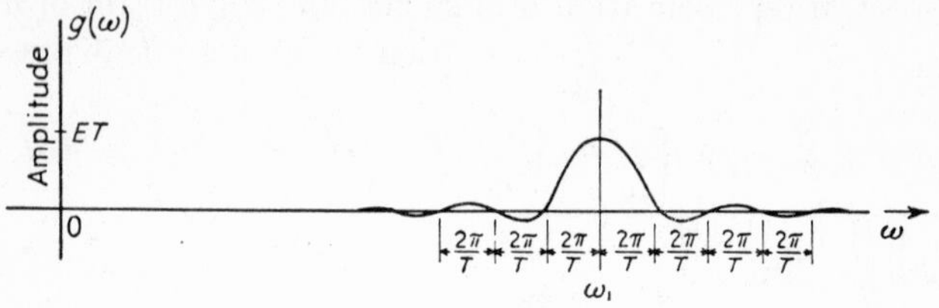

FIG. 2.

When the angular velocity in (3) is negative, we get

$$\begin{aligned} f(t) &= 0 & -\infty < t < -\frac{T}{2} \\ &= Ee^{-j\omega t} & -\frac{T}{2} < t < \frac{T}{2} \\ &= 0 & \frac{T}{2} < t < \infty \end{aligned} \tag{10}$$

Substituting (10) into (1), we get

$$g(\omega) = E\int_{-T/2}^{T/2} e^{-j(\omega_1+\omega)t}\,dt \tag{11}$$

$$= ET\frac{\sin(\omega_1+\omega)(T/2)}{(\omega_1+\omega)(T/2)} \tag{12}$$

The spectrum corresponding to Eq. (12) is pictured in Fig. 3. Note that the $(\sin\theta)/\theta$ representation is now displaced from the origin by the wave-train angular velocity $-\omega_1$.

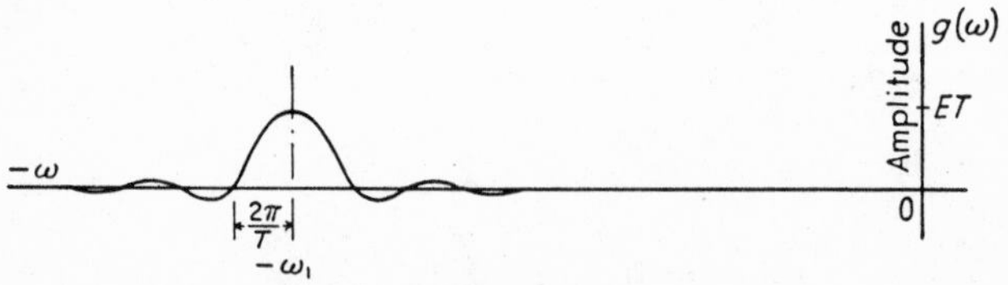

FIG. 3.

3. Discussion of Limits. Consider the wave train

$$
\begin{aligned}
e &= 0 & -\infty < t < 0 \\
&= Ee^{j\omega_1 t} & 0 < t < T \\
&= 0 & T < t < \infty
\end{aligned}
\tag{13}
$$

Then

$$g(\omega) = E \int_0^T e^{j(\omega_1 - \omega)t}\, dt \tag{14}$$

$$= ET \frac{e^{+j(\omega_1 - \omega)T} - 1}{j(\omega_1 - \omega)T} \tag{15}$$

$$= ET \left[\frac{\sin (\omega_1 - \omega)T}{(\omega_1 - \omega)T} - j \frac{\cos (\omega_1 - \omega)T - 1}{(\omega_1 - \omega)T} \right] \tag{16}$$

The real and imaginary parts of Eq. (16) will permit us to investigate the phase spectrum more fully. Equation (16) may be written in the form of Eq. (2) as follows:[1]

$$g(\omega) = G(\omega)e^{j\Theta(\omega)} \tag{2}$$

$$= ET \sqrt{\left[\frac{\sin (\omega_1 - \omega)T}{(\omega_1 - \omega)T}\right]^2 + \left[\frac{\cos (\omega_1 - \omega)T - 1}{(\omega_1 - \omega)T}\right]^2} \cdot \exp\left[j \tan^{-1} \frac{\cos (\omega_1 - \omega)T - 1}{\sin (\omega_1 - \omega)T} \right] \tag{17}$$

$$= \frac{ET \sqrt{[\sin (\omega_1 - \omega)T]^2 + [\cos (\omega_1 - \omega)T]^2 - 2 \cos (\omega_1 - \omega)T + 1}}{(\omega_1 - \omega)T} \cdot \exp\left[j \tan^{-1} \frac{\cos (\omega_1 - \omega)T - 1}{\sin (\omega_1 - \omega)T} \right] \tag{18}$$

$$= ET \frac{\sin (\omega_1 - \omega)(T/2)}{(\omega_1 - \omega)(T/2)} e^{j(\omega_1 - \omega)T/2} \tag{19}$$

The $G(\omega)$ of (19) is seen to be identical to that of (6). Equation (19), however, contains a phase-shift term which follows from the shifting of the wave-train limits from $-T/2 < t < T/2$ to $0 < t < T$.

[1] Using the trigonometric identities

a. $\cos^2 x + \sin^2 x = 1$

b. $\sin \frac{x}{2} = \sqrt{\frac{1 - \cos x}{2}}$

c. If $\tan^{-1} A = \frac{1 - \cos B}{\sin B}$, $\quad A = \frac{B}{2}$

4. Fourier Transforms of Real Single-tone Finite Wave Trains. Consider the spectrum of the real finite wave train which is expressed as

$$\begin{aligned} e &= 0 & -\infty < t < -\frac{T}{2} \\ &= E \cos \omega_1 t & -\frac{T}{2} < t < \frac{T}{2} \\ &= 0 & \frac{T}{2} < t < \infty \end{aligned} \tag{20}$$

According to Eq. (1),

$$g(\omega) = E \int_{-T/2}^{T/2} \cos \omega_1 t e^{-j\omega t}\, dt \tag{21}$$

This may be written in exponential form as

$$g(\omega) = \frac{E}{2}\left(\int_{-T/2}^{T/2} e^{j(\omega_1-\omega)t}\, dt + \int_{-T/2}^{T/2} e^{-j(\omega_1+\omega)t}\, dt\right) \tag{22}$$

and the solution, which is pictured in Fig. 4, is the expression

$$g(\omega) = \frac{ET}{2}\left[\frac{\sin(\omega_1-\omega)(T/2)}{(\omega_1-\omega)(T/2)} + \frac{\sin(\omega_1+\omega)(T/2)}{(\omega_1+\omega)(T/2)}\right] \tag{23}$$

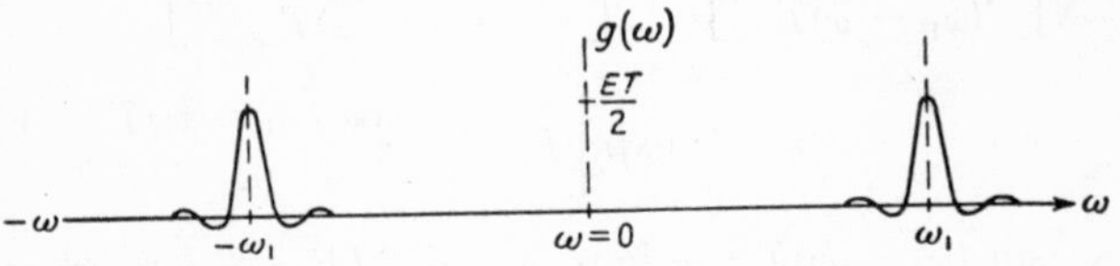

FIG. 4.

In like manner, let us consider the real, odd wave train which is described by the function

$$\begin{aligned} e &= 0 & -\infty < t < -\frac{T}{2} \\ &= E \sin \omega_1 t & -\frac{T}{2} < t < \frac{T}{2} \\ &= 0 & \frac{T}{2} < t < \infty \end{aligned} \tag{24}$$

Then

$$g(\omega) = E \int_{-T/2}^{T/2} \sin \omega_1 t e^{-j\omega t}\, dt \tag{25}$$

$$= -j\frac{ET}{2}\left[\frac{\sin(\omega_1-\omega)(T/2)}{(\omega_1-\omega)(T/2)} - \frac{\sin(\omega_1+\omega)(T/2)}{(\omega_1+\omega)(T/2)}\right] \tag{26}$$

5. Some General Considerations of Single-tone Finite Wave Trains. Consider the wave

$$
\begin{aligned}
e &= 0 & -\infty < t < -\frac{T}{2} \\
&= E \cos \frac{2\pi n t}{T_1} & -\frac{T}{2} < t < \frac{T}{2} \qquad (27) \\
&= 0 & \frac{T}{2} < t < \infty
\end{aligned}
$$

where T_1 is the period of the wave train and T is its duration. Then

$$g(\omega) = E \int_{-T/2}^{T/2} \cos \frac{2\pi n t}{T_1} \exp j \left(\frac{2\pi t}{T}\right) dt \qquad (28)$$

$$= \frac{E}{2} \int_{-T/2}^{T/2} \exp \left[j \left(\frac{2\pi n}{T_1} - \omega \right) t \right] dt + \frac{E}{2} \int_{-T/2}^{T/2} \exp \left[-j \left(\frac{2\pi n}{T_1} + \omega \right) t \right] dt \qquad (29)$$

$$= \frac{ET}{2} \left\{ \frac{\sin [\pi n(T/T_1) - \omega(T/2)]}{\pi n(T/T_1) - \omega(T/2)} + \frac{\sin [\pi n(T/T_1) + \omega(T/2)]}{\pi n(T/T_1) + \omega(T/2)} \right\} \qquad (30)$$

By trigonometric expansion of the numerator, Eq. (30) becomes

$$g(\omega) = \frac{ET}{[\pi n(T/T_1)]^2 - (\omega T/2)^2} \cdot \left(\pi n \frac{T}{T_1} \sin \pi n \frac{T}{T_1} \cos \frac{\omega T}{2} - \frac{\omega T}{2} \cos \pi n \frac{T}{T_1} \sin \frac{\omega T}{2} \right) \qquad (31)$$

In like manner, we may show that for the wave

$$
\begin{aligned}
e &= 0 & -\infty < t < -\frac{T}{2} \\
&= E \sin \frac{2\pi n t}{T_1} & -\frac{T}{2} < t < \frac{T}{2} \qquad (32) \\
&= 0 & \frac{T}{2} < t < \infty
\end{aligned}
$$

we get

$$g(\omega) = \frac{jET}{[\pi n(T/T_1)]^2 - (\omega T/2)^2} \cdot \left(\pi n \frac{T}{T_1} \cos \pi n \frac{T}{T_1} \sin \frac{\omega T}{2} - \frac{\omega T}{2} \sin \pi n \frac{T}{T_1} \cos \frac{\omega T}{2} \right) \qquad (33)$$

A comparison of Eqs. (31) and (33) will show the inherent difference between sinusoidal and cosinusoidal finite wave trains. Consider, for example, the $g(\omega)$'s which represent sinusoidal and cosinusoidal simple harmonic finite wave trains for the case when $T = T_1$ and $n = 1$. The $f(t)$'s corresponding to these functions are shown in Fig. 5*a* and *b*. By

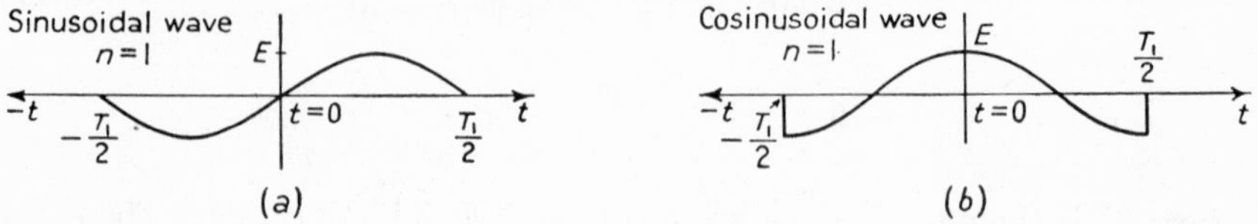

FIG. 5.

substituting $T = T_1$ and $n = 1$ into Eqs. (31) and (33), we get, for a sinusoidal wave,

$$g(\omega) = \frac{-jET_1}{\pi^2 - (\omega T_1/2)^2} \pi \sin \frac{\omega T_1}{2} \tag{34}$$

and for a cosinusoidal wave,

$$g(\omega) = \frac{ET_1}{\pi^2 - (\omega T_1/2)^2} \frac{\omega T_1}{2} \sin \frac{\omega T_1}{2} \tag{35}$$

Equations (34) and (35) differ by the fact that the numerator of (34) contains the constant π, whereas in the numerator of (35) we get the phase angle $\omega T_1/2$. The spectrum described by (35) will therefore be broader owing to the presence of this phase angle, this spectral broadening being attributable to the jumps at $t = T_1/2$ and $t = -T_1/2$.

6. Even and Odd Wave Considerations in Single-tone Finite-wave-train Spectra. As an extension of the discussion of sine and cosine simple harmonic wave trains, consider these wave trains in terms of their even and odd properties. Although the sine wave train is odd and the cosine wave train is even, it is not possible to use an integral value of n for both cases for a comparison because of the differences in the start and end of the wave train, such as were discussed in the preceding section. However, if n is an integer for the sine wave train, thus forcing the wave train to start and end at $f(t) = 0$, and if n is a half integer for the cosine train, thereupon also forcing it to start and end with zero amplitude, then the real and even properties are retained and a comparison of the waves may be made. Consider the case when $n = 1$ and $T = T_1$ for the sine train and $n = \frac{3}{2}$ and $T = T_1$ for the cosine train as illustrated in Fig. 6*a* and *b*, respectively. It follows that

Sine train:

$$g(\omega) = -j \frac{ET_1}{\pi^2 - (\omega T_1/2)^2} \pi \sin \frac{\omega T_1}{2} \qquad n = 1 \tag{36}$$

Cosine train:

$$g(\omega) = \frac{ET_1}{(3\pi/2)^2 - (\omega T_1/2)^2} \frac{3\pi}{2} \cos \frac{\omega T_1}{2} \qquad n = \frac{3}{2} \tag{37}$$

Inspection of Eq. (37) shows this to be even and real as compared with the odd and imaginary qualities of Eq. (36).

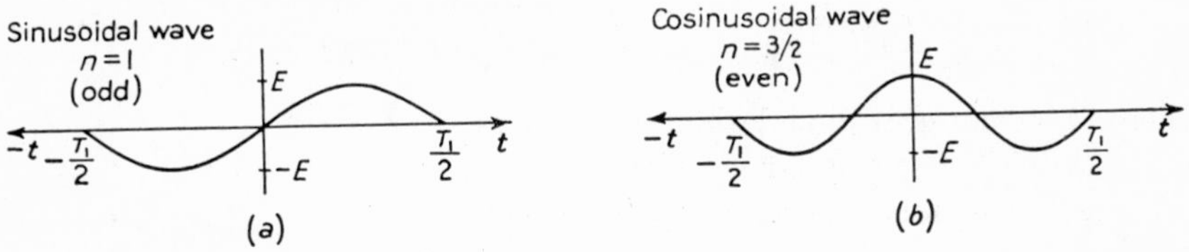

FIG. 6.

7. Fourier Analysis of Multitone and Amplitude-modulated Finite Wave Trains. Consider the Fourier analysis of finite wave trains which are produced when a set of simple harmonic finite wave trains of different periods are superimposed.

Case 1. *When Periods of the Component Waves Are Not Related to the Period of the Wave Train.* Consider the general wave

$$f(t) = E_1 e^{j\omega_1 t} + E_2 e^{j\omega_2 t} + \cdots + E_N e^{j\omega_N t} \tag{38}$$

which exists as a wave train in the period $-T/2 < t < T/2$ such that

$$T > \frac{2\pi}{\omega_1} \qquad \omega_1 > \omega_2 > \omega_3 > \cdots > \omega_N \tag{39}$$

Then, by Fourier-transform analysis,

$$g(\omega) = \int_{-T/2}^{T/2} f(t) e^{-j\omega t}\, dt \tag{40}$$

$$= E_1 \int_{-T/2}^{T/2} e^{j(\omega_1 - \omega)t}\, dt + E_2 \int_{-T/2}^{T/2} e^{j(\omega_2 - \omega)t}\, dt + \cdots + \int_{-T/2}^{T/2} e^{j(\omega_N - \omega)t}\, dt \tag{41}$$

$$= E_1 T \frac{\sin (\omega_1 - \omega)T/2}{(\omega_1 - \omega)T/2} + E_2 T \frac{\sin (\omega_2 - \omega)T/2}{(\omega_2 - \omega)T/2} + \cdots + E_3 T \frac{\sin (\omega_N - \omega)T/2}{(\omega_N - \omega)T/2} \tag{42}$$

Equation (42) shows that, for each component of the wave train, there exists a $(\sin \theta)/\theta$ spectrum.

Example. Consider the spectrum of a single-tone amplitude-modulated carrier which forms a wave train in the interval $-T/2 < t < T/2$; that is,

$$
\begin{aligned}
f(t) &= 0 && -\infty < t < -\frac{T}{2} \\
&= E(1 + M\cos\omega_1 t)e^{j\omega_0 t} && -\frac{T}{2} < t < \frac{T}{2} \qquad (43) \\
&= 0 && \frac{T}{2} < t < \infty
\end{aligned}
$$

where M = per cent modulation factor
ω_0 = carrier angular velocity
ω_1 = modulating-wave angular velocity

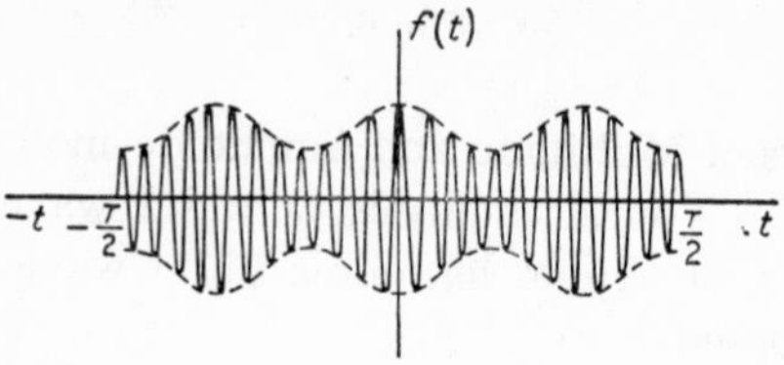

FIG. 7.

The real part of (43) is pictured in Fig. 7. It follows that

$$g(\omega) = E\int_{-T/2}^{T/2} (1 + M\cos\omega_1 t)e^{j\omega_0 t}e^{-j\omega t}\,dt \qquad (44)$$

$$= E\int_{-T/2}^{T/2} e^{j(\omega_0-\omega)t}\,dt + \frac{ME}{2}\int_{-T/2}^{T/2} e^{j(\omega_0+\omega_1-\omega)t}\,dt + \frac{ME}{2}\int_{-T/2}^{T/2} e^{j(\omega_0-\omega_1-\omega)t}\,dt \qquad (45)$$

$$= ET\frac{\sin(\omega_0-\omega)T/2}{(\omega_0-\omega)T/2} + \frac{MET}{2}\left[\frac{\sin(\omega_0+\omega_1-\omega)T/2}{(\omega_0+\omega_1-\omega)T/2} + \frac{\sin(\omega_0-\omega_1-\omega)T/2}{(\omega_0-\omega_1-\omega)T/2}\right] \qquad (46)$$

Equation (46) describes three separate spectra—a carrier spectrum centered at $\omega = \omega_0$, and two reduced amplitude spectra which are centered

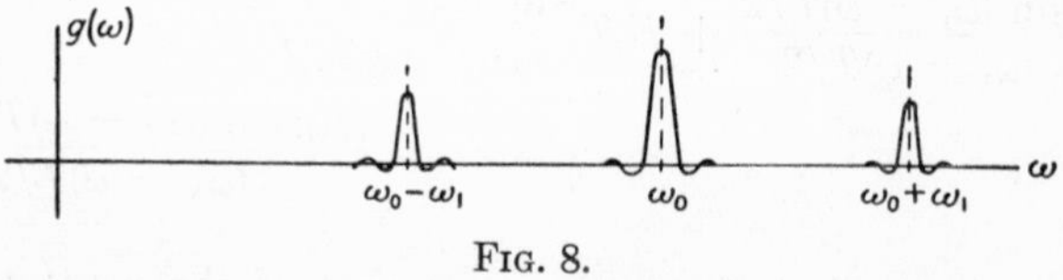

FIG. 8.

at $\omega = \omega_0 + \omega_1$ and $\omega = \omega_0 - \omega_1$, respectively. These spectra may be pictured as shown in Fig. 8. As T approaches infinity, the spectral width of the three spectra in Fig. 8 will decrease, thus yielding the three line spectra which result from continuous periodic single-tone amplitude modulation.

Case 2. *When the Period of the Fundamental of the Complex Wave Is Equal to the Duration Time of the Wave Train.* Consider the odd complex wave train $f(t)$ whose duration time is T and which may be expressed as follows:

$$\begin{aligned} f(t) &= 0 && -\infty < t < -\frac{T}{2} \\ &= \sum_{n=1}^{\infty} E_n \sin \frac{2\pi n t}{T} && -\frac{T}{2} < t < \frac{T}{2} \\ &= 0 && \frac{T}{2} < t < \infty \end{aligned} \tag{47}$$

where

$$E_n = \frac{1}{T} \int_{-T/2}^{T/2} f(t) \sin \frac{2\pi n t}{T}\, dt \tag{48}$$

This wave train is a real wave and is expressed as a Fourier sine series. Figure 9 shows a pictorial representation of (47) in which are also pictured the first three harmonics. All nth components go to zero at $t = -T/2$, 0, $T/2$.

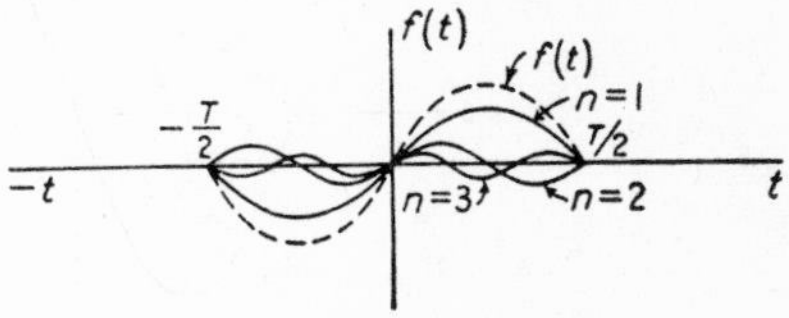

FIG. 9.

The $g(\omega)$ corresponding to Eq. (47) is

$$g(\omega) = \sum_{n=1}^{\infty} E_n \int_{-T/2}^{T/2} \sin \frac{2\pi n t}{T} e^{-j\omega t}\, dt \tag{49}$$

$$= \sum_{n=1}^{\infty} \left(\frac{E_n}{2j} \left\{ \int_{-T/2}^{T/2} e^{j[(2\pi n/T)-\omega]t}\, dt - \int_{-T/2}^{T/2} e^{-j[(2\pi n/T)+\omega]t}\, dt \right\} \right) \tag{50}$$

$$= \sum_{n=1}^{\infty} E_n T \left\{ \frac{\sin [\pi n - \omega(T/2)]}{2\pi n - \omega T} + \frac{\sin [\pi n + \omega(T/2)]}{2\pi n + \omega T} \right\} \tag{51}$$

Example. Consider the spectrum of the nonperiodic square wave which is pictured in Fig. 10 and which is represented as

$$\begin{aligned} f(t) &= 0 && -\infty < t < -\frac{T}{2} \\ &= -E && -\frac{T}{2} < t < 0 \\ &= E && 0 < t < \frac{T}{2} \\ &= 0 && \frac{T}{2} < t < \infty \end{aligned} \tag{52}$$

This wave train may be expressed as a Fourier series, the first two terms of which are shown in Fig. 10. It follows that, for the interval $-T/2 < t < T/2$,

$$f(t) = \frac{4E}{\pi}\left(\sin\frac{2\pi t}{T} + \frac{1}{3}\sin\frac{2\pi \times 3t}{T} + \frac{1}{5}\sin\frac{2\pi \times 5t}{T} + \cdots\right) \tag{53}$$

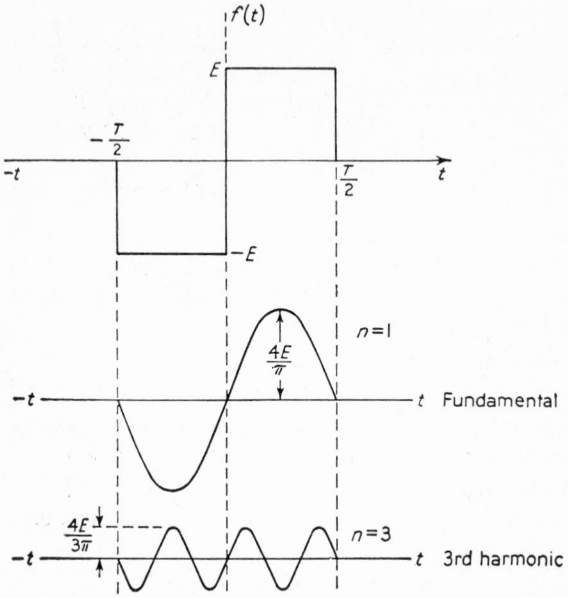

FIG. 10.

According to Eqs. (51) and (33),

$$g(\omega) = j4\left[-\frac{ET}{\pi^2 - (\omega T/2)^2}\sin\frac{\omega T}{2} - \frac{ET}{(3\pi)^2 - (\omega T/2)^2}\sin\frac{\omega T}{2} - \frac{ET}{(5\pi)^2 - (\omega T/2)^2}\sin\frac{\omega T}{2} + \cdots\right] \tag{54}$$

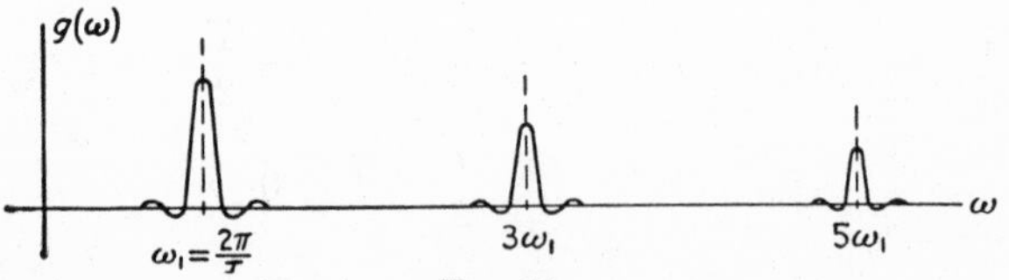

FIG. 11.

This shows that there are $(\sin\theta)/\theta$-form spectra centered at $\omega = \omega_1, 3\omega_1, 5\omega_1, \cdots$. These spectra are shown in Fig. 11.

Fourier Analysis of Frequency-modulated Wave Trains of Finite Duration[1]

8. Introduction. When the frequency of the finite wave train is modulated during the train duration, the problem is in many respects similar to the one dealing with periodic continuous FM waves. The analysis in the preceding chapters dealing with periodic frequency and amplitude modulation has shown that a generator whose output wave is frequency- or phase-modulated may be replaced by an infinite sum of generators in series which consist of a carrier-frequency generator plus an infinite number of upper and lower sideband generators which, for single-tone modulation, are separated in frequency by the frequency of the modulating wave. Except for the fact that finite-wave-train analysis no longer results in discrete spectral components, many of these concepts may be retained.

The analysis to follow will deal with even (cosine) frequency modulation and odd (sine) frequency modulation and will include only considerations of those waves whose modulating periods are equal to or multiples of the wave-train period.

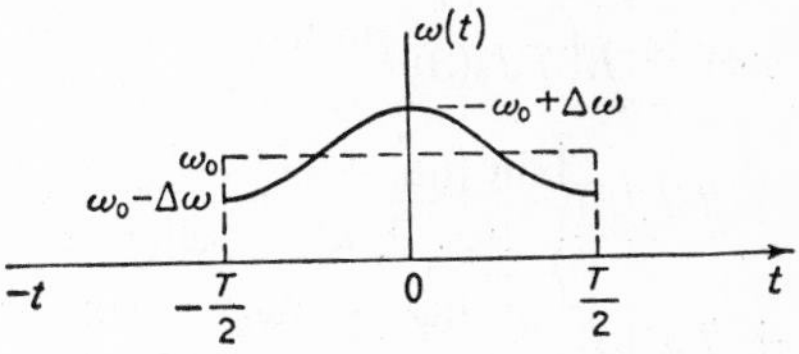

FIG. 12.

9. Single-tone Cosine FM Wave Train. Consider a single-tone cosinusoidally frequency-modulated wave train whose variation of angular velocity with time is shown in Fig. 12 for the wave-train interval T. This frequency variation is described as follows:

$$\omega(t) = \omega_0 + \Delta\omega \cos \omega_1 t \tag{55}$$

where

$$\omega_1 = \frac{2\pi}{T} \tag{56}$$

We may write $f(t)$ as

$$\begin{aligned} f(t) &= 0 & -\infty < t < -\frac{T}{2} \\ &= E \exp\left[j\left(\omega_0 t + \frac{\Delta\omega}{\omega_1} \sin \omega_1 t\right)\right] & -\frac{T}{2} < t < \frac{T}{2} \\ &= 0 & \frac{T}{2} < t < \infty \end{aligned} \tag{57}$$

[1] This is based in part on an unpublished report by W. D. Hershberger entitled *The Synthesis of Pulse Spectra by the Method of Paired Spectra.* The author is also very much indebted to Dr. Hershberger for many illuminating discussions on finite-wave-train spectra which have had considerable influence on this chapter.

Substituting Eq. (57) into Eq. (1), we get

$$g(\omega) = E \int_{-T/2}^{T/2} e^{j\beta \sin \omega_1 t} e^{j(\omega_0 - \omega)t} \, dt \qquad \beta = \frac{\Delta\omega}{\omega_1} \tag{58}$$

But according to Eq. (90), Chap. 2,

$$e^{j\beta \sin \omega_1 t} = \sum_{-\infty}^{\infty} J_n(\beta) e^{jn\omega_1 t} \tag{59}$$

Thus

$$g(\omega) = E \sum_{-\infty}^{\infty} J_n(\beta) \int_{-T/2}^{T/2} e^{j(\omega_0 + n\omega_1 - \omega)t} \, dt \tag{60}$$

The only portion of Eq. (59) to remain in the integrand is $e^{jn\omega_1 t}$. It follows from (60) that

$$g(\omega) = E \sum_{-\infty}^{\infty} TJ_n(\beta) \frac{\sin [(\omega_0 + n\omega_1) - \omega](T/2)}{[(\omega_0 + n\omega_1) - \omega](T/2)} \tag{61}$$

Written out, Eq. (61) becomes

$$\begin{aligned} g(\omega) = E\Bigg(& TJ_0(\beta) \frac{\sin (\omega_0 - \omega)(T/2)}{(\omega_0 - \omega)(T/2)} \\ & + TJ_1(\beta) \left\{ \frac{\sin [(\omega_0 + \omega_1) - \omega](T/2)}{[(\omega_0 + \omega_1) - \omega](T/2)} - \frac{\sin [(\omega_0 - \omega_1) - \omega](T/2)}{[(\omega_0 - \omega_1) - \omega](T/2)} \right\} \\ & + TJ_2(\beta) \left\{ \frac{\sin [(\omega_0 + 2\omega_1) - \omega](T/2)}{[(\omega_0 + 2\omega_1) - \omega](T/2)} + \frac{\sin [(\omega_0 - 2\omega_1) - \omega](T/2)}{[(\omega_0 - 2\omega_1) - \omega](T/2)} \right\} \\ & + \cdots \Bigg) \end{aligned} \tag{62}$$

Equation (62) shows that a $(\sin \theta)/\theta$-form spectrum is centered at the frequency of the carrier and at the frequency of each sideband which is produced during the frequency modulation of a wave train of infinite duration.

The nature of Eq. (62) may be demonstrated by considering the case of small β such that, as an excellent approximation,

$$J_0(\beta) \approx 1 \tag{63}$$

$$J_1(\beta) \approx \frac{\beta}{2} \tag{64}$$

We may rewrite Eq. (62) as follows:

$$\begin{aligned} g(\omega) &= TE \frac{\sin (\omega_0 - \omega)(T/2)}{(\omega_0 - \omega)(T/2)} + \frac{\beta}{2} TE \frac{\sin [(\omega_0 + \omega_1) - \omega](T/2)}{[(\omega_0 + \omega_1) - \omega](T/2)} \\ &\qquad - \frac{\beta}{2} TE \frac{\sin [(\omega_0 - \omega_1) - \omega](T/2)}{[(\omega_0 - \omega_1) - \omega](T/2)} \qquad (65) \\ &= E(g_0 + g_{1u} - g_{1L}) \qquad (66) \end{aligned}$$

The component spectra are illustrated in Fig. 13. Figure 13*a* shows g_0, which is a normal simple harmonic finite-wave-train spectrum. Figure 13*c* illustrates the upper sideband spectrum g_{1u}, which is displaced from the carrier by the angular velocity of the modulating wave. It is positive in sign, and its components will add directly to the corresponding components in the carrier spectrum. Figure 13*b* shows the lower sideband spectrum g_{1L}, which is also displaced from the carrier by the modulating-wave angular velocity. It is negative in sign, and its components will

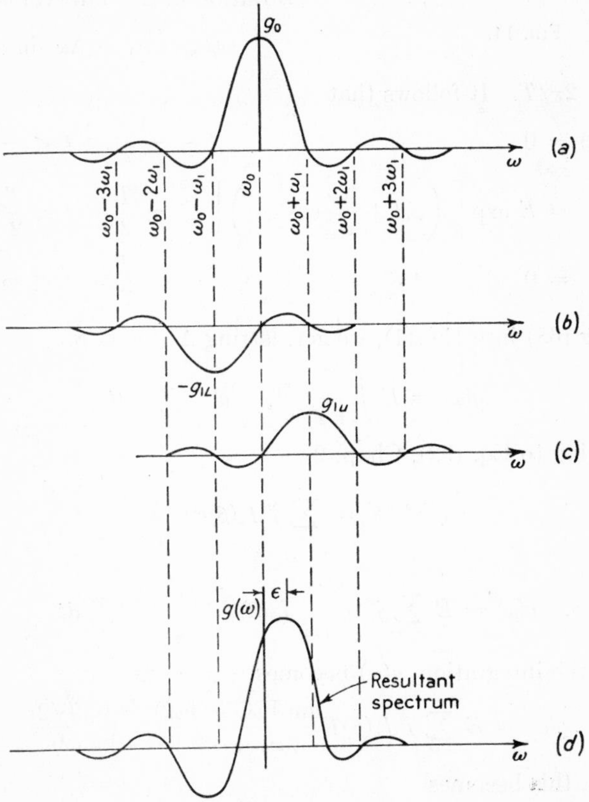

FIG. 13. Single-tone cosine FM spectra described by Eq. (66).

subtract from the corresponding components in the carrier spectrum. Figure 13*d* shows the resultant spectrum.

The addition of the odd first side spectrum pair to the carrier spectrum is clearly seen to cause the carrier spectrum to lose symmetry. The peak of the spectrum has been shifted by a value ϵ, and the first lower sideband lobe is seen to contain more energy than the first upper sideband lobe. This will be true for all odd-numbered side spectrum pairs, while the even-numbered side spectrum pair will serve to increase the sideband energy symmetrically.

10. Single-tone Sinusoidally Frequency-modulated Wave Train. Consider the single-tone sinusoidally frequency-modulated wave train whose variation of angular velocity with respect to time is shown in Fig. 14 for the interval T. The angular-velocity variation in this interval is

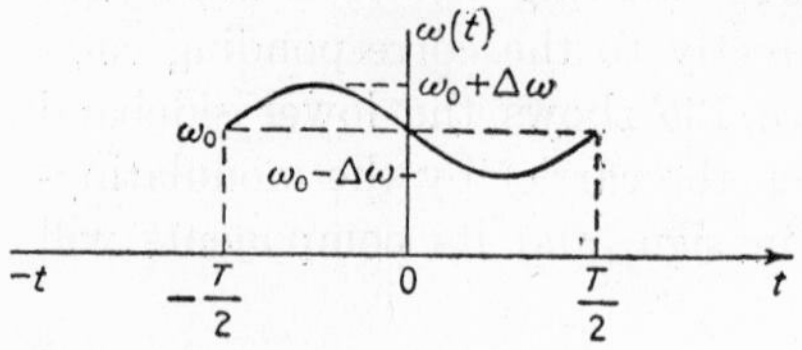

FIG. 14.

$$\omega(t) = \omega_0 - \Delta\omega \sin \omega_1 t \tag{67}$$

where $\omega_1 = 2\pi/T$. It follows that

$$\begin{aligned} f(t) &= 0 & -\infty < t < -\frac{T}{2} \\ &= E \exp\left[j\left(\omega_0 t + \frac{\Delta\omega}{\omega_1} \cos \omega_1 t\right)\right] & -\frac{T}{2} < t < \frac{T}{2} \\ &= 0 & \frac{T}{2} < t < \infty \end{aligned} \tag{68}$$

Substituting (68) into Eq. (1), we get, letting $\Delta\omega/\omega_1 = \beta$,

$$g(\omega) = E \int_{-T/2}^{T/2} e^{j\beta \cos \omega_1 t} e^{j(\omega_0 - \omega)t} \, dt \tag{69}$$

But, according to Eq. (92), Chap. 2,

$$e^{j\beta \cos \omega_1 t} = \sum_{-\infty}^{\infty} j^n J_n(\beta) e^{jn\omega_1 t} \tag{70}$$

Therefore

$$g(\omega) = E \sum_{-\infty}^{\infty} j^n \int_{-T/2}^{T/2} J_n(\beta) e^{j[(\omega_0 + n\omega_1) - \omega]t} \, dt \tag{71}$$

Performing the integration, $g(\omega)$ becomes

$$g(\omega) = E \sum_{-\infty}^{\infty} j^n J_n(\beta) T \frac{\sin [(\omega_0 + n\omega_1) - \omega](T/2)}{[(\omega_0 + n\omega_1) - \omega](T/2)} \tag{72}$$

Written out, this becomes

$$\begin{aligned} g(\omega) = E\Bigg(& T J_0(\beta) \frac{\sin (\omega_0 - \omega)(T/2)}{(\omega_0 - \omega)(T/2)} \\ & + jTJ_1(\beta)\left\{\frac{\sin [(\omega_0 + \omega_1) - \omega](T/2)}{[(\omega_0 + \omega_1) - \omega](T/2)} + \frac{\sin [(\omega_0 - \omega_1) - \omega](T/2)}{[(\omega_0 - \omega_1) - \omega](T/2)}\right\} \\ & - TJ_2(\beta)\left\{\frac{\sin [(\omega_0 + 2\omega_1) - \omega](T/2)}{[(\omega_0 + 2\omega_1) - \omega](T/2)} + \frac{\sin [(\omega_0 - 2\omega_1) - \omega](T/2)}{[(\omega_0 - 2\omega_1) - \omega](T/2)}\right\} \\ & + \cdots \Bigg) \end{aligned} \tag{73}$$

Again, as in cosinusoidal nonperiodic frequency modulation, the $g(\omega)$ is composed of an infinite number of $(\sin \theta)/\theta$ spectra arranged symmetrically about a carrier spectrum. Instead of having even and odd spectral pairs as in Eq. (62), we have in (73) real and imaginary spectral pairs in which the two members comprising a pair have the same sign. Inspection of (73) shows that all odd-numbered pairs are imaginary, while all even-numbered pairs are real.

The effect of the presence of real and imaginary spectral pairs may be seen by considering Eq. (73) when β is very small. Recalling from the discussion in Sec. 9 that

$$J_0(\beta) \approx 1 \tag{63}$$

$$J_1(\beta) \approx \frac{\beta}{2} \tag{64}$$

we may write Eq. (73) as

$$g(\omega) = ET \frac{\sin (\omega_0 - \omega)(T/2)}{(\omega_0 - \omega)(T/2)}$$

$$+ jTE \frac{\beta}{2} \left\{ \frac{\sin [(\omega_0 + \omega_1) - \omega](T/2)}{[(\omega_0 + \omega_1) - \omega](T/2)} + \frac{\sin [(\omega_0 - \omega_1) - \omega](T/2)}{[(\omega_0 - \omega_1) - \omega](T/2)} \right\} \tag{74}$$

$$= E[g_0 + j(g_{1u} + g_{1L})] \tag{75}$$

The carrier spectrum is pictured in Fig. 15*a* as g_0, and the upper and lower sideband spectral pair are pictured in Fig. 15*c* and *b* as jg_{1u} and jg_{1L}, respectively. Figure 15*d* shows the resultant spectrum, $|G(\omega)|$. We cannot add the carrier and sideband components arithmetically as in the case of even cosine frequency modulation. It is necessary now, owing to the fact that the first sideband spectra have been shifted in phase by an angle of 90°, to add vectorially each incremental component in the sideband spectrum with the corresponding incremental component in the carrier spectrum. As is seen in Fig. 15*d*, the spectrum broadens, but its peak does not shift. This is true of the effect due to all odd- and even-number pairs although the effect may be subtractive rather than additive, thus narrowing the resultant spectrum. In addition to the effect of the frequency modulation on spectral symmetry, the shifts in phase of the various spectral components in odd frequency modulation must also be taken into consideration.

11. Nonperiodic Multitone Frequency Modulation. In general the Fourier transform of an FM wave which may be represented by a single rotating vector may be shown to be

$$g(\omega) = E \int_{-\infty}^{\infty} \left\{ \exp \left[j \int f(\omega,t)\, dt \right] \right\} [\exp (-j\omega t)]\, dt \tag{76}$$

which may be written in terms of its Fourier expansion in the wave-train interval $-T/2 < t < T/2$ as

$$g(\omega) = E \int_{-T/2}^{T/2} \left\{ \sum_{-\infty}^{\infty} C_n \left[\exp\left(j \frac{2\pi n t}{T} \right) \right] \right\} [\exp(-j\omega t)]\, dt \tag{77}$$

where

$$C_n = \frac{1}{T} \int_{-T/2}^{T/2} \left\{ \exp\left[j \int f(\omega, t)\, dt \right] \right\} \left[\exp\left(-j \frac{2\pi n t}{T} \right) \right] dt \tag{78}$$

Equation (77) is the general expression for the spectrum corresponding to

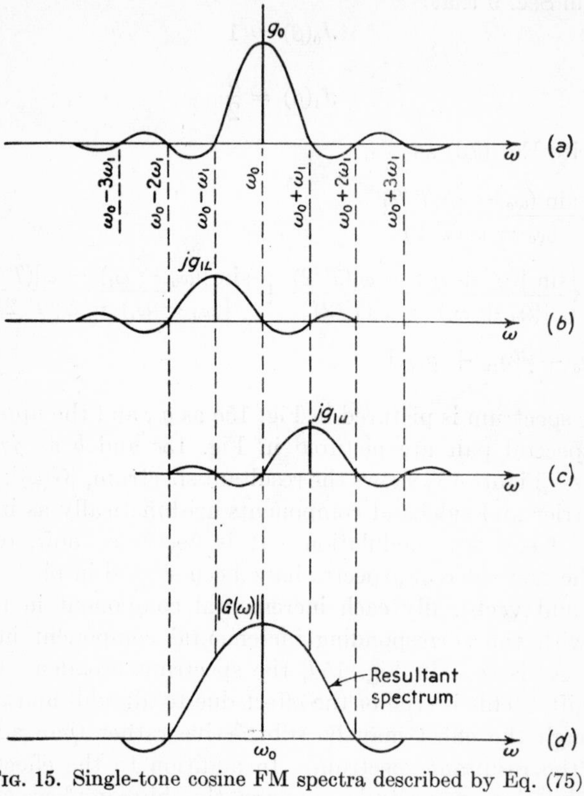

FIG. 15. Single-tone cosine FM spectra described by Eq. (75).

frequency variation in any interval $-T/2 < t < T/2$. After performing the integration, Eq. (77) becomes

$$g(\omega) = ET \sum_{-\infty}^{\infty} C_n \frac{\sin \{[\omega_0 + (2\pi n/T)] - \omega\}(T/2)}{\{[\omega_0 + (2\pi n/T)] - \omega\}(T/2)} \tag{79}$$

This expression shows the spectrum to be the sum of spectra which are of form $(\sin \theta)/\theta$ and which center at the frequencies of the sidebands which occur in the case of the wave of infinite duration.

In general, if the variation of frequency with respect to the carrier is even, asymmetry of the spectrum will result and the peak of the spectrum will be shifted. If the variation of frequency with respect to the carrier is odd, then no asymmetry will result but the spectrum will be broadened or narrowed.

A Study of the Transition of Wave Trains from Finite Duration to Infinite Duration

12. Effect of Duration Time on Spectral Shape. Figure 16 shows the spectrum representation of a simple harmonic finite wave train of fre-

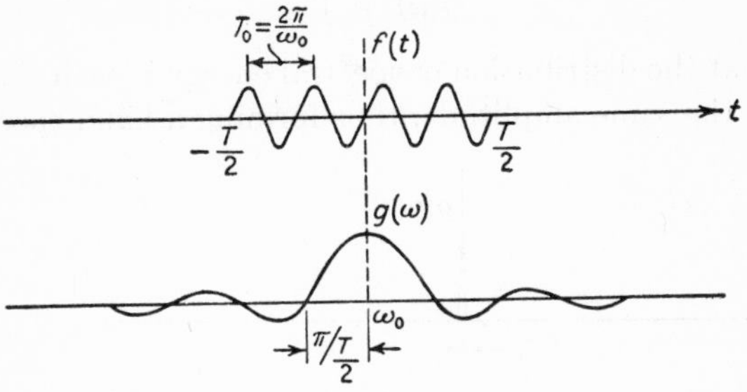

FIG. 16.

quency $\omega_0/2\pi = 1/T_0$ and duration interval $-T/2 < t < T/2$. $g(\omega)$ has been found to be

$$g(\omega) = ET \frac{\sin (\omega_0 - \omega)(T/2)}{(\omega_0 - \omega)(T/2)} \tag{6}$$

Figure 17 illustrates the behavior of the spectrum while the duration time T is varied and T_0 is kept constant. Let us start with Fig. 17*c* first. The duration time is T_c, and the $g(\omega)$ for this duration time will be used as a reference shape. If the duration time is increased to T_b, the zeros become spaced apart by $2\pi/T_b$. Figure 17*b* shows that the spectrum has become narrower. As the duration time goes to infinity, Fig. 17*a* shows that, for this case ($T_a \to \infty$), $g(\omega)$ yields a line spectrum. This is certainly to be expected since it represents the output of a continuous-wave simple-harmonic-wave generator. However, if the duration time decreases to T_d, then it is seen from Fig. 17*d* that the spectrum broadens. Finally, if the duration time is made infinitesimal, Fig. 17*e* for $T_c \to 0$ shows that the spectrum is a band spectrum with spectral energy present at all values of angular velocity.

13. The Delta Function $\delta(t - t_0)$. The limiting case of $T_e \to 0$ which yields the band spectrum illustrated in Fig. 17*e* may be derived by using the Fourier transform of the delta function.

Let a delta function $\delta(t - t_0)$ take place at t_0. This is an impulse or force of infinitesimal duration which conforms to the specification that

$$\int_{-\infty}^{\infty} \delta(t - t_0)\, dt = 1 \tag{80}$$

The Fourier transform of $\delta(t - t_0)$ is

$$g(\omega) = \int_{-\infty}^{\infty} \delta(t - t_0) e^{-j\omega t}\, dt \tag{81}$$

If the impulse takes place at the origin $t = 0$, then, as is shown in Sec. 8, Chap. 3,

$$g(\omega) = 1 \tag{82}$$

which shows that the distribution of spectral energy is such that all angular velocities have the same amplitude, thus forming a band spectrum.

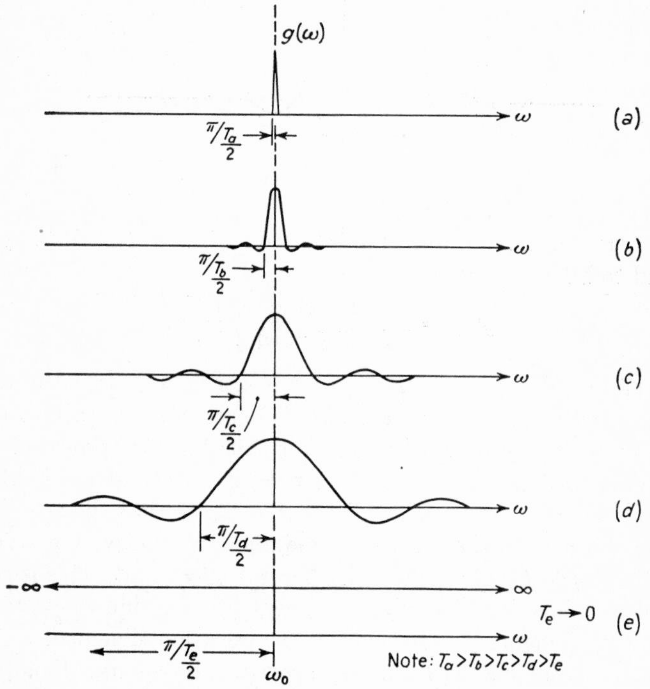

FIG. 17. Finite wave-train spectra as a function of duration time.

14. Transition from Finite to Infinite Wave-train Duration. It has been shown that each component wave of a complex wave train of finite duration may be represented by a single rotating vector which will produce a $(\sin \theta)/\theta$-form spectrum centered at the angular velocity of this vector.

As the wave-train duration is increased so that the only change is in the total number of repetitions of each component, the zeros of each $(\sin\theta)/\theta$-form spectrum will move closer together and for a wave train of infinite duration the space between zeros will vanish and line spectra will result. This behavior serves to illustrate the transition from a Fourier transform to a Fourier series. In practical applications, wave trains of infinite duration do not exist, but since the zeros of $(\sin\theta)/\theta$-form spectra move together rapidly as the duration time of a wave train is increased, a Fourier series may be used to represent accurately a wave train of finite duration provided that the duration time is considerably larger than the period of the fundamental.

FOURIER AND LAPLACE ANALYSIS OF TRANSIENTS IN CONTINUOUS WAVES

15. Introduction. The analysis up to this point has dealt with wave trains of finite duration. We shall consider here those waves which are continuous for all time and experience a transient disturbance during some finite interval and also those waves which start at some specified time and continue for the rest of time. The transients involved may be in the form of amplitude or angular-velocity variations.

Two Fundamental Wave Trains of Basic Importance

16. Fundamental Wave 1—The Kappa Function. Consider the case of the kappa function which is represented by a unit-amplitude simple harmonic wave which starts at $t = 0$ and which continues for all positive time. This may be written

$$f(t) = 0 \qquad -\infty < t < 0$$
$$= e^{j\omega_1 t} \qquad 0 < t < \infty \tag{83}$$

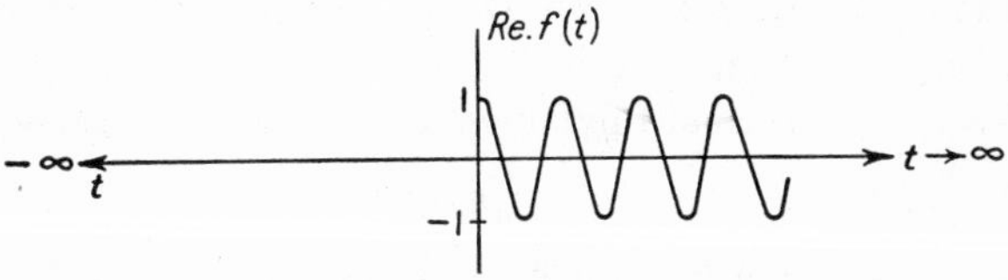

Fig. 18.

Its real part is pictured in Fig. 18. We cannot substitute Eq. (83) into the Fourier transform (1) directly since $f(t)$ does not vanish at infinity and the integral

$$g(\omega) = \int_0^\infty e^{j(\omega_1-\omega)t}\,dt \tag{84}$$

will not converge. It is necessary to resort to a more general formulation, *viz.*, the Laplace transform, which is written as

$$\mathfrak{L}[f(t)] = \int_0^\infty f(t)e^{-st}\,dt \tag{85}$$

where

$$s = \alpha + j\omega \tag{86}$$

Substituting Eq. (83) into Eq. (85), we find, for a wave of unit amplitude,

$$\mathfrak{L}[f(t)] = \int_0^\infty e^{(j\omega_1 - s)t}\,dt \tag{87}$$

$$= \frac{1}{j\omega_1 - s} \tag{88}$$

The Fourier transform may be recovered from Eq. (88) by taking the limit as α approaches zero as follows:

$$g(\omega) = \lim_{\alpha\to 0} \frac{1}{j\omega_1 - (\alpha + j\omega)} \tag{89}$$

$$= \frac{1}{j(\omega_1 - \omega)} \tag{90}$$

This expression shall be referred to as the kappa function of ω_1, that is,

$$\mathcal{K}(\omega_1 - \omega) = \frac{1}{j(\omega_1 - \omega)} \tag{91}$$

If the wave train starts at some arbitrary time T, then the kappa function is described as follows:

$$\mathcal{K}_T(\omega_1 - \omega) = \frac{e^{j(\omega_1 - \omega)T}}{j(\omega_1 - \omega)} \tag{92}$$

17. Fundamental Wave 2—The Delta Function of Angular Velocity. The delta function of angular velocity, $\delta(\omega_1 - \omega)$, which represents a line spectrum at ω_1, is the second fundamental wave to be considered.

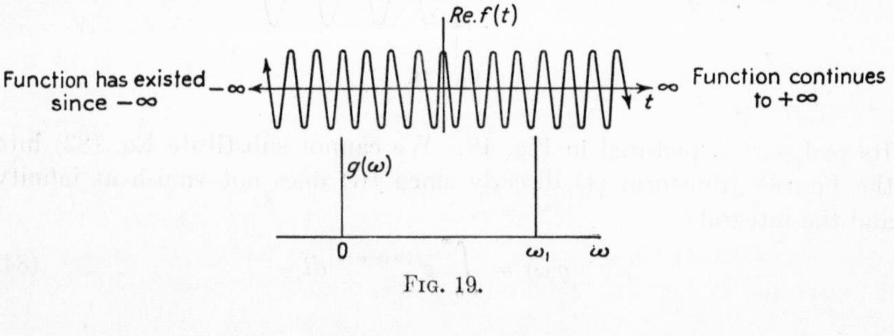

FIG. 19.

Consider a delta function which is located at ω_1 and which is multiplied by an amplitude factor E. $g(\omega)$ may be expressed as follows:

$$g(\omega) = E\delta(\omega_1 - \omega) \tag{93}$$

The inverse Fourier transform of this function is found by writing

$$f(t) = \frac{E}{2\pi} \int_{-\infty}^{\infty} \delta(\omega_1 - \omega) e^{j\omega t}\, d\omega \tag{94}$$

The exponential may be removed from within the integral sign since ω does not vary appreciably as we integrate across the point $\omega = \omega_1$. Then,

$$f(t) = \frac{E}{2\pi} e^{j\omega_1 t} \int_{-\infty}^{\infty} \delta(\omega_1 - \omega)\, d\omega \tag{95}$$

$$= \frac{E}{2\pi} e^{j\omega_1 t} \tag{96}$$

since the integral remaining in Eq. (95) is equal to unity by definition. The rotating vector resulting from the time recovery is one producing a wave train with angular velocity ω_1 over all time. $f(t)$ and $g(\omega)$ are illustrated in Fig. 19.

Spectral Analysis of Continuous Wave Trains by Wave Superposition

18. Amplitude-transient Analysis. Consider the spectral analysis of continuous waves which have nonperiodic amplitude variations or transients.

Case 1. Consider the case when the wave $E_1 e^{j\omega_1 t}$, which has existed since $t = -\infty$, changes amplitude suddenly at $t = 0$ so that the wave may

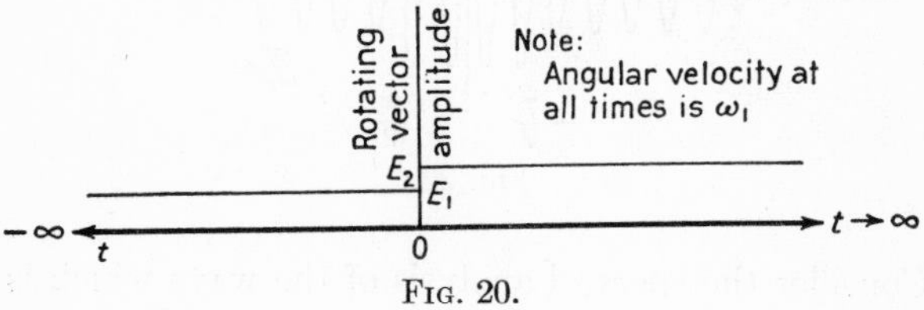

Fig. 20.

be written $E_2 e^{j\omega_1 t}$ for the interval $0 < t < \infty$. This wave configuration is illustrated in Fig. 20 and may be written as

$$\begin{aligned} f(t) &= E_1 e^{j\omega_1 t} \qquad -\infty < t < 0 \\ &= E_2 e^{j\omega_1 t} \qquad 0 < t < \infty \end{aligned} \tag{97}$$

Equation (97) may be analyzed by resolving it into two component waves as illustrated in Fig. 21. Figure 21a shows the wave train $E_1 e^{j\omega_1 t}$, which is continuous and exists for all time. Figure 21*b* shows a wave train $E_3e^{j\omega_1 t}$, which exists in the interval $0 < t < \infty$. $f(t)$ may be expressed as the sum of two wave trains $f_1(t)$ and $f_2(t)$; that is,

$$f(t) = f_1(t) + f_2(t) \tag{98}$$

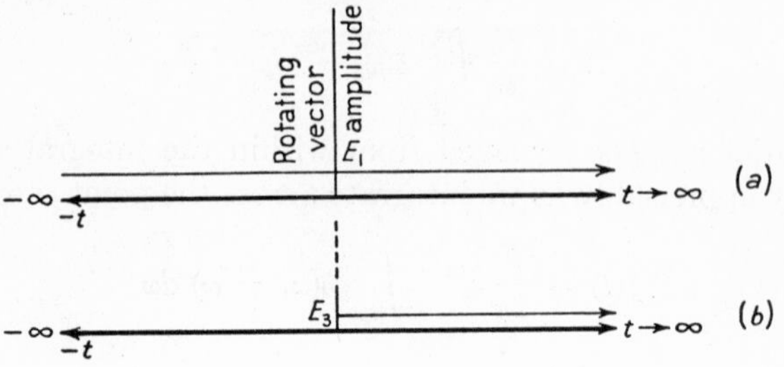

FIG. 21.

$$f_1(t) = E_1e^{j\omega_1 t} \quad -\infty < t < \infty; \qquad f_2(t) = 0 \quad -\infty < t < 0$$
$$= E_3e^{j\omega_1 t} \quad 0 < t < \infty \tag{99}$$

where

$$E_3 = E_2 - E_1 \tag{100}$$

Since the Fourier transform of $f_1(t)$ is the delta function $E_1\delta(\omega_1 - \omega)$ and the Fourier transform of $f_2(t)$ is the kappa function $E_3\mathcal{K}(\omega_1 - \omega)$, it follows that

$$g(\omega) = 2\pi E_1\delta(\omega_1 - \omega) + E_3\mathcal{K}(\omega_1 - \omega) \tag{101}$$

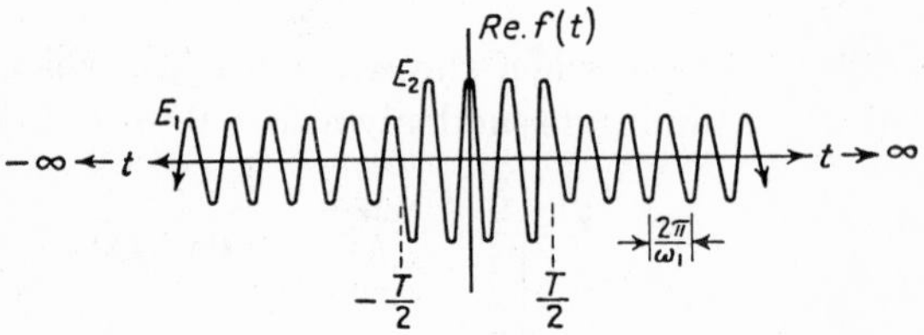

FIG. 22.

Case 2. Consider the spectral analysis of the wave which is illustrated in Fig. 22 and which is expressed mathematically as follows:

$$f(t) = E_1e^{j\omega_1 t} \qquad -\infty < t < -\frac{T}{2}$$
$$= E_2e^{j\omega_1 t} \qquad -\frac{T}{2} < t < \frac{T}{2} \tag{102}$$
$$= E_1e^{j\omega_1 t} \qquad \frac{T}{2} < t < \infty$$

The wave $E_1 e^{j\omega_1 t}$, which has existed for all time prior to $t = -T/2$, suddenly increases its amplitude to E_2 in the interval $-T/2 < t < T/2$ and back to E_1 for $T/2 < t < \infty$. The Fourier analysis of this wave may be simplified by rewriting (102) in the following way:

$$\begin{aligned} f(t) = \quad & E_1 e^{j\omega_1 t} \qquad -\infty < t < \infty \\ & + E_3 e^{j\omega_1 t} \qquad -\frac{T}{2} < t < \frac{T}{2} \end{aligned} \tag{103}$$

where

$$E_3 = E_2 - E_1 \tag{104}$$

Then

$$g(\omega) = E_1 \int_{-\infty}^{\infty} e^{j(\omega_1-\omega)t}\, dt + E_3 \int_{-T/2}^{T/2} e^{j(\omega_1-\omega)t}\, dt \tag{105}$$

The first integral will yield a delta function. The second integral has already been discussed in the first portion of this chapter [see Eq. (6)]. Thus we may write

$$g(\omega) = 2\pi E_1\, \delta(\omega_1 - \omega) + E_3 T \frac{\sin(\omega_1 - \omega)(T/2)}{(\omega_1 - \omega)(T/2)} \tag{106}$$

19. Nonperiodic Changes from One Frequency to Another. Another commonly met phenomenon in nonperiodic angular-velocity variation is that variation which takes place when a wave of infinite duration whose amplitude remains constant abruptly changes from one angular velocity to another at some time during the duration.

Consider the wave

$$\begin{aligned} f(t) &= E e^{j\omega_1 t} \qquad -\infty < t < 0 \\ &= E e^{j\omega_2 t} \qquad 0 < t < \infty \end{aligned} \tag{107}$$

whose angular velocity changes from ω_1 to ω_2 at $t = 0$. This wave may be decomposed into the three waves, which are listed as follows:

Wave I:

$$f_{\mathrm{I}}(t) = E e^{j\omega_1 t} \qquad -\infty < t < \infty \tag{108}$$

Wave II:

$$f_{\mathrm{II}}(t) = E e^{j\omega_2 t} \qquad 0 < t < \infty \tag{109}$$

Wave III:

$$f_{\mathrm{III}}(t) = -E e^{j\omega_1 t} \qquad 0 < t < \infty \tag{110}$$

The $g(\omega)$ for wave I is a delta function, whereas waves II and III yield kappa functions. Thus we find the Fourier transform of (107) to be

$$g(\omega) = E[2\pi\,\delta(\omega_1 - \omega) - \mathcal{K}(\omega_1 - \omega) + \mathcal{K}(\omega_2 - \omega)] \tag{111}$$

20. General Aspects. An analysis of the spectra of transients in continuous waves using step functions, infinite, and semiinfinite wave trains is not very rewarding if only a graphic representation of a spectrum due to some particular transient or sets of transients in a continuous wave train is desired.

For example, consider the single-tone wave train of finite duration which is pictured in Fig. 1 and described by Eq. (3). It is evident that the spectrum of this wave can be described by two kappa functions, *i.e.*,

$$g(\omega) = E[\mathcal{K}_{-T/2}(\omega_1 - \omega) - \mathcal{K}_{T/2}(\omega_1 - \omega)] \tag{112}$$

Equation (112) is a spectral function which is, of course, identical to Eq. (6). It is produced by two semiinfinite wave trains—the first starting at $t = -T/2$ and continuing to $t = \infty$, and the second starting at $t = T/2$ and continuing to $t = \infty$ with its magnitude equal but opposite in sign to the first, thereby canceling the first wave after $t = T/2$, leaving the wave shown in Fig. 1.

If either of the two kappa functions listed in (112) were to exist alone, it could be observed on a suitable spectrum analyzer. However, by combining them as in (112), they form a $(\sin \theta)/\theta$-function spectrum [see Eq. (6)] which bears no simple resemblance to either of the component kappa spectra as a result of the phase shifts involved.

It is obvious, therefore, that it is entirely out of the question to formulate a spectral representation of important continuous wave signals composed of *successive transients* such as television images, by using kappa and delta functions. On the other hand, as will be seen in Sec. 29 of the next chapter, these functions are of utmost importance in solutions leading to the response of linear networks to successive-transient signals in continuous wave transmission.

PROBLEMS

1. Determine the amplitude spectrum of the single-tone wave train of unit peak amplitude whose duration time is 1 μsec and whose wave frequency is 10^9 cycles.

2. Determine the amplitude spectrum of the symmetrical single-tone wave train of unit amplitude whose duration time is 1 μsec and whose wave frequency is 10^6 cycles. Repeat for a duration time of 1/2 μsec, and compare the spectra.

3. Discuss an extension of Prob. 1 in which the finite wave train is repeated 1,000 times per second. To what extent are the spectral distribution and density affected?

4. *a.* Diagram the amplitude spectrum of a sinusoidally frequency-modulated wave train of finite duration for the case when $\beta = 1$.

b. Diagram the amplitude spectrum of a cosinusoidally frequency-modulated wave train of finite duration for the case when $\beta = 1$.

5. Determine the amplitude spectrum of each of the following wave trains:

a. A wave train of infinite duration which experiences a cosine-loop amplitude disturbance at $-T_1/2 < t < T_1/2$ as shown in the figure.

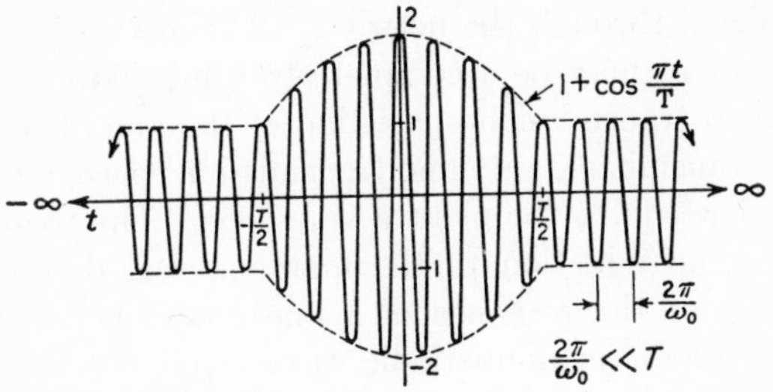

PROB. 5*a*.

b. A wave train of infinite duration which experiences a cosine-loop frequency disturbance at $-T_1/2 < t < T_1/2$ and whose nature is illustrated in the figure.

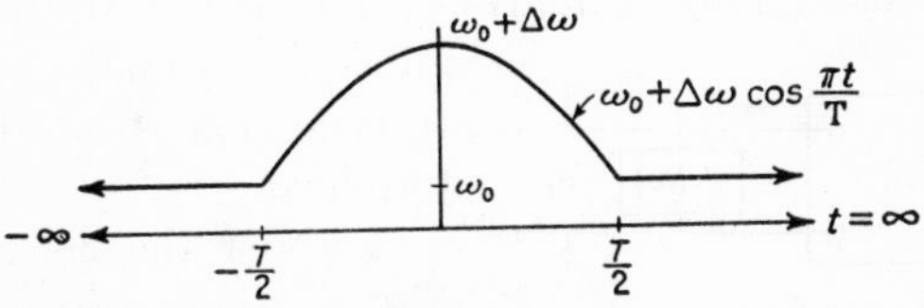

PROB. 5*b*.

c. A wave train of infinite duration which simultaneously experiences the amplitude and frequency changes shown in the figures.

CHAPTER 20

WAVE TRANSMISSION THROUGH LINEAR NETWORKS

1. Introduction. The preceding chapters have treated in great detail the decomposition of complex and modulated waves into their Fourier components. If these waves are transmitted through a linear network whose transmission characteristics are functions of frequency, then the response of the network will be made up of the contributions of each Fourier component transmitted through the network. This network may be a simple single-loop circuit or may be a complete transmission system such as the one used in video transmission consisting of the amplifiers from the television camera, transmitter, antenna, transmission space, receiving antenna, receiver, amplifier—up to the picture kinescope. The treatment to follow will serve as an introduction to the mathematical determination, using Fourier analysis, of the response of a linear communications system at whose input a periodic or nonperiodic wave or electric force is impressed.

TRANSMISSION CHARACTERISTICS OF LINEAR NETWORKS

2. The Complex Transmission-frequency Function $h(\omega)$. Before linear-system response using Fourier analysis can be obtained, the complex transmission-frequency function for the transmission network must be determined.

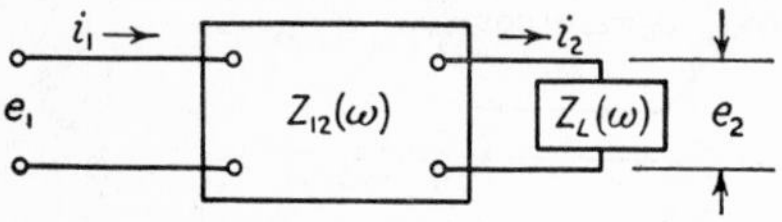

FIG. 1. Linear transfer network.

Consider the network pictured in Fig. 1, whose transfer impedance is $Z_{12}(\omega)$. This network is terminated in the impedance $Z_L(\omega)$. If an input voltage e_1 is applied to the input, causing a current i_1 to flow, a current i_2 will pass through the terminating impedance, thus causing a voltage e_2 to appear across this impedance. If e_1 may be described by a single rotating vector of amplitude E_1 with constant angular velocity ω_1 so that

$$e_1 = E_1 e^{j\omega_1 t} \tag{1}$$

then the output voltage will be a single rotating vector of some new amplitude E_2 with the same constant angular velocity ω_1 as the input but shifted in phase so that

$$e_2 = E_2 e^{j[\omega_1 t + \psi(\omega_1)]} \tag{2}$$

Let us write

$$H(\omega_1) = \left|\frac{e_2}{e_1}\right| = \frac{E_2}{E_1} \tag{3}$$

$H(\omega)$ and $\psi(\omega)$ are amplitude and phase functions which are determined by the network.

The output voltage e_2 which appears across $Z_L(\omega)$ may be written as follows:

$$e_1 = i_2 Z_L(\omega) \tag{4}$$

Then, in general, we may write the complex transmission-frequency function[1] as

$$h(\omega) = H(\omega)e^{j\psi(\omega)} \tag{5}$$

where

$$H(\omega)e^{j\psi(\omega)} = \frac{e_2(\omega)}{e_1(\omega)} \tag{6}$$

$h(\omega)$ may be described in terms of the transfer impedance and the load impedance as

$$h(\omega) = \frac{Z_L(\omega)}{Z_{12}(\omega)} \tag{7}$$

In general, $H(\omega)$ will be an even function, and $\psi(\omega)$ will be an odd function.

Since $h(\omega)$ is a function of ω, Eq. (6) must be determined for each significant or important Fourier component of any complex periodic or nonperiodic wave impressed at the input and the output response will consist of the superposition of all of the transferred component waves appearing across $Z_L(\omega)$.

3. Approximate Representation of $h(\omega)$. In general, exact expressions for $h(\omega)$ are of academic interest only because of the inherent and almost insurmountable complexity which is encountered in even the most simple networks. In fact, if it were not for our ability to obtain closely correct expressions for response using approximate expressions for $h(\omega)$, the Fourier integral and similar formulations would be of academic interest alone.

Consider, as an illustration, the approximate amplitude and phase characteristics of a low-pass filter; these characteristics may be described as follows:

$$\begin{aligned} H(\omega) &= 0 \qquad -\infty < \omega < -\omega_c \\ &= K \qquad -\omega_c < \omega < \omega_c \\ &= 0 \qquad \omega_c < \omega < \infty \end{aligned} \tag{8}$$

[1] W. L. Sullivan, Analysis of Systems with Known Transmission-frequency Characteristics by Fourier Integrals, *Elec. Eng.*, vol. 61, pp. 248–256, May, 1942.

$$\begin{aligned}\psi(\omega) &= 0 \qquad & -\infty < \omega < -\omega_c \\ &= \omega t_d & -\omega_c < \omega < \omega_c \\ &= 0 & \omega_c < \omega < \infty\end{aligned} \tag{9}$$

$H(\omega)$ and $\psi(\omega)$ are pictured in Fig. 2*a* and *b*, respectively. The quantities K and t_d which appear in (8) and (9) are constants whose actual significance will be discussed in the next section.

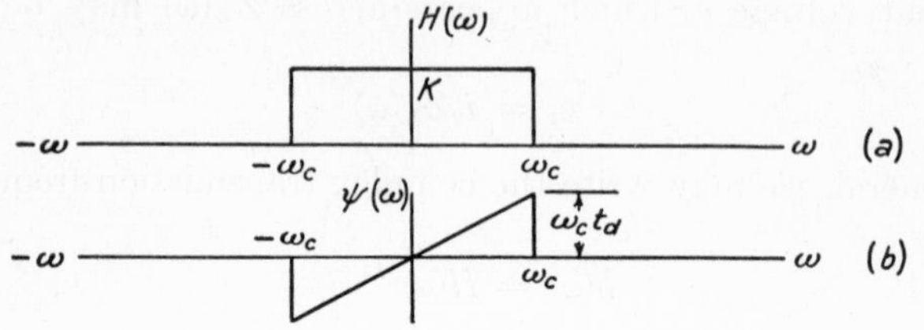

FIG. 2. Approximate amplitude and phase characteristics of a low-pass filter.

4. Amplitude and Phase Distortion in Linear-network Transmission. Before entering upon a discussion of the Fourier formulation associated with complex-wave transmission, it is convenient at this point to present a discussion of the actual roles played by amplitude and phase transmission characteristics.

Consider a wave made up of a fundamental and the third and fifth harmonics (see Fig. 2, Chap. 2),

$$e_1 = E_1(\sin \omega_1 t + 0.333 \sin 3\omega_1 t + 0.2 \sin 5\omega_1 t) \tag{10}$$

In order to avoid phase distortion, the transmission of e_1 through any network which does not yield amplitude distortion must be of the form

$$e_2 = E_1[\sin \omega_1(t - t_d) + 0.33 \sin 3\omega_1(t - t_d) + 0.2 \sin 5\omega_1(t - t_d)] \tag{11}$$

t_d is called the *delay time* of the network.

It is also evident that in order to avoid amplitude distortion as a result of transmission through a constant-t_d network, the amplitude of each component must be increased or decreased by a constant percentage so that the output will be a replica of the input. Equation (10), for instance, may be written

$$e_2 = KE_1[\sin \omega_1(t - t_d) + 0.33 \sin 3\omega_1(t - t_d) + 0.2 \sin 5\omega_1(t - t_d)] \tag{12}$$

where K is a constant which is determined by the network.

5. Idealized Networks. An idealized network is a network which will transmit all components in its pass band according to the requirements

$$H(\omega) = K \tag{13}$$

$$\text{Delay time} = t_d \tag{14}$$

It is important to realize that these qualities of an idealized transmission network apply only to the pass band or bands and do not imply that the output is necessarily a replica of the input since, in general, complex waves are represented by Fourier series or transforms and an infinite-bandwidth network would be necessary to pass all the components and in this way exactly reproduce the input wave.

TRANSMISSION OF PERIODIC COMPLEX AND MODULATED WAVES THROUGH LINEAR NETWORKS

6. Complex Waves. In Chap. 2, it has been shown that the complex Fourier-series representation of a periodic nonsinusoidal wave may be written as follows:

$$e_1(t) = \sum_{-\infty}^{\infty} C_n e^{jn\omega_1 t} \tag{15}$$

$$C_n = \frac{\omega_1}{2\pi} \int_{-\pi/\omega_1}^{\pi/\omega_1} e_1(t) e^{-jn\omega_1 t}\, dt \tag{16}$$

If this wave is passed through a linear network whose complex transmission-frequency function is $h(\omega)$, then the output wave is

$$e_2(t) = \sum_{-\infty}^{\infty} C_n H(n\omega_1) e^{j[n\omega_1 t + \psi(n\omega_1)]} \tag{17}$$

where C_n is expressed by Eq. (16). The product $C_n H(n\omega_1)$ describes the amplitude of each harmonic component as it appears across the output of the network and $[n\omega_1 t + \psi(n\omega_1)]$ gives the phase of each.

7. Square Wave through a Video Amplifier. Consider the response of the video amplifier pictured in Fig. 12, Chap. 10, when the square wave pictured in Fig. 3 is applied to its input terminals. (The harmonic and

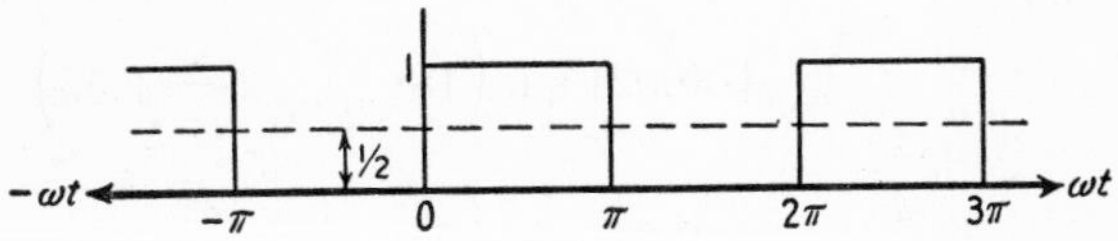

FIG. 3.

transient responses of this amplifier have been discussed in Secs. 3 and 10, Chap. 10).

The Fourier-series representation of the square wave pictured in Fig. 3 is

$$e_1(t) = \frac{1}{2} + \frac{1}{\pi} \sum_{n=1}^{\infty} \frac{1 - (-1)^n}{n} \sin n\omega_1 t \tag{18}$$

Let the period of this periodic square wave be such that the duration time of a half period[1] is slightly in excess of the time which is necessary for the response of a step-function voltage to attain its steady-state value in this circuit.

The amplitude and phase portions of the complex transmission-frequency function $h(\omega)$ for this circuit may be shown, using Kirchhoff's laws, to be

$$H(\omega) = g_m R_L \sqrt{\frac{1 + (f/kf_0)^2}{[(kf/f_0)]^2 + [(f/f_0)^2 - 1]^2}} \tag{19}$$

$$\psi(\omega) = \tan^{-1} \frac{f}{kf_0} \left[\left(\frac{f}{f_0} \right)^2 + k^2 - 1 \right] \tag{20}$$

where f is the driving frequency and f_0 and k are described by (81) in Chap. 10.

This half-period time can be obtained from Fig. 12, Chap. 10. The curve for $k = 1.41$ in Fig. 12 achieves a near-steady value for an elapsed time of 0.8 k/f_0 sec. The total period of the impressed square wave is then 1.6 (k/f_0) sec. Using values of $H(\omega)$ and $\psi(\omega)$ obtained from Eqs. (19) and (20) for the various harmonic components of this square wave, the normalized response becomes, using components of significant magnitude only,

$$\begin{aligned} e_0(t) = \frac{1}{2} + \frac{2}{\pi} \Big[\; & 1.02 \sin \left(2\pi \frac{f_0}{2.26} t - 0.358 \right) \\ & + 0.225 \sin \left(6\pi \frac{f_0}{2.26} t - 1.20 \right) \\ & + 0.074 \sin \left(10\pi \frac{f_0}{2.26} t - 1.46 \right) \\ & + 0.036 \sin \left(14\pi \frac{f_0}{2.26} t - 1.53 \right) \\ & + 0.021 \sin \left(18\pi \frac{f_0}{2.26} t - 1.55 \right) \\ & + 0.014 \sin \left(22\pi \frac{f_0}{2.26} t - 1.56 \right) \\ & + 0.010 \sin \left(26\pi \frac{f_0}{2.26} t - 1.56 \right) \Big] \end{aligned} \tag{21}$$

[1] If the assumed half period is too long, the solution, though correct, will be laborious since the Fourier series will converge less rapidly. If the assumed half period is too short, the response will not attain the steady-state value which is necessary for the next half-cycle response to start correctly.

Values from Eq. (21) are compared with values from Eq. (80), Chap. 10, in the following table:

$t\frac{f_0}{k}$	From (80), Chap. 10	From (21)
0	0	0.04
0.05	0.30	0.30
0.10	0.60	0.58
0.20	0.93	0.92
0.40	1.06	1.07
0.60	1.02	1.02
0.80	1.00	0.96

The excellence of the agreement at all points, except the points of discontinuity in the square wave at $t = 0$ and $t = 0.8\ k/f_0$, is demonstrated by this table.

Bedford and Fredendall[1] have extended the solution of the transient response of the shunt-compensated amplifier to include the response of multistage shunt-compensated amplifiers to step-function voltages. Up to 64 cascaded stages have been considered.

The amplitude and phase characteristics for n stages are found by raising

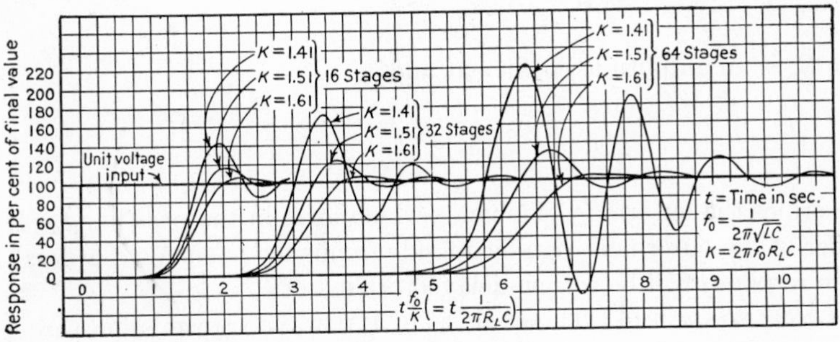

FIG. 4. Response of cascaded amplifiers to a unit step function. (*After Bedford and Fredendall, courtesy of Institute of Radio Engineers.*)

the amplitude response of one stage to the nth power and by multiplying the phase delay by n. Using the same Fourier-series approach as used for a single stage, response curves for $k = 1.41, 1.51, 1.61$ and $n = 16, 32, 64$ are computed and are plotted in Fig. 4.

8. Square Wave through a Low-pass Filter. If the square wave is being transferred through a low-pass filter with ideal characteristics and with

[1] Bedford and Fredendall, Transient Response of Multistage Video-frequency Amplifiers, *Proc. IRE*, vol. 27, pp. 277–284, April, 1939.

cutoff at ω_c, it is evident that

$$e_2(t) = \frac{K}{2} + \frac{K}{\pi} \sum_{n=1}^{n<\omega_c/\omega_1} \frac{1-(-1)^n}{n} \sin n\omega_1(t - t_d) \tag{22}$$

If n is made sufficiently large, then $e_2(t)$ will be a faithful replica of $e_1(t)$. Otherwise distortion will result.

9. Modulated Waves. The output response of a linear network to an amplitude modulated wave is written

$$e_2(t) = \sum_{n=-\infty}^{n=\infty} \mathfrak{M}_A(t)H(\omega)e^{j[(\omega_0+n\omega_1)t+\psi(\omega_0+n\omega_1)]} \tag{23}$$

Such an expression is actually of little more than academic interest since it is not practical to resort to a summation of output components, this being possible only with transferred complex waves.

If the wave described in Eq. (23) is passed through an idealized bandpass filter whose pass band is centered at ω_0 and which transmits in the band from $\omega_0 + \Omega/2$ to $\omega_0 - \Omega/2$, then, for this simple but highly practical case, the degree to which e_2 resembles e_1 may be determined by investigating the sideband content in this pass band. If a single-tone AM wave is being transferred through this idealized bandpass filter, then

$$e_2(t) = K \sum_{n=-n_s}^{n=n_s} C_n e^{j(\omega_0+n\omega_1)(t-t_d)} \tag{24}$$

where C_n is an amplitude coefficient and

$$n_s \approx \frac{\Omega}{2\omega_1} \tag{25}$$

n_s describes the outermost sidebands which exist in the pass band. If the number of the outermost significant side frequency is equal to or less than n_s, the response will be a time-delayed replica of e_1.

FM-wave Response.[1] The analysis of FM-wave transmission through a linear network is not as straightforward as that for AM-wave transmission since the analysis must include an additional consideration of great importance, *i.e., the transient effects due to the continual frequency variation of the FM wave.*

If the transient effects may be neglected so that the response of the linear

[1] Several authors have published methods of obtaining output envelopes and descriptions of phase in the transmission of FM waves. See, for example, W. J. Frantz, The Transmission of a Frequency Modulated Wave through a Network, *Proc. IRE*, vol. 34, pp. 114–125, March, 1946; H. Roder, Effects of Tuned Circuits upon a Frequency-modulated Signal, *Proc. IRE*, vol. 25, pp. 1617–1648, December, 1937; L. J. Giacoletto, Network Transmission of a Frequency Modulated Wave, *Proc. IRE*, vol. 35, pp. 1105–1106, October, 1947.

network at any instant is the same as the steady-state sine-wave behavior that would be calculated on the basis of a sinusoidal voltage having a frequency equal to the frequency of the FM wave at that instant, then the analysis involved is known as the *quasi-steady-state* method of analysis. This method and the validity and errors involved will be studied in the next section. [For a discussion of a useful criterion of validity based on a Fourier expansion of $h(\omega)$, see Frantz's paper.]

If the quasi-steady state may be validly used, then an elementary concept may be stated as follows: If the expression in Eq. (24) describes a single-tone FM wave such that

$$C_n = J_n(\beta) \qquad n_s\omega_1 \approx \Delta\omega < \frac{\Omega}{2} \tag{26}$$

where $\beta = \Delta\omega/\omega_1$, then, as in the case of the AM wave, the output will be a time-delayed replica of e_1. However, if $\Delta\omega > \Omega/2$, for large β, a large amount of the outer sideband energy will not appear at the output and distortion will take place.

10. Fourier Analysis Using a Power-series Expansion of $h(\omega)$.[1] The analysis to be presented yields the quasi-stationary response of a linear transfer network to an FM wave. This method uses a power-series expansion of $h(\omega)$ and is relatively simple and straightforward provided that the errors involved using the quasi-stationary approach are negligible. Let the output voltage $e_2(t)$ be represented by the Fourier integral

$$e_2(t) = \frac{Ee^{j\omega_0 t}}{2\pi} \int_{-\infty}^{\infty} g(\omega)h(\omega_0 + \omega)e^{j\omega t}\, d\omega \tag{27}$$

where

$$g(\omega) = \int_T \mathfrak{M}(t)e^{-j\omega t}\, dt \tag{28}$$

$g(\omega)$ being described in the finite epoch $0 \le t \le T$.

It follows from power-series formulation that

$$h(\omega_0 + \omega) = h(\omega_0) + \sum_1^\infty \frac{\omega^n}{n!}\frac{d^n h(\omega_0)}{d\omega_0{}^n} \tag{29}$$

Substituting this expression into Eq. (27), we get

$$e_2(t) = \frac{Ee^{j\omega_0 t}}{2\pi}\left[h(\omega_0)\int_{-\infty}^{\infty} g(\omega)e^{j\omega t}\, d\omega + \sum_1^\infty \frac{1}{n!}\frac{d^n h(\omega_0)}{d\omega_0{}^n}\int_{-\infty}^{\infty} \omega^n g(\omega)e^{j\omega t}\, d\omega\right] \tag{30}$$

where only the term ω^n is inserted into the integrand.

[1] Carson and Fry, Variable Frequency Electric Circuit Theory, *Bell System Tech. J.*, vol. 16, pp. 513–540, October, 1937.

Consider the development of Eq. (30), where $\mathfrak{M}(t)$ is a periodic phase- or a frequency-modulating function. Let

$$\mathfrak{M}(t) = e^{j\Delta\Theta_t} = \exp\left(j \int \Delta\omega_t \, dt\right) \tag{31}$$

The inverse Fourier transform of $\omega^n g(\omega)$ may then be shown to be as follows,

$$\int_{-\infty}^{\infty} \omega^n g(\omega) e^{j\omega t} \, d\omega = Q_n(t) e^{j\Delta\Theta_t} \tag{32}$$

where

$$Q_n(t) = \left(\Delta\dot{\Theta}_t - j\frac{d}{dt}\right)^{n-1} \Delta\dot{\Theta}_t \tag{33}$$

Substituting (32) into Eq. (30), we get

$$e_{2_s}(t) = Ee^{j(\omega_0 t + \Delta\Theta_t)}\left[h(\omega_0) + \sum_1^\infty \frac{1}{n!}\frac{d^n h(\omega_0)}{d\omega_0^{\ n}} Q_n(t)\right] \tag{34}$$

Although Eq. (27) included the initial transients, differentiation with respect to time has eliminated them, leaving the final equation (34) in quasi-stationary form.

As it stands, Eq. (34) is of limited practical value[1] since any computation using it would be very laborious. We may evolve a more informative form of $e_{2_s}(t)$, using suitable approximations as follows:

$\Delta\omega_t$ is of the form $\Delta\omega S(t)$; it has been seen in Chap. 18 that the spectral energy is contained in the region from $\omega_0 + \Delta\omega$ to $\omega_0 - \Delta\omega$ in most practical cases. If $\Delta\omega \gg \omega_1$ where $2\pi/\omega_1$ is the period of the modulating wave, then Carson has shown that the expression $Q_n(t)$ may be approximated by the terms

$$Q_n(t) = \Delta\omega_t^{\ n} - j\frac{n(n-1)}{2}\Delta\omega_t^{\ n-2}\,\Delta\dot{\omega}_t \tag{35}$$

Note that if $h(\omega) = h(j\omega)$ and $\omega_t = \omega_0 + \Delta\omega_t$, then

$$h(\omega_t) = h(\omega_0) + \sum_{n=1}^\infty \frac{\Delta\omega_t^{\ n}}{n!}\frac{d^n h(\omega_0)}{d\omega_0^{\ n}}$$
$$\frac{d^2 h(\omega_t)}{d\omega_t^{\ 2}} = \sum_{n=1}^\infty \frac{-n(n-1)}{n!}\Delta\omega_t^{\ n-2}\frac{d^n h(\omega_0)}{d\omega_0^{\ n}} \tag{36}$$

Substituting Eqs. (35) and (36) into Eq. (34), we find that, for $\Delta\omega \gg \omega_1$,

$$e_{2_s}(t) = E_1\left[\exp\left(j\int \omega_t \, dt\right)\right]\left[h(\omega_t) + j\frac{\Delta\dot{\omega}_t}{2}\frac{d^2 h(\omega_t)}{d\omega_0^{\ n}}\right] \tag{37}$$

[1] For an application of the general theory to circuits using tuned amplifiers, see D. L. Jaffe, A Theoretical and Experimental Investigation of Tuned-circuit Distortion in Frequency Modulation Systems, *Proc. IRE*, vol. 33, pp. 318–333, May, 1945.

The first term is the steady-state response of the linear network at the instantaneous angular velocity ω_t. The second term is a measure of the error involved. This error may be rendered minimum under two conditions:

1. When $h(\omega_t)$ is substantially linear over the ranges of frequency involved.

2. When the rates of change of frequency are small to the extent of also making the linearity of $h(\omega_t)$ unimportant.

Note that if we let

$$h(\omega_t) = h_1 + jh_2 \qquad u = \Delta\dot{\omega}_t/2$$
$$\frac{d^2h(\omega_t)}{d\omega_t^2} = h_1^2 + jh_2^2 \tag{38}$$

then we may write the output wave as described by (37) in the following form:

$$e_{2_s}(t) = \sqrt{(h_2 + h_1^2u)^2 + (h_1 - h_2^2u)^2}\, E_1 \cdot \exp\left(j\int \omega_t\, dt - \tan^{-1}\frac{h_2 + h_1^2u}{h_1 - h_2^2u}\right) \tag{39}$$

Equation (39) may be evaluated once ω_t and $h(\omega_t)$ are known, provided that $\Delta\omega \gg \omega_1$.

Illustration of the Use of (37). Consider the distortion described by (37) for the case when the frequency-modulated wave, $E \exp[j(\omega_0 + \Delta\omega \cos \omega_1)t]$, is applied at the input of the tuned amplifier pictured in Fig. 5. If the tuned circuit in this amplifier is adjusted to the carrier frequency, $\omega_0/2\pi$, it can be shown that for this amplifier (compare with Prob. 2, Chap. 10)

$$h(\omega_t) \cong g_mR \frac{1}{1 + j2\dfrac{\omega_0L}{R}\left(\dfrac{\omega_0 - \omega_t}{\omega_0}\right)} \tag{40}$$

where ω_t is the instantaneous angular velocity. Equation (40) is developed on the premise that $R \ll R_g$ and that the presence of C_s and C_c may be ignored.

It follows then that

$$\Delta\dot{\omega}_t = \frac{d}{dt}(\Delta\omega \cos \omega_1 t) = -\omega_1\Delta\omega \sin \omega_1 t$$
$$\frac{d^2h(\omega_t)}{d\omega_t^2} = \frac{2}{\pi^2}\frac{g_mR}{\Delta f'^2} \tag{41}$$

where $\Delta f' = \omega_0R/2\pi\omega_0L$ and is the bandwidth in cycles describing the region of the gain curve of the amplifier between the 0.707 gain points. Substituting these expressions with (37), we get

$$e_{2_s} = Ee^{j(\omega_0 + \Delta\omega\cos\omega_1 t)}\left[h(\omega_t) - j\frac{g_mR}{\pi^2}\frac{\omega_1}{\Delta f'}\frac{\Delta\omega}{\Delta f'}\sin \omega_1 t\right] \tag{42}$$

Thus we see that the distortion incurred in using the quasi-stationary method on the amplifier in Fig. 5 is a function of $\omega_1/\Delta f'$ and $\Delta\omega/\Delta f'$. By proper selection of these parameters, this distortion may be minimized.

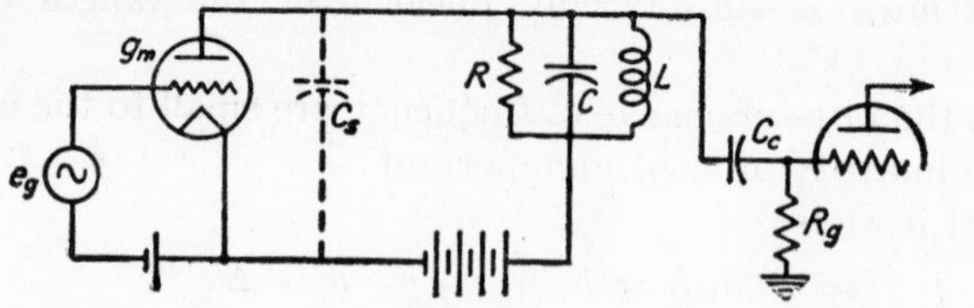

FIG. 5.

THE RESPONSE OF A LINEAR TRANSFER NETWORK

11. Fundamental Fourier Integral Relationships. The most important application of the Fourier integral for the electrical engineer or physicist is the determination of the response of a linear network upon whose input a nonperiodic wave force is impressed. This integral analysis is, in general, more rewarding than that for periodic-wave transmission analysis since useful expressions for response in closed form, rather than the point-by-point summations necessary in periodic-wave transmission analysis, may be obtained.

In the formulations to follow, the integrations demanded by the Fourier integral will be made possible through the use of idealized networks which yield approximate and functional representations of $h(\omega)$.

Consider the transfer network pictured in Fig. 1. If $e_1(t)$ is a nonperiodic function of time, then, using the Fourier transform, we get

$$g_1(\omega) = \int_{-\infty}^{\infty} e_1(t)e^{-j\omega t}\,dt \tag{43}$$

$$= G_1(\omega)e^{j\Theta_1(\omega)} \tag{44}$$

If the complex transmission-frequency function of the network is $h(\omega)$, the output spectrum corresponding to $e_2(t)$ is

$$g_2(\omega) = \int_{-\infty}^{\infty} e_2(t)e^{-j\omega t}\,dt = G_1(\omega)H(\omega)e^{j[\Theta_1(\omega)+\psi(\omega)]} \tag{45}$$

where $G_1(\omega)H(\omega)$ is the amplitude spectrum and $\Theta_1(\omega) + \psi(\omega)$ is the phase spectrum.

The time function $e_2(t)$ may be recovered from the spectrum equation in Eq. (45) to yield

$$e_2(t) = \frac{1}{2\pi}\int_{-\infty}^{\infty}\int_{-\infty}^{\infty} e_1(t)e^{-j\omega t}\,dt\,e^{j\omega t}\,d\omega \tag{46}$$

$$= \frac{1}{2\pi}\int_{\omega=-\infty}^{\infty} G_1(\omega)H(\omega)e^{j[\omega t+\Theta_1(\omega)+\psi(\omega)]}\,d\omega \tag{47}$$

12. Transmission through an Idealized Network Having Infinite Bandwidth. Consider the idealized network having infinite bandwidth for which

$$H(\omega)e^{j\psi(\omega)} = Ke^{j\omega t_d} \qquad -\infty < \omega < \infty \tag{48}$$

It is evident that the response of this network to an input wave is

$$e_2(t) = \frac{K}{2\pi}\int_{\omega=-\infty}^{\infty} g(\omega)e^{j\omega(t-t_d)}\,d\omega \tag{49}$$

$$= Ke_1(t - t_d) \tag{50}$$

which is the original wave whose amplitude is modified by K and which is delayed by the delay time t_d.

However, infinite-bandwidth networks are not realizable in practice, and the general equation (47) or the idealized-network equation (49) must be solved by integrating over only the finite-width pass band which is found in practical networks.

LINEAR-NETWORK RESPONSE TO STEP FUNCTIONS[1]

13. Introduction. In addition to providing a method for determining the response of a linear network to pulse excitation, step-function response is an important subject in its own right since it has many applications in the communications field. It also provides concepts which are useful for the understanding of the general theory of network response.

14. Sine-integral Representation of a Unit Step Function. An expression, due to Dirichlet, for the unit step function which is pictured in Chap. 4 may be obtained using a Fourier integral. This new representation will be seen to be a fundamental tool in nonperiodic-linear-network-response analysis.

This step function is expressed as

$$\begin{aligned} f(t) &= 0 \qquad -\infty < t < 0 \\ &= 1 \qquad 0 < t < \infty \end{aligned} \tag{51}$$

The $g(\omega)$ of this expression has been found in Chap. 4 to be

$$g(\omega) = \frac{1}{j\omega} \tag{52}$$

[1] The response of a linear-transmission system to a step voltage contains all the information necessary to determine both the a-c phase and frequency characteristics of the system. For a detailed discussion of the synthesis of square-wave response from a given set of amplitude and phase characteristics, see Bedford and Fredendall, *Proc. IRE*, vol. 30, pp. 440–457, October, 1942.

Substituting Eq. (52) into Eq. (40), the Fourier-integral representation of (51) is found to be

$$f(t) = \frac{1}{2\pi} \int_{-\infty}^{\infty} \frac{e^{j\omega t}}{j\omega} \, d\omega \tag{53}$$

This may be written

$$f(t) = \frac{1}{2\pi} \int_{-\infty}^{\infty} \frac{\sin \omega t}{\omega} \, d\omega + \frac{1}{2\pi j} \int_{-\infty}^{\infty} \frac{\cos \omega t}{\omega} \, d\omega \tag{54}$$

The second integral of Eq. (54) is a well-known integral whose solution is

$$\frac{1}{2\pi j} \int_{-\infty}^{\infty} \frac{\cos \omega t}{\omega} \, d\omega = \frac{1}{2} \tag{55}$$

Because of the evenness of the function $(\sin \omega t)/\omega$, we may write $f(t)$ in the form

$$f(t) = \frac{1}{2} + \frac{1}{\pi} \int_{0}^{\infty} \frac{\sin \omega t}{\omega} \, d\omega \tag{56}$$

15. Sine and Cosine Integrals.[1] The sine integral Si (x), whose form appears in Eq. (56) and which will be met frequently in transient analysis, is written as follows:

$$\text{Si}\,(x) = \int_{0}^{x} \frac{\sin u}{u} \, du \tag{57}$$

The value of u does not actually contribute to the result of the integration. As is seen in Eq. (57), Si (x) is a function of the limit x alone.

Si (x) is a well-known function which has been tabulated in numerous

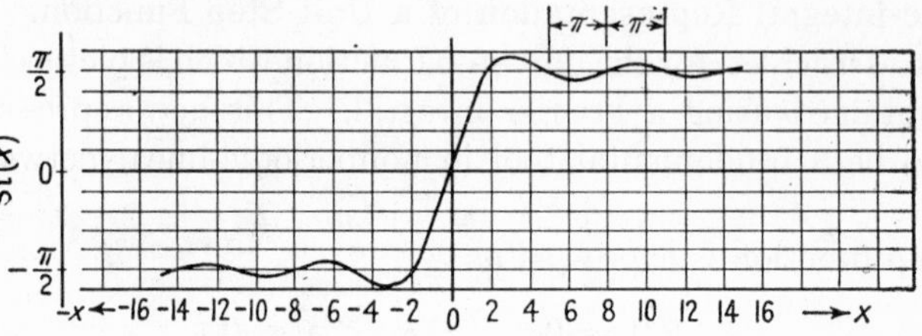

FIG. 6. Si (x) function.

volumes. Its behavior for $\pm x$ is pictured in Fig. 6. The function is odd and passes through the origin with unity slope. For increasing values of x, it oscillates about the value $\pi/2$, with its amplitude decreasing and with its zeros spaced apart by π. For negative values of x, the function oscillates about $-\pi/2$.

[1] For a discussion of the Gibbs phenomenon which bears directly on this subject, see E. A. Guillemin, "The Mathematics of Circuit Analysis," Chap. VII, John Wiley & Sons, Inc., New York, 1949.

Another frequently encountered integral is the cosine integral Ci (x), where

$$\mathrm{Ci}\,(x) = -\int_x^\infty \frac{\cos u}{u}\,du \tag{58}$$

As in the case of the sine integral, the actual value of Ci (x) is a function of the integration limit (which is the lower one in this case) alone. This function has been tabulated and is pictured in Fig. 7.

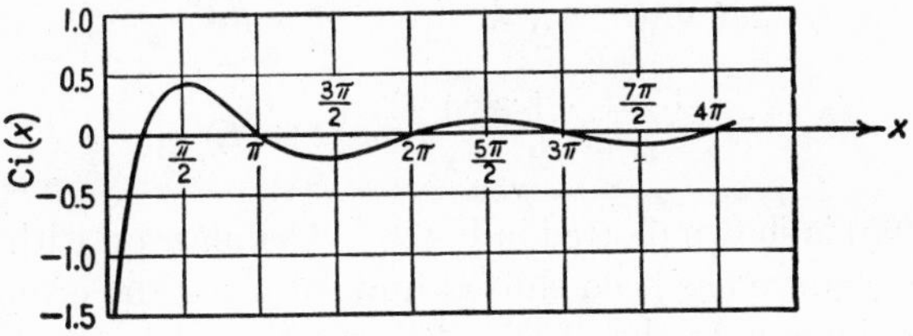

FIG. 7. Ci (x) function.

For large x, Ci (x) yields values of near-zero magnitude. For small x near the origin, the function is best evaluated using the expansion

$$\mathrm{Ci}\,(x) = 0.57721 + \log x - \frac{x^2}{2\cdot 2!} + \frac{x^4}{4\cdot 4!} - \frac{x^6}{6\cdot 6!} + \cdots \tag{59}$$

16. The Step Function and Linear-network Response. The unit step function, which is also known as the Heaviside unit voltage, is one of the most important functions to engineers and physicists interested in networks capable of wide-band transmission. In video and pulse transmission amplifiers, a criterion of fidelity based on amplifier response to a unit step function, in many cases, has replaced the one based on steady-state characteristics.[1]

The response of any network having a complex transmission-frequency function $h(\omega)$ to a unit step function is, using Eq. (56),

$$e_2(t) = \frac{H(0)}{2} + \frac{1}{2\pi}\int_{-\infty}^{\infty} \frac{H(\omega)\sin\,(\omega t - \psi(\omega))}{\omega}\,d\omega \tag{60}$$

This formulation is very difficult to solve for any but the simplest networks, and the following sections are devoted to some general treatments of unit-voltage response solutions.

17. The Unit Step Function and an Idealized Low-pass Filter. Consider the response of the idealized low-pass filter pictured in Fig. 5*a* and *b*, where the cutoff frequency is ω_c and

$$H(\omega) = 1 \qquad \psi(\omega) = \omega t_d \tag{61}$$

[1] See also D. L. Waidelich, Steady-state Testing with Saw-tooth Waves, *Proc. IRE*, vol. 33, pp. 339–348, June, 1944.

Substituting (61) into Eq. (60), we get,

$$e_2(t) = \frac{1}{2} + \frac{1}{\pi} \int_0^{\omega_c} \frac{\sin \omega(t - t_d)}{\omega} \, d\omega \tag{62}$$

If

$$u = \omega(t - t_d) \qquad u_c = \omega_c(t - t_d) \tag{63}$$

then Eq. (62) may be rewritten as follows:

$$e_2(t) = \frac{1}{2} + \frac{1}{\pi} \int_0^{u_c} \frac{\sin u}{u} \, du \tag{64}$$

$$= \frac{1}{2} + \frac{1}{\pi} \operatorname{Si} \omega_c(t - t_d) \tag{65}$$

Equation (65) is shown plotted in Fig. 8.[1] Comparison with Fig. 6 shows that the Si (u_c) curve has been shifted upward along the ordinate axis and shifted along the axis of the abscissa by the time delay t_d, to show a de-

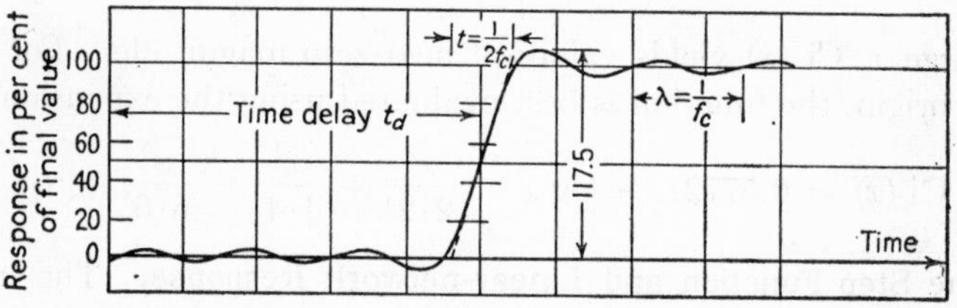

Fig. 8.

layed unit step function which very closely approximates the impressed function.

The build-up time of the step of the response is $t = \pi/\omega_c$, which is also equal to one-half of the period of the oscillations. Thus, the greater the bandwidth of the network, the steeper will be the step front and the oscillation zeros will be closer together. For an infinite-bandwidth idealized network with time delay t_d, the response will be a perfect step function which has been delayed by the time t_d.

18. Anticipatory Nature of Eq. (65). Note in Fig. 8 that at $t = 0$ the function yielding the response is not equal to zero, showing that the net-

[1] Many years before step-function response became an important consideration in communication engineering, Lord Rayleigh studied the Fourier integral, using a set of boundary conditions similar to those used for step-function formulation in a linear transfer network of ideal characteristics and limited bandwidth and in almost uncanny fashion evolved the waveform pictured in Fig. 8. [See Some Calculations in Illustration of Fourier's Theorem, *Proc. Roy. Soc. A*, vol. 90, pp. 318–322, 1914.] It is of interest that Lord Rayleigh made the following comment in his paper with regard to the results of his calculations: ". . . although the results include no novelty of principle, they may be worth putting upon record."

work apparently anticipates the step function. This apparent anomaly is due to the fact that the idealized network does not exactly represent the amplitude and phase characteristics of a true physical network. The idealized amplitude characteristic has an essential singularity at $\omega = \infty$ as the bandwidth is increased and the exact phase curve resembles an arcsine curve. This discrepancy is actually trivial since the wave in Fig. 8 is, in general, a highly satisfactory representation of step-function response of physically realizable circuits. Had $\psi(\omega)$ and $H(\omega)$ been given by exact expressions, then this anomaly would not have occurred.

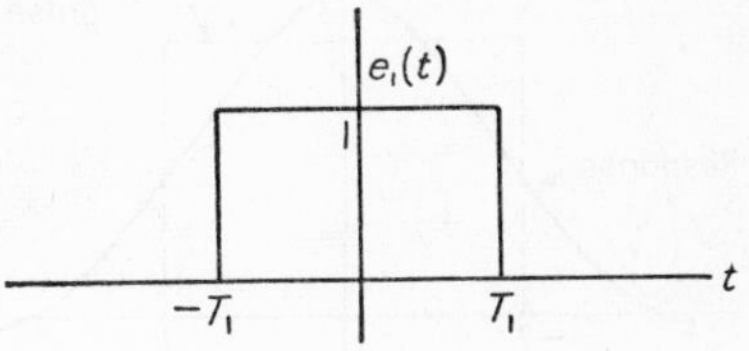

FIG. 9.

19. Response of an Idealized Low-pass Filter to an Impressed Pulse. Consider the unit pulse pictured in Fig. 9 which exists in the interval $-T_1 < t < T_1$. Its Fourier transform is

$$g(\omega) = 2\frac{\sin \omega T_1}{\omega} \tag{66}$$

If this pulse is impressed on the input of the idealized low-pass filter whose transmission characteristics are

$$H(\omega) = 1 \qquad \psi(\omega) = \omega t_d \tag{67}$$

then the response, using Fourier-integral formulation, is

$$e_2(t) = \frac{1}{\pi}\int_{-\omega_c}^{\omega_c} \frac{\sin \omega T_1}{\omega} e^{j\omega(t-t_d)}\, d\omega \tag{68}$$

After some trigonometric manipulation with the integrand, Eq. (68) may be rewritten as follows,

$$e_2(t) = \frac{1}{\pi}\int_0^{\omega_c} \frac{\sin \omega(t - t_d + T_1)}{\omega}\, d\omega - \frac{1}{\pi}\int_0^{\omega_c} \frac{\sin \omega(t - t_d - T_1)}{\omega}\, d\omega \tag{69}$$

$$= \frac{1}{\pi}[\mathrm{Si}\, \omega_c(t' + T_1) - \mathrm{Si}\, \omega_c(t' - T_1)] \tag{70}$$

where

$$t' = t - t_d \tag{71}$$

The response is made up of two Si (x) functions which lead and lag the time delay t_d by the half interval T_1. This response is pictured in Fig. 10a and b for $\omega_c T_1 = \pi, 4\pi$. It is seen that as $\omega_c T_1$ increases (which means larger bandwidth) the output becomes a more faithful reproduction of the input. The role which is played by the two sine integrals is evident from

Fig. 10*b*. The leading sine integral produces the rise of the pulse as if a step function alone had been impressed upon the input. The trailing end of the pulse appears to the network as a negatively directed step function, and so a second sine integral returns the response to zero after the oscillations have stopped at some time after $t_d + T_1$.

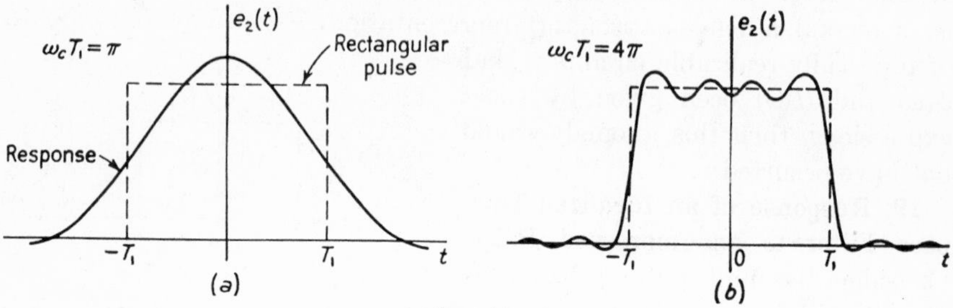

FIG. 10.

RESPONSE ANALYSIS USING THE METHOD OF MULTIPLE ECHOES

20. Introduction. The method of multiple echoes[1] is an auxiliary approach to the determination of network response using Fourier integral analysis. This type of analysis features the expansion of the complex transmission-frequency function $h(\omega)$ into a Fourier series, resulting in a very powerful analytic tool which is particularly suited to pulse and television transient analysis. In the following discussion, the method will be introduced in one of its simplest forms so that basic concepts may be established, concluding with an exposition of the general theory.

21. Interpretation of Distortion by Paired Echoes. In a paper bearing much the same title as the heading, H. A. Wheeler discusses the application of the method of multiple echoes to problems involving both amplitude and phase distortion. It is shown there that, for many practical applications in video transmission, a pair of echoes—one leading and one lagging—is adequate for distortion analysis.

Figure 11 pictures the transmission characteristics of a low-pass filter where only a single harmonic term in the expansion of both $H(\omega)$ and $\psi(\omega)$ is considered. Consider the case where amplitude distortion alone exists. This will produce a pair of positive replicas, or echoes, which is a function of the harmonic of the Fourier expansion of $H(\omega)$, which lead and

[1] Wheeler and Loughren, The Fine Structure of Television Images, *Proc. IRE*, vol. 26, pp. 540–575, May, 1938; H. A. Wheeler, The Interpretation of Amplitude and Phase Distortion in Terms of Paired Echoes, *Proc. IRE*, vol. 27, pp. 359–385, June, 1939. For some additional aspects of the subject of paired echoes, see R. V. L. Hartley, A More Symmetrical Fourier Analysis Applied to Transmission Problems, *Proc. IRE*, vol. 30, pp. 144–150, March, 1942.

lag the fundamental transferred wave. The time of lead or lag is a function of the harmonic of the Fourier expansion of $H(\omega)$ which is considered; as n increases, the lead and lag time *increases* linearly.

If only phase distortion induced by a single harmonic term is present, then two echoes will again appear. However, the leading echo will be negatively directed.

A simple illustration of the theory and application of paired echoes to distortion analysis is given as follows: Consider a pulse which is transferred through a linear network whose pass band is such that its response

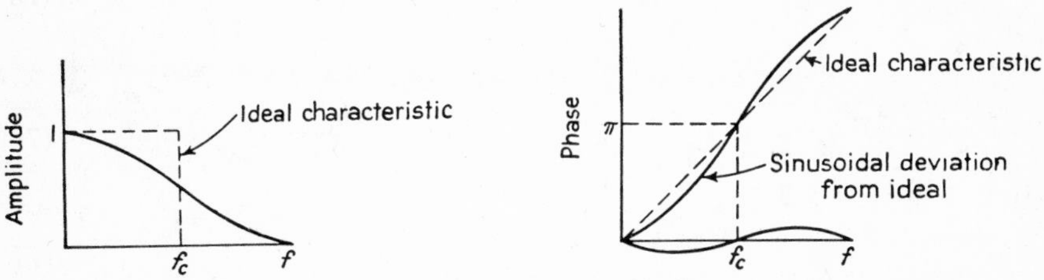

FIG. 11. Ideal and first-distortion terms in the Fourier representation of $\psi(\omega)$ for a low-pass filter.

shape is that shown in Fig. 10a. If phase distortion is present, then Fig. 12 shows how the pair of oppositely directed echoes add to or subtract from the fundamental wave to result in the distortion of its leading and trailing edges. The same type of effect will be realized from amplitude distortion except that both the leading and trailing sections of the fundamental wave will be affected in the same direction and if the transferred wave is symmetric, then the resulting distorted wave will also be symmetric.

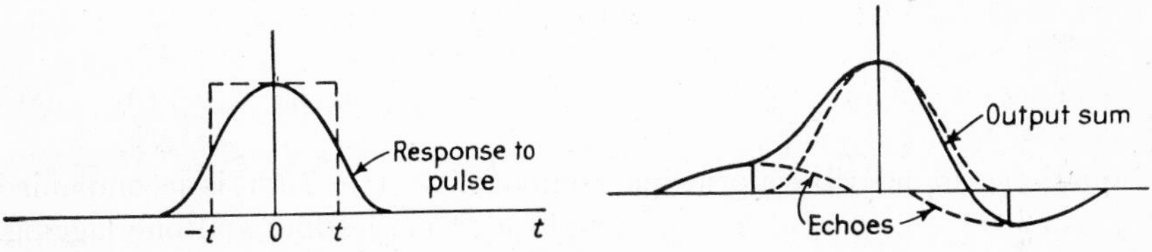

FIG. 12.

22. Paired Echoes Resulting from a Single Distortion Term. Consider the low-pass filter whose transmission characteristics are

$$\begin{aligned} H(\omega) &= K & -\omega_c < \omega < \omega_c \\ \psi(\omega) &= \omega t_d + b_1 \sin \omega t_0 & -\omega_c < \omega < \omega_c \end{aligned} \tag{72}$$

The term $b_1 \sin \omega t_0$ represents a first-order departure, in terms of harmonic representation of an odd function, from the linear phase characteristics of an idealized system. Substituting these characteristics into the Fourier integral (47), we get

$$e_2(t) = \frac{K}{2\pi} \int_{-\infty}^{\infty} g(\omega) e^{j[\omega(t-t_d)+b_1 \sin \omega t_0]} \, d\omega \tag{73}$$

$$= \frac{K}{2\pi} \int_{-\infty}^{\infty} g(\omega) e^{j\omega(t-t_d)} e^{jb_1 \sin \omega t_0} \, d\omega \tag{74}$$

But according to Eq. (90), Chap. 2,

$$e^{jb_1 \sin \omega t_0} = \sum_{-\infty}^{\infty} J_n(b_1) e^{jn\omega t_0} \tag{75}$$

If b_1 is very small, that is, $b_1 \ll \omega t_d$,

$$J_0(b_1) = 1 \qquad J_1(b_1) = \frac{b_1}{2} \tag{76}$$

from which we get

$$e^{jb_1 \sin \omega t_0} = 1 + \frac{b_1}{2} (e^{j\omega t_0} - e^{-j\omega t_0}) \tag{77}$$

Substituting (77) into (74), we get for the output wave

$$e_2(t) = \frac{K}{2\pi} \int_{-\infty}^{\infty} g(\omega) e^{j\omega(t-t_d)} \, d\omega + \frac{Kb_1}{4\pi} \int_{-\infty}^{\infty} g(\omega) e^{j\omega(t-t_d+t_0)} \, d\omega - \frac{Kb_1}{4\pi} \int_{-\infty}^{\infty} g(\omega) e^{j\omega(t-t_d-t_0)} \, d\omega \tag{78}$$

If we let

$$\frac{K}{2\pi} \int_{-\infty}^{\infty} g(\omega) e^{j\omega(t-t_d)} \, d\omega = e_{2_1}(t - t_d) \tag{79}$$

then (78) may be written in the form

$$e_2(t) = \frac{b_1}{2} e_{2_1}(t - t_d + t_0) + e_{2_1}(t - t_d) - \frac{b_1}{2} e_{2_1}(t - t_d - t_0) \tag{80}$$

Equation (80) describes a principal component $e_{2_1}(t - t_d)$; it is accompanied by a pair of echoes of decreased amplitude, one leading and one lagging. The leading echo is negative in sign, making the pair skew symmetric.

If the distortion takes place in the amplitude characteristic (which is an even function), let the transfer characteristics be

$$H(\omega) = K(1 + M \cos \omega t_0) \qquad \psi(\omega) = \omega t_d \tag{81}$$

It is easily shown that

$$e_2(t) = \frac{M}{2} e_{2_1}(t - t_d + t_0) + e_{2_1}(t - t_d) + \frac{M}{2} e_{2_1}(t - t_d - t_0) \tag{82}$$

which differs from (80) in that the pair of echoes is symmetric.

23. The Exact Theory for the Method of Multiple Echoes. Consider the exact theory, due to L. A. MacColl,[1] for the method of multiple echoes in which the amplitude and phase characteristics of a linear transfer network are represented by Fourier series. Letting $H(\omega)$ be expressed as a complex Fourier series and letting Ω be the bandwidth of the network, the general expression for $h(\omega)$ becomes

$$h(\omega) = e^{j\omega b_0} \sum_{m=-\infty}^{\infty} C_m e^{j(2\pi m\omega/\Omega)} \prod_{n=1}^{\infty} \sum_{k=-\infty}^{\infty} J_k(b_n) e^{j(2\pi nk\omega/\Omega)} \tag{83}$$

Substituting Eq. (83) into Fourier integral (47), the expression for the response is found to be

$$e_2(t) = \frac{1}{2\pi} \int_{-\infty}^{\infty} g(\omega) \sum_{m=-\infty}^{\infty} C_m e^{j(2\pi m\omega/\Omega)} \cdot \prod_{n=1}^{\infty} \sum_{k=-\infty}^{\infty} J_k(b_n) e^{j(2\pi nk\omega/\Omega)} e^{j\omega(t-b_0)}\, d\omega \tag{84}$$

This equation is not as pretentious as it appears to be at first glance. Let us for the time being replace the Fourier sine series representing phase by its symbol $\psi(\omega)$. Then the Fourier integral (84) may be written out as follows:

$$\begin{aligned} e_2(t) &= \frac{1}{2\pi} \int_{-\infty}^{\infty} g(\omega) C_0 e^{j[\omega t + \psi(\omega)]}\, d\omega \\ &+ \frac{1}{2\pi} \int_{-\infty}^{\infty} g(\omega) C_{+1} e^{j\{\omega[t+(2\pi/\Omega)]+\psi(\omega)\}}\, d\omega \\ &+ \frac{1}{2\pi} \int_{-\infty}^{\infty} g(\omega) C_{-1} e^{j\{\omega[t-(2\pi/\Omega)]+\psi(\omega)\}}\, d\omega \\ &+ \frac{1}{2\pi} \int_{-\infty}^{\infty} g(\omega) C_{+2} e^{j\{\omega[t+(4\pi/\Omega)]+\psi(\omega)\}}\, d\omega \\ &+ \frac{1}{2\pi} \int_{-\infty}^{\infty} g(\omega) C_{-2} e^{j\{\omega[t-(4\pi/\Omega)]+\psi(\omega)\}}\, d\omega \\ &+ \cdots \end{aligned} \tag{85}$$

In this form, the full significance of Eq. (84) is evident. $e_2(t)$ is made up of an idealized-amplitude-characteristic Fourier response integral, in which the constant K is replaced by the constant C_0, plus an infinite set of response replicas which are modified in amplitude by $C_{\pm m}$ and which lead and lag the first integral by the phase $2\pi m\omega/\Omega$. These replicas are

[1] MacColl's solution is discussed by C. R. Burrows in a communication at the conclusion of Wheeler's paper, The Interpretation of Distortion by Paired Echoes, *Proc. IRE*, vol. 27, pp. 359–385, June, 1939.

termed echoes and occur in pairs, one leading and one lagging, each with the same amplitude. The first pair of echoes, for example, has its amplitude determined by $C_{\pm 1}$ and leads and lags the first response integral by $\pm 2\pi\omega/\Omega$. Let us now reintroduce the Fourier-series expansion of $\psi(\omega)$ into the formulation.

Let the symbol $D(\omega)$ represent

$$D(\omega) = D_0(\omega) D_1(\omega) D_2(\omega) \cdots D_\nu(\omega) \cdots \tag{86}$$

where

$$D_0(\omega) = \sum_{m=-\infty}^{\infty} C_m e^{j[(2\pi m\omega/\Omega) - b_0\omega]} \tag{87}$$

and includes the Fourier-series representation of the amplitude characteristic and the constant term of the Fourier-series representation of the phase. Each succeeding term is found to be of the *form*

$$D_\nu(\omega) = e^{jb_\nu \sin(2\pi\nu\omega/\Omega)} \qquad \nu > 0 \tag{88}$$

$$= \sum_{k=-\infty}^{\infty} J_k(b_\nu) e^{j(2\pi k\nu\omega/\Omega)} \qquad \nu > 0 \tag{89}$$

Consider first the full significance of the term $D_0(\omega)$. If the wave whose Fourier transform is $g(\omega)$ is passed through a linear network having the transmission characteristics $D_0(\omega)$ alone, the output response may be written

$$e_{2_0}(t) = \sum_{m=-\infty}^{\infty} C_m e_2\left(t - b_0 + \frac{2\pi m}{\Omega}\right) \tag{90}$$

where

$$e_2(t) = \frac{1}{2\pi} \int_{-\infty}^{\infty} g(\omega) e^{j\omega t}\, d\omega \tag{91}$$

Equation (90) is a multiple-echo expression in which the fundamental response is delayed by b_0 and each succeeding echo leads and lags this representation by the phase $2\pi m\omega/\Omega$.

If the signal $e_{2_0}(t)$ is now passed through a network having the characteristics $D_1(\omega)$, where

$$D_1(\omega) = \sum_{k=-\infty}^{\infty} J_k(b_1) e^{j(2\pi k\omega/\Omega)} \tag{92}$$

then the response $e_{2_1}(t)$ will be

$$e_{2_1}(t) = \sum_{k=-\infty}^{\infty} J_k(b_1) e_{2_0}\left(t + \frac{2\pi k}{\Omega}\right) \tag{93}$$

Since we meet expressions of the form

$$J_k(b_\nu) e^{j(2\pi\nu k\omega/\Omega)} \tag{94}$$

which involve a constant $J_k(b_\nu)$ and a time-delay term $2\pi k\nu/\Omega$, we see that $D(\omega)$ represents a series of cascaded networks having the successive frequency transfer characteristics $D_0(\omega)$, $D_1(\omega)$, . . . through which the fundamental and response are transmitted, the output of one network being the input to the next. The output of the νth network is

$$e_{2_\nu}(t) = \sum_{k=-\infty}^{\infty} J_k(b_\nu) e_{2_{\nu-1}}\left(t + \frac{2\pi k\nu}{\Omega}\right) \qquad (95)$$

This process is repeated for all significant $D(\omega)$ to yield the final output.

The practical value of the exact method is vividly illustrated in the following table due to Burrows, which compares the magnitudes of the principal component and the first three pairs of echoes with those terms described by Eq. (80) (which used only a single distortion term) for the case when $b_1 = \frac{1}{2}$, 1, and 2 radians:

Amplitude of each component (absolute)	$b_1 = \frac{1}{2}$ radian		$b_1 = 1$ radian		$b_1 = 2$ radians	
	Eq. (95)	Eq. (80)	Eq. (95)	Eq. (80)	Eq. (95)	Eq. (80)
Principal component	0.938	1	0.765	1	0.224	1
1st pair of echoes	0.242	0.25	0.440	0.5	0.577	1
2d pair of echoes	0.062	0	0.115	0	0.353	0
3d pair of echoes	0.003	0	0.197	0	0.128	0

It is evident that for $b_1 = \frac{1}{2}$ radian which is typical of values encountered in applications to television (see H. W. Wheeler), the single pair of echoes due to a single distortion term (see Sec. 22) have amplitudes comparable to those yielded by the exact method. For larger values of b_1, a considerable discrepancy is seen to develop.

THE RESPONSE OF IDEALIZED FILTERS TO SUDDENLY APPLIED WAVE TRAINS

24. Introduction. The following treatment will discuss the response of certain idealized transmission networks upon whose input a wave train is suddenly impressed. The discussion will include the case where the impressed-wave angular velocity is outside of the transmission band. The first three sections to follow are based on treatments by K. Kupfmüller.[1]

[1] K. Kupfmüller, Über Einschwingvorgänge in Wellenfiltern, *Elek. Nachr.-Tech.*, vol. 1, pp. 141–152, 1924; Über Beziehungen zwischen Frequenz Charakteristiken und Ausgleichsvorgängen in linearen Systemen, *Elek. Nachr.-Tech.*, vol. 5, No. 1, p. 18, 1928.

25. Response of an Idealized Low-pass Filter to a Suddenly Applied Wave Train. Consider the response of an idealized low-pass filter described by (8) and (9) to a wave train impressed at time $t = 0$. This wave train, during its duration time $t = 0$, is represented by a rotating vector of constant amplitude E and constant angular velocity ω_0, that is,

$$\begin{aligned} e_1(t) &= 0 \qquad -\infty < t < 0 \\ &= Ee^{j\omega_0 t} \qquad 0 < t < \infty \end{aligned} \tag{96}$$

It has been seen in Chap. 19, Sec. 16, that the Fourier transform of this wave is the kappa function $\mathcal{K}(\omega_0 - \omega)$, where

$$\mathcal{K}(\omega_0 - \omega) = \frac{-j}{\omega_0 - \omega} \tag{97}$$

Then the network response voltage $e_2(t)$ may be written

$$e_2(t) = \frac{KE}{2\pi j}\int_{-\omega_c}^{\omega_c} \frac{e^{j\omega(t-t_d)}}{\omega - \omega_0}\,d\omega \tag{98}$$

If we let

$$\begin{aligned} u &= \omega(t - t_d) \\ u_1 &= (\omega_c - \omega_0)(t - t_d) \\ u_2 &= (\omega_c + \omega_0)(t - t_d) \end{aligned} \tag{99}$$

we may rewrite Eq. (98) as follows:

$$e_2(t) = \frac{KEe^{j\omega_0(t-t_d)}}{2\pi j}\left(\int_{-u_2}^{u_1} \frac{\cos u}{u}\,du + j\int_{-u_2}^{u_1} \frac{\sin u}{u}\,du\right) \tag{100}$$

This expression may be developed[1] into a form the real part of which is

$$\text{Re}\; e_2(t) = \Phi KE \cos\left[\omega_0(t - t_d) + \tan^{-1}\frac{\text{Ci}\,(u_2) - \text{Ci}\,(u_1)}{\pi + \text{Si}\,(u_2) + \text{Si}\,(u_1)}\right] \tag{101}$$

where Φ is an envelope function and is found to be

$$\Phi = \sqrt{\left[\frac{1}{2} + \frac{1}{2\pi}\,[\text{Si}\,(u_2) + \text{Si}\,(u_1)]\right]^2 + \left[\frac{1}{2\pi}\,(\text{Ci}\,(u_2) - \text{Ci}\,(u_1))\right]^2} \tag{102}$$

The contributions of the two cosine integrals will be of importance only in the vicinity of $t = t_d$ and will become increasingly large as ω_0 approaches ω_c. The sum of the two sine integrals will, in general, determine the envelope shape and represent the contributions of two sine integrals, where the zeros of one (u_2) are compressed and the zeros of the other (u_1) are spread out.

[1] See E. A. Guillemin, "Communication Networks," Vol. II, pp. 481–482, John Wiley & Sons, Inc., New York, 1935.

The processes of *build-up* are not as clear as they were for step-function excitation. However, the slope of the rise part of the envelope will be a function of ω_0/ω_c.

The frequency of the output wave may be found by differentiating the phase; that is,

$$f = \frac{\omega}{2\pi} = \frac{1}{2\pi}\frac{d}{dt}\left[\omega_0(t - t_d) + \tan^{-1}\frac{\mathrm{Ci}\,(u_2) - \mathrm{Ci}\,(u_1)}{\pi + \mathrm{Si}\,(u_2) + \mathrm{Si}\,(u_1)}\right] \tag{103}$$

After the sine and cosine integrals have achieved their steady-state values, the output wave will have a constant angular velocity ω_0. During build-up and until the oscillations of the integrals die out, the frequency will depart from $\omega_0/2\pi$ to an extent determined by ω_0/ω_c.

26. Response of an Idealized Bandpass Filter to a Suddenly Applied Wave Train. Consider an idealized bandpass filter whose pass band is $\omega_a < \omega < \omega_b$ and whose center frequency is adjusted to $\omega_0/2\pi$. Let the wave train which is described by Eq. (96), with its angular velocity adjusted to the same value as the angular velocity of the center of the pass band be impressed at the input of the filter. According to (98) the response $e_2(t)$ may be written[1]

$$e_2(t) = \frac{KEe^{j\omega_0 t_d}}{2\pi j}\int_{\omega_a}^{\omega_b}\frac{e^{j\omega(t-t_d)}}{\omega - \omega_0}\,d\omega \tag{104}$$

If we let $\Omega = \omega_b - \omega_a$ and write $\omega = \omega' + \omega_0$, then

$$e_2(t) = \frac{KEe^{j\omega_0 t}}{2\pi j}\int_{-\Omega/2}^{\Omega/2}\frac{e^{j\omega'(t-t_d)}}{\omega'}\,d\omega' \tag{105}$$

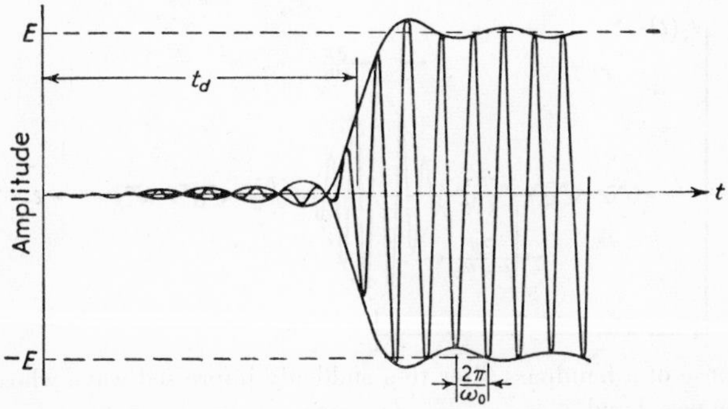

FIG. 13. Response of a bandpass filter to a suddenly impressed wave whose frequency is that of the *center* of the pass band.

[1] The integration is performed for positive values of ω since, for negative values of ω, the integrand denominator becomes large, thus reducing the contributions to the integration from this band. Note that for an idealized bandpass filter, $\psi(\omega) = (\omega - \omega_0)t_d$.

The real part of (105) is readily found to be

$$e_2(t) = KE\left\{\frac{1}{2} + \frac{1}{\pi}\,\text{Si}\left[\frac{\Omega}{2}(t - t_d)\right]\right\}\cos\omega_0 t \qquad (106)$$

From this equation, we see that the build-up of the wave train which is delayed by the time t_d is determined by an envelope whose characteristics are identical to the response of the network to an impressed step function. Equation (106) is plotted in Fig. 13 for a typical case.

27. Response When Wave-train Angular Velocity Is Outside of the Pass Band. Consider the case when the wave train described by (96) is applied to the input of an idealized bandpass filter whose pass band, centered at ω_1, is $\omega_a < \omega < \omega_b$ for the case when $\omega_b \ll \omega_0$. If it is assumed that $|\omega_0 - \omega_1| \gg \omega_b - \omega_a$, then $\omega - \omega_0$ may be replaced by $\omega_0 - \omega_1$ in (98) and we get

$$e_2(t) = \frac{EKe^{j\omega_1 t_d}}{2\pi j(\omega_1 - \omega_0)}\int_{\omega_a}^{\omega_b} e^{j\omega(t-t_d)}\,d\omega \qquad (107)$$

$$= \frac{EKe^{j\omega_1 t_d}}{2\pi j(\omega_1 - \omega_0)}\,\frac{e^{j\omega_b(t-t_d)} - e^{j\omega_a(t-t_d)}}{j(t - t_d)} \qquad (108)$$

This can be manipulated into the form[1]

$$e_2(t) = \frac{EK(\omega_b - \omega_a)}{2\pi(\omega_1 - \omega_0)}\,\frac{\sin\theta}{\theta}\,je^{j\omega_1 t} \qquad (109)$$

where

$$\theta = \frac{\omega_b - \omega_a}{2}(t - t_d) \qquad (110)$$

The general behavior of the wave described by (109) is pictured in Fig. 14.

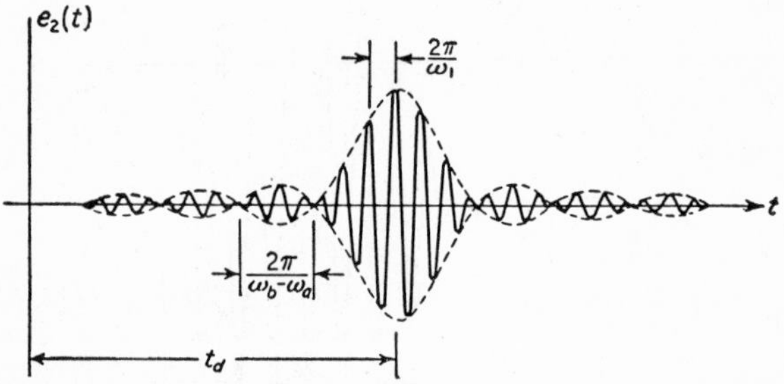

FIG. 14. Response of a bandpass filter to a suddenly impressed wave whose frequency is *outside* of the pass band.

The wave train with angular velocity ω_1 builds up and attains a maximum amplitude at a time t_d after the wave is impressed on the network. The wave then builds down again in the same fashion. Note that the oscilla-

[1] In the integration which yields (109), it can be shown that any contributions to the integration by inclusion of the limits $-\omega_b < \omega < -\omega_a$ will be negligible.

tory behavior of the envelope is due to a $(\sin \theta)/\theta$ function rather than to a sine-integral function. It is interesting to note that the output wave does not resemble the input wave in that its angular velocity is that of the center of the pass band and not of the impressed wave.

28. Laplace-transform Analysis of the Response of a Single-stage Amplifier. When a wave train is suddenly applied to communication network whose transmission characteristics are not suitable for use with the Fourier integral or if an exact expression is required, the Laplace transforms may be used.

As an illustration, consider the output of the circuit pictured in Fig. 7b, Chap. 10, due to a suddenly impressed sinusoidal wave train. This circuit is the equivalent circuit of a single-stage resistance-coupled amplifier. Let the impressed voltage μe_g be the wave train

$$\begin{aligned} \mu e_g &= 0 \qquad & -\infty < t < 0 \\ &= \sin \omega_0 t \qquad & 0 < t < \infty \end{aligned} \tag{111}$$

If the system is at rest, we see that (dropping the primes)

$$\mathcal{L}(\mu e_g) = \mathcal{L}[i(t)]\left[r_p + \frac{R/sC}{R + (1/sC)}\right] \tag{112}$$

$$= \mathcal{L}[i(t)]\frac{r_p + R + sCr_pR}{1 + sCR} \tag{113}$$

and

$$\mathcal{L}(e_0) = \mathcal{L}[i(t)]\frac{R}{1 + sCR} \tag{114}$$

It follows then that

$$h(s) = \frac{\mathcal{L}(e_0)}{\mathcal{L}(\mu e_g)} = \frac{1}{r_pC\{s + [(r_p + R)/CRr_p]\}} \tag{115}$$

The Laplace transform of μe_g is found to be

$$\mathcal{L}(\mu e_g) = \frac{\omega_0}{s^2 + \omega_0^2} \tag{116}$$

The network response is then

$$\begin{aligned} e_0 &= \mathcal{L}^{-1}[h(s)\mathcal{L}(\mu e_g)] \\ &= \frac{\omega_0}{r_pC}\frac{1}{2\pi j}\int_{\alpha - j\infty}^{\alpha + j\infty} \frac{e^{st}\,ds}{\{s + [(r_p + R)/CRr_p]\}(s + j\omega_0)(s - j\omega_0)} \end{aligned} \tag{117}$$

Equation (117) has poles at $s = (r_p + R)/CRr_p$, $s = -j\omega_0$, and $s = j\omega_0$. According to Eq. (127), Chap. 1, the solution of (117) is

$$\begin{aligned} e_0 = \frac{1}{r_pC\{[(r_p + R)/CRr_p]^2 + \omega_0^2\}} \bigg[\omega_0 \exp\left(-\frac{r_p + R}{CRr_p}t\right) \\ - \omega_0 \cos \omega_0 t - \frac{r_p + R}{CRr_p}\sin \omega_0 t \bigg] \end{aligned} \tag{118}$$

29. Response to a Sudden Amplitude Variation of a Continuous Wave Train. If the amplitude of the impressed continuous wave train suddenly changes at $t = 0$ so that the wave may be expressed over all time as

$$\begin{aligned} e_1(t) &= E_1 e^{j\omega_0 t} \qquad -\infty < t < 0 \\ &= E_2 e^{j\omega_0 t} \qquad 0 < t < \infty \end{aligned} \tag{119}$$

then this wave may be expressed as the sum of three wave trains of angular velocity ω_0 after $t = 0$, as follows,

$$e_1(t) = e_a(t) + e_b(t) + e_c(t) \tag{120}$$

where

$$\begin{aligned} e_a(t) &= E_1 e^{j\omega_0 t} \qquad -\infty < t < \infty \\ e_b(t) &= -E_1 e^{j\omega_0 t} \qquad 0 < t < \infty \\ e_c(t) &= E_2 e^{j\omega_0 t} \qquad 0 < t < \infty \end{aligned} \tag{121}$$

If this wave group is impressed upon the input of a linear transfer network whose response to a suddenly applied wave train of frequency $\omega_0/2\pi$ and unit amplitude is

$$e_0(t) = \Phi(t) K e^{j[\omega_0(t-t_d) - \vartheta(t)]} \tag{122}$$

where $\Phi(t)$ and $\vartheta(t)$ are envelope and phase functions, it is immediately evident that the response to $e_a(t)$ will be

$$e_{a_0}(t) = K E_1 e^{j\omega_0(t-t_d)} \tag{123}$$

The response due to $e_b(t)$ and $e_c(t)$ is easily deduced from (122), and it follows that

$$\begin{aligned} e_2(t) = K[E_1 e^{j\omega_0(t-t_d)} & \qquad -\infty < t < \infty \\ + (E_2 - E_1)\Phi(t) e^{j[\omega_0(t-t_d) - \vartheta(t)]}] & \qquad t \geq 0 \end{aligned} \tag{124}$$

This method of analysis may be extended to more complicated transients involving either (or both) variations in amplitude or frequency[1] by using the method of wave superposition which was discussed in the preceding chapter.

30. Considerations of the General Theory as Applied to Vestigial-sideband Transmission.[2] The general analysis presented in the preceding

[1] For a discussion of some engineering aspects of FM transients, see H. Salinger, Transients in Frequency Modulation, *Proc. IRE*, vol. 30, pp. 378–383, August, 1942.

[2] For some mathematical aspects of transient response and per cent modulation in vestigial-sideband systems, see S. Goldman, Television Detail and Selective Side-band Transmission, *Proc. IRE*, vol. 27, pp. 725–732, November, 1939; Kallman, Spencer, and Singer, Transient Response of Single-sideband Systems, *Proc. IRE*, vol. 28, pp. 557–563, December, 1940; Kell and Fredendall, Selective Side-band Transmission in Television,

section is not applicable to vestigial-sideband transmission using the envelope-function approach since the number of components involved makes the analysis too difficult to solve from the standpoint of response summation and it is difficult, using this approach,[1] to formulate a practical means of establishing the envelope of the modulated carrier during vestigial-sideband transmission. The situation is easily redeemed from an engineering standpoint by retaining the modulated wave train in its double-sideband form and shifting the response curve of the transfer network so that the lower side frequencies are attenuated to the degree prescribed by vestigial-sideband-transmission standards.

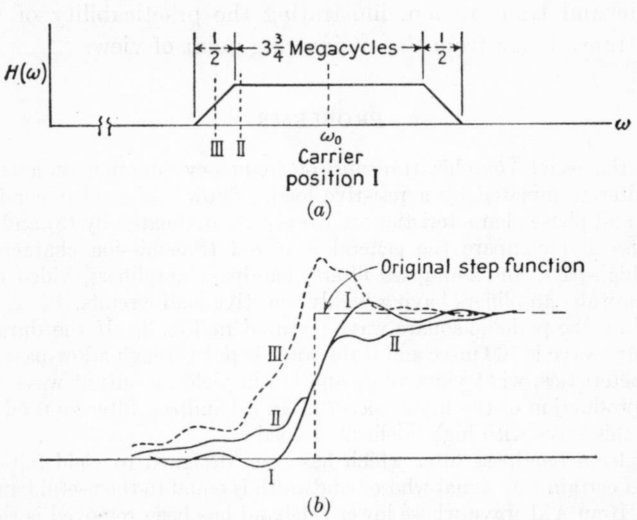

FIG. 15. Response of a bandpass filter having the amplitude-transfer characteristic illustrated in (*a*) to a step-function modulated wave train whose carrier frequency is adjusted to each of three frequencies. (*After S. Goldman, courtesy of Institute of Radio Engineers.*)

Consider as an illustration the case when a wave train is applied to the network whose amplitude-frequency transfer characteristics are illustrated in Fig. 15*a*. If the frequency of this wave train is positioned to carrier

---

RCA Rev., vol. 4, pp. 425–440, April, 1940; and Nyquist and Pfleger, Effect of the Quadrature Component in Single Sideband Transmission, *Bell System Tech. J.*, vol. 19, pp. 63–73, January, 1940.

[1] For a useful and illuminating Fourier-series approach, see Kell and Fredendall, Selective Side-band Transmission in Television, *RCA Rev.*, vol. 4, pp. 425–440, April, 1940. See also C. P. Singer's Fourier-integral approach in Kallman, Spencer, and Singer, Transient Response of Single-sideband Systems, *Proc. IRE*, vol. 28, pp. 557–563, December, 1940.

position I, the envelope response function will be that pictured in Fig. 15*b*, curve I, and is nearly identical to that pictured in Fig. 8.

If the frequency of the wave train is moved to carrier position II in Fig. 15*b*, it can be shown,[1] using the Fourier analysis, that the envelope response function is that given by curve II. This result corresponds closely to the result yielded in the case where a vestigial-sideband signal is applied to the transfer network with its carrier adjusted to carrier position I, taking into consideration a slight modification of the phase characteristics. Note that the use of vestigial-sideband transmission has resulted in a step-function envelope response not too different from that resulting from double-sideband transmission, illustrating the practicability of vestigial-sideband transmission from the engineering point of view.

PROBLEMS

1. Find the exact complex transmission-frequency function of a single-stage low-pass filter terminated by a resistive load. Show under what conditions the amplitude and phase characteristics are closely approximated by (8) and (9).

2. Discuss and compare the general idealized transmission characteristics of low-pass, high-pass, and bandpass filters, bandpass amplifiers, video amplifiers, and vacuum-tube amplifiers having highly selective load circuits.

3. Consider the periodic square wave pictured in Fig. 3. If the duration time of this square wave is 100 msec and if the wave is put through a low-pass filter with ideal characteristics, what value of ω_c and t_d will yield an output wave which is a faithful reproduction of the input wave? Can a bandpass filter be used for transmission of this wave with high fidelity? Explain.

4. Consider a bandpass filter which has been designed to yield faithful transmission of a certain FM signal whose bandwidth is equal to the useful bandwidth of the filter. If an AM wave whose lower sideband has been removed is then passed through the filter under the condition that the bandwidths are still commensurate, discuss the nature of the transmission involved and the realizable fidelity.

5. Discuss the application of the quasi-stationary method when used with a single-tone FM wave and with a square-wave FM wave of the same frequency.

6. Although a linear network with infinite bandwidth is not realizable in physical systems, many networks used in communication systems provide high-fidelity signal transmission even though their pass bands may have only limited range. Discuss the behavior in terms of the nature of the integrand and the limits of the integral (49).

7. Does Eq. (49) hold for the case where the input wave is a step function? Explain.

8. Prove that the build-up time, discussed in connection with Fig. 8, is equal to π/ω_c.

9. If the delay time of an idealized low-pass filter is 15 μsec, deduce from a table of Si(x) functions the magnitude of the anomalous voltage which is predicted to occur at $t = 0$ for the case where the output voltage comes to equilibrium at 175 volts and the cutoff frequency is 2 Mc.

[1] See S. Goldman, Television Detail and Selective Side-band Transmission, *Proc. IRE*, vol. 27, pp. 725–732, November, 1939. for the details of this Fourier analysis.

10. Consider a bandpass filter whose transmission characteristics in the pass band are described as follows:

$$h(\omega) \cong [1 + a \cos (\omega - \omega_0)t_1]e^{j[(\omega-\omega_0)t_d + a\sin(\omega-\omega_0)t_1]}$$

where $a \ll 1$ and ω_0 is the center of the pass band which extends from $\omega_0 + 3\omega_1$ to $\omega_0 - 3\omega_1$. Discuss the multiple-echo effects accompanying pulse transmission through the filter. HINT. Resolve $h(\omega)$ into the form $ke^{jx}/(1 - ye^{jz})$, and expand.

11. Determine the output response of an idealized low-pass filter whose cutoff frequency is $\omega_c/2\pi$ for the case when a continuous wave $E_1e^{j\omega_1 t}$ suddenly changes in both amplitude and frequency as prescribed as follows:

a. At $t = 0$, $e = E_2e^{j\omega_2 t}$ $\quad \omega_2 < \omega_1 < \omega_c$
b. At $t = 0$, $e = E_2e^{j\omega_3 t}$ $\quad \omega_1 < \omega_c < \omega_3$
c. At $t = 0$, $e = E_2e^{j\omega_3 t}$ $\quad \omega_3 < \omega_c < \omega_1$

12. Determine the output response of an idealized bandpass filter whose center frequency is 40 Mc, with a pass band $36 \times 10^6 < f < 44 \times 10^6$, to a modern television broadcast transmitter signal during transmission of the vertical synchronization signal if the carrier frequency is 40 Mc.

13. Prove the values corresponding to $b_1 = 1$ in the table in Sec. 23, using the exact method.

14. Discuss the method of analysis using paired echoes for the case when the impressed wave is a continuous wave and undergoes *no* transients.

15. Discuss and formulate the possibility of the echo on one side disappearing during simultaneous phase and amplitude distortion.

CHAPTER 21

TRAVELING WAVES IN COMMUNICATION SYSTEMS

1. Introduction. Traveling waves are found in systems which are associated with the wave equation, and their analysis in these systems must be approached differently from, for example, the case of linear-transfer networks. The general field of traveling-wave analysis is a tremendous one since not only are physical concepts involved but also *partial* differential equations are encountered for every case which must be solved for some set of boundary conditions. The treatment will therefore be introductory, more advanced studies being left to the student, and will include the general aspects of the wave equation and the more important aspects of traveling waves in transmission lines, free space, conducting media, and magnetrons.

THE WAVE EQUATION AND TRAVELING WAVES

2. The Wave Equation. One of the most widely encountered partial differential equations of physics and communication engineering is the wave equation, which is written in one-dimensional form, for the x direction, in terms of the wave function ψ as follows:

$$\frac{\partial^2 \psi}{\partial x^2} = \frac{1}{a^2} \frac{\partial^2 \psi}{\partial t^2} \tag{1}$$

where a is a constant.

3. Solution of the Wave Equation.[1] Let us determine the solution of the wave equation by using a classical method which employs the separation of variables. This method will also be used to solve other partial differential equations which will be encountered in this chapter.

First assume a solution

$$\psi = X(x)T(t) \tag{2}$$

where $X(x)$ and $T(t)$ are functions of only x and t, respectively. Then, substituting (2) into the term on the left in (1), we find

$$\frac{\partial^2 \psi}{\partial x^2} = X''(x)T(t) \tag{3}$$

[1] See R. V. Churchill, "Fourier Series and Boundary Value Problems," Sec. 13, McGraw-Hill Book Company, Inc., New York, 1941.

and substituting (2) into the right-hand term in (1), we get

$$\frac{1}{a^2}\frac{\partial^2\psi}{\partial t^2} = \frac{1}{a^2}X(x)T''(t) \tag{4}$$

It then follows that

$$X''(x)T(t) = \frac{1}{a^2}X(x)T''(t) \tag{5}$$

or

$$\frac{X''(x)}{X(x)} = \frac{1}{a^2}\frac{T''(t)}{T(t)} \tag{6}$$

Since each quotient is a function of either x or t alone, a change in $X(x)$ cannot produce a change in $T(t)$ and we can write

$$\frac{X''(x)}{X(x)} = \frac{1}{a^2}\frac{T''(t)}{T(t)} = \lambda \tag{7}$$

where λ is a constant. Two differential equations may be deduced from (7), *viz.*,

$$X''(x) - \lambda X(x) = 0 \tag{8}$$

$$T''(t) - \lambda a^2 T(t) = 0 \tag{9}$$

The characteristic equations of either of these differential equations are of the form,

$$m^2 - b^2 = 0 \tag{10}$$

such that since

$$\psi = X(x)T(t) \tag{11}$$

then for $\lambda > 0$

$$\psi = (c_1 e^{\sqrt{\lambda}\, x} + c_2 e^{-\sqrt{\lambda}\, x})(c_3 e^{a\sqrt{\lambda}\, t} + c_4 e^{-a\sqrt{\lambda}\, t}) \tag{12}$$

If $\lambda < 0$,

$$\psi = (c_5 \sin \sqrt{-\lambda}\, x + c_6 \cos \sqrt{-\lambda}\, x) \cdot (c_7 \sin a\sqrt{-\lambda}\, t + c_8 \cos a\sqrt{-\lambda}\, t) \tag{13}$$

and if $\lambda = 0$,

$$\psi = (c_9 x + c_{10})(c_{11} t + c_{12}) \tag{14}$$

The c's are arbitrary constants which must be solved for each problem in accordance with the boundary conditions involved.

4. The Rotating-vector Traveling Wave $Ee^{j\omega[t-(x/v)]}$ and the Wave Equation. Let us show that the traveling wave which can be represented by the rotating vector

$$e = Ee^{j\omega[t-(x/v)]} \tag{15}$$

satisfies the wave equation (1). It follows that

$$\frac{\partial e}{\partial x} = -\frac{j\omega}{v} Ee^{j\omega[t-(x/v)]} \qquad \frac{\partial e}{\partial t} = j\omega Ee^{j\omega[t-(x/v)]} \tag{16}$$

$$\frac{\partial^2 e}{\partial x^2} = -\left(\frac{\omega}{v}\right)^2 Ee^{j\omega[t-(x/v)]} \qquad \frac{\partial^2 e}{\partial t^2} = -\omega^2 Ee^{j\omega[t-(x/v)]} \tag{17}$$

Substituting (17) into (1), we get, letting $a = v$,

$$-\frac{\omega^2}{v^2} Ee^{j\omega[t-(x/v)]} = -\frac{1}{v^2}\omega^2 Ee^{j\omega[t-(x/v)]} \tag{18}$$

Since ω is completely general, (18) shows that any wave or component wave whose form is that given by (15) satisfies the wave equation.

5. Traveling Waves and the Wave Equation. Let us consider the rotating vector $Ee^{j\omega t}$, which travels in the x direction with velocity v. Since x/v has the dimension of time, then we may fully describe this traveling wave as follows:

$$\psi = Ee^{j\omega[t-(x/v)]} \tag{19}$$

Since the elementary wave (19), involving the distance factor x/v, was shown in the preceding section to satisfy the wave equation, let us now consider the following solution of the wave equation based on a portion of (12); *viz.*,

$$\psi = (c_1 e^{j(\omega/v)x} + c_2 e^{-j(\omega/v)x})e^{j\omega t} \tag{20}$$

Since c_1 and c_2 are arbitrary and may be functions of ω, let them be the Fourier transforms $G_1(\omega)$ and $G_2(\omega)$ such that

$$\begin{aligned} c_1 e^{j(\omega/v)x} &= g_1(\omega) = G_1(\omega)e^{j(\omega/v)x} \\ c_2 e^{-j(\omega/v)x} &= g_2(\omega) = G_2(\omega)e^{-j(\omega/v)x} \end{aligned} \tag{21}$$

Then it follows, using the inverse Fourier transforms of $g_1(\omega)$ and $g_2(\omega)$, that

$$\psi = \frac{1}{2\pi}\int_{-\infty}^{\infty} G_1(\omega)e^{j(x/v)\omega}e^{j\omega t}\,d\omega + \frac{1}{2\pi}\int_{-\infty}^{\infty} G_2(\omega)e^{-j(x/v)\omega}e^{j\omega t}\,d\omega \tag{21}$$

The boundary conditions may be introduced at this point. Let a wave generator be placed at $x = 0$ whose output is such that

$$\psi(0,t) = f(t) \qquad -\infty < t < \infty \tag{22}$$

$$\frac{\partial\psi}{\partial t}(0,t) = F(t) \tag{23}$$

Then, from (21), these boundary conditions yield the following expressions:

$$\psi(0,t) = \frac{1}{2\pi}\int_{-\infty}^{\infty} [G_1(\omega) + G_2(\omega)]e^{j\omega t}\,d\omega = f(t) \tag{24}$$

$$\frac{\partial\psi}{\partial t}(0,t) = \frac{j}{2\pi v}\int_{-\infty}^{\infty} \omega[G_1(\omega) - G_2(\omega)]e^{j\omega t}\,d\omega = F(t) \tag{25}$$

Solving these equations simultaneously for $G_1(\omega)$ and $G_2(\omega)$, we get

$$G_1(\omega) = \frac{1}{2}\int_{-\infty}^{\infty}\left[f(t) - j\frac{v}{\omega}F(t)\right]e^{-j\omega t}\,dt \tag{26}$$

$$G_2(\omega) = \frac{1}{2}\int_{-\infty}^{\infty}\left[f(t) + j\frac{v}{\omega}F(t)\right]e^{-j\omega t}\,dt \tag{27}$$

If we substitute (26) and (27) into (21), using τ as the variable of integration, we get

$$\psi(x,t) = \frac{1}{4\pi}\int_{-\infty}^{\infty} d\omega \int_{-\infty}^{\infty} f(\tau)[e^{j\omega[\tau+(x/v)-t]} + e^{j\omega[\tau-(x/v)-t]}]\,d\tau$$
$$- \frac{v}{2\pi}\int_{-\infty}^{\infty}\frac{d\omega}{\omega}\int_{-\infty}^{\infty} F(\tau)\sin\frac{x}{v}\omega e^{j\omega(\tau-t)}\,d\tau \tag{28}$$

Since it can be shown that

$$\int_{-\infty}^{\infty}\sin\frac{x}{v}\omega e^{j\omega(\tau-t)}\frac{d\omega}{\omega} = 0 \qquad \tau < t - \frac{x}{v}$$
$$= \pi \qquad t - \frac{x}{v} < \tau < t + \frac{x}{v} \tag{29}$$
$$= 0 \qquad \tau < t + \frac{x}{v}$$

then we may write Eq. (28) in the following form,

$$\psi(x,t) = \frac{1}{2}f\left(t + \frac{x}{v}\right) + \frac{1}{2}f\left(t - \frac{x}{v}\right) + \frac{v}{2}\int_{t-(x/v)}^{t+(x/v)} F(\tau)\,d\tau \tag{30}$$

$$= \frac{1}{2}f\left(t + \frac{x}{v}\right) + \frac{1}{2}f\left(t - \frac{x}{v}\right) + \frac{1}{2}h\left(t + \frac{x}{v}\right) + \frac{1}{2}h\left(t - \frac{x}{v}\right) \qquad (31)[1]$$

which shows the presence of two pairs of waves, one member of each pair traveling in the opposite direction with respect to the other member. The summation of these members is such that the first pair in (31) yields $f(t)$, whereas the second pair yields $F(t)$ at $x = 0$.

6. The Laplace Transform and the Wave Equation. We have seen that any wave of the form $f[t \pm (x/v)]$ satisfies the wave equation, and a demonstration of this property was made using the Fourier integral in the preceding section. If we are to employ the Fourier integral validly, we must observe the stipulation that $\int_{-\infty}^{\infty} |f(t)|\,dt$ converges. Actually, we need not place so severe a restriction on the wave function since waves of finite or semiinfinite duration of the form $f[t \pm (x/v)]$ are also solutions.

[1] See J. A. Stratton, "Electromagnetic Theory," Sec. 5.8, McGraw-Hill Book Company, Inc., New York, 1941, for a more detailed development of Eq. (31).

In such formulation, however, the Laplace transform becomes very useful since it permits the handling of solutions for both waves of finite duration and, in particular, those waves which start at some prescribed time and continue to $t = \infty$.

Consider first a general solution of the wave equation involving a set of boundary conditions. Let the problem be stated as follows:

$$\frac{\partial^2 \psi(x,t)}{\partial x^2} = \frac{1}{v^2} \frac{\partial \psi(x,t)}{\partial t^2} \tag{32}$$

$$\psi(x,0) = \frac{\partial \psi(x,0)}{\partial t} = 0 \tag{33}$$

$$\psi(0,t) = f(t) \qquad \lim_{x \to \infty} \psi(x,t) = 0 \tag{34}$$

The Laplace transforms of the derivatives in (32) may be described as follows:

$$\mathcal{L}\left[\frac{\partial^2 \psi(x,t)}{\partial t^2}\right] = s^2 y(x,s) - s\psi(x,0) - \psi'(x,0) \tag{35}$$

$$\mathcal{L}\left[\frac{\partial^2 \psi(x,t)}{\partial x^2}\right] = \int_0^\infty \frac{\partial^2}{\partial x^2} [e^{-st} \psi(x,t)]\, dt = \frac{\partial^2 y(x,s)}{\partial x^2} \tag{36}$$

where $y(x,s)$ is the Laplace transform of $\psi(x,s)$. Equation (35) follows from Sec. 7, Chap. 4; owing to the boundary conditions specified in (33), Eq. (35) yields simply, $s^2 y(x,s)$. The result in (36) is valid provided that the order of integration with respect to t and the differentiation with respect to x can be interchanged.

As a result of the application of the Laplace transform, the problem as stated by (32) to (34) may be written in the form

$$\frac{d^2 y(x,s)}{dx^2} - \frac{s^2}{v^2} y(x,s) = 0 \tag{37}$$

$$y(0,s) = f(s) \qquad \lim_{x \to \infty} y(x,s) = 0 \tag{38}$$

Equation (37) is an ordinary differential equation in x. It follows then that

$$y(x,s) = c_1 e^{-(s/v)x} + c_2 e^{(s/v)x} \tag{39}$$

where c_1 and c_2 may be functions of s. Since $y(x,s)$ approaches zero as x tends to infinity, c_2 must equal zero and we get $c_1 = f(s)$. Thus

$$y(x,s) = e^{-(s/v)x} f(s) \tag{40}$$

The inverse Laplace transform is easily evaluated to yield the following traveling-wave expression:

$$\psi(x,t) = f\left(t - \frac{x}{v}\right) \qquad t \geq \frac{x}{v}$$
$$= 0 \qquad t \leq \frac{x}{v} \tag{41}$$

Actually, we may generalize further by considering the following form of the wave equation:

$$\frac{\partial^2 \psi}{\partial x^2} = \frac{k'}{v^2}\frac{\partial^2 \psi}{\partial t^2} \tag{42}$$

where k' is a complex factor which completely determines the propagation of the wave. If the signal at $x = 0$ is defined as

$$f(0,t) = \frac{E}{2\pi j}\int_{\alpha - j\infty}^{\alpha + j\infty} \frac{e^{st}}{s + j\omega}\, ds = 0 \qquad t < 0$$
$$= Ee^{-j\omega t} \qquad t > 0 \tag{43}$$

then this rotating-vector wave may be described at any point x by (42) which is satified by solutions of the form exp $[st - (s\sqrt{k'}/v)x]$ from which we may evolve wave functions of the type

$$\psi(x,t) = \psi_0 e^{j(\omega t - \Gamma x)} \tag{44}$$

where

$$\Gamma = \frac{\omega}{v}\sqrt{k'} = \alpha + j\beta \tag{45}$$

Γ is the propagation constant; α is the attenuation constant, and β is the wavelength constant or phase constant.

7. Velocities of Traveling Waves. In considering the motion of a traveling wave, three types of wave velocities must be studied. They are phase velocity, group velocity, and wave-front velocity.

Phase velocity is perhaps easier to visualize than the other two types of velocity since it describes the velocity of a surface of equal phase of a wave function whose form is $f[t - (x/v)]$. Its phase velocity v_p is

$$v_p = \frac{dx}{dt} \tag{46}$$

An equiphase surface of this wave function is described by the relationship

$$\omega\left(t - \frac{x}{v}\right) = \omega t - \beta x = \text{constant} \tag{47}$$

where

$$\beta = \frac{\omega}{v} \tag{48}$$

The phase velocity of this equiphase surface does not necessarily coincide with the velocity of propagation of the energy of the wave and may or may not exceed the velocity v, which, in free space, is the velocity of light.

If the wave function is a single-tone harmonic wave traveling in the x direction, then, as is shown in Fig. 1, a plane drawn through some point a on the wave will travel in the x direction with phase velocity v_p.

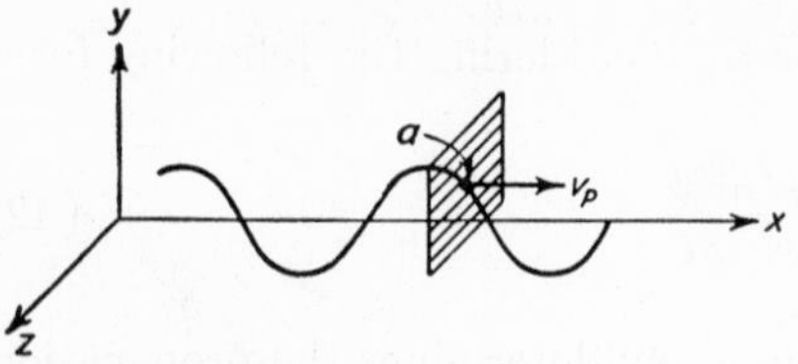

FIG. 1.

If the phase velocity of a wave passing through a medium is a *function of frequency*, that medium is said to be dispersive—if not, the medium is *nondispersive.* The quality of a medium which makes it dispersive is attributable to the presence of conductivity, which not only produces attenuation but also yields a functional relationship between phase velocity and frequency even though the conductivity may be almost completely negligible. If the conductivity is zero, then the phase velocity is a constant and a wave in the medium is propagated without distortion.

If two or more waves are concerned whose frequencies differ very slightly then the velocity of the group must be considered. This velocity is called the group velocity v_g, which is defined in terms of ω and β, as

$$v_g = \frac{1}{\partial\beta/\partial\omega} \tag{49}$$

In a nondispersive medium v_g may be shown to be equal to v_p as follows:

Since, from Eq. (48), we see that

$$\omega = v_p\beta \tag{50}$$

then, differentiating both sides with respect to ω, we get for the case where v_p is not a function of ω (which is the case in a nondispersive medium)

$$v_p \frac{\partial\beta}{\partial\omega} = 1 \tag{51}$$

Therefore

$$v_p = \frac{1}{\partial\beta/\partial\omega} = v_g \tag{52}$$

As an illustration of group velocity, let us consider the pair of traveling waves which are represented by rotating vectors as follows,

$$e_1 = e^{j(\omega_0 t - \beta x)} \tag{53}$$

$$e_2 = e^{j((\omega_0+\omega_1)t-(\beta+\delta\beta)x)} \tag{54}$$

where e_1 and e_2 represent a carrier and a first upper sideband, respectively, and δ is a very small but nonvanishing number. If we add these traveling waves together, we get

$$e = e_1 + e_2 = e^{j(\omega_0 t - \beta x)} + e^{j[(\omega_0 + \omega_1)t - (\beta + \delta\beta)x]} \tag{55}$$

$$= e^{j(\omega_1 t - \delta\beta x)}(e^{j[(\omega_0 - \omega_1)t - (\beta - \delta\beta)x]} + e^{j(\omega_0 t - \beta x)}) \tag{56}$$

and

$$\text{Re}\, e = \cos(\omega_1 t - \delta\beta x)\{\cos[(\omega_0 - \omega_1)t - (\beta - \delta\beta)x] + \cos(\omega_0 t - \beta x)\} \tag{57}$$

which contains an amplitude function $\cos(\omega_1 t - \delta\beta x)$ which represents the envelope of the pair of waves. If

$$\omega_1 t - \delta\beta x = \text{constant} \tag{58}$$

then the beats produced by the superposition of the wave pair are propagated with the group velocity

$$v_g = \frac{x}{t} = \frac{\omega_1}{\delta\beta} \tag{59}$$

If $\omega_1 \ll \omega_0$, then, letting $\omega_1 = \delta\omega_0$, we may write

$$v_g = \lim_{\delta \to 0} \frac{\delta\omega_0}{\delta\beta} = \frac{\partial\omega_0}{\partial\beta} = \frac{1}{\partial\beta/\partial\omega_0} \tag{60}$$

Note that if the medium is nondispersive

$$\frac{\partial\beta}{\partial\omega} = \frac{1}{v_p} \tag{61}$$

and so

$$\delta\beta = \frac{1}{v_p}\omega_1 \tag{62}$$

and Eq. (57) becomes

$$\cos\omega_1\left(t - \frac{x}{v_p}\right)\{\cos[(\omega_0 - \omega_1)t - (\beta - \delta\beta)x] + \cos(\omega_0 t - \beta x)\} \tag{57a}$$

which shows that the group velocity is now equal to the phase velocity and the envelope is propagated with the phase velocity.

We may investigate the property of group velocity leading to the relationship in Eq. (49) by considering the Fourier transform $g(\beta)$, with respect to β rather than ω, of the wave function $\psi(x,t)$. If we confine the significant spectral amplitudes of $g(\beta)$ to the region $\beta_0 - \delta\beta < \beta < \beta_0 + \delta\beta$, then we may write the inverse Fourier transform

$$\psi(x,t) = \frac{1}{2\pi}\int_{\beta_0 - \delta\beta}^{\beta_0 + \delta\beta} g(\beta)e^{j(\omega t - \beta x)}\, d\beta \tag{63}$$

This function is an important quantity used in quantum or wave mechanics and known as a wave packet.[1] If β is real and if ω is a known function of β, we may represent $\omega(\beta)$, when $\delta\beta$ is small, by the first two terms in its Taylor-series expansion as follows:

$$\omega(\beta) = \omega(\beta_0) + \left.\frac{d\omega}{d\beta}\right|_{\beta_0} (\beta - \beta_0) \tag{64}$$

Thus it follows that

$$\omega t - \beta x = \omega_0 t - \beta_0 x - (\beta - \beta_0)\left(x - \left.\frac{d\omega}{d\beta}\right|_{\beta_0} t\right) \tag{65}$$

whereupon we get

$$\psi(x,t) = \left(\frac{1}{2\pi} \int_{\beta_0 - \delta\beta}^{\beta_0 + \delta\beta} g(\beta) \cdot \exp\left\{-j\left[(\beta - \beta_0)\left(x - \left.\frac{d\omega}{d\beta}\right|_{\beta_0} t\right)\right]\right\} d\beta\right) \exp\left[j(\omega_0 t - \beta_0 x)\right] \tag{66}$$

By letting

$$x - \left.\frac{d\omega}{d\beta}\right|_{\beta_0} t = \text{constant} \tag{67}$$

we see that the group velocity of the spectral components lying in the range $\beta_0 - \delta\beta < \beta < \beta_0 + \delta\beta$ is

$$\left.\frac{d\omega}{d\beta}\right|_{\beta_0} = v_g \tag{68}$$

if $g(\beta)$ is essentially constant in this region.

If the packet is a single-tone wave packet, it follows from Eq. (66) that for $g(\beta) = g(\beta_0)$

$$\psi(x,t) = 2g(\beta_0)\, \delta\beta \frac{\sin 2\pi\, \delta\beta[x - (d\omega/d\beta)|_{\beta_0} t]}{2\pi\, \delta\beta[x - (d\omega/d\beta)|_{\beta_0} t]} e^{j(\omega_0 t - \beta_0 x)} \tag{69}$$

It is evident that the wave packet is described by the single-tone wave whose amplitude, as a function of distance, is a $(\sin \theta)/\theta$ function and whose peak, at some instant t, is located at $x = (d\omega/d\beta)|_{\beta_0} t$.

When the transmitting medium is dispersive, then the general problem of wave propagation becomes somewhat involved. If a wave train[2] whose Laplace transform is

$$\frac{e^{-s\sqrt{k'(s)}\,(x/v)}}{s + j\omega} \tag{70}$$

[1] V. Rojansky, "Introductory Quantum Mechanics," Sec. 40, Prentice-Hall, Inc., New York, 1942.

[2] See J. A. Stratton, "Electromagnetic Theory," Sec. 5.18, McGraw-Hill Book Company, Inc., New York, 1941.

is transmitted through the medium, then [compare with (43)]

$$\psi(x,t) = \frac{1}{2\pi j}\int_{\alpha-j\infty}^{\alpha+j\infty} \frac{e^{s[t-\sqrt{k'(s)}\,(x/v)]}}{s+j\omega}\,ds \qquad \alpha > 0 \tag{71}$$

The solution of this contour integral for $f(x,t)$ may be determined once $k'(s)$ is known. In general the solution will be of the form

$$\psi(x,t) = f_T(x,t) + f_{ss}(x,t) \tag{72}$$

where $f_T(x,t)$ is a transient wave and $f_{ss}(x,t)$ is a steady-state wave, the transmitting medium behaving somewhat as a transmission network.

Consider the behavior of some traveling wave $f[t - (x/v)]$ at the time $t = x/v$. It can be shown that nothing happens until $t = x/v$, up to which time the transient wave and the steady-state wave combine to yield zero for the total wave. After this time, the transient wave dies out, and the total wave builds up at a finite rate to the steady-state wave. This appearance and build-up of the wave appears to occur as follows: A first wave train, or first precursor, arrives with velocity v such that its amplitude is zero at $t = x/v$. Its frequency is very high, and its amplitude first grows and then diminishes. It is followed by a second precursor of larger amplitude but of lower frequency and then finally by the main wave train (steady state). Since the total wave is the superposition of the two precursors, which eventually die away, and the main wave train, it is difficult to determine just exactly when the signal arrives owing to the fact that, for all practical purposes, this arrival time is a function of the sensitivity of the detecting instruments since only on the basis of the readings of these instruments can we say exactly when the wave or signal has arrived and therefore attribute a signal velocity to it even though the initial wave front has arrived at $t = x/v$ and has traveled with the velocity v.

8. Other Wave-behavior Equations. In addition to the wave equation, we shall also encounter partial differential equations of the form

$$\frac{\partial^2\psi}{\partial x^2} - \frac{1}{v^2}\frac{\partial^2\psi}{\partial t^2} - \frac{1}{\xi}\frac{\partial\psi}{\partial t} = 0 \tag{73}$$

or

$$\frac{\partial^2\psi}{\partial x^2} - \frac{1}{\xi}\frac{\partial\psi}{\partial t} = 0 \tag{74}$$

Equation (73) is an extension of the wave equation as given by (1) and includes the effect of dissipation. Equation (74) is a famous partial differential equation of physics and engineering known as the diffusion equation.

TRANSMISSION LINES AND TRAVELING WAVES

9. Introduction. The Fourier and Laplace analyses have considerable application in systems involving transmission lines, from coaxial cables, used in television network systems, to pulse-forming lines, which are found in radar and pulser circuits.

The *Fourier analysis* may be used to determine the nature of *standing waves* and in some cases, the *traveling waves* which may exist on the transmission line. The *Laplace analysis,* however, is a far more powerful approach for it not only yields in a simple fashion the nature of the *traveling waves* which occur on transmission lines but also a more complete description of the transient phenomena which are associated with these waves.

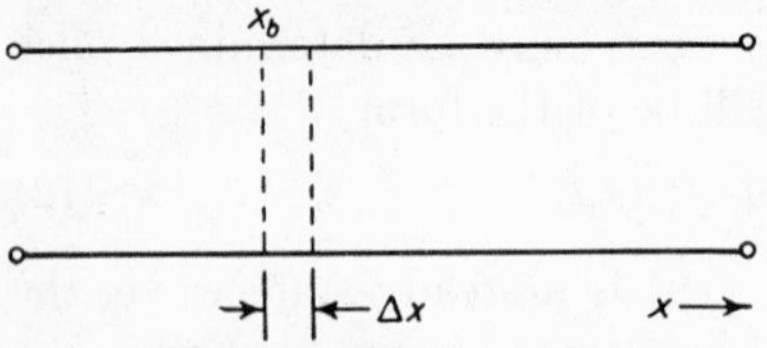

FIG. 2.

General Aspects of Transmission Lines

10. The General Transmission-line Equations. Let us consider the transmission-line section pictured in Fig. 2,

where $e = e(x,t)$ = potential in volts at x_0 at time t
$i = i(x,t)$ = current in amperes at x_0 at time t
r = resistance, ohms per mile
g = leakage to ground, mhos per mile
L = inductance, henrys per mile
C = capacitance, farads per mile

Consider now a segment Δx in this line. The voltage drop may be written

$$\Delta e = -r\,\Delta x\,i - L\,\Delta x\,\frac{\partial i}{\partial t} \tag{75}$$

If we divide (75) by Δx and take the limit as $\Delta x \to 0$, we get

$$\lim_{\Delta x \to 0} \frac{\Delta e}{\Delta x} = \frac{\partial e}{\partial x} = -ri - L\frac{\partial i}{\partial t} \tag{76}$$

The current drop in this line segment is

$$\Delta i = -g\,\Delta x\,e - C\,\Delta x\,\frac{\partial e}{\partial t} \tag{77}$$

Dividing by Δx and taking the limit as $\Delta x \to 0$, we get

$$\lim_{\Delta x \to 0} \frac{\Delta i}{\Delta x} = \frac{\partial i}{\partial x} = -ge - C\frac{\partial e}{\partial t} \tag{78}$$

If we differentiate (76) with respect to x and (78) with respect to t, we get

$$\frac{\partial^2 e}{\partial x^2} = -r\frac{\partial i}{\partial x} - L\frac{\partial^2 i}{\partial x\,\partial t} \tag{79}$$

$$\frac{\partial^2 i}{\partial t\,\partial x} = -g\frac{\partial e}{\partial t} - C\frac{\partial^2 e}{\partial t^2} \tag{80}$$

Substituting (76) and (78) into (79), we get

$$\frac{\partial^2 e}{\partial x^2} = LC\frac{\partial^2 e}{\partial t^2} + (rC + Lg)\frac{\partial e}{\partial t} + rge \tag{81}$$

and, in like manner,

$$\frac{\partial^2 i}{\partial x^2} = LC\frac{\partial^2 i}{\partial t^2} + (rC + Lg)\frac{\partial i}{\partial t} + rgi \tag{82}$$

Equations (81) and (82) are known as the telegraph equations and describe the general behavior of waves in a transmission line.

11. The Telegraph Equations and the Wave Equation. If the transmission line in Fig. 2 is presumed to be dissipationless so that $r = g = 0$, then we get from (81) and (82)

$$\frac{\partial^2 e}{\partial x^2} = \frac{1}{v^2}\frac{\partial^2 e}{\partial t^2} \tag{83}$$

$$\frac{\partial^2 i}{\partial x^2} = \frac{1}{v^2}\frac{\partial^2 i}{\partial t^2} \tag{84}$$

where

$$v = \frac{1}{\sqrt{LC}} \tag{85}$$

Equations (83) and (84) are wave equations, and waves of the form $f[t \pm (x/v)]$ will be transmitted on the transmission line with velocity v.

12. Rotating Vectors and the Telegraph Equations. Let us assume the rotating-vector solution

$$e(x,t) = E(x)e^{j\omega t} \tag{86}$$

for Eq. (81). Substituting (86) into (81), we get

$$\frac{\partial^2 E(x)}{\partial x^2}e^{j\omega t} = -LC\omega^2 E(x)e^{j\omega t} + j\omega(rC + Lg)E(x)e^{j\omega t} + rgE(x)e^{j\omega t} \tag{87}$$

$$= [-\omega^2 LC + (rC + Lg)j\omega + rg]E(x)e^{j\omega t} \tag{88}$$

$$= (r + j\omega L)(g + j\omega C)E(x)e^{j\omega t} \tag{89}$$

Thus,

$$\frac{d^2E(x)}{dx^2} - \Gamma^2 E(x) = 0 \tag{90}$$

$$\frac{d^2I(x)}{dx^2} - \Gamma^2 I(x) = 0 \tag{91}$$

where

$$\Gamma^2 = (r + j\omega L)(g + j\omega C) \tag{92}$$

Since Eqs. (90) and (91) are differential equations in x, they yield the following solutions:

$$E(x) = A_1 e^{-\Gamma x} + A_2 e^{\Gamma x} \tag{93}$$

$$I(x) = B_1 e^{-\Gamma x} + B_2 e^{\Gamma x} \tag{94}$$

This pair of equations contains four constants, which must be evaluated.

Let us now return to the original transmission-line equations

$$\frac{\partial e}{\partial x} = -ri - L\frac{di}{dt} \tag{76}$$

$$\frac{\partial i}{\partial x} = -ge - C\frac{de}{dt} \tag{78}$$

Substituting the rotating vectors $i = I(x)e^{j\omega t}$ and $e = E(x)e^{j\omega t}$ into (76) and (78), respectively, we get

$$\frac{dE(x)}{dx} = -(r + j\omega L)I(x) \tag{95}$$

$$\frac{dI(x)}{dx} = -(g + j\omega C)E(x) \tag{96}$$

If the values of $E(x)$ and $I(x)$ as given by (93) and (94) are differentiated with respect to x and substituted into these equations, we get

$$(Z_0B_1 - A_1)e^{-\Gamma x} + (Z_0B_2 + A_2)e^{\Gamma x} = 0 \tag{97}$$

$$(A_1 - Z_0B_1)e^{-\Gamma x} + (A_2 + Z_0B_2)e^{\Gamma x} = 0 \tag{98}$$

where

$$Z_0 = \sqrt{\frac{Z}{Y}} \tag{99}$$

$$Z = r + j\omega L \tag{100}$$

$$Y = g + j\omega C \tag{101}$$

Equations (97) and (98) can be valid only if

$$B_1 = \frac{A_1}{Z_0} \qquad B_2 = -\frac{A_1}{Z_0} \tag{102}$$

and it follows that

$$E(x) = A_1 e^{-\Gamma x} + A_2 e^{+\Gamma x} \tag{103}$$

$$I(x) = \frac{A_1}{Z_0} e^{-\Gamma x} - \frac{A_2}{Z_0} e^{+\Gamma x} \tag{104}$$

The number of boundary values to be evaluated has now been reduced to two.

Consider now the general transmission-line system, of length l, which is pictured in Fig. 3. For this system, we may specify the two following terminal conditions:

$$e(0) + I_S Z_S = e_S \qquad \text{at} \qquad x = 0 \tag{105}$$

$$e_r - I_r Z_r = 0 \qquad \text{at} \qquad x = l \tag{106}$$

Substituting these terminal conditions into (103) and (104), we get, for A_1 and A_2,

$$A_1 = e(t) \frac{(Z_r + Z_0)Z_0 e^{\Gamma l}}{(Z_0 + Z_S)(Z_0 + Z_r)e^{\Gamma l} - (Z_0 - Z_S)(Z_0 - Z_r)e^{-\Gamma l}} \tag{107}$$

$$A_2 = e(t) \frac{(Z_r - Z_0)Z_0 e^{-\Gamma l}}{(Z_0 + Z_S)(Z_0 + Z_r)e^{\Gamma l} - (Z_0 - Z_S)(Z_0 - Z_r)e^{-\Gamma l}} \tag{108}$$

which, when substituted into Eqs. (103) and (104), yield the general transmission-line equations

$$E(x) = \frac{Z_0}{Z_0 + Z_s} \frac{e^{-\Gamma x} - k_d e^{-\Gamma(2l-x)}}{1 - k_d k_0 e^{-2\Gamma x}} e(t) \tag{109}$$

$$I(x) = \frac{1}{Z_0 + Z_s} \frac{e^{-\Gamma x} + k_d e^{-\Gamma(2l-x)}}{1 - k_d k_0 e^{-2\Gamma x}} e(t) \tag{110}$$

where

$$k_0 = \frac{Z_0 - Z_S}{Z_0 + Z_S} \tag{111}$$

$$k_d = \frac{Z_0 - Z_r}{Z_0 + Z_r} \tag{112}$$

k_0 and k_d are reflection factors whose properties will be discussed later in this part.

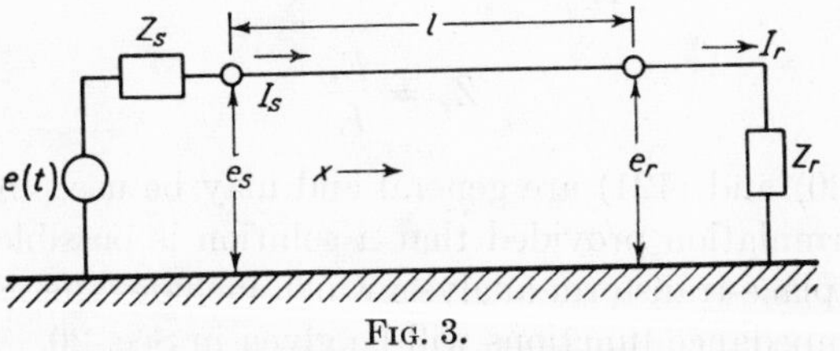

FIG. 3.

If considerations of input impedance and transfer impedance are of importance, it is of more interest to derive the transmission-line equations in another form. If we return and start again with Eqs. (76) and (78), it can be shown that[1]

[1] For the derivation of these equations, see, for example, Ware and Reed, "Communication Circuits," Chap. V, John Wiley & Sons, Inc., New York, 1944.

$$E(x) = E_r \cosh \Gamma x + I_r Z_0 \sinh \Gamma x \tag{113}$$

$$I(x) = I_r \cosh \Gamma x + \frac{E_r}{Z_0} \sinh \Gamma x \tag{114}$$

where Z_0 is the characteristic impedance of the line; *i.e.*,

$$Z_0 = \sqrt{\frac{Z}{Y}} \tag{115}$$

These equations describe the voltage and current at any part of the transmission line.

For a line of length l, we get for the input voltage and current, with l measured from the receiving end of the line,

$$E_S = E_r \cosh \Gamma l + I_r Z_0 \sinh \Gamma l \tag{116}$$

$$I_S = I_r \cosh \Gamma l + \frac{E_r}{Z_0} \sinh \Gamma l \tag{117}$$

and for the receiving-end voltage and current (for this case, l is measured from the sending end),

$$E_r = E_S \cosh \Gamma l - I_S Z_0 \sinh \Gamma l \tag{118}$$

$$I_r = I_S \cosh \Gamma l - \frac{E_S}{Z_0} \sinh \Gamma l \tag{119}$$

We may now describe the line in terms of impedances. For the input impedance,

$$Z_S = \frac{E_S}{I_S} = Z_0 \frac{Z_r \cosh \Gamma l + Z_0 \sinh \Gamma l}{Z_0 \cosh \Gamma l + Z_r \sinh \Gamma l} \tag{120}$$

and for the transfer impedance,

$$Z_T = \frac{E_S}{I_r} = Z_r \cosh \Gamma l + Z_0 \sinh \Gamma l \tag{121}$$

where

$$Z_r = \frac{E_r}{I_r} \tag{122}$$

Equations (120) and (121) are general and may be used in Fourier series or integral formulation provided that a solution is possible. An application of the Laplace-transform analysis which includes the use of the transmission-line impedance functions will be given in Sec. 20.

Fourier Analysis and Transmission Lines

13. A Solution of the Telegraph Equation.[1] Consider the representative solution of the telegraph equation (81) when the ends of a transmission

[1] See, for example, Reddick and Miller, "Advanced Mathematics for Engineers," 1st ed., Chap. VII, John Wiley & Sons, Inc., New York, 1938.

line (of length l), at $x = 0$ and $x = l$, are suddenly short-circuited at $t = 0$, yielding the following boundary conditions:

$$e(0,t) = 0 \qquad 0 < t < \infty \tag{123}$$

$$e(l,t) = 0 \qquad 0 < t < \infty \tag{124}$$

At $t = 0$, let the variation of e along the line be described by the following additional boundary conditions:

$$e(x,0) = e(x) \qquad 0 < x < l \tag{125}$$

$$\left.\frac{\partial e}{\partial t}\right|_{t=0} = 0 \qquad 0 < x < l \tag{126}$$

This problem is somewhat similar to the problem of the plucked string which experiences damping.

In order to solve the equation

$$\frac{\partial^2 e}{\partial x^2} = LC\frac{\partial^2 e}{\partial t^2} + (rC + Lg)\frac{\partial e}{\partial t} + rge \tag{81}$$

let us assume a solution of the form

$$e(x,t) = X(x)T(t) \tag{127}$$

Substituting (127) into (81), we get

$$X''T = LCXT'' + (rC + Lg)XT' + rgXT \tag{128}$$

Dividing through by XT, we get

$$\frac{X''}{X} = LC\frac{T''}{T} + (rC + Lg)\frac{T'}{T} + rg = \lambda \tag{129}$$

where λ is a constant. We therefore get two differential equations

$$X'' - \lambda X = 0 \tag{130}$$

$$T'' + \left(\frac{r}{L} + \frac{g}{C}\right)T' + \frac{rg - \lambda}{LC}T = 0 \tag{131}$$

Equations (130) and (131) yield, respectively, the roots,

$$m_{\pm 1} = \pm\sqrt{\lambda} \tag{132}$$

and

$$m_{\pm 2} = -\frac{1}{2}\left(\frac{r}{L} + \frac{g}{C}\right) \pm \sqrt{\frac{1}{4}\left(\frac{r}{L} + \frac{g}{C}\right)^2 - \left(\frac{rg - \lambda}{LC}\right)} \tag{133}$$

Consider the case when (134) can be written in the form[1]

$$m_{\pm 2} = a \pm j\sqrt{\lambda}\, b \tag{134}$$

We then arrive at the following solution of (81) using only negative values of λ so that e at any point may decrease as t increases:

$$e(x,t) = (c_1 \sin \sqrt{-\lambda}\, x + c_2 \cos \sqrt{-\lambda}\, x) \cdot (c_3 \sin \sqrt{-\lambda}\, bt + c_4 \cos \sqrt{-\lambda}\, bt)e^{at} \tag{135}$$

Let us now solve for the constants c_1, c_2, c_3, and c_4 in terms of the boundary conditions (123), (124), (125), and (126).

Since $e(0,t) = 0$, then we see immediately that $c_2 = 0$. Since $e(l,t) = 0$

$$\sin \sqrt{-\lambda}\, l = 0 \tag{136}$$

It follows from (136) that

$$\sqrt{-\lambda} = \frac{n\pi}{l} \tag{137}$$

As a result of (123) and (124), we find that

$$e(x,t) = c_1 \sin \frac{n\pi x}{l} \left(c_3 \sin \frac{n\pi bt}{l} + c_4 \cos \frac{n\pi bt}{l}\right)e^{at} \tag{138}$$

According to the third boundary condition, (125),

$$\left.\frac{\partial e}{\partial t}\right|_{t=0} = c_1 \sin \frac{n\pi x}{l}\, e^{at}\left(c_3 \frac{n\pi b}{l} \cos \frac{n\pi bt}{l} - c_4 \frac{n\pi b}{l} \sin \frac{n\pi bt}{l} + ac_3 \sin \frac{n\pi bt}{l} + ac_4 \cos \frac{n\pi bt}{l}\right) = 0 \qquad t = 0 \tag{139}$$

which can be true only if

$$ac_4 = c_3 \frac{n\pi b}{l} \tag{140}$$

Therefore

$$c_4 = c_3 \frac{n\pi b}{al} \tag{141}$$

Combining the coefficients c_3 and c_1 so that their product yields the constant c_5, we get

$$e(x,t) = c_5 \sin \frac{n\pi x}{l} \left(\sin \frac{n\pi bt}{l} + \frac{n\pi b}{al} \cos \frac{n\pi bt}{l}\right)e^{at} \tag{142}$$

[1] In a distortionless line, for example (see Sec. 17) $rC = Lg$. It follows that

$$m_{\pm 2} = -\frac{r}{L} \pm j\, \frac{\sqrt{\lambda}}{\sqrt{LC}}$$

Let us now assume that the initial voltage distribution $e(x)$ is described by the Fourier sine series

$$e(x) = \sum_{1}^{\infty} B_n \sin \frac{n\pi x}{l} \tag{143}$$

where

$$B_n = \frac{2}{l} \int_0^l e(x) \sin \frac{n\pi x}{l} \, dx \tag{144}$$

Then substituting $t = 0$ into Eq. (142) and equating the result with the nth term of the Fourier series (143), we get

$$c_5 \frac{n\pi b}{al} \sin \frac{n\pi x}{l} = B_n \sin \frac{n\pi x}{l} \tag{145}$$

which shows that

$$c_5 = \frac{al}{n\pi b} B_n \tag{146}$$

Therefore, $e(x,t)$ may be expressed by the following infinite set of terms:

$$e(x,t) = \sum_{1}^{\infty} B_n \frac{al}{n\pi b} e^{at} \sin \frac{n\pi x}{l} \left(\sin \frac{n\pi bt}{l} + \frac{n\pi b}{al} \cos \frac{n\pi bt}{l} \right) \tag{147}$$

This is the transient solution of the telegraph equations corresponding to the boundary-value conditions (123) to (126) and is seen to include the exponential decay factor e^{at}.

We may solve for the steady-state solution of the voltage telegraph equation by considering the form of Eq. (81) when e is made independent of time. Then

$$\frac{d^2e(x)}{dx^2} - rge(x) = 0 \tag{148}$$

The characteristic equation corresponding to (148) is

$$m^2 - rg = 0 \tag{149}$$

and we get

$$e(x) = Ae^{\sqrt{rg}\,x} + Be^{-\sqrt{rg}\,x} \tag{150}$$

If $e(x)$ is solved in terms of the boundary conditions which exist for $t < 0$, the resulting value of $e(x)$ may be substituted into (150), to permit the evaluation of the constants A and B.

As illustration of the evaluation of $e(x)$ in terms of boundary conditions, assume that, for $t < 0$,

$$e(0) = E_1 \tag{151}$$

$$e(l) = E_2 \tag{152}$$

Then, at $x = 0$ and $x = l$, respectively,

$$E_1 = A + B \tag{153}$$

$$E_2 = Ae^{\sqrt{rg}\,l} + Be^{-\sqrt{rg}\,l} \tag{154}$$

which is easily solved for A and B to yield

$$e(x) = \frac{E_2 - E_1 e^{-\sqrt{rg}\,l}}{2 \sinh \sqrt{rg}\,l} e^{\sqrt{rg}\,x} + \frac{E_1 e^{+\sqrt{rg}\,l} - E_2}{2 \sinh \sqrt{rg}\,l} e^{-\sqrt{rg}\,x} \tag{155}$$

14. Solution of the Telegraph Equations.[1] When $L = g = 0$, the general transmission-line equations (81) and (82) yield the telegraph equations

$$\frac{\partial^2 e}{\partial x^2} = rC \frac{\partial e}{\partial t} \tag{156}$$

$$\frac{\partial^2 i}{\partial x^2} = rC \frac{\partial i}{\partial t} \tag{157}$$

Let the following boundary conditions prevail for a line of length l which is short-circuited at both ends,

$$e(0,t) = 0 \tag{158}$$

$$e(l,t) = 0 \tag{159}$$

$$e(x,0) = e(x) \tag{160}$$

where $e(x)$ is the potential along the line at $t = 0$.

Consider a solution of (156) of the form

$$e(x,t) = X(x)T(t) \tag{161}$$

We get from (156)

$$\frac{X''(x)}{X(x)} = rC \frac{T'(t)}{T(t)} = \lambda \tag{162}$$

which yields the two following differential equations:

$$X''(x) - \lambda X(x) = 0 \tag{163}$$

$$T'(t) - \frac{\lambda}{rC} T(t) = 0 \tag{164}$$

It follows that

$$e(x,t) = (c_1 \sin \sqrt{-\lambda}\, x + c_2 \cos \sqrt{-\lambda}\, x)e^{-(\lambda/rC)t} \tag{165}$$

Let us now introduce the first boundary condition, (158). At $t = 0$

$$e(0,t) = c_2 \cos \sqrt{-\lambda}\, xe^{-(\lambda/rC)0} = 0 \tag{166}$$

[1] See Sec. 18 for a solution involving the Laplace transform.

This can be true only if $c_2 = 0$. Then

$$e(x,t) = c_1 \sin \sqrt{-\lambda}\, x e^{-(\lambda/rC)t} \tag{167}$$

The second boundary condition will be satisfied if

$$\sqrt{-\lambda} = \frac{n\pi}{l} \tag{168}$$

and we get

$$e(x,t) = c_1 \sin \frac{n\pi x}{l} e^{-(n^2\pi^2/l^2rC)t} \tag{169}$$

In applying the third boundary condition, (160), let us assume that the initial voltage distribution $e(x)$ at $t = 0$ may be expressed by the Fourier series

$$e(x) = \sum_1^\infty B_n \sin \frac{n\pi x}{l} \tag{170}$$

where

$$B_n = \frac{2}{l} \int_0^l e(x) \sin \frac{n\pi x}{l}\, dx \tag{171}$$

Then if we substitute $t = 0$ into (169) and equate its nth value with the nth term of the Fourier series (170), we get

$$c_1 \sin \frac{n\pi x}{l} = B_n \sin \frac{n\pi x}{l} \tag{172}$$

which shows that

$$c_1 = B_n \tag{173}$$

and we get finally

$$e(x,t) = \sum_1^\infty B_n \sin \frac{n\pi x}{l} e^{-(n^2\pi^2/l^2rC)t} \tag{174}$$

This is the transient solution and is seen to include the damping factor $e^{-(n^2\pi^2/l^2rC)t}$.

The steady-state solution, which is independent of time, may be found by letting

$$\frac{\partial^2 e(x)}{\partial x^2} = rC \frac{\partial e(x)}{\partial t} = 0 \tag{175}$$

since $e(x)$ does not depend on time. The solution of

$$\frac{\partial^2 e(x)}{\partial x^2} = 0 \tag{176}$$

is

$$e(x) = c_a x + c_b \tag{177}$$

which may be solved in terms of the boundary conditions for $t < 0$ and then substituted into (171) to yield the Fourier coefficients B_n.

Laplace Analysis and Traveling Waves in Transmission Lines

15. The General Transformed Equations. Consider the basic transmission-line equations

$$\frac{\partial e}{\partial x} = -ri - L\frac{\partial i}{\partial t} \tag{76}$$

$$\frac{\partial i}{\partial x} = -ge - C\frac{\partial e}{\partial t} \tag{78}$$

Let us take the Laplace transform of Eq. (76) by multiplying each member by e^{-st} and then integrating from $t = 0$ to $t = \infty$. Using the manipulations and the notation listed at the bottom of the page,[1] we get the following ordinary differential equations,

$$\frac{dE(x,s)}{dx} = Li_0(x) - (Ls + r)I(x,s) \tag{178}$$

$$\frac{dI(x,s)}{dx} = Ce_0(x) - (Cs + g)E(x,s) \tag{179}$$

where x is the independent variable and s is a continuously variable parameter. If we differentiate (178) with respect to x and substitute the expression for $dI(x,s)/dx$, as given by (179), into it, we get the following equation:

$$\frac{d^2E(x,s)}{dx^2} - L\frac{di_0(x)}{dx} + C(Ls + r)e_0(x) - \Gamma^2E(x,s) = 0 \tag{180}$$

which can be written in the form

$$\frac{d^2E(x,s)}{dx^2} - \Gamma^2E(x,s) = f(x,s) \tag{181}$$

where

$$f(x,s) = L\frac{di_0(x)}{dt} - C(Ls + r)e_0(x) \tag{182}$$

$$\Gamma^2 = (Ls + r)(Cs + g) \tag{183}$$

[1] Note that

$$\int_0^\infty e(x,t)e^{-st}\,dt = E(x,s)$$

$$\int_0^\infty \frac{\partial e(x,t)}{\partial x}e^{-st}\,dt = \frac{\partial}{\partial x}\int_0^\infty E(x,t)e^{-st}\,dt = \frac{\partial}{\partial x}E(x,s)$$

$$\int_0^\infty \frac{\partial e(x,t)}{\partial t}e^{-st}\,dt = e^{-st}e(x,t)\Big|_0^\infty + s\int_0^\infty e(x,t)e^{st}\,dt = -e_0(x) + sE(x,s)$$

The solution of (181) obviously consists of the sum of the complementary function [solution when $f(x,s) = 0$] and the particular integral; *i.e.*,

$$E(x,s) = Ae^{\Gamma x} + Be^{-\Gamma x} + \frac{e^{\Gamma x}}{2\Gamma}\int f(x,s)e^{-\Gamma x}\,dx - \frac{e^{-\Gamma x}}{2\Gamma}\int f(x,s)e^{\Gamma x}\,dx \quad (184)$$

and since, according to Eq. (178),

$$I(x,s) = \frac{1}{Ls + r}\left[-\frac{dE(x,s)}{dx} + Li_0(x)\right] \quad (185)$$

we get

$$I(x,s) = \frac{1}{Z_0}\left[-Ae^{\Gamma x} + Be^{-\Gamma x} - \frac{e^{\Gamma x}}{2\Gamma}\int f(x,s)e^{-\Gamma x}\,dx - \frac{e^{-\Gamma x}}{2\Gamma}\int f(x,s)e^{\Gamma x}\,dx + \frac{Li_0(x)}{\Gamma}\right] \quad (186)$$

where Z_0 is the characteristic impedance; *i.e.*,

$$Z_0 = \frac{Ls + r}{\Gamma} = \sqrt{\frac{Ls + r}{Cs + g}} \quad (187)$$

Equations (184) and (186) represent the complete transformed solutions of the general transmission-line problem in terms of the initial conditions $e_0(x)$ and $i_0(x)$ and the arbitrary constants A and B, whose values may be deduced from the other boundary conditions of the transmission line.

16. Waves in a Semiinfinite Transmission Line. If a transmission line extending from $x = 0$ to $x = \infty$ is initially at rest so that $f(x) = 0$, let us consider the current and voltage at some distance x, due to an impressed step voltage at $t = 0$. Then, from (184) and (186), we get

$$E(x,s) = Ae^{\Gamma x} + Be^{-\Gamma x} \quad (188)$$

$$I(x,s) = \frac{1}{Z_0}(-Ae^{\Gamma x} + Be^{-\Gamma x}) \quad (189)$$

Note the exponential $e^{\Gamma x}$. If $x \to \infty$, then A must equal zero if the real part of Γ is greater than zero. Moreover, if the voltage impressed at the input terminals at $t = 0$ is $e(t)$, then

$$E(0,s) = \mathcal{L}[e(t)] \quad (190)$$

and it follows that

$$B = E(0,s) \quad (191)$$

We find now the equations,

$$E(x,s) = \mathcal{L}[e(t)]e^{-\Gamma x} \quad (192)$$

$$I(x,s) = \frac{1}{Z_0}\mathcal{L}[e(t)]e^{-\Gamma x} \quad (193)$$

which describe the Laplace transformed current and voltage waves traveling down the line with their propagation a function of the exponential $e^{-\Gamma x}$.

Let us now look more closely at Γ. Note that

$$\Gamma^2 = (Ls + r)(Cs + g) \tag{194}$$

$$= \frac{1}{v^2}\left[(s + \rho_1)^2 + \rho_2^2\right] \tag{195}$$

where

$$v = \frac{1}{\sqrt{LC}} \qquad \rho_1 = \frac{1}{2}\left(\frac{r}{L} + \frac{g}{C}\right) \qquad \rho_2 = \frac{1}{2}\left(\frac{r}{L} - \frac{g}{C}\right) \tag{196}$$

Then we may rewrite (192) and (193) as follows:

$$E(x,s) = \mathfrak{L}[e(t)]e^{-(x/v)\sqrt{(s+\rho_1)^2-\rho_2^2}} \tag{197}$$

$$I(x,s) = \mathfrak{L}[e(t)](Cs + g)\,\frac{e^{-(x/s)\sqrt{(s+\rho_1)^2-\rho_2^2}}}{(1/v)\sqrt{(s + \rho_1)^2 - \rho_2^2}} \tag{198}$$

In Eq. (198), the relationship

$$Z_0 = \sqrt{\frac{Ls + r}{Cs + g}}\sqrt{\frac{Cs + g}{Cs + g}} = \frac{\Gamma}{Cs + g} \tag{199}$$

has been used.

The voltage and current at any point on the line may be found by taking the inverse Laplace transforms of (197) and (198); *i.e.*,

$$e(x,t) = \frac{1}{2\pi j}\int_{\alpha-j\infty}^{\alpha+j\infty} \mathfrak{L}[e(t)]e^{-(x/v)\sqrt{(s+\rho_1)^2-\rho_2^2}}e^{st}\,ds \tag{200}$$

$$i(x,t) = \frac{1}{2\pi j}\int_{\alpha-j\infty}^{\alpha+j\infty} \mathfrak{L}[e(t)](Cs + g)\,\frac{e^{-(x/v)\sqrt{(s+\rho_1)^2-\rho_2^2}}}{(1/v)\sqrt{(s + \rho_1)^2 - \rho_2^2}}\,e^{st}\,ds \tag{201}$$

Actually, the evaluation of the contour integrals (200) and (201) for even the simplest forms of $e(t)$ is very difficult, particularly if all of the four line parameters L, C, r, g are nonzero. L. F. Woodruff and J. R. Riordan[1] have shown, using different solutions which are based on Bessel-function recurrence formulas or on Tchebysheff polynomials, respectively, that for the case where $e(t)$ is a step-function voltage of amplitude E, that is,

$$\mathfrak{L}[e(t)] = \frac{E}{s} \tag{202}$$

then the solution for $e(x,t)$ is

$$e(x,t) = E\sum_{n=0}^{\infty}\mathcal{V}_n\left(\frac{\rho_1}{\rho_2}\right)u^n I_n(\rho_2\tau)e^{-\rho_1 t} \qquad x > vt \tag{203}$$

[1] L. F. Woodruff, Transmission Line Transients in Motion Pictures, *Trans. AIEE*, vol. 57, pp. 391–399, July, 1938. (Includes discussion by Riordan.)

where

$$u = \sqrt{\frac{vt - x}{vt + x}} \qquad \tau = [t^2 - (x/v)^2]^{\frac{1}{2}} \tag{204}$$

and

$$\begin{aligned}
\mathcal{V}_0\left(\frac{\rho_1}{\rho_2}\right) &= 1 \\
\mathcal{V}_1\left(\frac{\rho_1}{\rho_2}\right) &= 2\,\frac{\rho_1}{\rho_2} \\
\mathcal{V}_2\left(\frac{\rho_1}{\rho_2}\right) &= \left[4\left(\frac{\rho_1}{\rho_2}\right)^2 - 2\right] \\
\mathcal{V}_3\left(\frac{\rho_1}{\rho_2}\right) &= 8\left(\frac{\rho_1}{\rho_2}\right)^3 - 6\,\frac{\rho_1}{\rho_2} \\
\mathcal{V}_4\left(\frac{\rho_1}{\rho_2}\right) &= 16\left(\frac{\rho_1}{\rho_2}\right)^4 - 16\left(\frac{\rho_1}{\rho_2}\right)^2 + 2
\end{aligned} \tag{205}$$

etc.

$I_n(\rho_2\tau)$ is the Bessel function of the first kind with an imaginary argument, *viz.*, $j^{-n}J_n(j\rho_2\tau)$.

E. Weber[1] has derived the following solution for $i(x,t)$ due to step-function excitation using pairs 860 and 210 from the Campbell-Foster tables:[2]

$$i(x,t) = E\sqrt{\frac{C}{L}}\left(1 + \frac{g}{C}\int_{x/v}^{t} dt\right)\cdot\left[e^{-\rho_1 t} I_0\left(\rho_2\sqrt{t^2 - \left(\frac{x}{v}\right)^2}\right)\right] \tag{206}$$

where $t > x/v$ and the integration must be performed on the bracketed term. An application of the concepts associated with (206) will be presented in the next section in connection with nonleaky lines.

17. The Distortionless Line and the Nonleaky Line. Consider the propagation constant Γ of the transmission line for the case of the distortionless line which exists under the conditions

$$\rho_2 = 0 \tag{207}$$

$$\frac{r}{L} = \frac{g}{C} = \rho_1 \qquad Z_0 = \sqrt{\frac{L}{C}}\sqrt{\frac{LCs + gL}{LCs + rC}} = \sqrt{\frac{L}{C}} \tag{208}$$

Then,

$$\Gamma = \frac{s + \rho_1}{v} \tag{209}$$

[1] E. Weber, Traveling Waves on Transmission Lines, *Elec. Eng.*, vol. 61, pp. 302–309, June, 1942. This paper also contains a solution of (197) using pair 863.1 of the Campbell-Foster tables.

[2] See Campbell and Foster, "Fourier Integrals for Practical Applications," D. Van Nostrand Company, Inc., New York, 1942.

Substituting (209) into (193), we get

$$I(x,s) = \mathfrak{L}[e(t)] \sqrt{\frac{C}{L}} e^{-s/v} e^{-p_1/v} \tag{210}$$

If $e(t)$ is a step voltage of amplitude E, occurring at $t = 0$, then, using (202), we get

$$i(x,t) = Ee^{-p_1/v} \sqrt{\frac{C}{L}} \frac{1}{2\pi j} \int_{\alpha - j\infty}^{\alpha + j\infty} \frac{e^{-s/v} e^{-st}}{s} ds \tag{211}$$

which, owing to the shifting function $e^{-s/v}$, yields the solution

$$\begin{aligned} i(x,t) &= 0 & -\infty < t < -\frac{x}{v} \\ &= E \sqrt{\frac{C}{L}} e^{-p_1/v} & -\frac{x}{v} < t < \infty \end{aligned} \tag{212}$$

Equation (212) shows that the step function will be transmitted down the line without distortion, although it will decrease in amplitude because of the decay factor $e^{-p_1/v}$.

Let us compare this result with the case when a wave is transmitted down a nonleaky line, that is, $g = 0$. Substituting $g = 0$ into Eq. (206), we get

$$i(x,t) = E \sqrt{\frac{C}{L}} e^{-(r/2L)t} I_0\left(\frac{r}{2L} \sqrt{t^2 - \left(\frac{x}{v}\right)^2}\right) \qquad t > \frac{x}{v} \tag{213}$$

For a very short interval of time following $t = 0$,

$$i(x,t) = E \sqrt{\frac{C}{L}} e^{-(r/2L)t} \qquad t > \frac{x}{v} \tag{214}$$

which corresponds to Eq. (212) for the distortionless line. When t increases so that the first term of the modified Bessel function becomes important, we get,

$$i(x,t) = E \sqrt{\frac{C}{L}} e^{-(r/2L)t} \left[1 + \frac{[(r/2L)\sqrt{t^2 - (x/v)^2}]^2}{4\,\Gamma(2)}\right] \qquad t > \frac{x}{v} \tag{215}$$

which shows that the form of the transmitted step function is beginning to deteriorate. As t increases further so that more terms of (206) become important, the distortion will become even more pronounced.

18. Semiinfinite Transmission Line when $L = g = 0$. If $L = g = 0$ in a semiinfinite transmission line, then

$$\Gamma^2 = rCs \qquad Z_0 = \sqrt{\frac{r}{Cs}} \tag{216}$$

and it follows that

$$E(x,s) = \mathcal{L}[e(t)]e^{-\sqrt{rCs}\,x} \tag{217}$$

$$I(x,s) = \frac{\mathcal{L}[e(t)]}{Z_0}e^{-\sqrt{rCs}\,x} \tag{218}$$

$$= \mathcal{L}[e(t)]\sqrt{\frac{Cs}{r}}\,e^{-\sqrt{rCs}\,x} \tag{219}$$

The inverse Laplace transform of $I(x,s)$ is

$$i(x,t) = \sqrt{\frac{C}{r}}\,\frac{1}{2\pi j}\int_{\alpha-j\infty}^{\alpha+j\infty} \mathcal{L}[e(t)]e^{-\sqrt{rC}\,xs^{\frac{1}{2}}}s^{\frac{1}{2}}e^{st}\,ds \tag{220}$$

If $e(t)$ is a step function voltage of amplitude E, occurring at $t = 0$, Eq. (220) becomes

$$i(x,t) = \sqrt{\frac{C}{r}}\,\frac{1}{2\pi j}\int_{\alpha-j\infty}^{\alpha+j\infty} s^{-\frac{1}{2}}e^{-\sqrt{rC}\,xs^{\frac{1}{2}}}e^{st}\,ds \tag{221}$$

The solution of this integral involves branch points rather than simple poles and is somewhat similar to the illustration given in Sec. 19, Chap. 4. Its solution is

$$i(x,t) = E\sqrt{\frac{C}{\pi rt}}\,e^{-rCx^2/4t} \qquad t > 0 \tag{222}$$

which is of the same form as the solution obtained from the diffusion equation for certain problems in heat conduction.

19. Traveling Waves on a Distortionless Line of Finite Length.[1] If we replace $j\omega$ and $e(t)$ by s and $\mathcal{L}[e(t)]$, respectively, in Eqs. (109) and (110), we get, for a line of length l,

$$e(x,s) = \frac{Z_0}{Z_0 + Z_S}\,\frac{e^{-\Gamma x} - k_d e^{-\Gamma(2l-x)}}{1 - k_0 k_d e^{-2\Gamma l}}\,\mathcal{L}[e(t)] \tag{223}$$

$$i(x,s) = \frac{1}{Z_0 + Z_S}\,\frac{e^{-\Gamma x} + k_d e^{-\Gamma(2l-x)}}{1 - k_0 k_d e^{-\Gamma 2l}}\,\mathcal{L}[e(t)] \tag{224}$$

These equations completely describe the behavior of a line of finite length l which has been initially deenergized; $e(x,t)$ and $i(x,t)$ may be recovered by taking the inverse Laplace transforms of (223) and (224).

If we are willing to accept some loss of generality by considering Eqs. (223) and (224) for a distortionless line, a very vivid demonstration of the general behavior of traveling waves on transmission lines may be obtained.

[1] L. V. Bewley, "Traveling Waves on Transmission Systems," Part 1, John Wiley & Sons, Inc., New York, 1933.

E. Weber, Traveling Waves on Transmission Lines, *Elec. Eng.*, vol. 61, pp. 302–309, June, 1942.

For a distortionless line, $\rho_2 = 0$, and $r/L = g/C = \rho_1$. Therefore

$$\Gamma = \frac{s + \rho_1}{v} \tag{209}$$

If we specify that

$$Z_s = R_s \qquad Z_0 = \sqrt{\frac{L}{C}} \qquad Z_r = R_L \tag{225}$$

thus making the impedance coefficients in (223) and (224) independent of s, and if we recognize that

$$\frac{1}{1 + k_0 k_d e^{-\Gamma 2l}} = 1 - k_0 k_d e^{-2\Gamma l} + k_0^2 k_d^2 e^{-4\Gamma l} - k_0^3 k_d^3 e^{-6\Gamma l} + \cdots \tag{226}$$

then we get from Eqs. (223) and (224)

$$e(x,s) = \mathfrak{L}[e(s)](e^{-\Gamma x} - k_d e^{-\Gamma(2l-x)} + k_0 k_d e^{-\Gamma(2l+x)}$$
$$- k_0 k_d^2 e^{-\Gamma(4l-x)} + k_0^2 k_d^2 e^{-\Gamma(4l+x)} - \cdots) \frac{Z_0}{Z_0 + Z_s} \tag{227}$$

$$i(x,s) = \frac{\mathfrak{L}[e(s)]}{Z_0}(e^{-\Gamma x} + k_d e^{-\Gamma(2l-x)} + k_0 k_d e^{-\Gamma(2l+x)}$$
$$+ k_0 k_d^2 e^{-\Gamma(4l-x)} + k_0^2 k_d^2 e^{-\Gamma(4l+x)} + \cdots) \frac{Z_0}{Z_0 + Z_s} \tag{228}$$

In Eqs. (227) and (228) we have terms of the form

$$\mathfrak{L}[e(s)]e^{-\Gamma(nl-x)} \tag{229}$$

but, from (209), these become

$$\mathfrak{L}[e(s)]e^{-(s/v)(nl-x)}e^{-(\rho_1/v)(nl-x)} \tag{230}$$

and because of the translational properties of $e^{-(s/v)(nl-x)}$, it follows that

$$\frac{e^{-(\rho_1/v)(nl-x)}}{2\pi j} \int_{\alpha - j\infty}^{\alpha + j\infty} \mathfrak{L}[e(s)]e^{-(s/v)(nl-x)}e^{-st}\, ds$$
$$= e^{-(\rho_1/v)(nl-x)} e\left(t - \frac{nl - x}{v}\right) \qquad \frac{nl - x}{v} < t < \infty \tag{231}$$

The inverse Laplace transforms of (223) and (224) are, then,

$$e(x,t) = \Bigg[e^{-\rho_1(x/v)} \left(t - \frac{x}{v}\right) \qquad \frac{x}{v} < t < \infty$$
$$- k_d e^{-\rho_1[(2l-x)/v]} e\left(t - \frac{2l - x}{v}\right) \qquad \frac{2l - x}{v} < t < \infty$$

$$+ k_0 k_d e^{-\rho_1[(2l+x)/v]} e\left(t - \frac{2l+x}{v}\right) \qquad \frac{2l+x}{v} < t < \infty$$

$$- k_0 k_d^2 e^{-\rho_1[(4l-x)/v]} e\left(t - \frac{4l-x}{v}\right) \qquad \frac{4l-x}{v} < t < \infty$$

$$+ k_0^2 k_d^2 e^{-\rho_1[(4l+x)/v]} e\left(t - \frac{4l+x}{v}\right) \qquad \frac{4l+x}{v} < t < \infty$$

$$- \cdots \biggr] \frac{Z_0}{Z_0 + Z_S} \tag{232}$$

$$i(x,t) = \left[e^{-\rho_1(x/v)} e\left(t - \frac{x}{v}\right) \right. \qquad \frac{x}{v} < t < \infty$$

$$+ k_d e^{-\rho_1[(2l-x)/v]} e\left(t - \frac{2l-x}{v}\right) \qquad \frac{2l-x}{v} < t < \infty$$

$$+ k_0 k_d e^{-\rho_1[(2l+x)/v]} e\left(t - \frac{2l+x}{v}\right) \qquad \frac{2l+x}{v} < t < \infty$$

$$+ k_0 k_d^2 e^{-\rho_1[(4l-x)/v]} e\left(t - \frac{4l-x}{v}\right) \qquad \frac{4l-x}{v} < t < \infty$$

$$+ \cdots \biggr] \frac{1}{Z_0 + Z_S} \tag{233}$$

Consider now the behavior of the line voltage as a function of distance and time. The input wave $e(0,t)$ starts at $t = 0$ and travels down the line with velocity $v = 1/\sqrt{LC}$. For the time interval $0 < t < l/v$, the voltage on the line is described by

$$e(x,t) = e^{-\rho_1(x/v)} e\left(t - \frac{x}{v}\right) \frac{Z_0}{Z_0 + Z_S} \tag{234}$$

alone, the amplitude of the wave, as a function of x, being determined by the exponential $e^{-\rho_1(x/v)}$. Note that all of the other terms in (232) are equal to zero for $-\infty < t < (nl - x)/v$, where $n = 2, 4, 6, \ldots$.

For the time interval $l/v < t < 2l/v$,

$$e(x,t) = \left[e^{-\rho_1(x/v)} e\left(t - \frac{x}{v}\right) - k_d e^{-\rho_1[(2l-x)/v]} e\left(t - \frac{2l-x}{v}\right) \right] \frac{Z_0}{Z_0 + Z_S} \tag{235}$$

We now have superimposed on (234) the reflected wave which travels from $x = l$ back toward $x = 0$. Its amplitude at the start at $x = l$ is $k_d e^{-\rho_1(l/v)} e[t - (l/v)]\ [Z_0/(Z_0 + Z_S)]$, where k_d is the reflection factor at the line termination. The wave must travel from $x = l$ back to $x = 0$ since we can satisfy the criterion $t > (2l - x)/v$ only by having x decrease.

For the time interval $2l/v < t < 3l/v$

$$e(x,t) = \left[e^{-p_1(x/v)} e\left(t - \frac{x}{v}\right) - k_d e^{-p_1[(2l-x)/v]} e\left(t - \frac{2l - x}{v}\right) + k_0 k_d e^{-p_1[(2l+x)/v]} e\left(t - \frac{2l + x}{v}\right)\right] \frac{Z_0}{Z_0 + Z_S} \quad (236)$$

which shows that, superimposed on the first two waves, is a third wave $k_0 k_d e^{-p_1[(2l+x)/v]} e[t - (2l + x)/v]\ [Z_0/(Z_0 + Z_S)]$, which is a reflected wave which starts at $x = 0$ and travels toward $x = l$.

As more time goes by, more and more terms must be added to complete the general solution, that is, n terms needed for the time interval

$$(n - 1)\frac{l}{v} < t < n\frac{l}{v} \quad (237)$$

It is important to realize that, for the interval, n traveling wave terms must be summed—not merely one which has been reflected back and forth. If $e(x,t)$ is a wave of very short duration τ, where $\tau \ll l/v$, then the amplitude of all terms in the interval $(n - 1)(l/v) < t < n(l/v)$, with the exception of the nth term, will be equal to zero.

A useful picture of the wave behavior as a function of k_d may be obtained from the following illustration: If a step function is impressed on the line input and if the line is matched to the load, the voltage at the

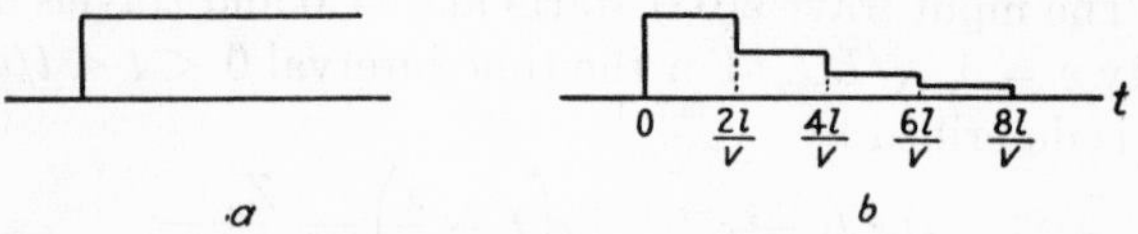

FIG. 4.

input will remain a step voltage as is shown in Fig. 4*a*. However, if the transmission-line termination is mismatched to the line, the reflected waves will introduce a series of steps into the wave which appears across the input. Such a series of steps is illustrated in Fig. 4*b*, the actual magnitude of the steps being a function of the mismatch and the step fronts occurring at $t = 2l/v, 4l/v, 6l/v, \ldots$.

If the terminating impedance is equal to the characteristic impedance, *i.e.*,

$$R_r = Z_0 \quad (238)$$

then

$$k_d = \frac{Z_0 - R_r}{Z_0 + R_r} = 0 \quad (239)$$

Under such a condition, no reflection will take place at $x = l$, and the line will act as infinite line.

20. Pulse-generating Property of a Short-circuited Transmission Line.[1] Consider the transmission-line circuit pictured in Fig. 5. The transmission line is shorted at a distance l from the input. This circuit is in use in pulsers for producing pulses and we shall demonstrate these pulse-forming qualities by use of the Laplace transform.

The input impedance of the shorted transmission line may be found by setting $Z_r = 0$ in Eq. (120). We get

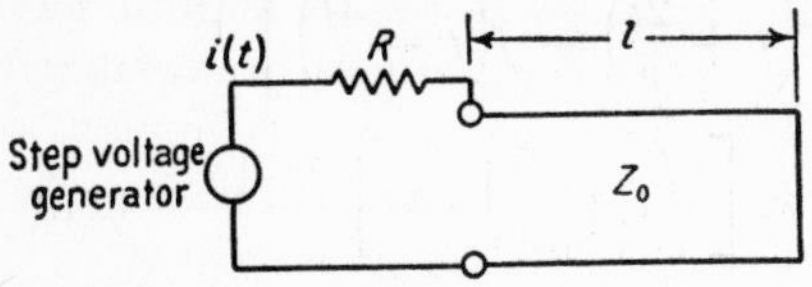

FIG. 5.

$$Z_S = Z_0 \coth \frac{j\omega l}{v} \tag{240}$$

$$= Z_0 \coth j\omega\tau \tag{241}$$

where $\tau = l/v$ is the time it takes a wave to travel the distance l along the line. Replacing $j\omega$ by s in (241), we get the Laplace-transformed impedance

$$Z_S(s) = Z_0 \coth s\tau \tag{242}$$

The current at the input due to a step-function voltage of amplitude E occurring at $t = 0$ is described by the equation

$$i(s) = \frac{E}{s} \frac{1}{R + Z_0 \coth s\tau} \tag{243}$$

This can be written in the form

$$i(s) = \frac{E}{s} \frac{1 - e^{-2s\tau}}{Z_0 + R} \frac{1}{1 - [(Z_0 - R)/(Z_0 + R)]e^{-2s\tau}} \tag{244}$$

Equation (244) can be expanded into the following series,

$$i(s) = \frac{E}{s(Z_0 + R)} [1 - e^{-2s\tau} - k_d(e^{2s\tau} - e^{-4s\tau})$$

$$- k_d^2(e^{4s\tau} - e^{-6s\tau}) + \cdots] \tag{245}$$

where

$$k_d = \frac{Z_0 - R}{Z_0 + R} \tag{246}$$

We must now find the inverse Laplace transform of functions of the type $e^{-ns\tau}/s$. This is quickly deduced by noticing that since

$$\frac{1}{2\pi j} \int_{\alpha - j\infty}^{\alpha + j\infty} \frac{e^{st}}{s} ds = 0 \qquad t < 0 \tag{247}$$

$$= 1 \qquad t > 0$$

[1] Compare with Sec. 8, Chap. 9, which presents a solution demonstrating pulse-forming qualities of an artificial line.

then, in virtue of the properties of the shifting operator $e^{-ns\tau}$ [see (212)],

$$\frac{1}{2\pi j}\int_{\alpha-j\infty}^{\alpha+j\infty}\frac{e^{-ns\tau}e^{st}}{s}\,ds = 0 \qquad t - n\tau < 0$$
$$= 1 \qquad t - n\tau > 0 \tag{248}$$

It follows then that the inverse Laplace transform of (245) is

$$i(t) = \frac{E}{R + Z_0}\left\{1 - f\left(t - \frac{2l}{v}\right) - k_d\left[f\left(t + \frac{2l}{v}\right) - f\left(t - \frac{4l}{v}\right)\right]\right.$$
$$\left. + k_d^2\left[f\left(t + \frac{4l}{v}\right)\cdots\right]\cdots\right\} \tag{249}$$

where

$$f\left(t - \frac{nl}{v}\right) = 0 \qquad -\infty < t - \frac{nl}{v} < 0$$
$$= 1 \qquad 0 < t - \frac{nl}{v} < \infty \tag{250}$$

If the line is matched to the load R so that $R = Z_0$, then the result of impressing a step function of amplitude E on the input will be a rectangular current pulse of amplitude $E/2Z_0$ and duration 2τ, since $k_d = 0$ and the second term in (249) will cancel the first term for all time after $t = 2\tau$.

TRAVELING WAVES AND MAXWELL'S EQUATIONS

21. Introduction. The remainder of this chapter will deal with the fundamentals of traveling waves in media in which the propagation and transfer characteristics are governed by Maxwell's equations. Waves in free space, waves in conducting media, and in magnetrons will be of particular interest to us.

The general subject of electromagnetic theory is a very extensive one and has been discussed with respect to its numerous phases in many volumes. We are not concerned here with a reconstruction or a recapitulation of this theory; the treatment will be limited to those basic concepts which play important parts in both the understanding and the mathematical analysis of those traveling waves which propagate in systems in which Maxwell's equations must be satisfied.

22. Maxwell's Equations.[1] Maxwell's equations state that

$$\text{(I)}\quad \text{curl}\,\mathbf{E} + \frac{\partial\mathbf{B}}{\partial t} = 0 \tag{251}$$

[1] See, for example, Sarbacher and Edson, "Hyper and Ultrahigh Frequency Engineering," John Wiley & Sons, Inc., New York, 1943, or J. C. Slater, "Microwave Transmission," Chap. II, McGraw-Hill Book Company, Inc., New York, 1942.

$$\text{(II)} \quad \operatorname{curl} \mathbf{H} - \frac{\partial \mathbf{D}}{\partial t} = \mathbf{J} \tag{252}$$

$$\text{(III)} \quad \operatorname{div} \mathbf{B} = 0 \tag{253}$$

$$\text{(IV)} \quad \operatorname{div} \mathbf{D} = \rho \tag{254}$$

These four equations are concerned with the four vector fields: **E**, the electric-field intensity; **B**, the magnetic induction; **D**, the electric displacement; **H**, the magnetic-field intensity. In Eq. (II), **J** denotes current density; in Eq. (IV), ρ denotes the charge density.

Each of these vector fields may be written in terms of unit-vector and scalar-field components. For example, **E** may be written as follows:

$$\mathbf{E} = \mathbf{i}E_x + \mathbf{j}E_y + \mathbf{k}E_z \tag{255}$$

where **i**, **j**, and **k** are unit vectors in the x, y, and z directions, respectively.

In a medium having a definite dielectric constant ϵ, permeability μ, and conductivity σ, we get what are known as the constitutive equations of the medium, *viz.*,

$$\mathbf{D} = \epsilon \mathbf{E} \tag{256}$$

$$\mathbf{B} = \mu \mathbf{H} \tag{257}$$

$$\mathbf{J} = \sigma \mathbf{E} \tag{258}$$

The units used here will be the rationalized meter-kilogram-second (mks) units (Giorgi units) such that

$\mathbf{E}$ = volts per meter

$\mathbf{B}$ = webers per square meter

$\mathbf{J}$ = amperes per square meter

$\mathbf{D}$ = coulombs per square meter

$\mathbf{H}$ = ampere turns per meter

In free space

$$\mu_0 = 4\pi \times 10^{-7} \text{ henry per m} \tag{259}$$

$$\epsilon_0 = 8.85 \times 10^{-12} \text{ farad per m} \tag{260}$$

$$\sqrt{\frac{\mu_0}{\epsilon_0}} = 376.6 \text{ ohms}$$

Maxwell's equations are valid at every point where the fields are continuous. When discontinuities occur, then the following boundary conditions must be satisfied at the surface of discontinuity:

Owing to (I), $\mathbf{E}_t$ is continuous.

Owing to (II), $\mathbf{B}_n$ is continuous.

Owing to (III), discontinuity in $\mathbf{H}_t$ = surface current density (current crossing unit length of line).

Owing to (IV), discontinuity in $\mathbf{D}_n$ = surface-charge density (charge per unit area in surface).

The subscripts t and n denote tangent and normal to the surface, respectively.

23. Plane-polarized Electromagnetic Waves in an Isotropic Medium. Maxwell's equations may be developed into a set of equations describing the propagation of a plane-polarized electromagnetic wave in an isotropic medium as follows: If we specify that $\mathbf{D} = \epsilon\mathbf{E}$, $\mathbf{B} = \mu\mathbf{H}$ in Eqs. (251) and (252), we may write these equations in terms of their components as follows:

$$\frac{\partial H_z}{\partial y} - \frac{\partial H_y}{\partial z} = \sigma E_x + \epsilon \frac{\partial E_x}{\partial t} \tag{261}$$

$$\frac{\partial H_x}{\partial z} - \frac{\partial H_z}{\partial x} = \sigma E_y + \epsilon \frac{\partial E_y}{\partial t} \tag{262}$$

$$\frac{\partial H_y}{\partial x} - \frac{\partial H_x}{\partial y} = \sigma E_z + \epsilon \frac{\partial E_z}{\partial t} \tag{263}$$

$$\frac{\partial E_z}{\partial y} - \frac{\partial E_y}{\partial z} = -\mu \frac{\partial H_x}{\partial t} \tag{264}$$

$$\frac{\partial E_x}{\partial z} - \frac{\partial E_z}{\partial x} = -\mu \frac{\partial H_y}{\partial t} \tag{265}$$

$$\frac{\partial E_y}{\partial x} - \frac{\partial E_x}{\partial y} = -\mu \frac{\partial H_z}{\partial t} \tag{266}$$

If we differentiate (261) with respect to t, (265) with respect to z, and (266) with respect to y, we get

$$\frac{\partial^2 H_z}{\partial t\,\partial y} - \frac{\partial^2 H_y}{\partial t\,\partial z} = \sigma \frac{\partial E_x}{\partial t} + \epsilon \frac{\partial^2 E_x}{\partial t^2} \tag{267}$$

$$\frac{\partial^2 E_x}{\partial z^2} - \frac{\partial^2 E_z}{\partial z\,\partial x} = -\mu \frac{\partial^2 H_y}{\partial z\,\partial t} \tag{268}$$

$$\frac{\partial^2 E_y}{\partial y\,\partial x} - \frac{\partial^2 E_x}{\partial y^2} = -\mu \frac{\partial^2 H_z}{\partial y\,\partial t} \tag{269}$$

If the following equalities are valid,

$$\frac{\partial^2 E_y}{\partial y\,\partial x} = \frac{\partial^2 E_y}{\partial x\,\partial y} \qquad \frac{\partial^2 H_z}{\partial t\,\partial y} = \frac{\partial^2 H_z}{\partial y\,\partial t} \qquad \frac{\partial^2 H_y}{\partial t\,\partial z} = \frac{\partial^2 H_y}{\partial z\,\partial t} \tag{270}$$

then, by combining (267), (268), and (269), where (267) and (269) are modified by $-1/\mu$ and $1/\mu$, respectively, we get

$$\frac{1}{\mu}\left[-\frac{\partial}{\partial x}\left(\frac{\partial E_y}{\partial y}+\frac{\partial E_z}{\partial z}\right)+\frac{\partial^2 E_x}{\partial y^2}+\frac{\partial^2 E_x}{\partial z^2}\right]=\sigma\frac{\partial E_x}{\partial t}+\epsilon\frac{\partial^2 E_x}{\partial t^2} \tag{271}$$

According to Eq. (254), when $\rho = 0$

$$\text{div } \mathbf{E} = 0 \tag{272}$$

from which we get

$$\frac{\partial E_y}{\partial y}+\frac{\partial E_z}{\partial z}=-\frac{\partial E_x}{\partial x} \tag{273}$$

When (273) is substituted into (271), we get

$$\frac{\partial^2 E_x}{\partial x^2}+\frac{\partial^2 E_y}{\partial y^2}+\frac{\partial^2 E_z}{\partial z^2}=\mu\sigma\frac{\partial E_x}{\partial t}+\mu\epsilon\frac{\partial^2 E_x}{\partial t^2} \tag{274}$$

We may proceed in like manner to derive similar equations for E_y, E_z, H_x, H_y, and H_z. We get, finally, the general equations ($\rho = 0$)

$$\nabla^2\mathbf{E}=\mu\epsilon\frac{\partial^2\mathbf{E}}{\partial t^2}+\mu\sigma\frac{\partial\mathbf{E}}{\partial t} \tag{275}$$

$$\nabla^2\mathbf{H}=\mu\epsilon\frac{\partial^2\mathbf{H}}{\partial t^2}+\mu\sigma\frac{\partial\mathbf{H}}{\partial t} \tag{276}$$

In an uncharged nonconducting medium, such that $\sigma = \rho = 0$, these equations become the wave equations

$$\nabla^2\mathbf{E}=\frac{1}{v^2}\frac{\partial^2\mathbf{E}}{\partial t^2} \tag{277}$$

$$\nabla^2\mathbf{H}=\frac{1}{v^2}\frac{\partial^2\mathbf{H}}{\partial t^2} \tag{278}$$

where

$$v=\frac{1}{\sqrt{\mu\epsilon}} \tag{279}$$

According to (259) and (260), it follows that in empty space

$$v=\frac{1}{\sqrt{\mu_0\epsilon_0}}=3\times10^8 \text{ m per sec} \tag{280}$$

which is the velocity of light.

24. Propagation of E_y in the x Direction. It is particularly instructive to investigate the behavior of an x-directed electric-field component E_y, for the case when the wave is in free space, and in a conducting medium.

The procedures and concepts derived from these simple but very important cases may be extended to waves of more complicated composition.

For E_y to exist as the only electric-field component present, it is necessary that $E_x = E_z = 0$. However, one or more magnetic-field vectors may be present; these will be prescribed by Maxwell's equations in accordance with the fundamental statements and boundary conditions corresponding to each problem.

25. The E_y Wave in Free Space. Since $\sigma = 0$ in free space, an E_y wave of the form

$$E_y\left(t - \frac{x}{v}\right)$$

may be propagated in the x direction (discussed in Sec. 5). A wave $E_y \sin \omega[t - (x/v)]$, with this form, is shown in Fig. 6 for $t = 0$; this wave will travel with the velocity 3×10^8 m per sec.

We may verify the dependence of the wave $E_y[t - (x/v)]$ on the wave equation and also demonstrate the nature of the associated magnetic-field vectors by considering Maxwell's equations as follows:

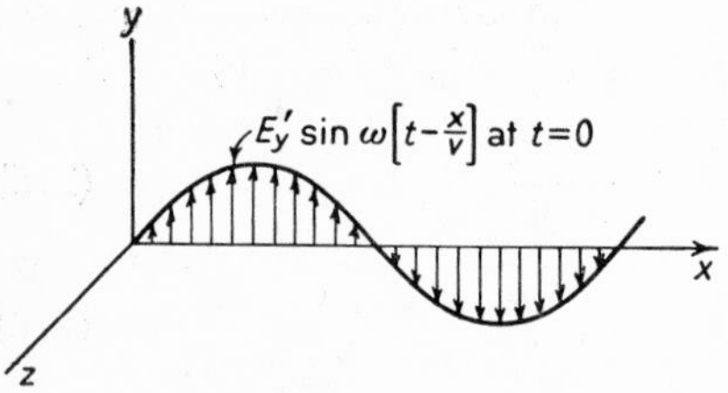

FIG. 6.

An equiphase surface for $E_y[t - (x/v)]$ will be normal with respect to the x axis and will lie in a yz plane. If no variation of electric-field intensity is permitted in this equiphase surface, we may specify that $\partial/\partial y = \partial/\partial z = 0$, which, when substituted into Eqs. (262) and (266), yields the following equations (recalling that $E_x = E_z = 0$):

$$-\frac{\partial H_z}{\partial x} = \epsilon_0 \frac{\partial E_y}{\partial t} \tag{281}$$

$$-\frac{\partial E_y}{\partial x} = \mu_0 \frac{\partial H_z}{\partial t} \tag{282}$$

If we differentiate (281) and (282) with respect to t and x, respectively, and add, we get

$$\left(\frac{\partial^2 H_z}{\partial x\, \partial t} - \frac{\partial^2 H_z}{\partial t\, \partial x}\right) - \epsilon_0 \frac{\partial^2 E_y}{\partial t^2} + \frac{1}{\mu_0} \frac{\partial^2 E_y}{\partial x^2} = 0 \tag{283}$$

If

$$\frac{\partial^2 H_z}{\partial x\, \partial t} = \frac{\partial^2 H_z}{\partial t\, \partial x} \tag{284}$$

we get the *wave equation*

$$\frac{\partial^2 E_y}{\partial x^2} = \mu_0 \epsilon_0 \frac{\partial^2 E_y}{\partial t^2} \tag{285}$$

In like manner, we find that for H_z

$$\frac{\partial^2 H_z}{\partial x^2} = \mu_0\epsilon_0 \frac{\partial^2 H_z}{\partial t^2} \tag{286}$$

Two facts are apparent from this development, *viz.*,

1. In addition to $\mathbf{j}E_y$, the magnetic-field vector $\mathbf{k}H_z$ is present which is in space quadrature with respect to $\mathbf{j}E_y$.

2. Both E_y and H_z behave in accordance with the wave equation and therefore have the form $E_y[t \pm (x/v)]$ and $H_z[t \pm (x/v)]$.

The magnetic-field intensity H_z is related to E_y by the equation

$$\frac{\partial H_z}{\partial x} = -\epsilon_0 \frac{\partial E_y}{\partial t} \tag{287}$$

Then, if E_y is known, the magnitude of H_z may be deduced from the expression

$$H_z = -\epsilon_0 \int \frac{\partial E_y}{\partial t}\, dx + c \tag{288}$$

If E_y is a rotating vector

$$E_y = E_y' e^{j\omega[t-(x/v)]} \tag{289}$$

where $v = 1/\sqrt{\mu_0/\epsilon_0}$, then

$$\frac{\partial E_y}{\partial t} = j\omega E_y' e^{j\omega[t-(x/v)]} \tag{290}$$

Substituting (290) into (288) and ignoring the constant of integration c, we get

$$H_z = -j\omega\epsilon_0 \int E_y' e^{j\omega[t-(x/v)]}\, dx \tag{291}$$

$$= \frac{1}{j\omega} j\omega\epsilon_0 v E_y' e^{j\omega[t-(x/v)]} \tag{292}$$

$$= \sqrt{\frac{\epsilon_0}{\mu_0}}\, E_y' e^{j\omega[t-(x/v)]} \tag{293}$$

Thus we see that the amplitude of H_z is $\sqrt{\epsilon_0/\mu_0}\, E'_y$.

26. The E_y Wave in a Conducting Medium. Consider the case when the E_y wave is propagated at $t = 0$ in the x direction in a conducting medium. Since this constitutes a source at the origin, the Laplace-transform analysis must be used.

In a conducting medium, $\sigma \neq 0$, and therefore, letting $E_x = E_z = \partial E_y/\partial y = \partial E_y/\partial z = 0$ in Eqs. (262) and (266), we get (recalling that only $H_z \neq 0$)

$$\frac{\partial H_z}{\partial x} + \epsilon \frac{\partial E_y}{\partial t} + \sigma E_y = 0 \tag{294}$$

$$\frac{\partial E_y}{\partial x} + \mu \frac{\partial H_z}{\partial t} = 0 \tag{295}$$

If we let x be the running variable, the Laplace transforms of $H_z(x,t)$ and $E_y(x,t)$ may be written as follows:

$$\mathcal{L}[H_z(x,t)] = H(x,s) \tag{296}$$

$$\mathcal{L}[E_y(x,t)] = E(x,s) \tag{297}$$

The Laplace transforms of (294) and (295) are found to be

$$\frac{\partial E(x,s)}{\partial x} + \mu s H(x,s) - \mu H_z(x,0) = 0 \tag{298}$$

$$\frac{\partial H(x,s)}{\partial x} + (\epsilon s + \sigma)E(x,s) - \epsilon E_y(x,0) = 0 \tag{299}$$

If we take the derivative of (298) with respect to x at $t = 0$, we get

$$\frac{\partial H(x,s)}{\partial x} = \frac{1}{\mu s}\left[\mu \left.\frac{\partial H_z(x,t)}{\partial x}\right|_{t=0} - \frac{\partial^2 E(x,s)}{\partial x^2}\right] \tag{300}$$

Using the relationship described in (294), (300) may be substituted into (299) to yield the following fundamental equation,

$$\frac{\partial^2 E(x,s)}{\partial x^2} - \Gamma E(x,s) = f(x,s) \tag{301}$$

where

$$\Gamma^2 = \mu\epsilon s^2 + \mu\sigma s \tag{302}$$

$$f(x,s) = -\frac{\Gamma^2}{s} f_1(x) - \mu\epsilon f_2(x) \tag{303}$$

$f_1(x)$ and $f_2(x)$ are defined by the expressions

$$f_1(x) = \lim_{t\to 0} E_y(x,t) \tag{304}$$

$$f_2(x) = \lim_{t\to 0} \frac{\partial E_y(x,t)}{\partial t} \tag{305}$$

which represent the initial conditions at $t = 0$.

It is evident that (301) is identical in form to (181), which describes the behavior of the voltage on a transmission line. Γ is a propagation constant which is now in terms of the parameters σ, ϵ, and μ, of the medium. Equation (301) is seen to be an ordinary differential equation whose general solution may be shown to be [see Eq. (184)]

$$E(x,s) = Ae^{\Gamma x} + Be^{-\Gamma x} + \frac{e^{\Gamma x}}{2\Gamma}\int e^{-\Gamma x} f(x,s)\,dx - \frac{e^{-\Gamma x}}{2\Gamma}\int e^{\Gamma x} f(x,s)\,dx \tag{306}$$

where A and B are constants which must satisfy the boundary conditions imposed on the problem.

Consider now the solution, as discussed by J. A. Stratton,[1] for the case when an electric-field generator located at $x = 0$ sends out the electric-field-intensity wave, $E_y[(t - (x/v)]$, the generator starting at $t = 0$. At $x = 0$, let

$$E_y\left(t - \frac{0}{v}\right) = E_y(t) \tag{307}$$

$$\mathfrak{L}\left[E_y\left(t - \frac{0}{v}\right)\right] = E_y(s) \tag{308}$$

If we now specify that the wave travels only in the x direction (A must therefore be equal to zero) and that the medium be field-free at $t = 0$ [$f(x,s) = 0$], we see that

$$E(x,s) = E_y(s)e^{-\Gamma x} \tag{309}$$

It is necessary to take the inverse Laplace transform of $E_y(s)e^{-\Gamma x}$ in order to recover $E_y(x,t)$. Before proceeding with the inverse transformation, let us investigate the following integral identity based on an integral relationship which is described by G. N. Watson,[2] *i.e.*,

$$\frac{e^{-\Gamma x}}{\Gamma} = v \int_{x/v}^{\infty} J_0\left(\frac{a}{v}\sqrt{x^2 - v^2t^2}\right) e^{-(a+s)t}\, dt \tag{310}$$

where

$$v = \frac{1}{\sqrt{\mu\epsilon}} \qquad a = \frac{\sigma}{2\epsilon} \tag{311}$$

If we differentiate (310) with respect to x, we get

$$\frac{d}{dx}\frac{e^{-\Gamma x}}{\Gamma} = e^{-\Gamma x}$$

$$= e^{-a(x/v)}e^{-s(x/v)} - v\int_{x/v}^{\infty} e^{-at}\frac{\partial}{\partial x}J_0\left(\frac{a}{v}\sqrt{x^2 - v^2t^2}\right)e^{-st}\, dt \tag{312}$$

$$= e^{-a(x/v)}e^{-s(x/v)} - v\int_{x/v}^{\infty} Q(x,t)e^{-st}\, dt \tag{313}$$

where

$$Q(x,t) = e^{-at}\frac{\partial}{\partial x}J_0\left(\frac{a}{v}\sqrt{x^2 - v^2t^2}\right) \tag{314}$$

$$= e^{-at}\frac{\partial}{\partial x}\left[1 - \frac{1}{4}\left(\frac{a}{v}\right)^2(x^2 - v^2t^2) + \frac{1}{64}\left(\frac{a}{v}\right)^4(x^2 - v^2t^2)^2 - \cdots\right] \tag{315}$$

$$= \frac{a^2t}{2}e^{-at}\left[1 - \frac{1}{8}\left(\frac{a}{v}\right)^2(x^2 - v^2t^2) + \cdots\right] \tag{316}$$

[1] J. A. Stratton, "Electromagnetic Theory," Sec. 5.13, McGraw-Hill Book Company, Inc., New York, 1941.

[2] See G. N. Watson, "Bessel Functions," 2d ed., p. 416, No. 4, The Macmillan Company, New York, 1944.

Note that the integral in (313) is the Laplace transform of the function $Q(x,t)$; this function exists only for $x/v < t < \infty$.

We may now substitute (313) into (309) to get

$$E(x,s) = e^{-ax/v}E_y(s)e^{-s(x/v)} - vE_y(s)\mathfrak{L}[Q(x,t)] \tag{317}$$

It is evident that, owing to the translational properties of $e^{-s(x/v)}$,

$$\mathfrak{L}^{-1}[E_y(s)e^{-s(x/v)}] = E_y\left(t - \frac{x}{v}\right) \tag{318}$$

Let us use the Faltung theorem on the product term on the right-hand side of (317); *i.e.*,

$$\mathfrak{L}^{-1}\{E_y(s)\mathfrak{L}[Q(x,s)]\} = \int_{x/v}^{t} E_y(t - \tau)Q(x,\tau)\, d\tau \tag{319}$$

$$= \int_0^{t-(x/v)} E_y(\lambda)Q(x,\, t - \lambda)\, d\lambda \tag{320}$$

where $\lambda = t - \tau$. Substituting (318) and (320) into (317), we get, for the inverse Laplace transform of $E(x,s)$,

$$E_y(x,t) = e^{-ax/v}E_y\left(t - \frac{x}{v}\right) - \frac{\sigma^2 v}{8\epsilon^2}\int_0^{t-(x/v)} E_y(\lambda)e^{-(\sigma/2\epsilon)(t-\lambda)}(t - \lambda) \cdot \left\{1 - \frac{1}{8}\left(\frac{a}{v}\right)^2[x^2 - v^2(t - \lambda)^2] + \cdots\right\} d\lambda \tag{321}$$

which may be evaluated once $E_y(\lambda)$ is prescribed.

When $\sigma = 0$, $E_y(x,t)$ reduces to

$$E_y(x,t) = E_y\left(t - \frac{x}{v}\right) \tag{322}$$

which is the result predicted by the wave equation for a nonconducting medium. However, when σ is no longer equal to zero, the wave behavior becomes quite involved.

The more important aspects of (321) may be summarized as follows: The traveling wave $e^{-ax/v}E_y[t - (x/v)]$ decays with increasing distance in accordance with the nature of the exponential $e^{-ax/v}$. In addition, as the wave travels, it leaves behind it a tail which decays exponentially with time. This tail is described by contributions of the integral relationship in (321), these contributions persisting for all time at each point which the wave front has passed.

27. Fourier Analysis of the Traveling Electric Field in the Cavity-magnetron Anode-Cathode Space. A cavity-magnetron anode[1] such as the

[1] Fisk, Hagstrum, and Hartman, The Magnetron as a Generator of Centimeter Waves, *Bell System Tech. J.*, vol. 25, pp. 167–348, April, 1946; G. B. Collins, "Microwave Magnetrons," Chap. 2, McGraw-Hill Book Company, Inc., New York, 1948.

one pictured in Fig. 7 can resonate at an infinite number of frequencies. There is, however, one frequency or mode of operation at which the magnetron has been found to oscillate efficiently. This mode of operation is known as the π mode and is that mode at which the charges on alternate vane tips are of the same polarity. It is the traveling electric field in the anode-cathode space corresponding to this mode which will be analyzed.

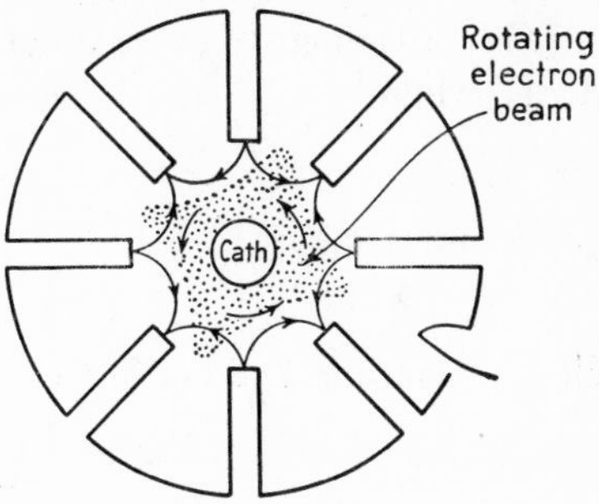

FIG. 7. Rotating electron spokes in a cavity magnetron.

The basic operation of an oscillating cavity magnetron may be summarized as follows: When the resonant cavity system of a magnetron is excited, an electric fringe field emanates from the vane tips into the cathode-anode space (see Fig. 8). This electric field has three components E_z, E_r, and E_Θ. E_z is constant since in an ideal tube it is parallel to the axis of the cathode. E_r and E_Θ interact with the electrons which leave the cathode and spiral with ever-increasing radius on their way to the anode. The interactions form the electron *spokes* which are pictured in Fig. 7. These spokes have an angular velocity which is equal to

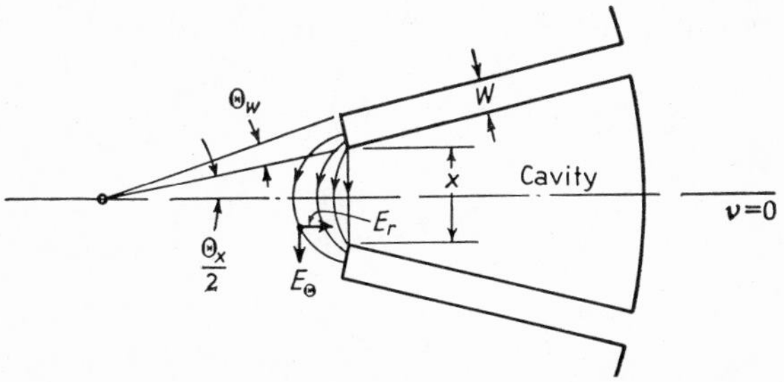

FIG. 8.

that of E_Θ, and the phase between the two is such that E_Θ decelerates the electrons in the electron spokes. The energy corresponding to the electron deceleration goes into the cavity fields and thence to the magnetron load.

Consider a Fourier analysis, due to L. P. Smith,[1] for E_Θ in the anode-cathode space of a cavity magnetron. In this discussion, we shall assume that the cavity-magnetron anode has an even number of cavities, that $E_z = 0$, and that the radius is r_a.

[1] Unpublished work. For a more detailed and advanced approach, see Kroll and Lamb, The Resonant Modes of the Rising Sun and Other Unstrapped Magnetron Blocks, *J. Applied Phys.*, vol. 19, pp. 166–186, February, 1948.

Two further assumptions are made—that no charge and no cathode is present. The latter represents little deviation from the actual conditions governing the true analysis since, as we shall see, the field strength is very small at the cathode position.

It is convenient to express the electric field in terms of a vector potential $\mathbf{A}(r,t)$, where[1]

$$-\frac{d\mathbf{A}}{dt} = \mathbf{E} \tag{323}$$

where, by definition,

$$\text{curl } \mathbf{A} = \mathbf{B} \tag{324}$$

Since, according to Maxwell's equations, when $\mathbf{J} = 0$,

$$\text{curl } \mathbf{H} = \epsilon \frac{\partial \mathbf{E}}{\partial t} \tag{325}$$

it follows then that

$$\text{curl curl } \mathbf{A} + \epsilon\mu \frac{\partial^2 \mathbf{A}}{\partial t^2} = 0 \tag{326}$$

The problem is one in cylindrical coordinates. Therefore, letting $z = z$, $x = r \cos \Theta$, and $y = r \sin \Theta$, Eq. (326) reduces to the following two scalar equations:

$$\frac{1}{r}\frac{\partial}{\partial \Theta}\frac{1}{r}\left(\frac{\partial}{\partial r} rA_\Theta - \frac{\partial}{\partial \Theta} A_r\right) + \mu\epsilon \frac{\partial^2 A_r}{\partial t^2} = 0 \tag{327}$$

$$\frac{\partial}{\partial r}\frac{1}{r}\left(\frac{\partial}{\partial r} rA_\Theta - \frac{\partial}{\partial \Theta} A_r\right) - \mu\epsilon \frac{\partial^2 A_\Theta}{\partial t^2} = 0 \tag{328}$$

If we let

$$A_\Theta = -\frac{\partial \Psi}{\partial r} \tag{329}$$

$$A_r = \frac{1}{r}\frac{\partial \Psi}{\partial \Theta} \tag{330}$$

where Ψ is a scalar function, then (327) and (328) reduce to

$$\frac{1}{r}\left(\frac{\partial}{\partial r} r \frac{\partial \Psi}{\partial r} + \frac{1}{r}\frac{\partial^2 \Psi}{\partial \Theta^2}\right) - \mu\epsilon \frac{\partial^2 \Psi}{\partial t^2} = 0 \tag{331}$$

This equation can be solved to yield a particular solution of the form

$$\Psi_n = [a_n J_n(kr) + b_n N_n(kr)]e^{-i(\omega t - n\Theta)} \tag{332}$$

where

$$k = \mu\epsilon\omega^2 = \frac{\omega^2}{v^2} \tag{333}$$

$$n = 0, \pm 1, \pm 2, \pm 3, \cdots \tag{334}$$

[1] In general, $\mathbf{E} = -(d\mathbf{A}/dt) - \text{grad } \phi$, where ϕ is a scalar potential. Since no charge or current is present, ϕ may be assumed to be identically zero.

$N_n(kr)$ is the Bessel function of the second kind. However, for $r < r_a$, when no conductor is present in the anode, it is necessary to let $b_n = 0$ in order to eliminate the singularity which occurs in $N_n(kr)$ at $r = 0$. Therefore

$$\Psi_n = a_n J_n(kr) e^{-j(\omega t - n\Theta)} \tag{335}$$

The general solution of (331) can be expressed as a linear combination of all of the particular solutions of the form given by (355). If the smallest period in E_Θ is $2\pi/m$, where, for an N-cavity magnetron, $1 \leq m \leq N/2$, we may write, using m as a superscript with Ψ and a_n,

$$\Psi^m = \sum_{n=-\infty}^{\infty} a_n{}^m J_{mn}(k_m r) e^{-j(\omega_m t - nm\Theta)} \tag{336}$$

If Eq. (336) is to be made applicable to the π mode, it then may be written as

$$\Psi^\pi = \sum_{n=-\infty}^{\infty} a_n{}^\pi J_{n(N/2)}(k_\pi r) \exp\left[-j\left(\omega_\pi t - n\frac{N}{2}\Theta\right)\right] \tag{337}$$

$N/2$ represents the number of periods of the fundamental wave occurring in the anode-cathode space for the π mode. However, in order to express the equation in its most readable form, π is used as a subscript or superscript, rather than $N/2$, to represent this mode except when an actual multiplication takes place.

Continuing with the π-mode formulation, it then follows from (329) that[1]

$$E_\Theta(r,\Theta,t) = \frac{\partial \dot{\Psi}^\pi}{\partial r}$$

$$= -j\omega_\pi k_\pi \sum_{n=-\infty}^{\infty} a_n{}^\pi J'_{(N/2)n}(k_\pi r) \exp\left[-j\left(\omega_\pi t - n\frac{N}{2}\Theta\right)\right] \tag{338}$$

where the prime denotes a derivative with respect to $k_\pi r$. This equation may be written in terms of the electric fields at the vane tips (where $r = r_a$), as follows:

$$E_\Theta(r,\Theta,t) = \sum_{n=-\infty}^{\infty} C_n \frac{J'_{(N/2)|n|}(k_\pi r)}{J'_{(N/2)|n|}(k_\pi r_a)} \exp\left[-j\left(\omega_\pi t - n\frac{N}{2}\Theta\right)\right] \tag{339}$$

provided that this represents the case where the fields of the traveling wave are matched to those in the cavity. C_n is related to $a_n{}^\pi$ by the expression

$$a_n{}^\pi = j\frac{C_n}{\omega_\pi k_\pi J'_{(N/2)|n|}(k_\pi r_a)} \tag{340}$$

[1] Considerations of $E_r(r,\Theta,t)$ are omitted here for reasons of space. $E_r(r,\Theta,t)$, which plays an important part in producing the space-charge spokes, may be deduced, using (330).

C_n being the Fourier coefficient integral

$$C_n = \frac{1}{2\pi} \int_0^{2\pi} E_\Theta(r_a,\Theta) e^{-in(N/2)\Theta} \, d\Theta \tag{341}$$

Let us now solve for C_n. Assume that the distance between vane tips is x and that w is the width of the vane tip. Then, as is shown in Fig. 8, if $\Theta = 0$ is taken as the center of the intervane-tip space, where we shall let $\nu = 0$—the openings running from $\nu = 0$ to $\nu = N - 1$—and if Θ_x and Θ_w are the angular displacements corresponding to x and w, we may write

$$\begin{aligned} x &= \Theta_x r_a \qquad & Nx + Nw &= 2\pi r_a \\ w &= \Theta_w r_a \qquad & \Theta_x + \Theta_w &= \frac{2\pi}{N} \end{aligned} \tag{342}$$

Let the variation of $E_\Theta(r_a,\Theta,t)$ be described by the following approximate but highly representative expression:

$$\begin{aligned} E_\Theta(r_a,\Theta,t) & \\ &= E_0 \cos 0 \qquad & 0 < \Theta < \frac{\Theta_x}{2} \\ &= 0 \qquad & \frac{\Theta_x}{2} < \Theta < \frac{\Theta_x}{2} + \Theta_\omega \\ &= E_0 \cos \pi \qquad & \frac{\Theta_x}{2} + \Theta_w < \Theta < \frac{3}{2}\Theta_x + \Theta_w \\ & \cdots\cdots\cdots\cdots\cdots\cdots & \\ &= E_0 \cos N\pi \qquad & \frac{(2N-1)}{2}\Theta_x + N\Theta_w < \Theta < N(\Theta_x + \Theta_w) \end{aligned} \tag{343}$$

Substituting (343) into (341), we get

$$C_n = \frac{E_0}{2\pi} \sum_{\nu=0}^{N-1} \cos \nu\pi \int_{(2\pi/N)\nu - (\Theta_x/2)}^{(2\pi/N)\nu + (\Theta_x/2)} \cos n \frac{N}{2} \Theta \, d\Theta \tag{344}$$

which, when integrated, becomes

$$C_n = \frac{2}{\pi} \frac{E_0}{N} \sum_{\nu=0}^{N-1} \frac{1}{n} \cos \nu\pi \cos \nu n\pi \sin n \frac{N}{2} \frac{\Theta_x}{2} \tag{345}$$

which can be easily evaluated once E_0, N, and Θ_x are determined.

It is seen from Eq. (339) that the electric field in the anode-cathode space is formed by the superposition of harmonic waves rotating in a clockwise and counterclockwise (positive) direction similar to those encountered in a synchronous motor. The angular velocity of the nth harmonic wave is

$$\dot{\Theta}_n = \frac{2\omega}{Nn} \tag{346}$$

Waves traveling in the clockwise direction correspond to $n > 0$, those traveling in the counterclockwise direction to $n < 0$. The wave corresponding to $n = 0$ either cannot satisfy the formulation or is not of interest. The wave for $|n| = 1$, on the other hand, is the most important one since it is the first harmonic and is that wave which produces the main interaction with the electron stream.

We may gain insight into the physical implications of Eq. (339) by considering the special case when $0 < k_\pi r < 0.4$. In this case, we may replace the Bessel functions by the first term in their power-series representations; *i.e.*,

$$J_{(N/2)n}(k_\pi r) = \frac{1}{[(N/2)n]!}\left(\frac{k_\pi r}{2}\right)^{n(N/2)} \tag{347}$$

$$J'_{(N/2)n}(k_\pi r) = \frac{1}{2}\frac{1}{[(N/2)n - 1]!}\left(\frac{k_\pi r}{2}\right)^{n(N/2)-1} \tag{348}$$

Substituting (347) and (348) into (339), we get

$$\operatorname{Re} E_\Theta(r,\Theta,t) = \sum_{n=-\infty}^{\infty} C_n\left(\frac{r}{r_a}\right)^{(N/2)|n|-1} \cos\left(n\frac{N}{2}\Theta - \omega_\pi t\right) \tag{349}$$

The term $[(r/r_a)]^{(N/2)|n|-1}$ shows that as the harmonic wave number n increases, the wave penetration into the anode-cathode space decreases. The wave penetration for $|n| = 1$ in modern magnetrons does not extend to the area which is occupied by the magnetron cathode.

Electrons leaving the cathode and pursuing their spiral or cycloidal path on the way to the anode will first meet the fundamental harmonic electric wave and subsequently each higher harmonic. In an ideal tube, the net energy exchange between the field harmonics for $|n| \neq 1$ is zero, the main interaction for power exchange taking place between the electron spokes which are formed and the component of $E_\Theta(r,\Theta,t)$ for which $|n| = 1$.

PROBLEMS

1. Calculate the phase at $t = 10$ msec of a simple harmonic traveling wave after traveling in free space from the earth to the moon (256,000 miles), having left the earth at $t = 0$. The frequency of the wave is 450 Mc.

2. Show that the complex Fourier series

$$e(t) = \sum_{-\infty}^{\infty} C_n e^{jn\omega[t-(x/v_n)]}$$

satisfies the wave equation. What restriction must be placed on v_n for the traveling wave to arrive at some destination without distortion?

3. Does the wave

$$e(t) = e^{-ax}Ee^{j\omega[t-(x/v)]}$$

satisfy the wave equation if a is a real number? Explain in detail.

4. Prove the relationship described by Eq. (44).

5. Discuss the block design of an electronic system for investigating the dispersive qualities of a transmission medium. Can the dissipative qualities of the medium also be deduced by this system?

6. Compare the problem of the transmission line in which $L = g = 0$ and whose sending and receiving terminals are short-circuited at $t = 0$ with the well-known problem of the temperatures in a slab with faces at zero temperature (see, for example, R. V. Churchill)[1]. Discuss the restrictions which must be made in setting up the initial distribution of voltage or temperature for each case.

7. Equation (222) is derived for the case of a step function applied to a semi-infinite transmission line for which $L = g = 0$. Can any comparison be made between this solution and the solution leading to Eq. (174) for the case when a unit voltage applied to the terminals of the transmission line describing (174) is suddenly reduced to zero amplitude, thus possibly implying the application of a negative step function. (The line used is very long, with the other terminal short-circuited.) Is the implication referred to correct? Explain fully.

8. Consider the case of a distortionless line 1,000 miles long which is terminated with a resistance whose magnitude is equal to 0.4 of the characteristic impedance of the line. Some of the important properties of this line are, per mile, $L = 3.75$ mh, $C = 0.005\ \mu$f, $g = 0.3\ \mu$mho. If a step voltage with a magnitude of 50 volts is applied to the input terminals at $t = 0$, determine the voltage appearing at the input as a function of time.

9. Consider the transmission-line system pictured in Fig. 5. What must be the value of R and the length of line to yield a voltage pulse of amplitude 500 volts and duration time 10 μsec?

10. Determine the nature of the associated magnetic-field vectors if either E_x or E_z exists alone in free space traveling in the y or x directions, respectively. Repeat for the case where E_y and E_z exist with $E_x = 0$.

11. If a standing wave is to be set up in an isotropic nonconducting medium with the electric-field intensity oriented in some particular plane, discuss the nature of the waves necessary for this condition to be fulfilled. What is the part played by the magnetic-field vectors in setting up these standing waves?

12. The general solution [see (306)] for wave propagation in a conducting medium has been seen to be identical to that prescribing transmission-line behavior [see (184)]. Discuss fully and give illustrations of the fundamental differences involved in the respective problems, based on the boundary conditions encountered in each system. Are there any wave phenomena present in transmission-line systems which might be considered to be a counterpart of the tail encountered in electromagnetic-wave propagation as described in Eq. (321)?

13. Solve (337) and set up (343) for the case of the $n = 4$ mode in a 12-cavity magnetron.

[1] R. V. Churchill, "Modern Operational Mathematics in Engineering," Chap. VI, McGraw-Hill Book Company, Inc., New York, 1944.

CHAPTER 22

RECEPTION IN ELECTRICAL COMMUNICATIONS

THE RECEIVER

1. The Superheterodyne Receiver. In the early days of radio reception, it was customary to receive a signal and pass this signal through an r-f amplifier into a detector (only AM wave transmission was in use at the time). The recovered intelligence was then passed through an audio amplifier and amplified to the desired level. During the First World War, E. A. Armstrong and W. Schottky, working independently, introduced the superheteorodyne receiver, which has become virtually the standard receiver for the reception of AM and FM waves.

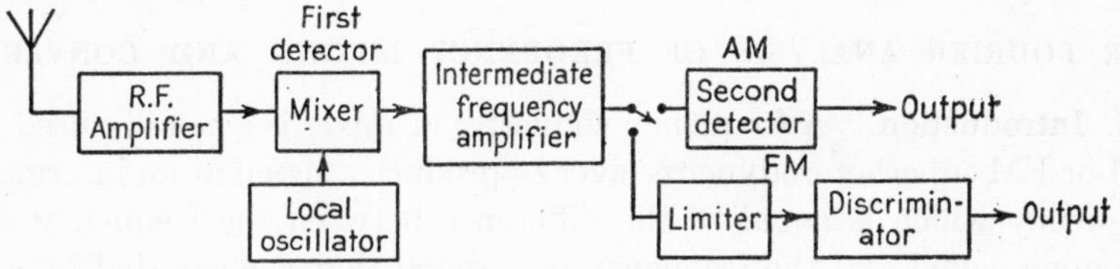

FIG. 1. Superheterodyne receiver.

The basic superheterodyne receiver is pictured in Fig. 1. The incoming signal from the antenna is passed through an r-f amplifier[1] into a frequency mixer, where it is beat against a signal from a local oscillator. The output of the mixer is then passed through an i-f amplifier. This i-f amplifier is a highly selective amplifier which will pass and amplify the difference component of the beating waves while rejecting the other components. The output of the i-f amplifier is then passed into the "second" detector in the case of an AM wave or into a limiter plus frequency discriminator in the case of an FM wave. The output of either is then passed through an audio or video amplifier to a loudspeaker or to a video output system.

L. Malter[2] has succinctly summarized the chief reasons for the use of the superheterodyne principle in radio receivers as follows:

[1] The use of an r-f amplifier is, of course, preferred but not essential in superheterodyne reception. Many receivers feed the antenna directly to the first detector.

[2] Herold and Malter, Aspects of Reception at Ultra-high Frequency, Part IV, General Superheterodyne Considerations at Ultra-high Frequencies, *Proc. IRE*, vol. 31, pp. 567–575, October, 1943.

1. The tuned circuits in intermediate amplifiers are fixed in frequency whereas in radio-frequency amplifiers, they require tuning to the individual signal. If the receiver is to cover an extended frequency range, the tuning problem for the radio-frequency amplifier may be a serious one.
2. It is often possible to secure a higher gain per stage at intermediate frequencies than at radio-frequencies.
3. Better control of frequency response can generally be achieved at intermediate frequencies, particularly if the receiver is to operate over an extended frequency range.
4. It may be possible, at the ultra-high frequencies, to achieve greater signal-to-noise ratio with a superheterodyne type receiver than with a radio-frequency amplifier type of receiver.

In this chapter we shall be primarily concerned with the Fourier analysis and general aspects of frequency mixing and modulated-wave demodulation since the basic elements of the Fourier and Laplace analyses which may be applied to r-f and i-f amplifiers have already been discussed. For other items such as automatic volume control, automatic frequency control, noise suppression, etc., the reader is referred to the literature of the communication-engineering field.

THE FOURIER ANALYSIS OF FREQUENCY MIXING AND CONVERSION

2. Introduction. A frequency converter or mixer is generally used in an AM or FM superheterodyne receiver to produce a signal at an intermediate frequency which is equal to the difference between the frequency of the incoming signal and the frequency of a signal that is generated by a local oscillator. In general, if the frequency-changing tube contains its own local oscillator, it is called a converter; if a separate source is used for the local oscillator, then it is known as a mixer.[1]

This section will discuss the various ways in which the Fourier analysis may be used to produce a solution for mixer or converter action and is based in general on the writings of E. W. Herold, who has contributed extensively in this field.

3. Conversion Transconductance. Conversion transconductance is defined as follows:

Conversion transconductance g_C is the ratio[2] of the magnitude of a single beat-frequency component $(f_1 + f_0)$ or $(f_1 - f_0)$ of the output current to the magnitude of the input voltage of frequency, f_1, under the conditions that all direct voltages and the magnitude of the second imput voltage f_0 (local oscillator) must remain constant. As most precisely used, it refers to an infinitesimal magnitude of the voltage of frequency f_1.

[1] E. W. Herold, Operation of Frequency Converters and Mixers for Superheterodyne Reception, *Proc. IRE*, vol. 30, pp. 84–102, February, 1942.

[2] Note that the conversion transconductance is not defined as a partial derivative as is the mutual transconductance.

Conventional tubes[1] have conversion transconductances which, for the ideal case, are equal in magnitude to $1/\pi$ times the mutual transconductance for fundamental operation, 16 per cent for second harmonic conversion, and 10 per cent for third harmonic conversion.

4. Frequency Mixing in an Ideal Mixer. Frequency mixing can be performed only in nonlinear circuits. As a demonstration of the elementary principle of frequency mixing, consider an ideal mixer in which two waves are beat together without resulting in any distortion terms other than the normal beat frequencies.

Let the input wave from the antenna be the modulated wave

$$i_1 = I_1 \sum_{n=-\infty}^{\infty} C_n e^{j(\omega_0 + n\omega_1)t} \tag{1}$$

where C_n is the amplitude coefficient which may be determined for amplitude, frequency, or phase modulation. Let i_1 be beat against the real wave

$$i_2 = I_2 \cos \omega_2 t \tag{2}$$

from the local oscillator. It follows that

$$i_1 i_2 = I_1 I_2 \cos \omega_2 t \sum_{n=-\infty}^{\infty} C_n e^{j(\omega_0 + n\omega_1)t} \tag{3}$$

$$= \frac{I_1 I_2}{2} (e^{j\omega_2 t} + e^{-j\omega_2 t}) \sum_{n=-\infty}^{\infty} C_n e^{j(\omega_0 + n\omega_1)t} \tag{4}$$

which may be written as follows:

$$i_1 i_2 = \frac{I_1 I_2}{2} \left(\sum_{n=-\infty}^{\infty} C_n e^{j[(\omega_0 + \omega_2) + n\omega_1]t} + \sum_{n=-\infty}^{\infty} C_n e^{j[(\omega_0 - \omega_2) + n\omega_1]t} \right) \tag{5}$$

Equation (5) shows the resultant wave to consist of two sideband sets. One is located symmetrically about $\omega_0 + \omega_2$, and the other is located symmetrically about $\omega_0 - \omega_1$. In general, the lower frequency sideband set is termed the intermediate-frequency set.

5. Concerning the Conversion Transconductance, g_C. In considerations of amplifier design, numerical values of gain, as deduced from the tube characteristics and the associated circuit parameters, play an important part. In like manner, conversion transconductance (or conversion conductance in the case of a diode) is an important quantity in the design of mixers or converters.

Mixer Gain. The conversion transconductance yields the output com-

[1] For a discussion of the conversion transconductance of an unconventional tube, see E. W. Herold, Superheterodyne Conversion Using Phase Reversal Modulation, *Proc. IRE*, vol. 34, No. 4, pp. 184–197, April, 1946, for such aspects of the beam deflection tube whose transconductance was deduced in Sec. 8, Chap. 7.

ponent of current of the mixer at the intermediate frequency. The product of the current component and the output load impedance yields the output intermediate-frequency voltage. The ratio of this i-f voltage to the impressed signal voltage is referred to as the gain of the mixer. This mixer gain cannot exceed one-third of the gain of the same tube used as an amplifier.

Taylor-series Aspects. For many years, it was customary to describe converter or mixer action qualitatively in terms of a Taylor-series representation of the nonlinear dynamic characteristic of the associated tube. For example, it was often shown, using formulation identical to that described in Sec. 6, Chap. 7, that if a pair of waves of different frequency is impressed on a nonlinear device having a square-law characteristic, the output wave would include waves having sum and difference frequencies of the original frequencies (see the preceding section). However, as a means of yielding numerical results in analysis of conversion conductance and converter operation, the Taylor-series approach is very unsatisfactory because of the complex expressions involved and the laborious computations necessary despite the illuminating physical picture which it presents.

Fourier-series Approach. The most rewarding approach for deducing mixer or converter operation is one which recognizes the fact that the amplification, and therefore the conductance or the transconductance, of the device varies at the same rate as the local oscillator signal. This method of approach is described as follows:

Consider a converter or mixer whose output current is of the form

$$i = ge_s \tag{6}$$

where e_s is the input voltage and g is the conductance of the device. If the angular velocity of the local oscillator is ω_0, the conductance can be expressed in a Fourier series such that (6) becomes

$$i = \left(g_0 + \sum_{n=1}^{\infty} g_n \cos n\omega_0 t\right)e_s \tag{7}$$

where

$$\begin{aligned} g_0 &= \frac{1}{2\pi}\int_0^{2\pi} g \, d\omega_0 t \\ g_n &= \frac{1}{\pi}\int_0^{2\pi} g \cos n\omega_0 t \, d\omega_0 t \end{aligned} \tag{8}$$

If $e_s = E_s \sin \omega t$, the nth component of i will be

$$i_n = g_n \cos n\omega_0 t \sin \omega t = g_{c_n} \sin (\omega + n\omega_0)t + g_{c_n} \sin (\omega - n\omega_0)t \tag{9}$$

where

$$g_{c_n} = \frac{g_n}{2} \tag{10}$$

Mixer Noise. In the design of converters or mixers, it is necessary to include considerations of mixer noise with those of mixer gain.

As in the case of amplifier tubes, it is convenient to express the fluctuation noise in a mixer or a converter in terms of a noise equivalent resistance (see Sec. 13, Chap. 5). The value of the resistance is obtained by equating the thermal noise of a resistor at room temperature to the equivalent grid-noise voltage of the tube, *i.e.*,

$$R_{eq} = \frac{1}{4kT_R} \frac{\overline{i_{i-f}^2}}{g_c^2 \Delta f} \tag{11}$$

where $\overline{i_{i-f}^2}$ is the mean squared noise at the intermediate frequency, k is Boltzman's constant, T_R is the room temperature (293°K), and Δf is the noise bandwidth.

E. W. Herold[1] has shown that approximate formulas for noise equivalent resistance of various types of tubes can be developed to yield the following:
Triode mixers:

$$R_{eq} = \frac{4}{g_c}$$

Pentode mixers:

$$R_{eq} = \frac{I_b}{I_b + I_{c_2}} \left(\frac{4}{g_c} + \frac{20 I_{c_2}}{g_c^2} \right)$$

Pentagrid mixers:

$$R_{eq} = \frac{20 I_b}{g_c^2 I_{sp}} (I_{sp} - I_b)$$

where I_{sp} is the average total space current drawn from the cathode and I_b and I_{c_2} are the average plate and screen currents averaged over the oscillator cycle.

The significance of these equations can be illustrated as follows: Consider the following tabulation of typical values which were measured by Herold with an oscillator at 60 Mc using an i-f amplifier operating at 10 Mc:

Tube	g_c (micromhos)	R_{eq}
6J5 triode	1,000	5,800
6AC7/1852 pentode	3,600	3,000
6L7 pentagrid mixer	400	230,000

Note that the 6L7 pentagrid mixer tube, which is widely used in AM broadcast (spectrum 10 kc wide) receivers, would be unsuitable for television (spectrum 6 mc wide) because of its low gain and high noise. This is

[1] E. W. Herold, Superheterodyne Converter System Considerations in Television Receivers, *RCA Rev.*, vol. 4, No. 3, pp. 324–337, January, 1940.

due to the fact that the fluctuation noise sets a limit to the sensitivity of the receiver, and since this noise increases as the bandwidth of the signal spectrum is increased, the choice of such mixer or converter tubes as the 6AC7/1852 becomes imperative because of their low noise and high gain.

The noise of a diode mixer is difficult to calculate but may be approximated by a resistance equal to the output impedance of the diode. This resistance is then assigned a temperature between cathode temperature and room temperature, sufficient to account for the noise.

6. Theory of the Diode Frequency Mixer. In the u-h-f region, the diode, which is a two-element nonlinear device, enjoys considerable usage as a diode frequency mixer.[1] When suitably combined with a local oscillator and an incoming wave, it produces an i-f wave across a tuned circuit which is tuned to the intermediate frequency and which is included in the circuit.

The basic diode-mixer circuit is shown in Fig. 2, where we see a series circuit made up of a diode, a local oscillator and battery, and two tuned

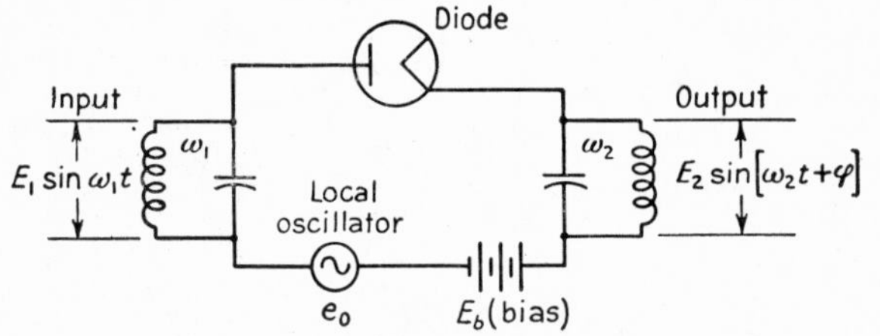

FIG. 2. Diode-mixer circuit.

circuits, one tuned to the input wave and the other to the intermediate frequency wave. In an analysis which is based on this circuit, we shall assume the phase angles to be arbitrary and that the produced i-f voltage exists as an impressed voltage. The current in the circuit may then be written

$$i = f(e_1 + e_2 + e_0) \tag{12}$$

where e_1, e_2, and e_0 represent the simple harmonic input voltage, i-f voltage, and the local oscillator voltage, respectively. Since the voltage-current characteristic curve in the conducting region is near-linear, let us express the current i as a Taylor series as follows:

$$i = f(e_0) + g[E_1 \sin \omega_1 t + E_2 \sin (\omega_2 t + \varphi)] \tag{13}$$

where the expansion is carried out about the point determined by e_0 and g represents the tube conductance di/de.

[1] Herold and Malter, Some Aspects of Radio Reception at Ultra-high Frequency, Part V, Frequency Mixing in Diodes, E. W. Herold, *Proc. IRE*, vol. 31, pp. 575–582, October, 1943.

The important consideration in this circuit is the fact that g varies periodically with time at the frequency $\omega_0/2\pi$ of the local oscillator voltage. Let us then expand g in a Fourier cosine series such that

$$g = g_0 + \sum_{n=1}^{\infty} g_n \cos n\omega_0 t \tag{14}$$

g_0 and g_n may be evaluated from the characteristic curve of the particular diode used. Substituting (14) into Eq. (13), we get, after some trigonometric manipulation,

$$\begin{aligned} i = {} & f(e_0) + g_0[E_1 \sin \omega_1 t + E_2 \sin (\omega_2 t + \varphi)] \\ & + \frac{E_1}{2} \sum_{n=1}^{\infty} g_n[\sin (\omega_1 + n\omega_0)t + \sin (\omega_1 - n\omega_0)t] \\ & + \frac{E_2}{2} \sum_{n=1}^{\infty} g_n\{\sin [(\omega_2 + n\omega_0)t + \varphi] + \sin [(\omega_2 - n\omega_0)t + \varphi]\} \end{aligned} \tag{15}$$

If we specify that

$$\omega_2 = \pm(\omega_1 - n\omega_0) \tag{16}$$

where the conversion is made to the nth harmonic of the local oscillator, we find that the current at the input frequency is

$$i(\omega_1) = g_0 E_1 \sin \omega_1 t + \frac{g_n}{2} E_2 \sin (\omega_1 t + \varphi) \tag{17}$$

and that the i-f current is (letting $g_n/2 = g_{c_n}$)

$$i(\omega_2) = g_0 E_2 \sin (\omega_2 t + \varphi) + g_{c_n} E_2 \sin (\omega_2 t + \varphi) \tag{18}$$

Because of the presence of the tuned circuit tuned to $\omega_2 = \pm(\omega_1 - n\omega_0)$, we may ignore all terms but the input and i-f terms, and we may drop our original conception of the voltage $E_2 \sin (\omega_2 t + \varphi)$ as an impressed voltage and consider it to be a voltage drop due to the current $i(\omega_2)$.

7. Application of Diode-mixer Theory to an Ideal Diode. We may study the behavior of g by considering the current-voltage characteristic curve and the g versus voltage curve of an idealized diode. These are plotted in Fig. 3a and b, respectively. It is seen there that, with a local oscillator voltage $E_0 \sin \omega_0 t$ and a d-c bias E_b, the behavior of the conductance as a function of time is pulselike in shape. If the peak value of g is $g_{\max}$, we may show from Chap. 3 that

$$g_0 = g_{\max} k \tag{19}$$

$$g_{c_n} = g_{\max} k \frac{\sin nk\pi}{nk\pi} \tag{20}$$

where k is the ratio of the pulse duration to the period $2\pi/\omega_0$ of the local oscillator and may be shown to be

$$k = \frac{1}{\pi} \cos^{-1} \frac{E_b}{E_0} \tag{21}$$

We may chart the magnitudes of g_0, g_{C_1}, g_{C_2}, and g_{C_3} as functions of g_{max} and E_b/E_0 as shown in Fig. 4.

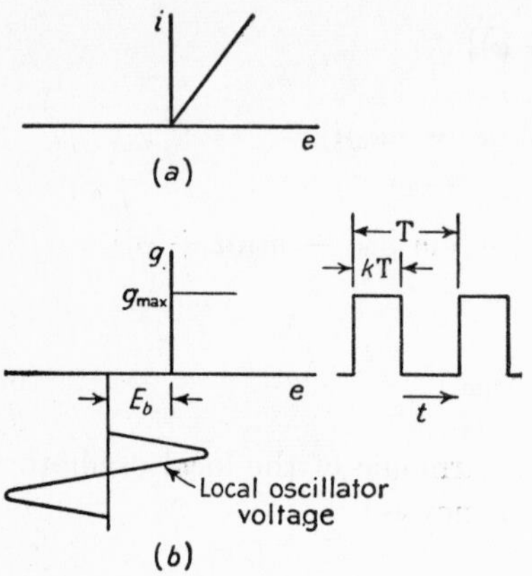

FIG. 3.

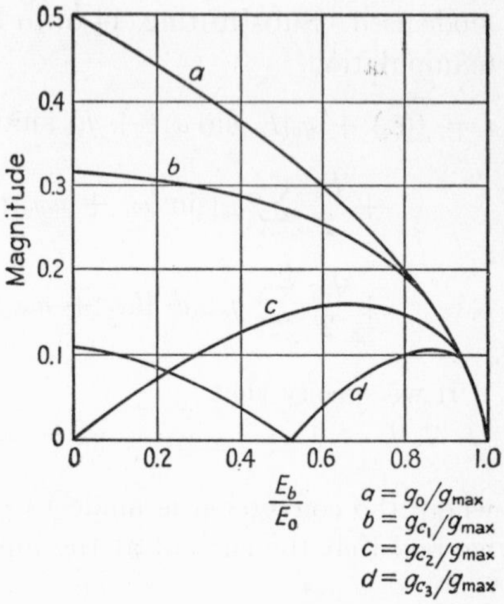

FIG. 4. (*Courtesy of Institute of Radio Engineers.*)

8. Mixer Action Using a Fourier-series Representation of the Transconductance. If the local oscillator voltage is sufficiently large, then the instantaneous signal electrode of the mixer circuit pictured in Fig. 5 may be considered to be varying periodically at the frequency of the local

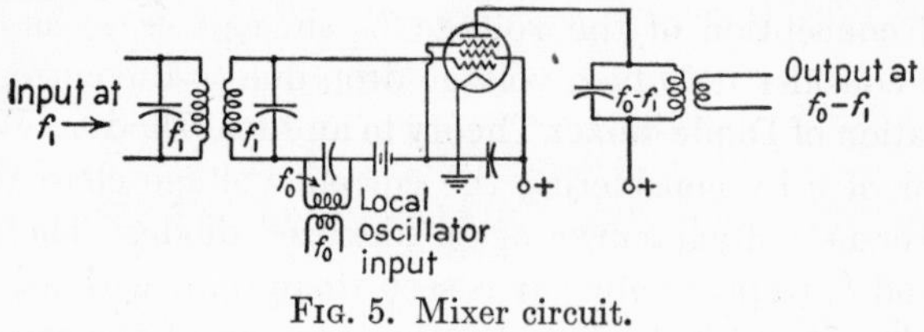

FIG. 5. Mixer circuit.

oscillator, as is shown in Fig. 6*a*, where e_s is the input oscillator voltage and $g_m(t)$ is the resultant time variation of the transconductance. Since transconductance variation is an even function, we may represent it by a Fourier cosine series as follows,

$$g_m(t) = a_0 + a_1 \cos \omega_0 t + a_2 \cos 2\omega_0 t + \cdots \tag{22}$$

where the a_n's are coefficients which depend on the operating point, the tube characteristics, and the amplitude of the local oscillator voltage. If an input signal $e_s = E_s \sin \omega_s t$ is applied to the control electrode, it follows that

$$i_p = g_m(t) E_s \sin \omega_s t \tag{23}$$

where i_p is the plate current of the tube. Substituting (22) into (23), we get

$$i_p = a_0 E_s \sin \omega_s t + E_s \sum_{n=1}^{\infty} a_n \sin \omega_s t \cos n\omega_0 t \tag{24}$$

$$= a_0 E_s \sin \omega_s t + \frac{E_s}{2} \sum_{n=1}^{\infty} a_n \sin (\omega_s + n\omega_0) t + \frac{E_s}{2} \sum_{n=1}^{\infty} a_n \sin (\omega_s - n\omega_0) t \tag{25}$$

If the resonant network in the plate circuit is tuned to $\omega_s - \omega_0$ or to any other frequency listed in (25), a voltage will appear across the resonant

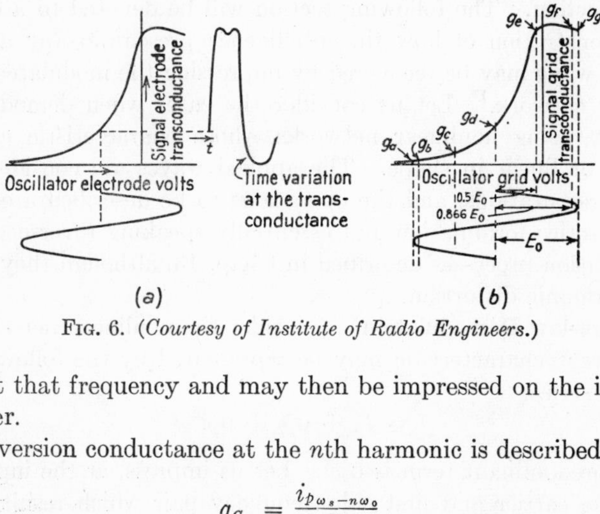

FIG. 6. (*Courtesy of Institute of Radio Engineers.*)

network at that frequency and may then be impressed on the input of an i-f amplifier.

The conversion conductance at the nth harmonic is described as

$$g_{c_n} = \frac{i_{p\,\omega_s - n\omega_0}}{E_s} \tag{26}$$

$$= \frac{a_n}{2} \tag{27}$$

which can be written in terms of the nth Fourier-series coefficient as

$$g_{c_n} = \frac{1}{2\pi} \int_0^{2\pi} g_m(t) \cos m\omega_0 t \, d\omega_0 t \tag{28}$$

We may find values of g_{c_n} by employing a graphical determination of the Fourier-series coefficients from the control-grid transconductance versus oscillator voltage curve of any modulator or mixer tube. Using a seven-point analysis (30° intervals) of the curve as shown in Fig. 6*b*, it follows that, using the indicated points on the curve,

$$g_{C_1} = \tfrac{1}{12}[(g_g - g_a) + (g_e - g_c) + 1.73(g_f - g_b)] \tag{29}$$

$$g_{C_2} = \tfrac{1}{12}[2g_d + \tfrac{3}{4}(g_c - g_e - g_f - g_b) - (g_g + g_a)] \tag{30}$$

$$g_{C_3} = \tfrac{1}{12}[(g_g - g_a) - 2(g_e - g_c)] \tag{31}$$

g_{C_1} is the most accurate of the three formulas, g_{C_3} being only a rough approximation. Note in Fig. 6*b* that the maximum possible value of g_{C_1} occurs when g_a, g_b, and g_c are equal to zero. This can be attained by operating the local oscillator so that the transconductance curve is cut off for slightly less than half of the cycle.

THE THEORY OF THE DEMODULATION OF AN AMPLITUDE-MODULATED WAVE USING A NONLINEAR CIRCUIT

9. Introduction. The following section will be devoted to a discussion and a demonstration of how the intelligence present in any amplitude-modulating wave may be recovered by impressing the modulated wave on a nonlinear network.[1] Let us consider the cases when demodulation is obtained by using nonlinear networks whose characteristic curves are square law or linear in shape. The applied waves are considered to be Fourier representations, and the operations to be described are based on the Taylor-series formulation and essentially speaking reverse the amplitude-modulation processes described in Chap. 13, although they may also produce harmonic distortion.

10. Square-law Demodulation. Consider the nonlinear network whose voltage-current characteristic may be represented by the following terms of a Taylor series,

$$i = I_b + G_1 e + G_2 e^2 \tag{32}$$

where the predominant term is $G_2 e^2$. Let us impress, at the input of this network, the carrier and first side-frequency pair which result from the amplitude modulation of the carrier $E_0 \sin \omega_0 t$ by the modulating wave $ME_0 \cos \omega_1 t$. The impressed voltage is then written

$$e = E_0 \sin \omega_0 t + \frac{ME_0}{2}[\sin(\omega_0 + \omega_1)t + \sin(\omega_0 - \omega_1)t] \tag{33}$$

[1] W. L. Everitt, "Communication Engineering," 2d ed., Chap. XIII, McGraw-Hill Book Company, Inc., New York, 1937. For a discussion of the limited Fourier-series approach to demodulation analysis in amplitude modulation, see W. L. Barrow, Contribution to the Theory of Nonlinear Circuits with Large Applied Voltages, *Proc. IRE*, vol. 22, pp. 964–980, August, 1934.

Substituting (33) into (32), we find that the square-law term will yield the waves

$$
\begin{aligned}
G_2 e^2 = G_2 E_0^{\,2}\left(\frac{1}{2} + \frac{M^2}{4}\right) \\
- G_2 \frac{E_0^{\,2}}{2}\left[\cos 2\omega_0 t + \frac{M^2}{4}\cos 2(\omega_0 + \omega_1)t\right. \\
\left. + \frac{M^2}{4}\cos 2(\omega_0 - \omega_1)t\right] \\
- G_2 \frac{ME_0^{\,2}}{2}[\cos (2\omega_0 + \omega_1)t + \cos (2\omega_0 - \omega_1)t] \\
- G_2 \frac{M^2E_0^{\,2}}{4}(\cos 2\omega_0 t - \cos 2\omega_1 t) \\
+ G_2 ME_0^{\,2} \cos \omega_1 t \qquad (34)
\end{aligned}
$$

The wave in (34) which corresponds to the original intelligence is

$$+ G_2 ME_0^{\,2} \cos \omega_1 t \qquad (35)$$

Its amplitude is seen to be proportional to the square of the voltage. This wave may be passed into an amplifier and amplified to the desired level. Note the presence of the second harmonic term

$$- G_2 \frac{M^2E_0^{\,2}}{4} \cos 2\omega_1 t \qquad (36)$$

The percentage of second harmonic distortion is found by taking the ratio of the maximum amplitudes of (35) and (36), which is found to be

$$\text{Per cent second} = \frac{M}{4} \times 100 \qquad (37)$$

We may qualitatively check the theory which yields (35) and (36) by considering the envelope of the current wave which is pictured in Fig. 7. Here the AM wave which is described by Eq. (33) is impressed on a square-law curve, and the resulting distortion of its envelope is cleariy shown. If E_b denotes a constant-bias voltage, then the positive envelope in Fig. 7 may be written

$$e_+ = E_b + E_0(1 + M \sin \omega_1 t) \qquad (38)$$

and the negative envelope is seen to be

$$e_- = E_b - E_0(1 + M \sin \omega_1 t) \qquad (39)$$

The average amplitude of the positive and negative envelopes is evidently equal to E_b.

After the AM wave (33) is impressed on the square-law characteristic curve, the output current envelope is represented by the following positive and negative envelopes:

$$i_+ = I_b + G_1E_0(1 + M \sin \omega_1 t) + G_2E_0^2(1 + M \sin \omega_1 t)^2 \tag{40}$$

$$i_- = I_b - G_1E_0(1 + M \sin \omega_1 t) + G_2E_0^2(1 + M \sin \omega_1 t)^2 \tag{41}$$

The average of i_+ and i_- is found to be

$$\frac{i_+ + i_-}{2} = I_b + G_2E_0^2\left(1 + \frac{M^2}{2} + 2M \sin \omega_1 t - \frac{M^2}{2} \cos 2\omega_1 t\right) \tag{42}$$

The amplitudes and frequencies of the two varying components in (42) are those predicted by (37).

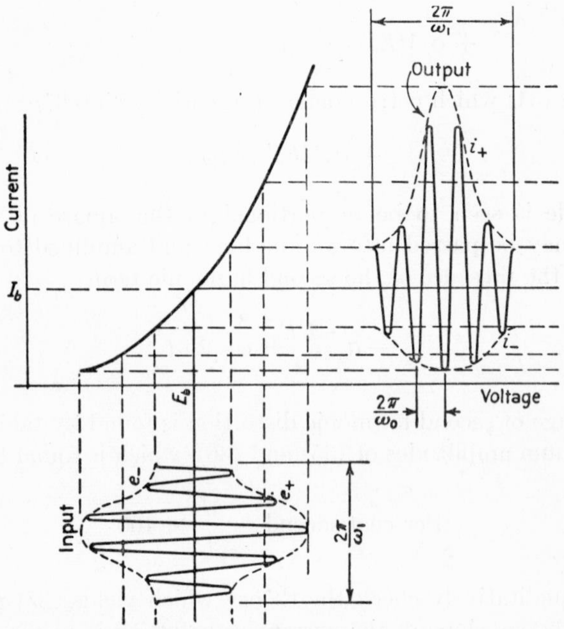

FIG. 7. AM wave impressed on a square-law characteristic curve.

11. The Linear Detector. Another important type of demodulation is that which is performed by a linear detector. The use of the term *linear* is perhaps misleading since, although it implies a completely linear voltage-current characteristic curve, it actually is applied to a characteristic curve which is made up of two linear sections of different slope, as shown in Fig. 8, so that their intersection produces as sharp a bend as possible. In practice, we can achieve only bends of the type shown by the dotted line, but by using sufficiently large input voltages, the errors involved can be made negligible.

Let the slopes of the upper and lower linear portions be S_1 and S_2, respectively. If the AM wave described by Eq. (33) is applied to the input of the linear detector and is biased so that the positive and negative

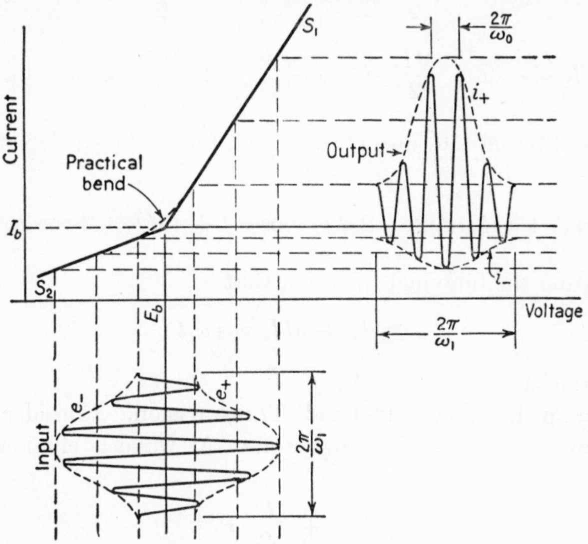

FIG. 8. AM wave applied to the characteristic curve of a linear detector.

envelopes at the input are described by (38) and (39), respectively, we obtain the following positive and negative envelopes in the output:

$$i_+ = I_b + S_1E_0(1 + M \sin \omega_1 t) \tag{43}$$

$$i_- = I_b - S_2E_0(1 + M \sin \omega_1 t) \tag{44}$$

Taking the average of (43) and (44), we find that

$$\frac{i_+ + i_-}{2} = I_b + \frac{S_1 - S_2}{2} E_0(1 + M \sin \omega_1 t) \tag{45}$$

$$= I_b + \frac{S_1 - S_2}{2} E_0 + (S_1 - S_2) \frac{ME_0}{2} \sin \omega_1 t \tag{46}$$

It is evident from Eq. (46) that the modulating wave has been recovered without harmonic distortion and that its amplitude is proportional to the first power of the voltage.

We may demonstrate the validity of this result analytically by considering the vector sum of the three rotating vectors,

$$i = I_1 e^{j\omega_0 t} + \frac{MI_1}{2} e^{j(\omega_0 + \omega_1)t} + \frac{MI_1}{2} e^{j(\omega_0 - \omega_1)t} \tag{47}$$

which, of course, represents a single-tone AM wave. The vector resultant i_r is described as follows,

$$i_r = \sqrt{i_x^2 + i_y^2} \tag{48}$$

where

$$i_x = I_1 \cos \omega_0 t + \frac{MI_1}{2} \cos (\omega_0 + \omega_1)t + \frac{MI_1}{2} \cos (\omega_0 - \omega_1)t \tag{49}$$

$$i_y = I_1 \sin \omega_0 t + \frac{MI_1}{2} \sin (\omega_0 + \omega_1)t + \frac{MI_1}{2} \sin (\omega_0 - \omega_1)t \tag{50}$$

Substituting (49) and (50) into (48), we get, for the linear-detector output, the wave

$$i_r = [I_1^2 + (MI_1)^2/2 + 2MI_1^2 \cos \omega_1 t + (MI_1)^2/2 \cos 2\omega_1 t]^{\frac{1}{2}} \tag{51}$$

It follows, using the binomial theorem, that

$$i_r \cong I_1 + MI_1 \cos \omega_1 t \tag{52}$$

which is in the same form as (46).

12. Detection in Single-sideband Transmission. Consider the case when the lower sideband of a single-tone AM wave is eliminated.[1] Let the resulting wave

$$i = I_1 e^{j\omega_0 t} + \frac{MI_1}{2} e^{j(\omega_0 + \omega_1)t} \tag{53}$$

be impressed on the input of a detector. If the detector is a linear detector, it follows from Eq. (48) that

$$i_r = I_1 \sqrt{1 + \frac{M^2}{4}} + \frac{MI_1}{2\sqrt{1 + (M^2/4)}} \cos \omega_1 t - \frac{M^2 I_1}{32[1 + (M^2/4)]^{\frac{3}{2}}} \cos^2 \omega_1 t + \cdots \tag{54}$$

When M is small,

$$i_r = I_1 \sqrt{1 + \frac{M^2}{4}} + \frac{MI_1}{2\sqrt{1 + (M^2/4)}} \cos \omega_1 t \tag{55}$$

This is a result of great importance since it shows that all of the information of the modulating signal may be contained in a spectral set composed of the carrier and either the upper or the lower sideband set. It is important that M be small so that the distortion as indicated in Eq. (54)

[1] For a general discussion of unsymmetrical-sideband theory, see H. A. Wheeler, The Solution of Unsymmetrical Side Band Problems with the Aid of the Zero-frequency Carrier, *Proc. IRE*, vol. 29, pp. 446–458, August, 1941.

will be minimized. W. J. Poch and D. W. Epstein[1] have calculated the per cent second and third harmonic distortion, and a chart which relates this distortion to the per cent modulation is shown in Fig. 9. It is seen that for 100 per cent modulation the amplitudes of the second and third harmonics will be equal in magnitude to 12 and 2.8 per cent of the fundamental amplitude, respectively. This per cent distortion would be intolerable in audio transmission, but it does not seriously cause the quality of the video picture to suffer.

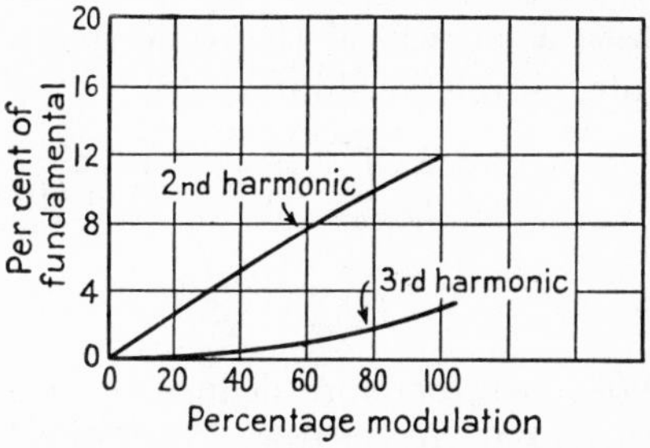

FIG. 9. (*Courtesy of Institute of Radio Engineers.*)

13. Practical Detector Considerations. A suitable detector circuit which is used extensively consists of a half-wave or full-wave diode rectifier system combined with a parallel *RC* network. The half-wave diode detector circuit is that which is pictured in Fig. 10. Note the parallel *RC* circuit which is in series with the diode. As the AM wave appears across the terminals *a*, *b* and is thus impressed on the series circuit consisting of the diode and the *RC* circuit, the diode rectifies the modulated wave. If the time constant *RC* is of the correct value, the *RC* circuit will follow the envelope of the rectified AM wave; this output wave yields the modulating intelligence which is recovered without distortion. This intelligence may then be fed into an amplifier and amplified to the desired level.

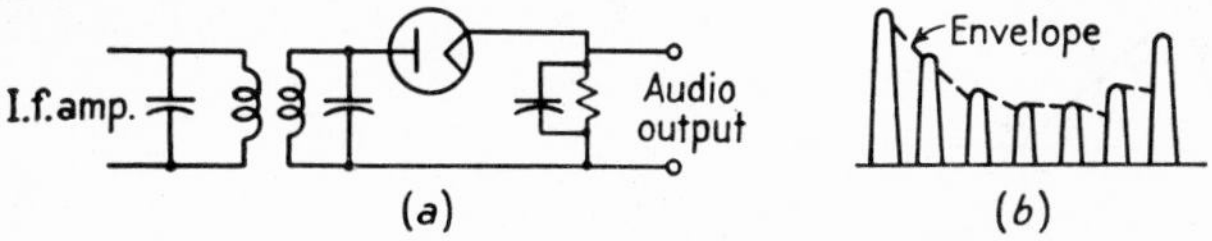

FIG. 10. Diode detector circuit.

14. Equivalent Resistance of a Diode Detector. An important consideration in the design of detector circuits is one of losses based on the equivalent resistance presented by the diode to the circuit. The equivalent resistance of a diode may be deduced as follows, using the Fourier analysis:

Consider the resistance presented by the diode to an impressed voltage $E_1 \cos \omega_1 t - E_b$. The current then consists of a series of cosinusoidal-loop pulses each of which has a duration time of less than half a cycle. For this discussion, let us assume that the plate-current–plate-voltage curve is linear and that the plate-current–plate-voltage relationship is

[1] Poch and Epstein, Partial Suppression of One Side Band in Television Reception, *Proc. IRE*, vol. 25, pp. 15–31, January, 1937.

$$\begin{aligned} i_p &= ge_p \qquad e_p > 0 \\ &= 0 \qquad e_p < 0 \end{aligned} \tag{56}$$

The a-c voltage $E_1 \cos \omega_1 t$ can yield power to the diode only when associated with a current of the same frequency through the diode, owing to the integral relationship

$$\begin{aligned} \frac{1}{2\pi} \int_0^{2\pi} E_1 \cos \omega_1 t \, I_1 \cos n\omega_1 t \, d\omega_1 t &= 0 \qquad n \neq 1 \\ &= \frac{E_1 I_1}{2} \qquad n = 1 \end{aligned} \tag{57}$$

We must therefore deduce the magnitude of the first Fourier harmonic current $I_1 \cos \omega_1 t$ from Eq. (56). Using a Fourier cosine series, it follows that

$$I_1 = \frac{2g}{\pi} \int_0^{\theta_c} (E_1 \cos \omega_1 t - E_b) \cos \omega_1 t \, d\omega_1 t \tag{58}$$

where θ_c is related to E_1 and E_b by the expression

$$\cos \theta_c = \frac{E_b}{E_1} \tag{59}$$

Continuing with the evaluation of (58), we get

$$I_1 = \frac{2g}{\pi} \left[E_1 \left(\frac{\theta_c}{2} + \frac{\sin 2\theta_c}{4} \right) - E_b \sin \theta_c \right] \tag{60}$$

Using Eq. (59), (60) can be rewritten as follows:

$$I_1 = \frac{gE_1}{\pi} (\theta_c - \sin \theta_c \cos \theta_c) \tag{61}$$

The effective resistance of the diode is therefore

$$R_{\text{eff}} = \frac{E_1}{I_1} = \frac{\pi}{g(\theta_c - \sin \theta_c \cos \theta_c)} \tag{62}$$

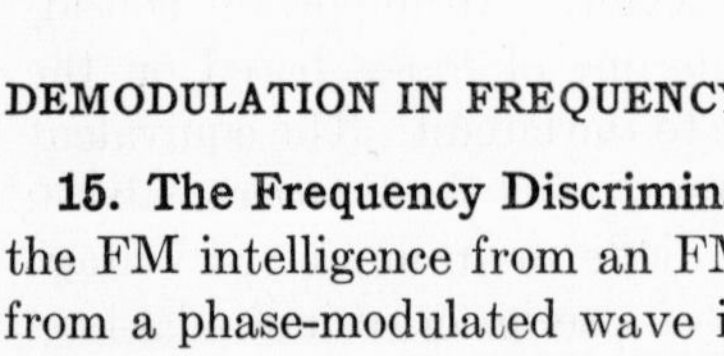

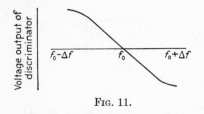

FIG. 11.

DEMODULATION IN FREQUENCY-MODULATION TRANSMISSION SYSTEMS

15. The Frequency Discriminator. The device which is used to recover the FM intelligence from an FM wave or the equivalent FM intelligence from a phase-modulated wave is known as a frequency discriminator;[1] it produces an output voltage which is directly proportional to the frequency deviation. A typical discriminator characteristic is illustrated in Fig. 11.

[1] For discussions of two of the most modern types of commercial frequency discriminators, see Seeley and Avins, The Ratio Detector, *RCA Rev.*, vol. 8, No. 2, pp. 201–236, June, 1947, and W. E. Bradley, Single-stage FM Detector, *Electronics*, vol. 19, No. 10, October, 1946.

16. An Elementary Approach to FM Demodulation. The most elementary type of frequency discriminator is a selective circuit which is used in conjunction with an AM-wave detector. Consider, for example, the parallel *RLC* circuit which is pictured in Fig. 12*a*. Let this circuit have the self-impedance diagram shown in Fig. 12*b*.

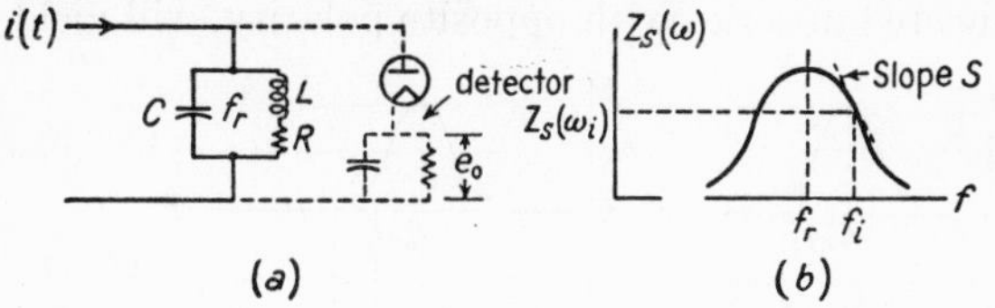

FIG. 12.

If the current through the resonant circuit is

$$i(t) = I \exp\left[j\left(2\pi f_i t + \int \Delta\omega \sin \omega_1 t\right)\right] \tag{63}$$

where f_i is the intermediate frequency, and if $f_i \neq f_r$ as shown, then, if the slope of the impedance curve at f_i is S, the output voltage $e(t)$ across the *RLC* circuit, for frequency deviations which are small compared with $f_i - f_r$, will be

$$e(t) = SZ(2\pi f_i) \sin \omega_1 t \, I \exp\left[j\left(2\pi f_i t + \int \Delta\omega \sin \omega_1 t\right)\right] \tag{64}$$

This wave has an envelope which is proportional to the modulating wave. Therefore, if $e(t)$ is impressed on the input of an AM-wave detector, the modulating intelligence may be recovered.

17. An Elementary Balanced Discriminator. Two of the chief drawbacks of the circuit in Fig. 12*a* are that, at the unperturbed carrier frequency, voltage appears across the output of the system and that the system is very sensitive to amplitude modulation. A balanced discrimi-

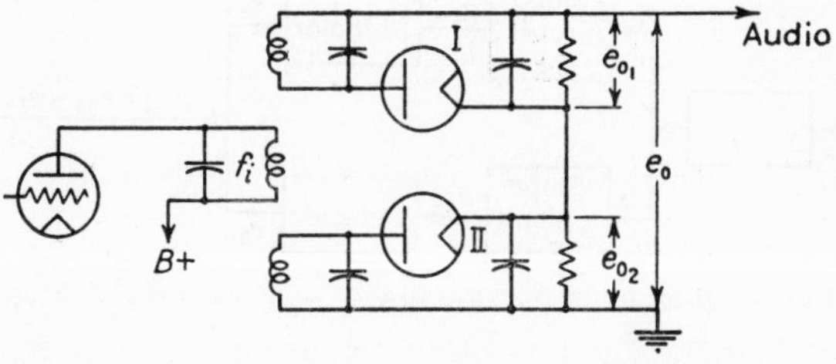

FIG. 13. Elementary balanced discriminator.

nator is a discriminator circuit whose output-voltage versus frequency-deviation curve is similar to that pictured in Fig. 11, where it is seen that the output e_0 is proportional to the frequency deviation alone. An elementary circuit of this type is shown in Fig. 13, where it is seen to consist of two tuned-circuit linear-rectifier systems which are coupled to the output circuit of the i-f amplifier.

Let $f_a > f_i$ and $f_b < f_i$, where f_b, f_a, and f_i refer to the resonant frequencies of the circuits in systems I and II and the intermediate frequency, respectively; then, as is shown in Fig. 14, the outputs of I and II, which are connected in series with opposite polarity, will yield a d-c output

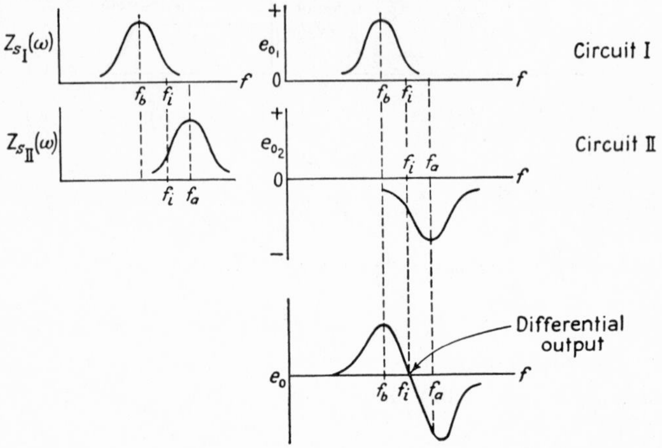

FIG. 14. Impedance and output curves of the circuits in Fig. 13.

voltage which is proportional to the frequency deviation. When $f = f_i$, the output is equal to zero. Because the output e_0 is, essentially speaking, a differential voltage, the system will be relatively insensitive to amplitude modulation.

18. General Discriminator Slope Factors. We have seen that a frequency discriminator may be produced by combining a circuit having a sloped impedance characteristic with an AM detector. Let us now extend

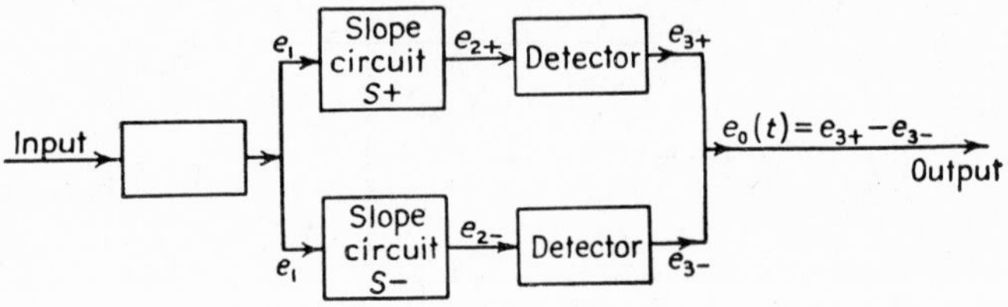

FIG. 15.

our discussion of frequency discriminators to considerations, due to H. A. Wheeler,[1] of general slope characteristics and linear and square-law detection in FM transmission.

Figure 15 pictures a block diagram which may be used to represent most

[1] H. A. Wheeler, Common-channel Interference between Two Frequency-modulated Signals, *Proc. IRE*, vol. 30, pp. 34–50, January, 1942.

frequency discriminators. In this diagram, we find two slope circuits (circuits with sloped impedance characteristics in the vicinity of the center frequency) of opposite slope which feed into detectors, the outputs of which are combined to yield the composite output signal which represents the recovered intelligence. Figure 16*a* and *b* illustrates the general slope

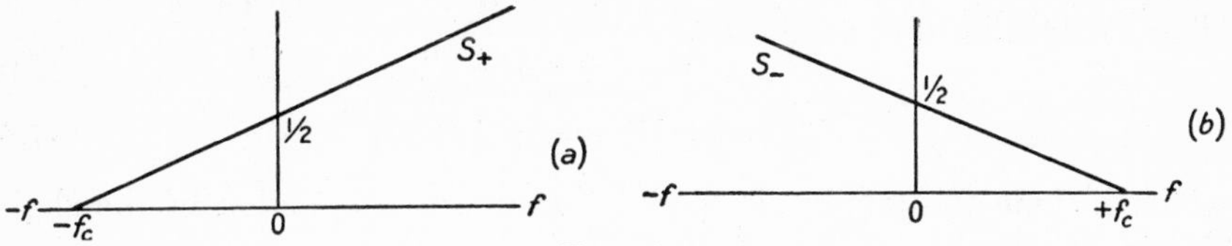

FIG. 16.

factors which describe the nature of linear slope circuits as a function of frequency. If the base-line intercepts are f_c and $-f_c$ and if $S_+(\omega)$ and $S_-(\omega)$ denote the positive and negative slope factors, we may write

$$S_+(\omega) = \frac{1}{2}\left(1 + \frac{f}{f_c}\right) \tag{65}$$

$$S_-(\omega) = \frac{1}{2}\left(1 - \frac{f}{f_c}\right) \tag{66}$$

Using the rotating-vector operator p (see Chap. 6), where

$$p = \frac{d}{dt} \tag{67}$$

Equations (65) and (66) may be written in the form,

$$S_\pm(\omega) = \frac{1}{2}\left(1 \pm \frac{p}{j\omega_c}\right) \tag{68}$$

whereby

$$e_{2\pm} = S_\pm(\omega)e_1(t) \tag{69}$$

Let us now introduce an FM wave at the input to the system [see $e_1(t)$ in Fig. 15]. In order to simpify the mathematics, let the carrier be a zero-carrier-frequency function such that we may write the input wave $e_1(t)$ as

$$e_1(t) = E_1 e^{j\Theta_t} \tag{70}$$

where

$$\Theta_t = \int \Delta\omega_t \, dt \tag{71}$$

$\Delta\omega_t$ describes the frequency variations which correspond to some original modulating voltage $e_m(t)$. $\Delta\omega_t$ may be written as the product

$$\Delta\omega_t = \omega_c e_m(t) \tag{72}$$

where ω_c may be described as a measure of the deviation per unit voltage of $e_m(t)$. It follows then that

$$pe_1(t) = j\omega_c e_m(t)e_1(t) \tag{73}$$

Substituting (73) into (68) and (69), we get, for the output of the slope circuits, the voltages

$$e_{2+}(t) = \tfrac{1}{2}[1 + e_m(t)]e^{j\Theta_t} \tag{74}$$

$$e_{2-}(t) = \tfrac{1}{2}[1 - e_m(t)]e^{j\Theta_t} \tag{75}$$

which include the amplitude modulation due to the action of the slope circuits.

19. Linear and Square-law Detectors in Frequency Discriminators. The preceding analysis leading to expressions for e_{2+} and e_{2-} (see Fig. 15) may be used to compare the discriminator output when either linear or square-law detectors are used. Figure 17*a* shows the output of each linear de-

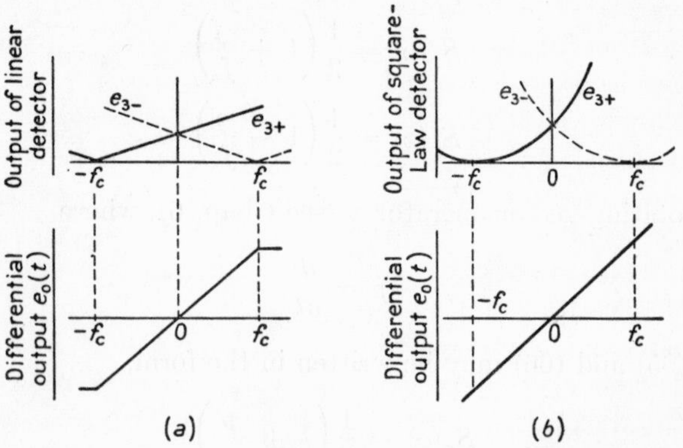

FIG. 17.

tector and the differential output due to both. This differential output may be expressed in terms of the absolute magnitudes of (74) and (75) (in order to describe the envelopes) as follows (where $e_{3\pm} = |e_{2\pm}|$):

$$e_0(t) = |e_{2+}| - |e_{2-}| \tag{76}$$

$$= \left|\frac{1}{2} + \frac{e_m(t)}{2}\right| - \left|\frac{1}{2} - \frac{e_m(t)}{2}\right|$$

$$= e_m(t) \qquad -f_c < f < f_c,\ -1 < e_m(t) < 1 \tag{77}$$

When square-law detectors are used in conjunction with the slope circuits, the individual outputs e_{2+} and e_{2-} and the differential output $e_0(t)$ are similar to those shown in Fig. 17*b*. $e_0(t)$ is found as follows:

$$e_0(t) = |e_{2+}|^2 - |e_{2-}|^2 \tag{78}$$

$$= [\tfrac{1}{4} + \tfrac{1}{2}e_m(t) + \tfrac{1}{4}e_m{}^2(t)] - [\tfrac{1}{4} - \tfrac{1}{2}e_m(t) + \tfrac{1}{4}e_m{}^2(t)] = e_m(t) \tag{79}$$

which is valid over an unlimited range as compared with the limited range of validity when linear detectors are used. Note that the effect of the curvature has canceled out.

In general, linear-detector usage in discriminators is more desirable than square-law-detector usage for the reasons that the latter usage demands that the discriminator balance be maintained perfect for efficient operation. Also, the relative response to amplitude modulation when linear detectors are used is much less than that when square-law detectors are used.

THE RECEPTION OF TELEVISION SIGNALS

20. The Television Receiver.[1] The television receiver is one of the most outstanding examples of ingenuity which has emerged from research and engineering in the field of electrical communications. Unlike the relatively simple operation of a modern AM broadcast receiver, which receives audio information confined to a band of frequencies 10 kc wide in the range of frequencies between 500 and 1,500 kc, the television receiver must perform the following basic functions in ranges of frequencies from 50 Mc up:

1. It must separate the sound, which is being transmitted using frequency modulation, from the video signal, which is being transmitted using amplitude modulation.
2. It must provide suitable means for demodulation and reproduction of the sound signal.
3. It must provide video circuits which have bandwidths adequate for a single-sideband video spectrum 4 Mc wide and must provide means for demodulation and for eliminating cochannel and adjacent-channel interference.
4. It must provide a means for establishing a reference level for the video output signal corresponding to black-level at the transmitter, thus making possible blacker than black and various tones in the scale between black and white.
5. It must separate the synchronizing and equalizing pulses from the picture information; the pulses are in turn reseparated into information relating to horizontal and vertical scanning and blanking.
6. Using the synchronizing information, the television receiver must produce a properly scanned and phased picture on the face of the kinescope.

Many additional functions[2] are demanded of modern television receivers. However, the six functions listed form the true basis of operation

[1] For a general discussion of television-receiver circuits, see S. Helt, "Practical Television Engineering," Murray Hill Books, Inc., New York, 1950.

[2] See Wendt and Schroeder, Automatic Gain Control for Television Receivers, *RCA Rev.*, vol. 9, No. 4, pp. 602–631, December, 1948.

of any television receiver, and the following discussion will describe briefly how these basic functions are fulfilled in a modern high-efficiency receiver.

It is particularly fitting that this volume end with a brief discussion of television-receiver practice. Amplitude and frequency modulation, phase control, pulses, bandwidth, high-fidelity response, scanning, mixing, conversion, demodulation, and many other topics discussed in this volume are encountered in considerations of television reception, in addition to applications of many specialized circuits such as discriminators, reactance tubes, and saw-tooth-wave generators. In the study of the basic aspects of television-receiver behavior, the student will find answers to many of the inevitable "whys" which occur to him as he studies mathematical and circuit

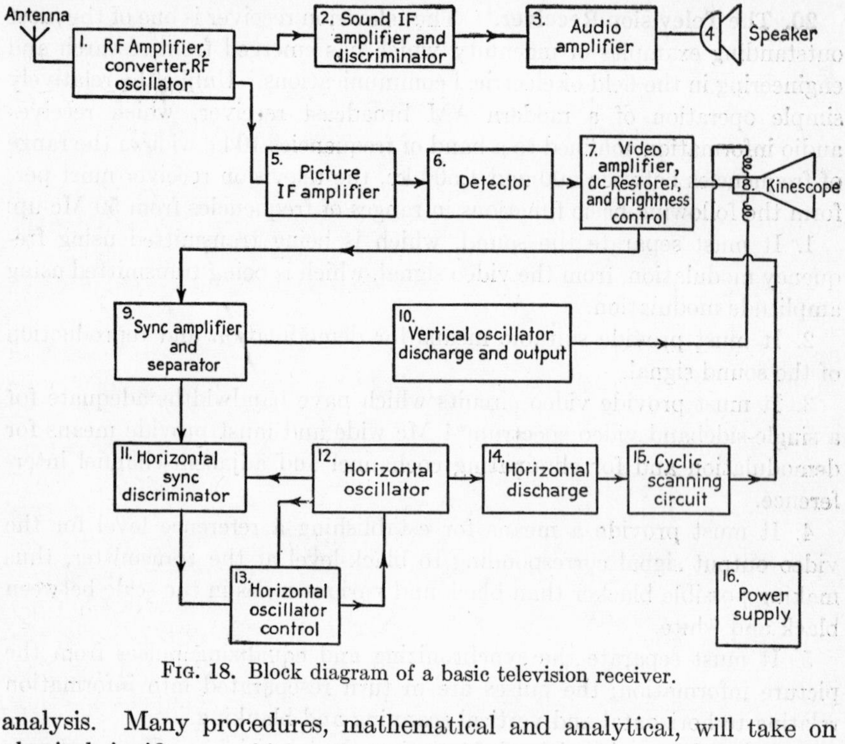

FIG. 18. Block diagram of a basic television receiver.

analysis. Many procedures, mathematical and analytical, will take on physical significance which will aid in his further studies of communication circuits. The general aspects of television-receiver circuits, also, form an excellent introduction to the complexities of modern communication systems.

21. The Basic Principles of Operation of a Television Receiver. The block diagram of a basic modern television receiver is pictured in Fig. 18.[1]

[1] This block diagram is based on the well-known RCA 630 circuit. See A. Wright, Television Receivers, *RCA Rev.*, vol. 8, No. 1, pp. 5–28, March, 1947.

It is seen to consist of 16 blocks representing components necessary to produce the sound and the picture.

The r-f amplifier receives the television signal from the antenna and delivers it to the converter, whose basic principles of operation are described earlier in this chapter. The output of the converter contains both the video and audio information. Before any further operation is performed, this information must be separated,[1] the FM sound and the video going to their respective intermediate amplifiers. The device used to separate the sound from the combined signal appearing at the converter plate is a special network in the plate circuit of the converter which contains a high-Q resonator tuned to the center frequency of the FM sound spectrum, which is $4\frac{1}{2}$ Mc removed from the carrier frequency. The output of this high-Q resonator is the sound signal at the intermediate frequency; this signal goes to the sound i-f amplifier, which has a transmission band sufficiently wide for undistorted amplification of the FM i-f signal. From there the sound signal goes to a discriminator whose output goes to the audio amplifier and finally to the loudspeaker.

The video signal proceeds from the converter through the picture i-f amplifier to the second detector, where it is demodulated, the output going through a video amplifier to the grid of the kinescope.

The final video output stage performs several functions in addition to supplying an amplified video signal to the kinescope. It provides dc restoration, brightness adjustment, and the initial separation of the synchronizing information from the video information. Consider first the dc restoration:

The dc component[2] (not d-c, normally read as direct-current) of a television picture is the varying unidirectional component of the picture which is a measure of the intensity of the light in that picture. This dc component is transmitted to the receiver by amplitude-modulating the a-c portion of the signal with this component. It is received and passed into a special detector which measures the signal peaks, recovers the dc component, and adds it to the a-c components. This detector is called the dc restorer and essentially speaking holds the black level of the picture signal at a fixed dc value regardless of the picture illumination, thus eliminating the necessity of readjusting the kinescope illumination after each change of scene.

[1] For a system in which the sound is separated from the video in the final output video amplifier, see R. B. Dome, Carrier-difference Reception of Television Sound, *Electronics*, pp. 102–105, January, 1947; see also S. W. Seeley, Design Factors for Intercarrier Television Sound, *Electronics*, vol. 21, pp. 72–75, July, 1948.

[2] For a detailed discussion of this important and often little understood component in image transmission, see K. R. Wendt, Television DC Component, *RCA Rev.*, vol. 9, pp. 85–111, March, 1948.

A typical dc-restorer circuit is shown in Fig. 19*a*. Consider first a simplified version of this circuit, which is shown in Fig. 19*b*. If the driving generator suddenly impresses a horizontal synchronizing pulse on the circuit in Fig. 19*b*, current will flow through C, R, and the diode if the

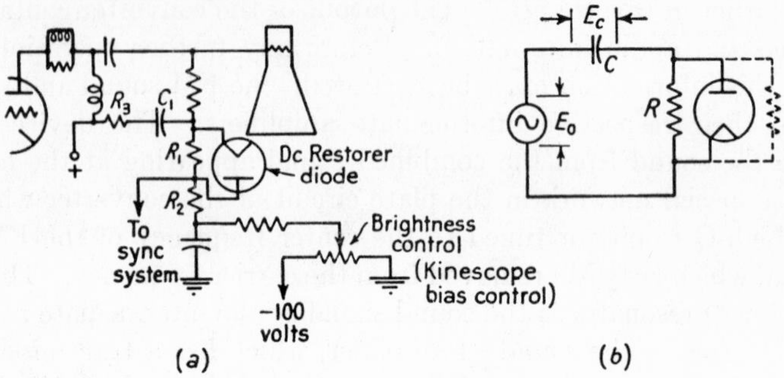

FIG. 19. Dc-restorer circuit.

polarity of the picture signal is correct. During the horizontal scan following this pulse, the diode does not conduct. During the next pulse, the diode conducts, etc. Because of the action of the diode, the charge into the capacitor is not equal to the charge leaving the capacitor during a cycle, resulting in a voltage appearing across the capacitor. This is the dc-restoration bias voltage, which readjusts the level of the picture voltage in the output stage—in effect restoring the dc component to the group of a-c components comprising the picture signal. If the time constant of the *RC* network is such that $RC < 0.3$, the voltage across the capacitor will follow the average brightness of the picture.

The restoration of the dc component has an important effect on the

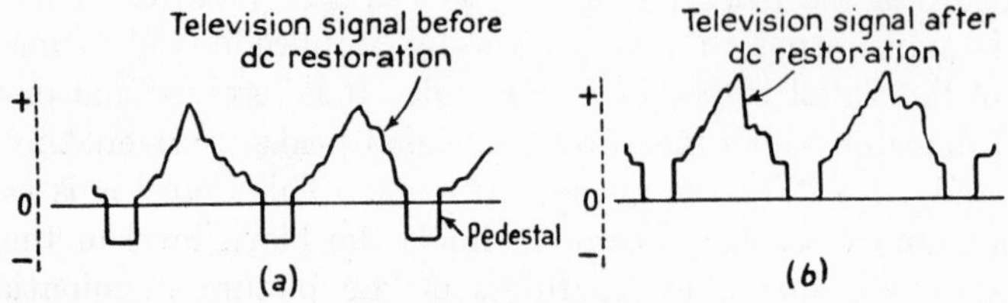

FIG. 20.

picture signal. The *pedestals* of the signal, as formed by the synchronizing pulses, are raised in voltage to such a level that their bases follow the zero-voltage axis shown in Fig. 20. This effect is entirely automatic, resulting in a lining up of the pedestals regardless of the value of average brightness.

Because of the action of the diode, which permits current to flow through the resistor R_2 only when the synchronizing pulses occur, the synchronizing signals will appear across R_2 with near-complete rejection of the picture information. This resistor provides a convenient place from which the synchronizing signals may be introduced into the synchronizing system.

The synchronizing signals are passed through a synchronizing amplifier in which the synchronizing signals are amplified and the rejection of picture information is made complete. At the output of this circuit, the information relating to vertical and horizontal synchronization part company. As is shown in Fig. 21*a* the output is fed to both an integrating and a differentiating network.

Consider first the vertical-synchronizing system. The integrating circuit

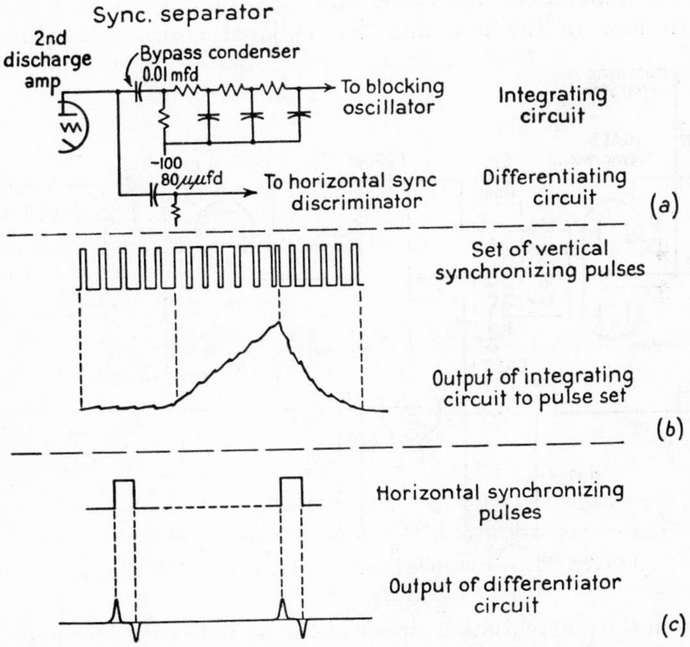

FIG. 21. Circuit and operation of a synchronization separator.

will respond only to the vertical-synchronization pulse, yielding the wave pictured in Fig. 21*b*. This wave is then applied to a blocking-oscillator circuit which drives a vertical-scanning circuit which produces vertical deflection in the kinescope of correct frequency and deflection.

Because of the fact that the horizontal-scanning rate is much greater than the vertical-scanning rate, the horizontal-scanning system employs a radically different circuit from that required for vertical scanning. The heart of this system is the horizontal-scan-system oscillator shown in Fig. 22. This oscillator employs a Hartley circuit and oscillates at the scan frequency of 15,750 cycles, the oscillations taking place between the cathode and the screen grid of the 6K6GT, using the primary of the transformer as its coil.

The horizontal-scan oscillator performs two functions:

1. By oscillating with a large driving voltage, a clipped sine wave (a near-square wave) appears at the output of the oscillator.
2. The oscillator impresses a sine voltage on the plates of the twin diode.

The voltage fed to the transformer by the oscillator presents a reference wave which can be compared with the incoming horizontal-synchronization information, thus making it possible to adjust the oscillator frequency and phase to those prescribed by the picture signal, using a synchronization discriminator and a reactance tube as the control mechanism.[1]

Return now to the incoming differentiated horizontal-synchronizing

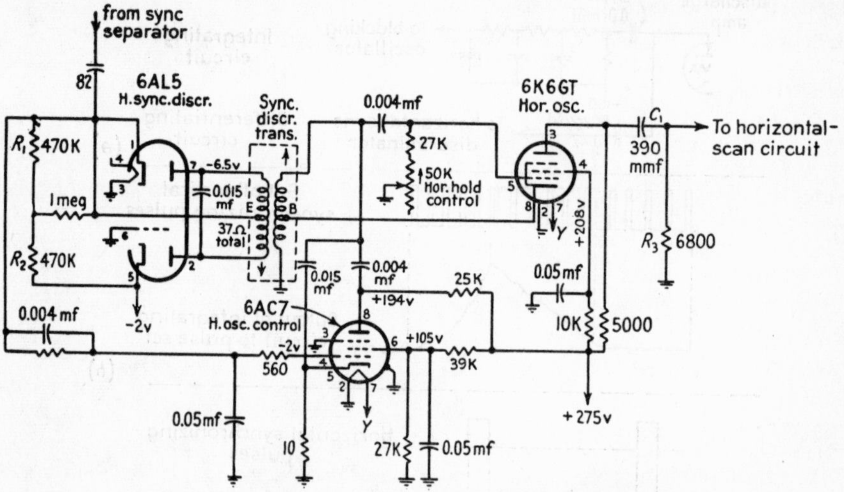

FIG. 22. Phase-controlled horizontal-scan-oscillator circuit.

pulses from the differentiating circuit in the output of the second synchronization amplifier. The general shape of these differentiated pulses is shown in Fig. 21*c*. These pulses arrive at the synchronization discriminator and are applied to the plates of the twin diode. If the pulses and the sine wave from the oscillator are properly phased, the sum of the voltage appearing across R_1 and R_2 is equal to zero. For other than proper phase, a d-c voltage appears as a sum voltage which is proportional to the difference in phase. This voltage is used to control the reactance-tube circuit, this circuit in turn controlling the phase of the horizontal-scan-circuit oscillator, which is thus maintained in proper phase.

The square wave appearing in the plate circuit of the oscillator tube is

[1] See Wendt and Fredendall, Automatic Frequency and Phase Control of Synchronization in Television Receivers, *Proc. IRE*, vol. 31, pp. 7–15, January, 1943.

differentiated by C_1 and R_3 and applied to the input of the cyclic-scanning circuit (see Chap. 11), which creates the horizontal deflection necessary to produce the picture on the kinescope face in conjunction with the vertical-deflection system and the video information applied to the kinescope grid.

PROBLEMS

1. Compare the specifications necessary for the design of an intermediate amplifier which is to be used for either or both amplitude and frequency modulation.

2. Discuss the operation of a double-superheterodyne receiver in which the second detector is replaced by another converter or mixer which feeds into a second intermediate amplifier plus demodulator circuit. What advantages would this system have over a conventional superheterodyne?

3. The video carrier and the sound carrier of a television signal being transmitted on channel 3 are located at 61.25 and 65.75 Mc, respectively. Discuss the characteristics of a local oscillator in the television receiver necessary to yield the video and sound carriers at the intermediate frequencies of 25.75 Mc and 21.25 Mc, respectively.

4. Discuss the mixer current for the circuit in Fig. 5 for the case when $i_p = \text{G}_0 + \text{G}_1(e_s + e_0) + \text{G}_3(e_s + e_0)^3$.

5. Consider the mixer circuit shown in Fig. 2. If the diode current obeys a three-halves-power law, deduce, using graphical analysis, the conversion transconductance g_{C_1}. If the maximum value of g is the same both for the ideal diode case and for the case studied in this problem, compare the curves of $g_{C_1}/g_{\max}$ versus E_b/E_0 for both cases.

6. Consider a triode converter obeying the plate-current–grid-voltage relationship

$$\begin{aligned} i_p &= 0 & -\infty < E_c < E_{c_0} \\ &= k[E_{c_0} + E_c]^2 & E_{c_0} < E_c \end{aligned}$$

where k is a constant and E_c is the grid potential. Find g_{c_1} and g_{c_2} for the case where the instantaneous grid potential is $E_{c_0}[1 + 1.2 \cos \omega_0 t]$.

7. Consider a carrier which is amplitude-modulated by a simple harmonic wave so that the per cent modulation is 35 per cent. If this modulated wave is applied to a square-law detector, what is the per cent second harmonic distortion which will result? Repeat for a linear detector (ideal case).

8. Using Eq. (51), deduce the per cent second harmonic distortion resulting from a linear detector.

9. If the detector is to be a crystal detector which is to be used as a probe on a transmission line for measuring standing-wave ratios, discuss the merits of using this device as a linear detector or as a square-law detector.

10. Discuss the possibility of using as a detector a vacuum tube whose plate-current versus grid-voltage curve is a cubic.

11. Compare square-law and linear detection from the standpoint of the fundamental properties of a Taylor series.

12. Discuss fully the fact that vestigial-sideband transmission is suitable for video signals but not for audio signals in commercial broadcasting. Include a comparison on the basis of the per cent modulation used for each in AM transmission.

13. Discuss the possibility of using single-sideband FM broadcasting for television.

14. Let an FM wave $Ee^{i(\omega_0 + 5\sin\omega_1)t}$ be impressed across a resonant circuit having a linear slope factor $S(\omega) = 0.4$ in the region of the frequency $\omega_0/2\pi$. Deduce the characteristics of the envelope of the current flowing in the circuit. Discuss the side frequencies comprising this current with respect to both amplitude and phase.

15. Discuss the behavior of the circuit in Fig. 13 if the filament of the diode in circuit $-I$ were to burn out.

16. Deduce the general aspects of a phase-discriminator circuit. Discuss. Can the circuit in Fig. 13 be employed as a phase discriminator? Discuss fully, making recommendations for any changes deemed necessary.

17. Let an FM wave in which the modulating wave is simple harmonic be applied to the input of a balanced discriminator whose characteristic curve is that pictured in Fig. 14. If the frequency deviation Δf of the applied wave is equal to $f_b - f_a$, deduce the shape of the wave appearing at the discriminator output. Write a Fourier-series representation of this output wave.

18. Let an FM wave $2.2e^{i(2\pi \times 40 \times 10^6 + 3\sin 2\pi \times 10^3)t}$ be applied to the input of the circuit pictured in Fig. 15. Determine the outputs of the slope circuits.

19. Prepare a short monograph discussing important modifications, improvements, and refinements which have been made in modern television-receiver circuits.

APPENDIX

BESSEL FUNCTIONS OF THE FIRST KIND

1. The General Bessel Equation and Its Solution. The general Bessel equation is written

$$x^2 \frac{d^2y}{dx^2} + x\frac{dy}{dx} + (x^2 - n^2)y = 0 \qquad (1)$$

This is a second-order differential equation, and its complete solution is

$$y = J_n(x) + N_n(x) \qquad (2)$$

where $J_n(x)$ is the Bessel function of the first kind
$N_n(x)$ is the Bessel function of the second kind, or Neumann function
n is the order of the solution
x is the argument of the function corresponding to the independent variable in Eq. (1)

In the analysis of communication spectra, the Bessel function of the first kind is encountered in problems dealing with changes in frequency or phase of waves. In these cases, the Bessel equation itself does not appear. Infinite series are encountered, which, upon inspection, prove to be Bessel functions. These functions appear as coefficients of the Fourier series which are associated with phase and frequency modulation, and once the order and the argument of each Bessel function are determined, the coefficients may be easily evaluated by consulting one of the many comprehensive sets of tables of Bessel functions which have been published.

In general, the solution of (1), yielding the Bessel function of the first kind, may be shown to be[1]

$$J_n(x) = \sum_{k=0}^{\infty} (-1)^k \frac{x^{n+2k}}{2^{n+2k}k!\Gamma(n + k + 1)} \qquad (3)$$

If n is a positive integer or is equal to zero, Eq. (3) becomes

$$J_n(x) = \sum_{k=0}^{\infty} (-1)^k \frac{x^{n+2k}}{2^{n+2k}k!(n + k)!} \qquad (4)$$

[1] See R. V. Churchill, "Operational Mathematics in Engineering," Sec. 13, McGraw-Hill Book Company, Inc., New York, 1944, for a Laplace-transform solution, yielding this equation.

Consider the case when n is replaced by $-n$; we get

$$J_{-n}(x) = \sum_{k=0}^{\infty} (-1)^k \frac{x^{-n+2k}}{2^{-n+2k} k! \Gamma(-n+k+1)} \tag{5}$$

As n approaches a positive integer N,

$$1/\Gamma(-n+k+1) = 0 \qquad k = 0, 1, \ldots, N-1 \tag{6}$$

Thus the series (5) must start with N; (5) takes the *form*

$$J_{-N}(x) = \sum_{k=N}^{\infty} (-1)^k \frac{x^{-N+2k}}{2^{-N+2k} k!(-N+k)!} \tag{7}$$

It is easily shown that (7) yields $(-1)^N J_N(x)$; therefore

$$J_{-n}(x) = (-1)^n J_n(x) \tag{8}$$

2. Trigonometric and Exponential Integrals Which Yield Bessel Functions. Integrals of the type

$$\int_0^{2\pi} e^{j(\beta \sin \varphi - n\varphi)} \, d\varphi \tag{9}$$

$$\int_0^{2\pi} e^{j(\beta \cos \varphi - n\varphi)} \, d\varphi \tag{10}$$

are encountered in the Fourier analysis of modulated and complex waves.

The solutions of these integrals may be deduced from the properties of the Bessel generating function, which is written

$$e^{(x/2)[t-(1/t)]} \tag{11}$$

Let us deal with the expansion of (11). From simple exponent theory

$$e^{(x/2)[t-(1/t)]} = e^{xt/2} e^{-x/2t} \tag{12}$$

$$= \left[1 + \frac{xt}{2} + \frac{1}{2!}\left(\frac{xt}{2}\right)^2 + \cdots\right] \cdot \left[1 - \frac{x}{2t} + \frac{1}{2!}\left(\frac{x}{2t}\right)^2 + \cdots\right] \tag{13}$$

By multiplying together the two infinite series in (13), an infinite number of terms for each power of t will result, that is, $\ldots t^2, t, t^0, t^{-1}, t^{-2}, t^{-3}, \ldots$. After grouping together the terms which are associated with each power of t, we find that the coefficients of the various powers of t are Bessel functions; *i.e.*,

$$e^{(x/2)[t-(1/t)]} = J_0(x) + J_1(x)t + J_2(x)t^2 + \cdots + J_{-1}(x)\frac{1}{t} + J_{-2}(x)\frac{1}{t^2} + \cdots \tag{14}$$

$$= \sum_{n=-\infty}^{n=\infty} t^n J_n(x) \tag{15}$$

where n is an integer.

The solutions of the integrals (9) and (10) may be found by starting with the substitution of $t = e^{j\Theta}$ into Eq. (11):

$$\exp\left[\frac{x}{2}\left(t - \frac{1}{t}\right)\right] = \exp\left[\frac{x}{2}(e^{j\Theta} - e^{-j\Theta})\right] \tag{16}$$

$$= \exp(jx \sin \Theta) \tag{17}$$

Substituting (17) into (14), we get

$$e^{jx\sin\Theta} = J_0(x) + e^{j\Theta}J_1(x) + e^{j2\Theta}J_2(x) + \cdots + e^{-j\Theta}J_{-1}(x) + e^{-j2\Theta}J_{-2}(x) + \cdots \tag{18}$$

But

$$J_{-n}(x) = (-1)^n J_n(x) \tag{19}$$

and

$$\sin\Theta = \frac{e^{j\Theta} - e^{-j\Theta}}{2j} \tag{20}$$

$$\cos\Theta = \frac{e^{j\Theta} + e^{-j\Theta}}{2} \tag{21}$$

The substitution of (8), (20), and (21) into Eq. (18) yields the expression,

$$e^{jx\sin\Theta} = J_0(x) + 2[J_2(x)\cos 2\Theta + J_4(x)\cos 4\Theta + \cdots] + 2j[J_1(x)\sin\Theta + J_3(x)\sin 3\Theta + \cdots] \tag{22}$$

But

$$e^{jx\sin\Theta} = \cos(x\sin\Theta) + j\sin(x\sin\Theta) \tag{23}$$

By equating the real and the imaginary parts of Eqs. (22) and (23), we get

$$\cos(x\sin\Theta) = J_0(x) + 2[J_2(x)\cos 2\Theta + J_4(x)\cos 4\Theta + \cdots] \tag{24}$$

and

$$\sin(x\sin\Theta) = 2[J_1(x)\sin\Theta + J_3(x)\sin 3\Theta + \cdots] \tag{25}$$

These are known as the Jacobi equations and may be written in compact mathematical form as follows:

$$\cos(x\sin\Theta) = J_0(x) + 2\sum_{k=1}^{\infty} J_{2k}(x)\cos 2k\Theta \tag{26}$$

$$\sin(x\sin\Theta) = 2\sum_{k=1}^{\infty} J_{2k-1}(x)\sin(2k-1)\Theta \tag{27}$$

Let us now make use of the orthogonality of sets of sine and cosine functions:

$$\begin{aligned} \int_0^{2\pi} \cos n\Theta \cos m\Theta \, d\Theta &= 0 \qquad m \neq n \\ &= \pi \qquad m = n \neq 0 \\ &= 2\pi \qquad m = n = 0 \end{aligned} \tag{28}$$

$$\begin{aligned} \int_0^{2\pi} \sin n\Theta \sin m\Theta \, d\Theta &= 0 \qquad m \neq n \\ &= \pi \qquad m = n \end{aligned} \tag{29}$$

Multiply the series in equation (26) through by $\cos n\theta$ and integrate from 0 to 2π. Thus

$$\begin{aligned} \int_0^{2\pi} \cos (x \sin \Theta) \cos n\Theta \, d\Theta &= \int_0^{2\pi} J_0(x) \cos n\Theta \, d\Theta \\ &+ 2 \int_0^{2\pi} J_2(x) \cos 2\Theta \cos n\Theta \, d\Theta \\ &+ 2 \int_0^{2\pi} J_4(x) \cos 4\Theta \cos n\Theta \, d\Theta + \cdots \end{aligned} \tag{30}$$

Using Eq. (28), we find that, for all even values of n and for $n = 0$,

$$\int_0^{2\pi} \cos (x \sin \Theta) \cos n\Theta \, d\Theta = 2\pi J_n(x) \tag{31}$$

Now multiply the series in Eq. (27) through by $\sin n\Theta$, and integrate from 0 to 2π. Thus

$$\begin{aligned} \int_0^{2\pi} \sin (x \sin \Theta) \sin n\Theta \, d\Theta &= 2 \int_0^{2\pi} J_1(x) \sin \Theta \sin n\Theta \, d\Theta \\ &+ 2 \int_0^{2\pi} J_3(x) \sin 3\Theta \sin n\Theta \, d\Theta + \cdots \end{aligned} \tag{32}$$

It is easily verified that, for all odd n,

$$\int_0^{2\pi} \sin (x \sin \Theta) \sin n\Theta \, d\Theta = 2\pi J_n(x) \tag{33}$$

Since the integral in (31) has been evaluated for even values of n and the integral in (33) has been evaluated for odd values of n, we may combine the two integrals and write, for all n,

$$\int_0^{2\pi} [\cos (x \sin \Theta) \cos n\Theta + \sin (x \sin \Theta) \sin n\Theta] \, d\Theta = 2\pi J_n(x) \tag{34}$$

where n is a positive integer. Equation (34) may be rewritten, using a trigonometric identity, in the form

$$\int_0^{2\pi} \cos (n\Theta - x \sin \Theta)\, d\Theta = 2\pi J_n(x) \tag{35}$$

It is easily verified that

$$\int_0^{2\pi} \sin (n\Theta - x \sin n\Theta)\, d\Theta = 0 \tag{36}$$

Since $e^{j\Theta} = \cos \Theta + j \sin \Theta$, we may combine (35) and (36) as follows:

$$\int_0^{2\pi} e^{j(n\Theta - x\sin\Theta)}\, d\Theta = 2\pi J_n(x) \tag{37}$$

Since the imaginary portion of (37) is equal to zero,

$$\int_0^{2\pi} e^{\pm j(n\Theta - x\sin\Theta)}\, d\Theta = 2\pi J_n(x) \tag{38}$$

This yields Eq. (90), Chap. 2.

3. Derivations of Other Forms of Integral (38). There are several other important forms of integral (38). They may be derived by making suitable substitutions for Θ. As an illustration, consider the following:

Substituting $\Theta - \pi$ for Θ in Eq. (38), we get, for the positive exponent,

$$\int_0^{2\pi} e^{j[x\sin(\Theta-\pi) - n(\Theta-\pi)]}\, d\Theta = 2\pi J_n(x) \tag{39}$$

Since

$$\sin (\Theta - \pi) = \sin \Theta \cos \pi - \cos \Theta \sin \pi = -\sin \Theta \tag{40}$$

we get

$$\int_0^{2\pi} e^{j(-x\sin\Theta - n\Theta)} e^{jn\pi}\, d\Theta = 2\pi J_n(x) \tag{41}$$

But

$$e^{jn\pi} = (-1)^n \tag{42}$$

Thus we see that

$$\int_0^{2\pi} e^{-j(x\sin\Theta + n\Theta)}\, d\Theta = (-1)^n 2\pi J_n(x) \tag{43}$$

This yields Eq. (91), Chap. 2. Equation (93) in that chapter may be verified by making the substitution $\theta - 3\pi/2$.

NAME INDEX

SUBJECT INDEX